Juan Ramírez-Muñoz took his degrees in chemistry at the Universities of Granada (1947) and Madrid (D.Sc. 1950). After research studies in the fields of spectrographic analysis and flame photometry in Belgium, Britain and Spain, he was appointed Senior Lecturer in Analytical Chemistry at the University of Madrid and Scientific Research Collaborator of the High Council of Scientific Research of Spain. Dr. Ramírez-Muñoz became Associate Professor of Spectrography, Metallography and Analytical Chemistry at the University of Santander, Bucaramanga, Colombia in 1958 and was Full Professor from 1959 until 1963. During this period he was also Director of the Scientific Research Division of the university.

In 1962 he was selected as Director of the First International Course on Flame Photometry and has been elected to honorary membership of the chemical societies of Peru and Mexico. Having joined the staff of Beckman Instruments, Inc., Fullerton, California in 1963, Dr. Ramírez-Muñoz is now Principal Application Chemist with this firm.

This distinguished scientist has published four books and about 140 research papers on analytical chemical subjects.

ATOMIC-ABSORPTION SPECTROSCOPY

and Analysis by Atomic-Absorption
Flame Photometry

ATOMIC-ABSORPTION SPECTROSCOPY

and Analysis by Atomic-Absorption Flame Photometry

JUAN RAMÍREZ-MUÑOZ

Principal Application Chemist at Beckman Instruments, Inc.
and Scientific Research Collaborator
of the High Council of Scientific Research of Spain

ELSEVIER PUBLISHING COMPANY

Amsterdam - London - New York

1968

ELSEVIER PUBLISHING COMPANY
335 Jan van Galenstraat
P.O. Box 211, Amsterdam, The Netherlands

ELSEVIER PUBLISHING CO. LTD.
Barking, Essex, England

AMERICAN ELSEVIER PUBLISHING COMPANY, INC.
52 Vanderbilt Avenue
New York, New York 10017

Library of Congress Catalog Card Number: 68-10412

With 156 illustrations and 23 tables

Printed in The Netherlands

Preface

In writing this book, the author has had two basic aims: first, to assemble an informative work on the methods of atomic-absorption spectroscopy which can provide the professional analyst with a coherent exposition of this relatively new method of instrumental analysis; and secondly, to make a selection of the available material in those areas of greatest interest in order to provide a proper survey of the potentialities of the general technique.

When it was decided to begin work on this book, consideration was given to the relative youth enjoyed by this new method of instrumental analysis. At that time, it was not thought that a format similar to that of the earlier book, *Flame Photometry*, would be justified. In the course of writing, however, so much new material has been added that the two books are in fact very similar in volume. Even so, there are still many potential applications which have not yet been studied while others are at the experimental stage and have not yet been published. The present text will therefore in due course doubtless deserve further enlargement.

It is hoped that this volume may help to acquaint the reader with a new constantly expanding method, which has now attained a certain degree of maturity but which still offers many interesting paths of research. It is also hoped that the book may assist enthusiasts for flame photometry by presenting, in a readily available form, a survey of the recent literature of new instrumental systems and of new analytical possibilities.

In order to avoid repetition, the reader is occasionally referred to certain chapters of *Flame Photometry*, especially in those areas which are in some ways common to emission and atomic-absorption work. The present limited treatment is compensated to some extent by an extensive subject index referring to original sources on specific topics which are treated too briefly, or not at all, in the text. Drawings have been introduced whenever they seemed useful; many of these, as well as some parts of the text itself, are the products of lectures given by the author in Colombia in 1962 at the First International Conference on Flame Photometry, organized and sponsored by the Department of Scientific Affairs of the Pan American Union.

References to the experimental work and publications of many authors have been included. It is likely that some papers published very recently or in journals hard to obtain have been overlooked. The author will welcome all suggestions or information concerning work not discussed or mentioned, in order that they may be included in future editions. He would also be grateful for suggestions and constructive criticism which would improve the text, and for advice on any misinterpretation of details obtained from lectures, round-table discussions, or other oral presentations. In any case, such details can usually be considered only as preliminary information which awaits confirmation from the eventual publications in scientific journals.

To save space, it has been necessary to reduce to a minimum the description of commercial equipment and of experimental instruments recommended by various specialists. However, for the information of those interested in commercial instruments, notes have been included to acquaint them with what is at present available.

Fullerton, California
December, 1967

JUAN RAMÍREZ-MUÑOZ

Acknowledgements

This English version of the original Spanish manuscript was prepared by Dr. Walter D. Kline, Professor of Spanish Language at California State College, Fullerton, whom the author wishes to thank for his efforts in achieving a fluent translation. Careful and detailed editing of the English version has been carried out by Dr. Alison M. G. Macdonald, Editor of *Analytica Chimica Acta*. The author is deeply grateful for her valuable and patient editing work which has so much improved the manuscript.

The author is also very grateful to several members of Beckman Instruments, Inc., Fullerton: Dr. William F. Ulrich, for reading the complete manuscript and for his comments and suggestions; Mr. Paul T. Gilbert, also for his comments and suggestions in some parts of the book; Dr. August Hell and Mr. Norm Shifrin, for their constant help during the experimental work, and ideas: Mr. Robert O. Brace, Mr. Richard W. Claus, Mr. M. Galassi and Mr. M. E. Roth, for their personal collaboration in experimental work; Mrs. B. M. Steidl, for her constant help at the Research Library; and Mrs. Pat Detro, for her aid in compiling some literature references and in the meticulous typing of the bibliography.

Thanks are also due to Mr. J. R. Alamilla for his impartial assistance in providing literature in connection with his activities as Director of the Department of Scientific Publications of the Universidad Industrial de Santander, Colombia; and to Mrs. Eladia Gaya-Angás de Ramírez-Muñoz for her tireless help in the revision and classification of scientific material and in the preparation of the indexes.

The author also wishes to thank Beckman Instruments, Inc., for the facililities made available for scientific documentation and experimentation in flame methods.

He also wishes to express his gratitude to the scientists who so kindly sent reprints, manuscripts and various other documents, and to all those who from the very beginning have published their contribution on atomic-absorption spectroscopy, since their discoveries and publications have necessarily constituted the basis of this book. The author greatly appreciates the publications, pamphlets and general information which have been so generously sent to him by various firms producing instruments for atomic-absorption spectroscopy.

Fullerton, California
December, 1967.

JUAN RAMÍREZ-MUÑOZ

Acknowledgments

Contents

Preface v
Acknowledgements vii

PART I. FUNDAMENTALS

INTRODUCTION 3

Chapter 1. ORIGINS OF THE METHOD AND NOMENCLATURE 6
1. Origin of the method 7
2. Nomenclature 8

Chapter 2. GENERAL PRINCIPLES AND CHARACTERISTICS 11
1. General principles 11
2. Qualitative characteristics 13
3. Quantitative characteristics 13

Chapter 3. ABSORPTION AND EMISSION 15
1. Comparison of the two methods 15
2. Advantages of atomic-absorption spectroscopy 18
3. Disadvantages of atomic-absorption spectroscopy 20
4. The choice of atomic-absorption flame photometry 22
5. Comparison with other instrumental methods 23

Chapter 4. THE LITERATURE OF ATOMIC-ABSORPTION SPECTROSCOPY 24
1. Books 24
2. Reviews 25
3. Conferences and lectures 26
4. Future perspectives 27

Chapter 5. THEORY 29
1. The absorption process 29
2. Quantitative aspects of the absorption process 38

PART II. INSTRUMENTAL SYSTEMS

Chapter 6. INSTRUMENTAL SYSTEMS 45

Chapter 7. EMISSION SYSTEM 47
1. Continuous emitters 47
2. Discrete emitters 49
1. The flame as a source 49; 2. Laboratory vapor-discharge lamps 50; 3. Hollow-cathode lamps 51; 4. Other sources 84

Chapter 8. ABSORPTION SYSTEM 87
1. The flame 87
1. Uses of the flame. Flame characteristics 88; 2. Different kinds of flames 97; 3. Absorption phenomena produced by the flame itself 104; 4. Modulation 107; 5. Selected zone 108
2. The burner 113
1. Different kinds of burners 114; 2. Multiburner couplings 124
3. The sprayer 124
1. Optimum conditions of the sprayer 126; 2. Feed rate 127; 3. Heated spray chambers 130; 4. Tube feeding 131

4. Mechanical parts 131
1. Auxiliary mechanisms of the burner 131; 2. Long beam-path adapters 134; 3. Chimneys 139; 4. Vents 139; 5. Mechanisms for supplying the solutions 140
5. Optical parts 140
1. Lenses 140; 2. Masking devices 140; 3. Splitting devices and beam combiners 140; 4. Optical multi-path devices 142; 5. Periscope couplings 146; 6. Mirrors 146
6. Other techniques which do not involve the use of conventional flames 146
1. Laser 147; 2. Plasmas 147; 3. Spark 148; 4. L'vov furnace technique 149; 5. Vidale furnace technique 150; 6. Other furnace techniques 150; 7. Cathodic sputtering technique 150; 8. Flash heating technique 152

Chapter 9. SELECTION SYSTEM 153
1. Filters 153
2. Monochromators 155
1. Slit 156
3. Use of the resonance radiation 158

Chapter 10. PHOTOMETRIC SYSTEM 160
1. Detection 160
2. Amplification 161
3. Measurement 161
1. Modulation 164; 2. Noise 167; 3. Recording 168; 4. Scale expansion 168; 5. Measuring procedure described by Lang 169; 6. Measuring procedure described by Warren 169; 7. Other measuring procedures 169
4. Double-beam operation 170
5. Other measurement procedures involving comparison of two light signals. 171
6. Multi-element measurement 172
7. Internal standard operation 172

Chapter 11. INSTRUMENTS 174
1. Home-made instruments 175
2. Commercial instruments 182

PART III. RANGE AND LIMITATIONS OF ATOMIC-ABSORPTION METHODS

Chapter 12. DETERMINABLE ELEMENTS. CHOICE OF LINES 205
1. Determinable elements 205
2. Choice of lines 208
1. Lines in the far ultraviolet 211; 2. Bands 215
3. Measurement of line profiles 215
4. Lines utilized in atomic-absorption 215

Chapter 13. SENSITIVITY 216
1. Definition of sensitivity 216
1. Diverse units used to express limits 218; 2. Factors governing the absolute sensitivity 220; 3. Different definitions of relative sensitivity 220; 4. Qualitative sensitivity and qualitative limits 221; 5. Quantitative sensitivities and quantitative limits 232
2. Some advantages in the use of sensitivity values 237
3. Procedures for determining concentration limits and sensitivities 241
1. Percentual qualitative concentration limits 241; 2. Fluctuational qualitative concentration limits 242
4. Sensitivities obtainable by atomic-absorption 243
5. Superior values of sensitivity in atomic-absorption 248
6. Factors which influence sensitivity in atomic-absorption 250
1. Methods of increasing the slope 250; 2. Methods of minimizing noise 251; 3. Methods of decreasing reading time 251; 4. Factors which decrease sensitivity 252
7. Experimental reduction of sensitivity 253
8. Special case of heavy elements 255

Chapter 14. LIMITATIONS IN ATOMIC ABSORPTION 256
1. Accuracy 256

2. Precision 258
3. Disturbances and interferences 260
4. Limiting factors depending on the instrumental system 262
5. Limiting factors associated with operation 263
6. Limiting factors depending on the sample 265
1. Physical interferences 266; 2. Chemical interferences 268
7. Graphic representation of interference phenomena 277

PART IV. EXPERIMENTAL METHODS

Chapter 15. EXPERIMENTAL PROCESS 281
1. Known analytical processes 281
1. Switching lamps 282
2. Unknown analytical processes 283
3. Optimum operating conditions 284

Chapter 16. STANDARD SOLUTIONS 286
1. Substances for the preparation of standards 286
2. Stock solutions and standards 287
1. Glassware 288; 2. Weighing procedure 289; 3. Dilution process 289; 4. Storage of the solutions 289; 5. Polyethylene bottles 289; 6. Additions 290; 7. Calculations 290
3. Series of standards 291
4. Concentration range 292
5. Graphical aids 292

Chapter 17. PREPARATION OF THE SAMPLE 296
1. Treatment of solid samples 297
2. Separations 297
1. Selective adsorption 298; 2. Selective extraction 298
3. Previous dilution 300
4. Preliminary concentration 301
5. Secondary preparation of samples 301
1. Addition of non-aqueous solvents 302; 2. Various other additives 304

Chapter 18. EXPERIMENTAL MEASUREMENTS AND CALIBRATION 311
1. Experimental measurements 311
1. Order of the measurements 312
2. Calibration 313
1. Types of calibration and working curves in atomic-absorption 314; 2. Shape of the curves 322; 3. Concentration range 327; 4. Special cases in working curves 328
3. Calculations 338
4. Precautions 341
1. Instrumental precautions 341; 2. Precautions with respect to the samples 343; 3. Precautions of a personal nature 343

PART V. APPLICATIONS

Chapter 19. APPLICATIONS 349
1. Analysis of waters 350
1. Preparation of samples 351; 2. Determinable elements 352; 3. Interference effects 352; 4. Standards 353
2. Analysis of agricultural materials 353
1. Fertilizers 353; 2. Plant materials 355; 3. Soils 358
3. Analysis of biological materials 361
1. Blood 362; 2. Saliva 365; 3. Milk 366; 4. Urine 366; 5. Feces 368; 6. Tissues 369; 7. Bones 369; 8. Cerebrospinal fluid 370; 9. Special studies 370; 10. Shellfish 370
4. Analysis of mineral products and related materials 370
1. Solid mineral products (rocks, minerals and ores) 370; 2. Petroleum and petroleum products 374
5. Analysis of metallurgical products 376
1. Preparation of samples 377; 2. Determinable elements 379; 3. Interference effects 380; 3. Standards 381

6. Analysis of foods and beverages 382
7. Analysis of industrial products 383
1. Cement 383; 2. Industrial solutions 383; 3. Chemical products 384; 4. Plastics and related products 385; 5. Fungicides 385; 6. Silicate samples and refractories 385; 7. Glass and ceramics 386; 8. Miscellaneous applications 386
8. Isotopic analysis 387
9. Special studies 388

APPENDIX
Conversion table to transform % absn. and % T to absorbance values 392
Hollow-cathode lamps for atomic-absorption spectroscopy 395
Dilution series for standards 399
Concentration conversion factors 400
Recommended operating conditions for determinations by atomic-absorption flame photometry 401

BIBLIOGRAPHY 409
Appendix. Addendum to bibliography 448

JUNIOR AUTHOR INDEX 453

SUBJECT INDEX 457

PART I

FUNDAMENTALS

Introduction

In the course of a relatively short time the analytical methodology of flame photometry has acquired a characteristic personality within the general field of spectral analysis. Several factors have contributed to this rapid development. Suitable equipment became commercially available shortly after the first developments were published in the scientific literature; and an informative literature was quickly amassed, since flame photometry solved quantitative problems that were difficult or almost impossible to solve by classical or earlier instrumental methods. In recent years, many spectroscopists and analytical chemists have been attracted to the examination of flame methods, and many new developments in instrumentation, in applications to chemical problems, in the theoretical interpretation of the related phenomena and in their adaptation for practical purposes, have ensued. The high sensitivity of flame methods, and the ease of achieving an adequate precision and accuracy, have justified the efforts devoted to the general method. The initial tentative analytical procedures have evolved into complete standardized techniques which have been adopted for routine analytical work and as an aid in other branches of research.

The high sensitivity of flame photometry has made the method particularly suitable for the analysis of micro-components or trace elements, whether as impurities or normal components of samples. Despite possible interferences from other components—generally macro-components—of the sample, the sensitivity generally justifies the selection of this method in preference to other techniques and instrumental methods. All these factors have contributed to the rapid expansion of flame photometry in the field of chemical analysis.

Tangible evidence of the great interest in this type of analysis is given by the amount of published work, which shows no sign of levelling off in either quantity or quality; the field does not seem to become saturated, as has happened with other analytical techniques. In fact, it is increasingly difficult to keep a complete record of all the publications dealing with flame analysis, since many articles on the most diverse subjects contain references to flame procedures and results obtained by flame photometry.

After the extensive development of flame photometry, various workers proposed, utilized and developed a new use of the flame in chemical analysis—not as a source of excitation of emission, but as a medium for absorbing radiation; both the emission and the absorption are characteristic of the qualitative and quantitative composition of a sample. A new branch of flame photometry was thus developed and a logical division arose between *emission flame photometry* and *absorption flame photometry*. The development of this new branch, *atomic-absorption analysis by the flame* (the widest division of *atomic-absorption spectroscopy*; see later), with its own distinctive principles and instrumentation, has paralleled in speed and extent, the earlier development of emission flame photometry.

The method of atomic absorption provides a means of analysis for elements that are difficult or impossible to determine by conventional emission methods, and even offers freedom from interfering factors that are traditional to the emission method. Many problems which are intractable to emission methods, can be readily solved by the absorption method. In the course of only a few years—an extremely short period in terms of scientific development and communication—the method of atomic absorption has become fully established and accepted as a vital area of spectral analysis.

With most instrumental methods, progress normally follows the scheme: proposal of the method, home-made instrumentation, analytical applications, commercial instrumentation, extension of the applications and adaptation to routine analysis, and finally, investigation of new potentialities. In the case of atomic absorption, the development of commercial and home-made instrumentation proceeded simultaneously, and the investigation of new potentialities has surpassed the analytical applications. Theoretical studies have been made on certain elements for which no applications to specific practical cases, much less to routine analysis, have yet been developed. Nevertheless, some determinations have already become a part of routine analysis; for example, magnesium is now determined by atomic absorption with the same simplicity that the routine determination of sodium, potassium and calcium enjoys in emission flame photometry.

A series of brilliant advances has facilitated the general acceptance of the method. These include solutions of the following problems.

(*a*) The determination of calcium and magnesium in biological analysis. Although calcium has been, and continues to be, frequently determined by flame emission, the difficulties encountered can be largely avoided in atomic absorption. The determination of magnesium is, of course, a brilliant achievement in bioanalysis. To these may be added the determinations of zinc, nickel, iron, manganese, lead, and other elements, which are simpler than by other instrumental methods.

(*b*) The determination of calcium, magnesium and various minor elements in vegetable matter and soil extracts. The minor elements are of great importance in studies of deficiency diseases and of mobilization and uptake of micro-nutrients from the soil in the processes of plant nutrition.

(*c*) The determination of lead in the petroleum industry and the possibility of including in analytical programs other elements of interest, e.g. vanadium, in catalysts, crude oils and other products.

(*d*) The rapid determination of lead, zinc, gold, silver and other elements, in the great range of metallurgical materials, minerals and concentrates. The method also provides an excellent means of determining impurities in precious metals.

(*e*) An effective method of isotopic analysis.

(*f*) A great improvement in the sensitivity for some elements, which makes atomic absorption one of the best methods for the determination of trace elements.

(*g*) The determination of various metals which show poor sensitivity in emission flame photometry. Excellent methods have been developed—in emission as well as in absorption—through the use of fuel-rich flames.

(*h*) Specific determination of the rare earth elements singly or mixed. This application has not yet been fully worked out.

(*i*) The specific determination of metals at toxicological levels.

(*j*) The determination of metallic elements extracted as a group by organic solvents (preferably with chelation). A single extract is used, without subsequent separation, but the method becomes specific because of the inherent spectral selection of atomic absorption.

A curious phenomenon that has accompanied the development of this branch of analysis is the profusion of reviews, expository reports, notes, bibliographies, and summaries which have appeared, sometimes as integrated contributions in journals, sometimes as chapters in general volumes. These have testified to the definite and powerful impact of this innovation in instrumental analysis, as have the frequent scientific meetings held nationally and internationally.

Chapter 1

Origins of the method and nomenclature

Atomic absorption and atomic-absorption methods form a distinctive new offshoot of spectroanalysis by flame methods. However, there are other means of producing absorption which may be used in a similar way for analysis, *without the use of flame*, hence it seems wise to define the method in general terms, on the basis of the absorption process.

This new branch of instrumental analysis is usually called *atomic-absorption spectroscopy*. This term, which was introduced by Walsh, denotes any analytical method in which an element is *atomized* in order to permit the observation, selection and measurement of its absorption spectrum. But since the method can also be considered as a new break-through in flame photometry, it has also been called absorption flame photometry, or more precisely, absorption flame spectrophotometry.

The method could be defined in general terms as an instrumental spectroanalytical method which is based on the measurement of the absorption produced, in a beam of radiation of suitable wavelength proceeding from an emitting source of constant intensity, by a medium composed of atoms of the element to be determined. Under these conditions, the amount of absorption increases with the concentration of atoms in the absorbing medium, and thus with the concentration of the sample solution used in producing the absorbing medium. If the sample is used in solid form, the absorption measured will increase with the concentration of the element in the solid sample, whether it be in its original condition or subjected to pretreatment.

The qualifier *atomic* stems from the fact that the absorbing medium contains atoms of the element to be determined. Atomic vapors at moderate temperatures and ordinary pressures have absorption spectra consisting of sharp lines which lie within a very convenient range of wavelength—from 1800 to 9000 Å—for selection with monochromators and spectrophotometers, and which are narrow enough to provide excellent specificity. To achieve the highest performance in atomic-absorption measurements, the absorption must be measured at the wavelength corresponding to the peak of the absorption line, or within a rather narrow wavelength range very close to the peak. The inclusion of absorption flame photometry within the general method atomic-absorption spectroscopy is due to the fact that the flame is used as a carrier of the absorbing medium formed of atoms. The flame is an effective means for producing and maintaining a suitable concentration of atoms, and the first experimental steps in this field were generally made with the aid of flames.

Nevertheless, any procedure whose basis can be covered by the above definition may be considered a true method of atomic absorption. Those procedures (which are most widespread today) that use discrete emitters and flames to obtain atomic populations constitute only one of many possible cases falling under that definition.

In atomic-absorption flame photometry, a sample in liquid form—a real solution or a suspension—is sprayed[1] into an appropriate flame, and the analyte or analytes[2] present are atomized. The analytes are determined by measuring the absorption of a beam of light passing through the flame. Each determination is made at the wavelength at which each analyte absorbs. The flame is placed between a constant-intensity source of light and a wavelength selector. Experimental readings are taken of the intensity of the light, as seen through the flame (by spraying the standards, the blank, and the samples).

The general definition would be susceptible to modification if one wished to include molecular absorption—molecular-absorption spectroscopy. However, although many types of molecules emit spectra of sufficient intensity to be used in emission work, their absorption spectra are too weak to be utilized under the conditions for atomic-absorption spectroscopy. The spectra are distributed among a great number of lines. In later sections, other experimental techniques that do not necessarily use flames in the production of atomic populations are mentioned.

1. ORIGIN OF THE METHOD

The ultimate origins of the method are, of course, to be found in the observations of Fraunhofer on the solar spectrum, and in the subsequent identification of the emission spectra of various elements, discovered by Bunsen and Kirchhoff. Mention must also be made of the studies of the composition of the stellar atmospheres, and of the studies on the elucidation

---

[1] For a long time the verb *atomize* has been used in flame photometry as a synonym of *spray*; thus the sprayers commonly incorporated in flame photometers are called atomizers. As atomic-absorption spectroscopy involves a conversion of a sample to a vapor formed by free atoms, it seem logical to reserve the verb *atomize* for the action of converting to atomic vapor.

[2] The English term *analyte* was introduced by Glenn E. Pollard in 1955. Here it is used in the sense of element to be determined. The author has published (*932*) some comments on the convenience of the adoption of the Spanish term *analito*.

of atomic spectra. From the analytical point of view, the sporadic efforts made to determine mercury in the vapour state (mercury did not present difficulties since it easily yields atomic vapor at room temperature—cold vapor)[3] deserve notice.

However, as a definite point of departure, the independent publications of Walsh (*797*) and of Alkemade and Milatz (*5,6*) are of the greatest importance. These publications demonstrated the effective potential of atomic absorption as a new and *universal analytical* tool in the instrumental field. After this start, some time passed before the appearance of the first applications and the descriptions of the first laboratory-built instruments for the research undertaken by various authors in Australia, New Zealand, Europe, South Africa and North America. It was these instruments and their analytical applications that first aroused widespread interest in the new method. In those early years, some publications mentioned and described an apparatus which, although very simple, easily built, and of low cost, could be used for the routine determination of various analytes (*108*).

The same phenomenon occurs with many analytical methods. Some observations and studies are made, followed by a period of silence, and then there is a rebirth as a new and flourishing branch of instrumental analysis. For example a considerable time elapsed between the observation of some colored lines and the presentation of the first emission flame photometer to the analytical world.

In many of the relevant publications paragraphs are devoted to the origin and history of atomic-absorption spectroscopy. The reader who wishes to pursue this interesting and frequently discussed topic, can readily find abundant information (see (*384, 438, 615, 800, 833*)).

2. NOMENCLATURE

The topic of nomenclature deserves further attention. The paragraphs that Gilbert (*274, 275*) devotes to this subject are of interest. A definite terminology should be established while the method may still be considered young, otherwise confusion in nomenclature will later hamper the classification, indexing and retrieval of documents and information.

Since atomic-absorption spectroscopy utilizes the absorption of spectral radiation produced by atomic populations, as observed by spectral selection and measurement, there can be no doubt that the terms *atomic, absorption*

[3] See, for instance, the contributions corresponding to references (*238, 360, 471, 484, 538, 649, 811, 834, 854, 855, 879*).

Kuznetsov and Chabovskii have published a method for mercury determination in powdered samples (*414*).

and *spectroscopy* (or some term related to spectroscopy) are correct. If further investigations into the true root of spectroscopy were made, some would prefer *spectrometry* or *spectrophotometry* in view of the true etymological meaning of *spectroscopy*. To shorten it conveniently, one could simply use the term *photometry*. The transmitted radiation is measured photometrically, spectral separation preceding the measurement.

The addition of the word *flame* implies a subdivision within atomic-absorption spectroscopy, in which the atomic population is produced by a flame, which also acts as a carrier. Similar subdivisions would introduce *furnace, hollow-cathode sputtering* and other ways of producing concentrations of atoms capable of absorption. The suppression of *atomic* might be objected to on the grounds that the phrase *absorption flame photometry* suggests optical extinction methods such as are used in some kinds of emission spectroscopy (*125*).

One other point remains to be considered. From the analytical point of view it is necessary to specify that the method is used for analytical purposes, and not for some other type of measurement. Therefore, the use of *analytical* or *analysis by* is imperative, except in an obviously analytical context.

These considerations are summarized in the following chart.

Indicating analytical application	*Indicating the fundamental process*		*Indicating the auxiliary experimental technique*	*Indicating the method as a spectral method in its different variants*
1	2	3	4	5
Analytical Analysis by	atomic	absorption	flame furnace hollow-cathode sputtering etc.	spectroscopy spectrometry spectrophotometry photometry

Terms 2 and 3 (atomic-absorption) are inseparable if one wishes to retain the concept of the basic process. Since the use of flames is inherent in the widespread technique utilizing discrete emitters and a flame, there is a strong argument for the consistent use of *flame* to distinguish this from other similar techniques. The use of *spectrophotometry*, which implies spectral selection and measurement is also justifiable, though the use of *photometry* has become quite common.

In summary, the general term *atomic-absorption spectrophotometry* and the special term *atomic-absorption flame spectrophotometry* (or *photometry*) are the fullest and most specific names for the general method and for its commonest variety. If *spectroscopy* is accepted, not in its strict etymological sense, but rather as a generic term for spectral methods, there is no objection to the term *atomic-absorption spectroscopy*.

With regard to the special case of flames, the retention of four words becomes inconvenient, hence some authors prefer the simpler term *absorption flame photometry*. This terminology has been discussed by Gilbert (*275*), and the term has been used by Alkemade and Milatz (*5*), Allan (*17*), and Leithe and Hofer (*428–430*). In their 1955 publication, Alkemade and Milatz had already called their instrument an *absorption flame photometer* in describing their tests with a constant monochromatic light source (*5*).

All the admissible terms will be used in this book, although to avoid excessive repetition, frequent use is made of *absorption* and *atomic absorption*.

With respect to *photometry*, it should be made clear that when this term is used in the description of procedures or instruments, it does not mean that in that particular case filters are used; *photometry* and *spectrophotometry* are used synonymously. The spectral selection of radiation by monochromators or by filters is used in flame methods—in emission as well as in absorption—as a means of giving a spectroselective photometric measurement. *Spectrophotometry* can be taken as a restrictive term within *photometry* if there is spectral pre-selection before the measurement[4].

---

[4] In a recent publication, Celsi considers that photometers provided with filters can be studied and classified under the same criteria as those commonly called spectrophotometers; the former are built according to the same principles, the only difference being in the device used for wavelength selection. See S. A. Celsi, Colorimetry and spectrophotometry: Revision of their theoretical fundamentals, *Bol. Soc. Quim. Peru*, 30 (4) (1964) 141 (in Spanish).

Chapter 2

General principles and characteristics

If some particular branch of an analytical method grows more rapidly than others and becomes more widely known, then it is obviously necessary, in considering the total picture, to give this branch special attention. Accordingly, in this book, much more consideration is given to the so-called atomic-absorption flame photometry, than to the other branches of atomic absorption mentioned in the previous Chapter.

1. GENERAL PRINCIPLES

Like every spectral method, atomic absorption utilizes two inherent analytical variables: a *qualitative variable,* represented here by the characteristic wavelength at which the absorption is manifest, and a *quantitative variable* provided by the magnitude of the absorption under fixed experimental conditions.

The qualitative variable is specific for each element, inasmuch as the absorption occurs at the same wavelengths at which the element produces its characteristic emissions when excited (see also Chapter 5, p. 29). It must be noted that although emission can appear at all wavelengths where absorption occurs, absorption does not necessarily occur at all the wavelengths where there is emission. Preference is given to the wavelengths corresponding to the resonance lines of each element. The line that represents a transition between the ground state and a higher state is known as *resonance line*. Although it is admissible to recognize as resonance lines those lines with their lower states just a little above the ground state, it is better to consider as *the* resonance line of an element the ground-state line corresponding to the longest wavelength.

The qualitative variable also gains selectivity by the addition of two selective principles to the experimental process an increase in selectivity increases the certainty of qualitative analytical separation and may even lead to specific identification). Firstly, there is a pre-selection in the absorption process with the use of discrete emitters, which produce narrow emission lines corresponding to the element to be determined; and secondly, the radiation already subjected to absorption is passed through a selective spectral system (filters and/or monochromators) before being measured photoelectrically.

The quantitative variable, like all variables that can be measured instrumentally, is conditioned by various experimental factors that can influence the instrumental response to the absorption phenomenon, which itself depends on the absolute or relative concentration of the components of the sample being analyzed.

Atomic-absorption spectroscopy is based on the utilization of a complete instrumental system composed of the following: an emitter system, which in most cases produces a spectrum characteristic of the element sought but may be a source producing a continuous spectrum; a system producing atomic vapor—a population of atoms—(generally a flame into which an aerosol of the sample is injected); a system of spectral selection (filters, monochromators); a photodetection system; and finally, a measurement system (direct or by recording or printing).

The measurement system is concern only with displaying the electrical signal from the photodetection system, which in turn responds to the transmitted radiation emerging from the absorbing medium.

If there are no atoms capable of producing measurable absorption in the absorbing medium, the emission from the source does not diminish and a constant intensity is recorded[1]. In other words, if an aerosol produced simply from distilled water or from a solution of substances that do not yield absorbing vapor is injected into the flame, the measurement represents practically all the emitted intensity. In this case, a reading is made of the *blank*, representing the absence of the element sought in the flame, which is the medium of optical absorption. When a certain quantity of absorbing atoms is injected into the flame, only a fraction of the light emitted by the source reaches the photodetector. The measurement is then a *direct* measurement inasmuch as the absorption is a function of the concentration present. From another point of view, the measurement is *by difference*, since the unabsorbed fraction of the emitted radiation is measured.

It may be noted that the selector system, in the case of discrete sources emitting a discontinuous spectrum (a spectrum of lines) of the element being determined, is expected only to isolate the characteristic and useful emission coming from the source. In this *post-selective* action (the first selective action, as already indicated, is in the emitting source), the selector system can contribute its second selective step by isolating the desired line

---

[1] "Constant intensity" must be understood to mean that the intensity should be constant. In fact, the source, is subject to variations that deprive the emitter system of constancy. Some instruments are prepared to avoid or compensate as much as possible those variations.

from a complex emission spectrum or by eliminating adjacent radiations that originate in the emitter or in the flame itself.

This subordination of the spectral selector system to the emitting source implies at the very outset a serious limitation to the qualitative possibilities of the analytical method. Any qualitative orientation is governed primarily by the nature of the source rather than by the variable selectivity of the spectral apparatus.

2. QUALITATIVE CHARACTERISTICS

Although mention has already been made of the difficulty of using atomic-absorption apparatus for qualitative analysis, nevertheless it actually possesses several qualitative characteristics, as is shown below.

(*a*) The absorption occurs at definite and characteristic wavelengths for each element examined (qualitative variable). Thus specificity can be achieved, but if the radiations of different elements are superposed, the specific character may be practically lost (at least at the peak wavelength; it should be noted that other components can produce a general background absorption). If other components affect the absorption process, they will raise or lower the absorption of the element sought.

(*b*) The use of different emitting sources makes possible the successive identification of absorptions by different elements present in the same sample solution. Detection of absorption may be considered to indicate the presence of the element in question.

(*c*) Since the absorption is peculiar to each element, the effects detected can persist in the presence of other elements or radicals or other components which do not affect the absorption process (at least at a given peak absorption wavelength). This circumstance enhances the qualitative character of the instrumental selection. When the components of the sample affect the absorption process for the element sought, there will be a reduction or an increase in the relative qualitative sensitivity attainable under ideal conditions in the absence of other components (for concepts and definitions of sensitivity, see Chapter 13).

(*d*) The utilization of subsequent optical methods of selection contributes to the overall instrumental selection, as has already been indicated.

3. QUANTITATIVE CHARACTERISTICS

Instruments for atomic-absorption analysis are predominantly quantitative, thus it is appropiate to consider the following quantitative characteristics.

(*a*) The absorption is quantitatively a function of the concentration of atoms in the path of the beam from the source. This concentration is a function of the instantaneous rate at which the sample is consumed in producing the atomic absorbing vapor, and it is also related to the concentration of the element to be determined in the sample or the solution. The instrumental response, which is translated into a meter reading or a permanent recording, is thus a definite function of the concentration of the element to be determined in the sample prepared for the instrument. Whether or not these prepared samples are of the same nature and composition as the original sample supplied, the instrumental response will still be directly related to the concentration of the sought component in the original sample.

(*b*) The magnitude of the absorption for a given concentration in the sample supplied to the instrument depends on an aggregate of experimental conditions previously established. Various factors greatly affect the magnitude of the absorption. The selection of instrumental and operational conditions can, within certain limits, reduce or increase the response obtained. A change in the response is produced by any variation of any of the instrumental or operational conditions (voltage or current supply to the emitter unit, pressures and flow-rates of the gases feeding the flame, the path of the beam through the flame, addition of non-aqueous solvents to the sample, sample flow-rate, by positive pumping or free flow, etc.). One cannot state the useful range of concentration for the quantitative measurement, in a strict sense, without defining all the conditions that may influence the final quantitative response.

(*c*) Just as in the qualitative selection, quantitative measurement is influenced by the presence of other components which may affect the absorption process. Once operating have been fixed, the quantitative response can be related to the concentration of concomitant components in the prepared solution.

(*d*) Atomic absorption is highly sensitive. The lower limit of the concentration scale for an element will be set in each case by the variability of the readings on the blank solution, for which the absorption is nearly zero (see Chapter 13).

(*e*) Atomic absorption has shown good precision and accuracy for an instrumental method. These concepts will be discussed in later chapters. The precision and accuracy are improved through proper calibration by comparison with standards of known concentration. In the case of low concentrations that are very near or below the limits of sensitivity for quantitative purposes, both precision and accuracy can be improved by a preliminary concentration process, provided that there is no risk of losses and/or contaminations.

Chapter 3

Absorption and emission

When atomic-absorption spectroscopy began to advance, it became necessary to clarify the relationship between it and the widely used emission flame photometry. This need increased when it became clear that atomic absorption was another flame method, since most atomic-absorption methods used the flame. Two questions immediately came to mind. What fundamental differences, not only in principle but also in range, exist between the two branches? Could absorption succeed in displacing and even putting an end to emission in the field of flame photometry? As immediate consequences of these questions: What are the advantages offered by atomic-absorption spectroscopy and particularly by atomic-absorption flame photometry? What difficulties exist?

And along with these questions, is another question, always the same, but always different, directed to the resolution of a specific problem: For this or that analytical problem, which should be used, emission or absorption?

An attempt will here be made to answer the above questions as briefly as possible within the limits of present knowledge. The answer may fail to be of lasting validity if new results favoring one method or the other later come to light.

1. COMPARISON OF THE TWO METHODS

Many of the publications on the subject will be found to contain more or less profound comments on the differences and similarities of the two methods[1]. The two branches of flame photometry differ greatly in their physical basis and in their experimental methodology. Their main points of contact are their use of a flame, a monochromator and a similar photometric system.

For emission flame photometry, use is made of radiation emitted by a sample introduced into the flame and excited in it. In atomic-absorption flame photometry, the absorption of a beam of radiation by a sample

[1] The reader should note the remarks of Gilbert (*275*) and the opinions summarized by Herrmann (*320*). See also the comments in other publications (*213, 615, 833, 912*).

brought to a flame traversed by the beam is measured. Aside from this difference there are many points in common. For example, the sample, usually in solution (it should not be forgotten that the sample may also be brought to the flame in solid form as a suspension), is introduced as an aerosol into a flame, where emission of excited atoms is utilized in the one case, and absorption by atoms in the ground state in the other. In both cases, the radiation emerging from the flame is received, selected and measured by a spectrophotometer. Again, in both cases, all the processes and factors governing the uniformity, constancy, qualitative and quantitative composition, repeatability, form, height, etc., of a flame fed by an aerosol, intervene and affect the behaviour and quantitative output of the emitting or absorbing medium. These facts, together with others given in the later sections on advantages and disadvantages of atomic absorption, may serve to illustrate the differences and similarities of the two methods.

The range of each of the two branches depends on the present and future means of producing emitting and absorbing media that yield signals of sufficient magnitude with samples of low concentration. Since the attainment of this objective is usually based on the flame itself (kind, temperature, form, width, height of the selected zone), it is clear that some of the possibilities of extending the range depend on modifications of the flames employed or on the production of new phenomena in these flames[2], along with the use of accessories to raise the intensity of emission obtained with the common flames (i.e., the use of sheathed burner and reversed flame). In short, the range depends on methods of increasing the proportion of atoms susceptible to excitation and the stability of flames.

In atomic absorption, the utilization of fuel-rich flames, and nitrous oxide–acetylene flames, adapters to increase the length of the optical path through the flame, and multiple passage of the beam though the absorbing medium (see Chapter 8), serve to provide media of higher absorption by presenting more atoms in a state suitable for absorbing the light from the emitting source. Every means of providing these conditions for determinable components, will undoubtedly increase the range of one or both kinds of flame photometry.

It is interesting that the recent attention given to fuel-rich flames in emission has resulted in an increase in the number of elements determinable by both types of flame photometry. Thus emission flame photometry has here contributed to the progress of one of the aspects of atomic-absorption flame photometry.

It is difficult to answer categorically the question about the obsolescence

---

[2] The modern use of fuel-rich flames (see Chapter 8) and the phenomena of chemiluminescence (*278*) in emission flame photometry may be cited as examples.

of emission flame photometry. A few years ago the supremacy of emission in almost all aspects could be defended. The recent advances in atomic absorption oblige one to be cautious in defending emission methods, but it must be recognized that atomic absorption still possesses some serious limitations that are largely absent from emission methods. At the 2nd Australian Spectroscopy Conference (*798*) Walsh discussed the status of both methods at that time, with special attention to those elements determinable by emission flame photometry by utilizing their atomic lines.

Emission methods still offer the following advantageous characteristics.

(a) *Qualitative analysis.* Emission flame photometry allows a complete inspection of the spectrum by recording the emission as a function of wavelength. In a matter of minutes, with an adequate scan, a qualitative analysis may be obtained.

(b) *Semiquantitative analysis.* By the same procedure a semiquantitative analysis is possible by estimating the intensity recorded at each wavelength at which the components of the sample emit. The spectrogram is a graphic representation of the quantitative variable of this analytical system as a function of the qualitative variable.

(c) *Quantitative analysis.* In quantitative work an instrument set up for emission analysis can be switched rapidly from one element to another; one need only change some of the instrumental controls (filters or wavelength setting of the monochromator, gain, slit, etc.), keeping the same emitting system, except that one may have to change the burner and/or the gases, instal the sheath for some elements, or make other changes, all of which naturally prolongs the time required for switching from one element to another in some cases. In atomic absorption one must have special emitters for each element to be determined[3]. Not much difference between the methods is noticeable for those cases in which it is necessary to make changes in the emitting system, in addition to the changes in settings.

(d) *Sensitivity.* Emission flame photometry offers considerably greater sensitivity for some elements (e.g., alkali metals). However, atomic-absorption methods possess greater sensitivity for other elements and offer the possibility of determining some elements which cannot easily be determined by emission. The absence of interelement interferences in many cases and various other factors also favor atomic-absorption and balance out the factors favoring emission listed in paragraphs (a)–(c).

---

[3] Kahn and Slavin (*384*), in discussing the inconveniences in switching from one element to another, indicate that the resetting of wavelength, electronic gain, lamp current, monochromator bandwidth and other factors could of course be made automatic, although at considerable instrumental cost, but that in any case, a skilled operator will not have much trouble in resetting the instrument for each analysis.

(e) *Band emission.* Emission flame photometry still offers many opportunities for the use of band emission. In atomic absorption, resonance and other lines emitted by the source are primarily used.

(f) *Multicomponent analysis.* Emission flame photometry may be successfully used for simultaneous multicomponent analysis with a single source, the selected radiation corresponding to each analyte being received by suitably placed photodetectors. However, multicomponent analysis can also be done by atomic absorption, with several monoelement sources or with single multielement sources.

(g) *Chemiluminescence.* Chemiluminescence phenomena in emission work offer a notable increase of sensitivity for some elements (*278*).

Since atomic-absorption flame photometry does not readily lend itself to qualitative or semiquantitative analysis and is primarily a quantitative method, it is applied only when it may be assumed on the basis of prior evidence that the analyte exists in the sample.

2. ADVANTAGES OF ATOMIC-ABSORPTION SPECTROSCOPY

Besides the points discussed above, there are others points in favor of atomic-absorption. For one thing, the experimental procedure, as in emission, is very simple, being reduced in many cases to dissolving the sample, without any kind of separation, and carrying out the instrumental process.

It has been proved that the absorption process is independent of the excitation potential and hence of the wavelength, a fact that makes the qualitative concentration limits for elements such as zinc and cadmium with resonance lines of very short wavelength, similar to those of the alkali metals with their much longer wavelengths. The independence from excitation potential makes the method independent of all factors which, in emission, may affect the percentage of excited atoms[4]. For elements with resonance lines of high excitation potential, atomic-absorption flame photometry gives higher sensitivity with average instrumentation than the emission method; this has been proved with magnesium, cadmium and zinc.

Emission flame photometry is, of course, a relative analytical method i.e. the sample must always be compared with standards. Atomic-absorption flame photometry is likewise a comparative method, but both methods are capable of absolute analysis, provided that all the factors affecting the final readings can be accurately accounted for (*442*).

[4] Some of the factors which alter the excitation conditions and thus affect the emission, e.g. changes in surface tension and viscosity or the nature of the solvent, may also have an effect in absorption, but from another point of view, viz., by altering the efficiency of atomization.

Atomic-absorption flame photometry is almost free of spectral interference effects (see Chapter 14). This is one of its greatest advantages: avoidance of the disturbances so often found in emission which require complicated methods for correcting the resulting errors; even in the determination of alkali metals one may find complicated cases of mutual interference. Owing to its relative freedom from interferences, atomic-absorption flame photometry is considered as one of the few methods which is almost free from matrix effects.

Since the absorption process is due to a physical property of the matter in the state of free atomic vapor, its specificity may be understood from the fact that a radiation characteristic of the element to be determined will be absorbed only by atoms of that element. Free atoms of any other element will not absorb that radiation. Atoms of the element to be determined will act *independently*, which results in freedom of spectral interferences; the other atoms present will not be limiting factors. However, any elements or other components that *chemically* bind the atoms of the element of interest forming undissociated or undissociable compounds, and thus preventing them from participating in the absorption process, are limiting factors.

In absorption processes there is the further advantage that the absorption is less dependent on the temperature of the flame than in emission, since only atoms in the ground state are utilized. However, there are maybe chemical interferences present (e.g. the condensed-phase interference described on p. 268), in which another component forms a compound with the analyte that does not vaporize readily in the flame, preventing the formation of atomic vapor.

One of the most significant advantages of atomic-absorption spectroscopy is its versatility. The availability of lamps for many different analytes and the possibility of varying the instrumental sensitivity to determine low and high concentrations, provide the analyst with a wide area of applicability.

The high sensitivity of the absorption method is another prominent advantage. Several elements are now easily detected and determined in the range between p.p.m. and p.p.b., and of course, the sensitivity may be further increased by preliminary concentration in many cases.

The good repeatability obtained in practice leads to results of good accuracy and precision. Reliability (insensitivity of the reading to alteration of instrumental parameters) is sometimes limited, but is often good enough for closely similar results to be obtained even when some of the instrumental variables such as slit width (when the source emits a well isolated line with low background), lamp current or height of the burner, are varied within wide limits.

Finally, there are two other advantages: relatively low price and the small amount of training required. Instrumental equipment may seem expensive to some potential users, but when one considers the great number of analyses that can be completed per year, the cost of atomic-absorption equipment is very low when calculated as instrumental cost per analysis. Besides, the man-hour factor is very small—only a few seconds are required to take each analytical reading and calculate the result.

Any operator acquainted with conventional emission flame photometry can switch to atomic absorption with little further instruction. Untrained operators need only a few hours' training to be able to work by themselves without constant help or supervision. Preparation of samples usually requires only a general analytical skill. Thus sample preparation and operation of the instrument can easily be done by technicians, once the instrument has been set up, aligned and tested. Naturally, the planning of new methods, preliminary calibration, study of performance, and the interpretation of results must be carried out by specialists or at least by persons at professional level.

3. DISADVANTAGES OF ATOMIC-ABSORPTION SPECTROSCOPY

Mention has been made in this chapter of several circumstances that favor emission flame photometry but are disadvantageous to atomic-absorption. Additional points are brought out below.

Some elements do not readily yield ground-state atomic vapor when they reach the flame as undissociated oxides or other stable compounds, and this hampers their detection and determination. Aluminum, molybdenum, silicon, titanium, and tungsten are examples. The determination of these elements is facilitated by the use of fuel-rich oxygen–acetylene flames, enriched air–acetylene flames and nitrous oxide–acetylene flames (see Chapter 8).

Certain solvents which may help to raise the concentration of atoms in the absorbing medium can show an absorption of their own in the flame. If this is due to the combustion process of the solvent, interference can be avoided by selecting a zone above that in which the unwanted absorption occurs.

For a single determination of a single element, a sample of limited volume may be used perhaps without difficulty. However, if determinations of several components are being attempted, repeated readings can consume the available sample before the analysis is complete. Dilution to increase the volume may not be permissible if one (or several) of the desired components is present at very low concentration.

In absorption there is less flexibility than in emission for varying the instrumental sensitivity in order to work with a given element over a wide range of concentration. To diminish the absorption when it is too great for a given element, it is usually necessary to make a preliminary dilution or to shorten the optical path through the flame, though it may be possible to utilize a different line of smaller absorptivity.

The precision achieved in atomic-absorption may vary from one element to another, since it is closely associated with the stability of both the emitting source and the flame, whereas in emission the precision is limited mostly by the stability of the flame. Since the lamp is a basic part of the source system, its stability is a basic factor; a very noisy lamp decreases the precision of the measurements and its fluctuations are an unavoidable component of the total noise of the measurement. It should also be remembered that a very noisy lamp will diminish the attainable qualitative fluctuational sensitivity (see Chapter 13).

Some analysts have cited as an objection to atomic-absorption flame photometry, the fact that the sample has to be supplied as a solution. However, this is not a disadvantage since solutions are the most convenient homogeneous form in which most elements in a sample can be introduced into an instrument. Most natural or artificial samples can easily be brought into solution; when this is not easy, it is often possible to utilize a *suspension* of known concentration.

The price of lamps has also been pointed out as a disadvantage because each element requires its own lamp[5]. But many laboratories use atomic-absorption for only two to five elements, so that lamps required do not add significantly to the cost of purchase and/or maintenance of the equipment. Research, educational and other specialized laboratories are the only ones faced with the problem of having to stock a large number of hollow-cathode and vapor lamps.

Because some flames more appropriate for some particular elements, an additional analyte may require not only a change of source and settings, but also of flame, burner and gas supply; fortunately, such cases are comparatively rare.

A serious disadvantage is the fact that the best absorption lines for some elements lie in the far ultraviolet. In conventional spectroanalysis, vacuum techniques can be utilized but these are not easily applied to atomic-absorption flame photometry. Nevertheless, *indirect analysis*, such as is used in emission flame photometry when elements or components

[5] Considering the topic of the individual lamps, Brech (*112*) mentioned the fact that in atomic-absorption any additional element requires additional capital outlay, and that this justifies much of the modern work done on the use of continuum sources and multichannel instruments for multi-element determinations.

that do not emit measurable characteristic radiations are to be determined, can also be applied to atomic-absorption. Operation in the far ultraviolet is impeded by the low transparency of the air, the optical components and the flame itself in those regions of the wavelength scale. Valuable work has recently been done in the far ultraviolet (*17*).

In some cases, atomic-absorption requires a greater volume of solution, and therefore a greater weight of element, for a given feeding time, than conventional emission methods, hence lower absolute sensitivity (see Chater 13) is achieved. However, a greater qualitative relative sensitivity is achieved for many elements in atomic-absorption, so that a given quantity of original sample may be more diluted.

Mention was made earlier of the possibility of carrying out qualitative and semiquantitative analysis by emission. Spectral scanning can be carried out in atomic-absorption only with great difficulty. A qualitative analysis by absorption would require a series of *specific qualitative tests* for all the elements sought, with a series of lamps, one for each element, the presence of absorption being tested at each wavelength. This would be very cumbersome and would require a great deal of time for the analysis of each sample. The difficulty of scanning arises again in the preparation of absorption spectrograms, for which measurements must be made at the various wavelengths, alternating blank and analyte solutions.

4. THE CHOICE OF ATOMIC-ABSORPTION FLAME PHOTOMETRY

The final decision by which an analytical chemist may select atomic-absorption from among other instrumental methods or in preference to emission flame photometry, must be based on a critical consideration of the elements to be determined, the type of sample, the nature of the solution prepared for analysis and its other components, the sensitivity required, the question of single or multiple analysis of the sample, the quantity of sample, the number of samples and number of analysis required each day. The advantages and disadvantages listed in the preceding sections may help in making that decision for a given case.

There are very clear cases, such as the determination of zinc in very small concentrations, which would call for atomic-absorption. Other cases are less definite and straightforward, especially in multiple and very complex systems, and require careful balancing of the various considerations.

The ideal solution is, of course, to have at one's disposal both an emission and an atomic-absorption flame spectrophotometer, but this is often impossible owing to economic factors, and often unnecessary when the analysis is not complex but must be repeated many times. This requirement of two kinds of flame photometer to take care of all applications to all elements and components that can be determined by flame photometry (some by emission and others by atomic-absorption) is satisfied in the available multi-purpose instruments.

5. COMPARISON WITH OTHER INSTRUMENTAL METHODS

The reader is undoubtedly familiar with the characteristics, advantages and disadvantages of other instrumental methods that are widely used. It is therefore not necessary here to present elaborate comparisons. A brief comparison with some other methods outside the field of flame photometry has been made by Elwell and Gidley (*213*). A detailed comparison has been given by the author (*586*), covering the instrumental methods that may offer precision, accuracy and sensitivity similar to those obtained with atomic-absorption spectroscopy.

In closing this chapter, the author wishes to state clearly that although he has a predilection for flame photometry, he does not fail to recognize that it is not universally applicable to all analytical problems involving the determination of elements, and that many other methods are probably more appropriate and convenient in certain cases.

Chapter 4

The literature of atomic-absorption spectroscopy

The appearance of the earliest publications on atomic-absorption spectroscopy and the subsequent output of original contributions and reviews have been mentioned. It is surprising that in such a short time so many compendious, critical, theoretical, and experimental contributions have been made[1]. There may soon be difficulty, as there has long been in emission flame photometry, in maintaining a complete file of all publications on atomic-absorption. Unfortunately, some contributions presented at conferences are not published for some time in accessible journals or remain unpublished, and so information is already becoming lost. Publications printed in countries with which there is little exchange of information and those printed in journals of limited circulation contribute to the difficulty of making a complete compilation of the literature.

The bibliography included in this volume tries to offer the reader a guide in his search for further information; an attempt has been made to include all the publications treating the basic subject or its different aspects and applications, along with some that mention the method only briefly. A few other references less closely related to the topic have been included because they are relevant to the text. A few references are also included in some of the footnotes.

Many of the references on flame photometry published prior to the book *Flame Photometry*, of which the author of this volume is co-author (*125*), have been excluded although they would serve as a complement, especially in those experimental or instrumental aspects that are common to both absorption and emission. The interested reader may extend his acquaintance with the field by reading the pertinent chapters of that book.

1. BOOKS

Up to the time of preparing the manuscript for this volume, the only book which has been published is that of Elwell and Gidley (*213*), a short

[1] In the search "Trends in Analytical Chemistry 1965" published by R. B. Fischer, *Anal. Chem.*, 37 (13) (1965) 27 A, (following those of 1946 and 1955), atomic-absorption papers are included under the heading "flame". Flame papers represent for 1965 2.4% in the classification according to method, in comparison with 1.3% for 1955. The percentage 2.4 is the same shown for infrared methods, larger than the percentage for X-ray fluorescence methods (2.2%), and close to photometric methods (2.7%).

but interesting work with a good review of fundamentals, equipment, and applications, containing valuable experimental results in the area of metallurgical analysis. This book, the first in this field, will always be esteemed for its value in spreading the technique of atomic-absorption spectroscopy in its early stages.

As was the case with emission flame photometry, the topic of atomic-absorption has been treated in special chapters of certain books or at least mentioned in the general text. The books of Dean (*186*), Herrmann and Alkemade (*321*), Mavrodineanu and Boiteux (*479*), and Pinta (*555*) treat atomic-absorption spectroscopy at some length. Special chapters of certain books have been written by David (*172*), Malmstadt (*449*), Robinson (*624*), Walsh (*800*) and Willis (*835*). All are chapters of lasting value and worthy of careful reading. Briefer references to atomic-absorption appear in texts by Mitchell (*505*) and in books edited by Strouts *et al.* (*740*) and by Kolthoff *et al.* (*787*)[2].

2. REVIEWS

The published reviews are very numerous. Some very extensive and thoroughly documented reviews, condensed so as to present information in the least space, are valuable as compilations and for their careful ordering of references. Other are less extensive but always offer some contribution or comment to enhance the knowledge of the specialist or of the person wishing to familiarize himself with the topic. Sometimes the references included are not numerous, since the review was published at a time when the available information was meager. Some contain only brief items.

The following reviews may be cited: Allan (*16*), a few anonymous (*23, 26, 30, 56*), Bermejo (*95, 896*), Brech (*112, 113*), Butler (*127*), Cooke (*156*), David (*164, 169, 176, 178*), Dawson (*181*), Dean (*187, 188*), Fassel (*227, 228*), Franswa (*247*), Gilbert (*274–276*), Herrmann (*319, 320*), Kahn (*373, 377, 379, 381*), Kahn and Slavin (*384*), Krampitz and Doepfmer (*412*), Leithe (*428*), Lockyer (*432–435*), Makino and Yasudo (*447*), Mansell (*467*), Menzies (*492–496*), Milazzo (*499*), Müller (*512–515*), Parellada (*541*), Poluéktov (*560, 561*), Poluéktov and Zelyukova (*566*), Pungor and Konkoly-Thege (*575*), Ramírez-Muñoz (*582*), Robinson (*614, 615, 619, 621, 623–626*), Rossi (*636*), Russell *et al.* (*647*), Sawyer (*652–654*), Scribner and Margoshes (*660, 661*), Shelton and Walsh (*667*), Sikorski and Copeland (*672*), Slavin (*679, 683, 685, 686, 693–695, 699, 700, 702*), Sullivan (*744, 745*), Svehla (*753*), Ulrich (*782, 783*), Ulrich and Shifrin (*784*), Walsh (*797, 799–806*), and

---

[2] Two pages are devoted to atomic-absorption in the chapter on *Flame photometry* by Vallee and Thiers in the *Treatise on Analytical Chemistry* (*787*), (see also ref. *863*).

Willis (*830, 833*). Some information is also included in the following references (*43, 136, 233, 252, 273, 305, 367, 400, 401, 427, 440, 534, 569, 574, 580, 613, 628, 629, 631, 633, 639, 644, 645, 650, 655, 698, 762, 765, 786, 809, 870, 890, 907, 914, 915, 926–928*).

The papers by Allan, Butler, Cooke, David, Dean, Fassel, Gilbert, Kahn *et al.*, Menzies (see ref. (*579*)), Robinson, Slavin, Ulrich, Ulrich and Shifrin, Walsh and Willis are probably the most suitable for initial reading and orientation in the subject.

Several manufacturers have published rather detailed reviews in their brochures or house organs. The contributions that appear periodically in the *Atomic Absorption Newsletter* published by The Perkin Elmer Corporation are valuable in presenting some of the most recent advances, original research, and current bibliographies.

Since the year 1965, special sections, under the title of *Information on Flame Photometry* has been published by Ramírez-Muñoz in the journal *Información de Química Analítica*; in these sections, informative comments on salient aspects of emission and atomic-absorption flame photometry are summarized under the headings *Instrumentation*, *New Methods*, and *New Experimental Techniques* (*592–596*).

Some bibliographies have been published separately (*27, 35, 692*). Many of the reviews cited above include extensive bibliographies.

Some articles of a general character describe and comment on the selected research of a few authors. Thus, the investigations of Walsh, Allan and Gidley were discussed in a review published in the *Hilger Journal* (*23*). The publications of Robinson and Menzies were discussed by Müller (*512*), who also described the development of the commercial atomic-absorption equipment available at that time.

Anonymous editorial articles or reports have appeared in several journals, describing new equipment or commenting on the new advances or advantages of atomic-absorption (*24, 26, 31, 32, 38, 47–49, 55, 56*).

Reviews devoted to some particular application of atomic-absorption spectroscopy are mentioned in later Chapters.

Various theses have been prepared which include work on atomic-absorption spectroscopy (*306, 509, 539, 603, 674*).

3. CONFERENCES AND LECTURES

A growing number of communications have been first presented at conferences and national or international meetings reporting basic results and specific applications as well as new instrumentation. The frequent contributions of British authors at the meetings of the Society for Analytical

Chemistry of Great Britain have been noteworthy in this respect; among them are the contributions of Menzies (*493*), Lockyer (*432*), Elwell (*209*), Elwell and Gidley (*212*) and Baker (*65*).

The number of papers dealing with atomic-absorption presented at the 10th International Conference on Spectroscopy at College Park, in 1962, constituted a real advance. The series of Australian Spectroscopy Conferences has produced a wealth of information. Ham (*303*), Durie (*203*) and Coogan *et al.* (*153*) have attempted to keep scientists informed of the rich contents of these conferences. Many excellent atomic-absorption papers have also been presented at various Conferences and Symposia in the United States in 1965 and 1966; a Panel Discussion provided many items of interest during the 1966 Pittsburgh Symposium (*928*).

Lectures have been given at the meetings of the Atomic-Absorption Spectroscopy Discussion Panel in Great Britain (*57, 180*).

Other individual lectures, which have been presented are those by Alkemade (*4*), Budd (*118*), Gilbert and Ulrich (*277, 281*), Hell (*312*), Manning (*465*), Ramírez-Muñoz (*582, 585–587, 589, 591, 597, 598*), Slavin (*688*), and Ulrich (*781*).

4. FUTURE PERSPECTIVES

The future will unquestionably bring many further interesting contributions to atomic-absorption spectroscopy, and further progress in emission flame photometry will undoubtedly help some areas of atomic-absorption. Already it has been stated (*191*) that the application of the advances in flame emission equipment and techniques to atomic absorption has contributed to its rapid development.

Among particular future developments, Butler anticipates the use of multiple detectors, multi-element sources, better means of atomization and more studies of the direct analysis of solid samples (*127*).

Walsh (*804*) believes that future efforts will be directed toward the use of double-beam methods, equipment that will permit the determination of several elements simultaneously or in rapid succession, and the development of better hollow-cathode lamps. Greater attention will also be given to the processes of atomization and the production of flames, as well as to the use of cathode sputtering and the arc furnace.

In his lecture in January 1964, at the Fondazione Carlo Erba, Alkemade listed as possible advances: increase in sensitivity by improvement of the optical system, increase in precision, perhaps by the extension of null-point methods, increase in the dynamic range, adoption of the internal-standard method, and finally, more attention to cathode sputtering (*4*).

The most important current trends of development, judged from recent published papers and from lectures etc. (see references (*532*, *597*, *699*, *782*)) are as follows.

(a) Use of the nitrous oxide–acetylene flame.
(b) Use of plasmas.
(c) Laser volatilization potentialities.
(d) Use of sputtering chambers and furnaces.
(e) The continuum emitter as a source.
(f) Polychromators adapted to atomic-absorption and emission methods simultaneously.
(g) Signal integration methods.
(h) Ratio systems, by using absorbing standards.
(i) Interference control.

5.1. Atomic-fluorescence flame spectrometry

The most recent contributions of Winefordner *et al.*[3] under the title of *atomic-fluorescence flame spectrometry* mark a new departure that may be the start of an extensive research effort.

In atomic-fluorescence flame spectrometry, the quantity measured instrumentally is the fluorescent emission coming from an atomic vapor that is irradiated by light of the wavelength that it absorbs. New instrumentation has been developed and the method presents interesting capabilities for the analytical determination of a series of elements. Mansfield *et al.* (*472*) have reported improvements in instrumentation that allow very low concentration limits for cadmium, zinc, mercury and thallium to be attained. They also report concentration limits for indium and gallium.

---

[3] See references (*472, 727, 789, 842–844, 848, 849, 852*).

Chapter 5

Theory

This book is intended primarily as a practical manual, but some discussion of the theoretical basis of atomic-absorption spectroscopy is essential for a proper appreciation of the value of the general method.

1. THE ABSORPTION PROCESS

If an atomic vapor containing free atoms of an element in the ground state is illuminated by a light source that radiates light of a frequency characteristic of the element present in the vapor, the neutral free atoms can absorb the resonant frequency[1]. The excited atoms return to their original state of energy re-emitting at the same frequency.

In fact, when such a vapor is illuminated by an appropriate light beam, an atom in that state absorbs a photon of light, and the energy of the photon produces a change in the distribution of an electron in the atom, bringing it to the so-called excited state. The net energy of this state is equal to the energy of the absorbed photon. As each species of atom can exist only in certain excited states with definite energies, only photons of definite energy can be absorbed (definite energy corresponds to definite frequency, and then to definite wavelength). In other words, only the photons of those wavelengths corresponding to the lines of the atomic-absorption spectrum of the element are absorbed.

For a preliminary understanding of the phenomenon involved in atomic-absorption processes, attention is drawn to Fig. 5–1, which shows the transition between the energy level or state E to state $E + \mathbf{h}\nu$. This transition is produced in an atom as a result of an absorption of radiant energy corresponding to frequency ν. The return from the upper level to level E is accomplished by emitting radiant energy[2].

---

[1] See comments on the characteristics of resonance lines in Chapter 2, p. 11. For those elements with complex spectrum, several resonance lines can be found suitable for the absorption process; if possible, the resonance line of longer wavelength is used for analytical purposes.

[2] The difference of energy between two levels is related to the frequency by the well-known equation $E_1 - E_2 = \mathbf{h}\nu$, where $\nu = \mathbf{c}/\lambda$; in which $\mathbf{c}$ = velocity of the light and λ = wavelength.

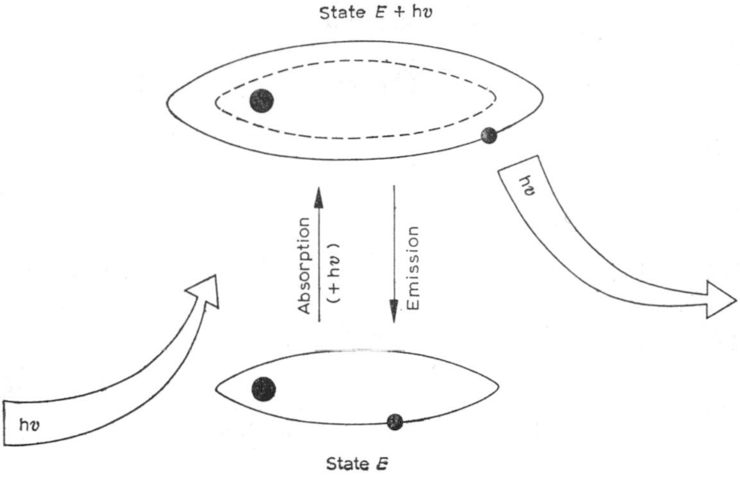

Fig. 5–1. Transitions between two energy states.

These phenomena, excitation and radiation, recall the excitation processes traditionally utilized in emission flame photometry. However, there is a fundamental difference: the energy is supplied in absorption methods in the form of a radiation—the flame should only help to produce the atom population—and in emission flame photometry the energy is supplied by the flame itself, which atomizes and energizes at the same time.

In Fig. 5–2, a more elaborate diagram shows a comparison of the processes involved in emission and atomic absorption when an atom at the energy level E is brought to the level $E + \mathbf{h}\nu$. These processes have been distributed into three consecutive steps, for each case.

In emission one can suppose that the atom receives the energy in the form of thermal energy at the excitation source (i.e. at the flame). A part of the energy provided is used in exciting the atom, which returns the energy in the form of radiant energy at the characteristic wavelength of the element involved (this is the fundamental phenomenon used in emission flame photometry), according to the difference of energy between the two levels. This radiant energy is transmitted in all directions, but the spectrophotometer observes only the fraction of the transmitted light that enters through the entrance slit, along the optical axis (according to the optical characteristics of the instrumental set up).

In the case of absorption (see also Fig. 5–2), a beam of light of definite intensity and specific wavelength comes from the source and passes through the absorbing medium. If there were no absorption (as in the case when a blank solution is sprayed into the flame; if there were some small absorption, the instrument should be zeroed) all the light would reach the entrance optics of the spectrophotometer. But if there are some atoms (free neutral atoms in the ground state) that can absorb a part of the radiant energy, this part is used in exciting the atoms. They, of course, also return energy as radiant energy, but it is transmitted in all directions, and in most cases the fraction observed by the spectrophotometer does not

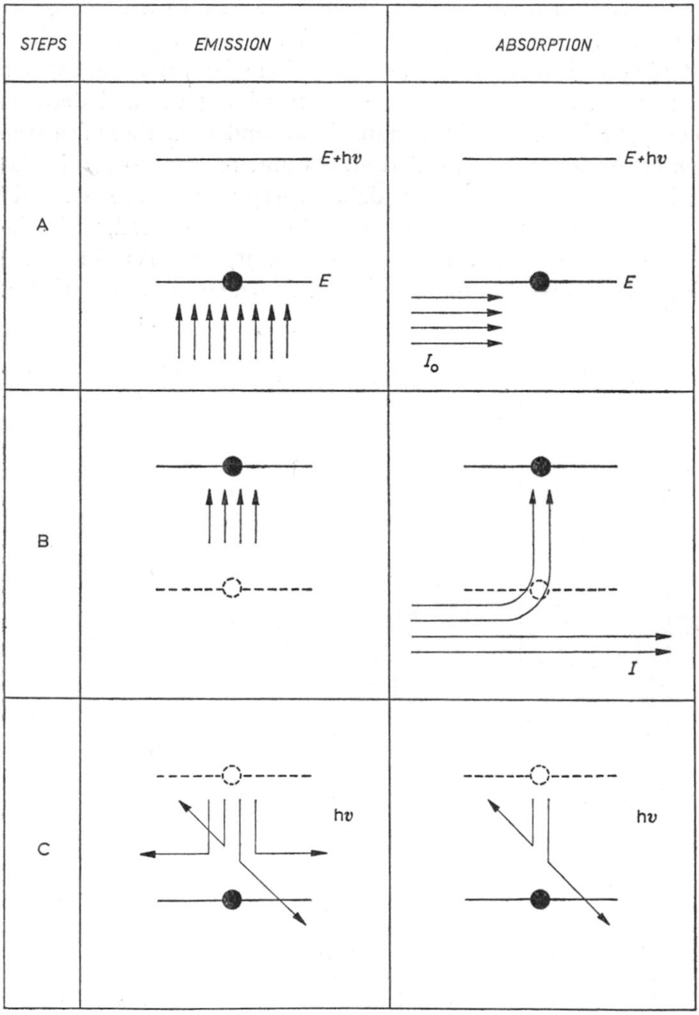

Fig. 5–2. Comparison of the processes involved in emission and in atomic-absorption.

produce any noticeable disturbance in the measurement of the remaining unabsorbed radiation coming from the source.

In the interpretation of Fig. 5–2 for the case of absorption, it should be understood that the lower energy state corresponds to the ground state of the free neutral atoms, in order to be close to the real behaviour of this type of absorbing system.

Actually, things are not so simple. Now, the whole process will be considered when a solution is introduced into the flame. If a solution (a dilute aqueous solution of a simple salt) is introduced into a flame in the form of a fine spray, a complex process occurs. Some steps are quite simple, being simple physical processes of evaporation of solutions and vaporization of solids; others are chemical processes involving thermal decomposition of the compounds existing in gaseous form, and then there are transitions from non-excited states to excited states and returns to the initial states by emitting radiant energy. The higher energy states are reached by the atoms in the flame because of the thermal energy supplied, which increases the kinetic energy of the atomic species present, and also as a consequence of the inelastic collisions produced there. A whole picture of this complex

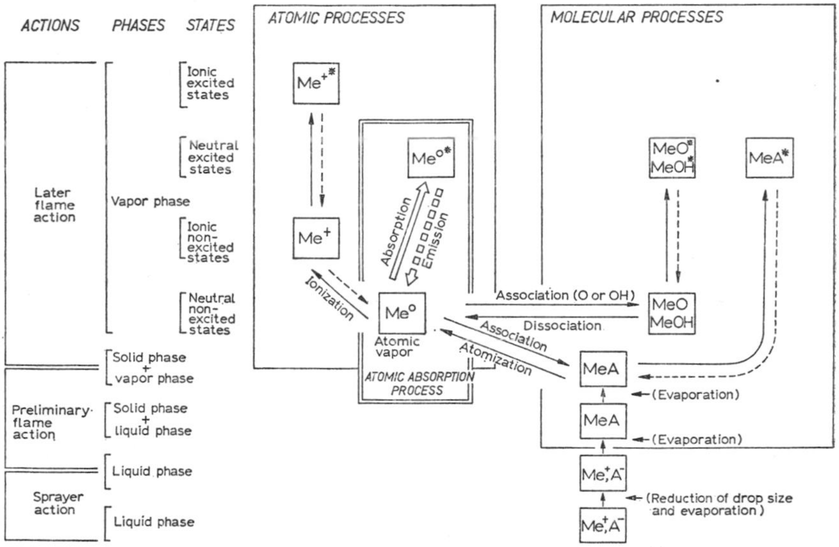

Fig. 5–3. Actions, phases and transitions involved in the transference of a solution containing a metallic element, Me, into a hot flame by means of a sprayer. (This figure is a modification of Fig. 12, p. 22 of the book *Techniques in Flame Photometric Analysis* by N. S. Poluéktov, Consultants Bureau, New York, 1961 (by permission of Consultants Bureau Enterprises, Inc.).

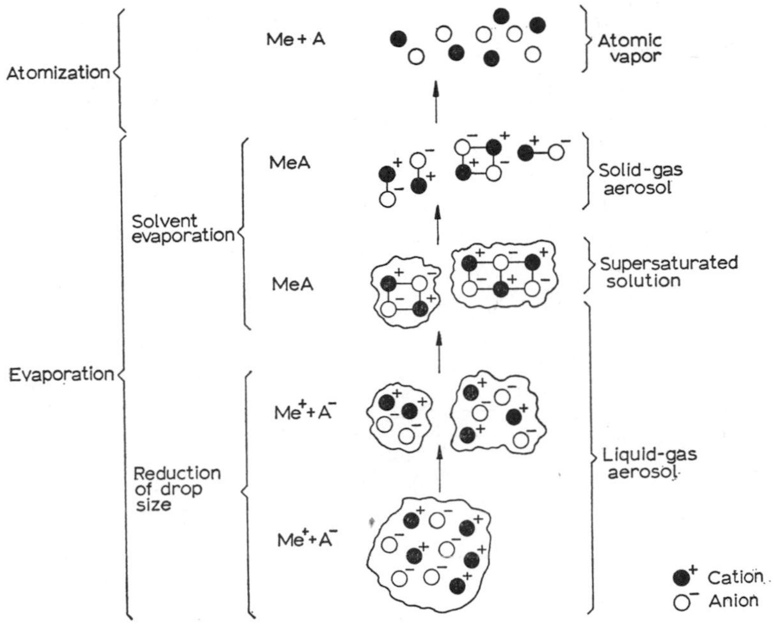

Fig. 5–4. Evaporation, vaporization of solids and thermal dissociation in flames.

process is represented in Fig. 5–3, for the particular case of a simple salt in the sprayed solution.

This figure is naturally not a representation of the well-known term diagrams[3], but shows the principal equilibria and transitions in this type of process. For this reason a real distinction has not been made between particular excited levels.

It is interesting to point out that in emission it is possible to take advantage of many of the transitions shown in Fig. 5–3, because they correspond to emissions that can be used in practical work: for example, those emissions produced by excitation of the molecular compounds formed in the flame by means of the oxygen or the OH (band emission). In atomic-absorption attention is concentrated on the transition corresponding to the step: ground state to excited state (neutral atom). See zone encircled in Fig. 5–3.

Most of the atoms of an atomic vapor in a flame are in the ground state, i.e., the electrons of the atoms are in their lowest energy states. Efforts

[3] Those readers interested in a thorough theoretical treatment of the term diagrams of interest in the flame field will find the necessary information in Part II of the book by Mavrodineanu and Boiteux (*479*).

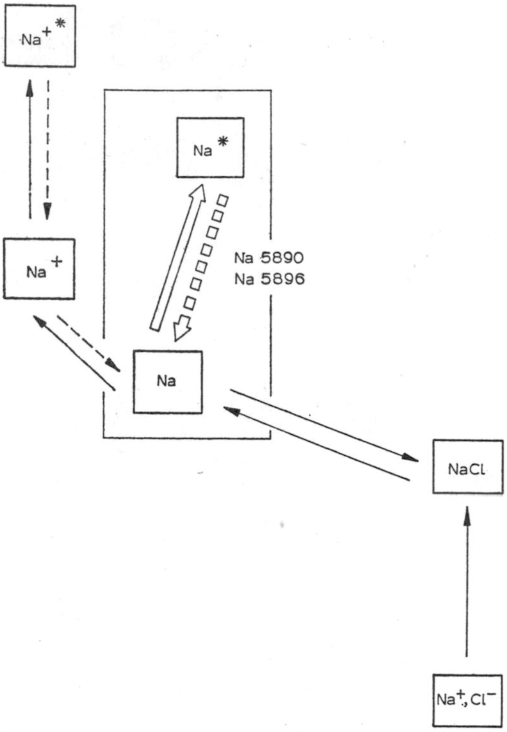

Fig. 5–5. Processes involved for a solution containing sodium. See Fig. 5–3.

are made to avoid losses of neutral atoms by ionization or condensation (forming molecular compounds), and to avoid the formation of molecular compounds by means of the components of the solution (condensed-phase interference; see Chapter 14), while trying to dissociate them with proper conditions of the flame.

The lower steps of the diagram in Fig. 5–3 (evaporation, vaporization of solids, and thermal dissociation) are represented in Fig. 5–4, which shows the decrease in size of the droplets until the moment in which the atomic vapor is formed. The transitions followed by the free atoms after this step are schematized in Fig. 5–5 and in Fig. 5–6 for two common cases (sodium and calcium). The most important phases for atomic-absorption purposes are marked in each figure[4].

---

[4] These diagrams (Figs. 5–4, 5–5, and 5–6) are modifications of some slides presented by Ulrich in one of his lectures (*781*), presented at Newport, Calif., in 1964 (by permission of W. F. Ulrich).

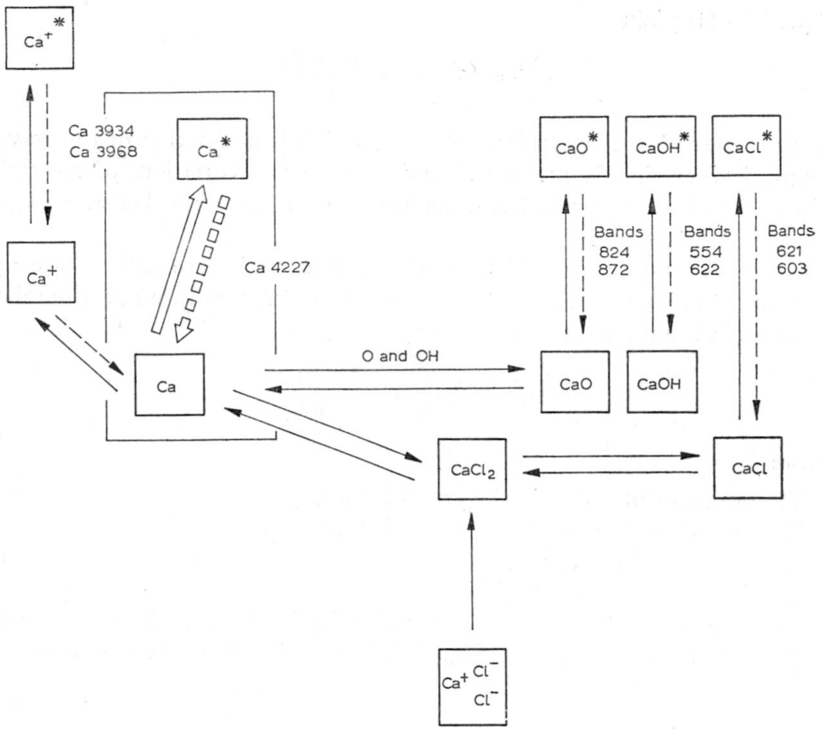

Fig. 5–6. Processes involved for a solution containing calcium. See Fig. 5–3.

1.1. Significance of the number of atoms in the ground state

If two energy states are considered at the same temperature, the number of atoms in each state will be given by the equations

$$\left.\begin{aligned} N_1 &= Cg_1 \exp -\frac{E_1}{\mathbf{k}T} \\ N_2 &= Cg_2 \exp -\frac{E_2}{\mathbf{k}T} \end{aligned}\right\} \qquad (1)$$

where

N_1 and N_2 = numbers of atoms in each state,
C = constant independent of the values E_1 and E_2,
T = absolute temperature,
$\mathbf{k}$ = the Boltzmann constant,
g_1 and g_2 = statistical weights.

Equations (1) yield

$$\frac{N_1}{N_2} = \frac{g_1}{g_2} \exp -\frac{E_1 - E_2}{\mathbf{k}T}$$

In this expression the exponential term, which is a function of the wavelength, is very significant. One should consider the variations of the ratio of number of atoms when the difference of energies varies because longer wavelengths are used.

Considering now a transition between the ground state and a state E_j, with the atomic vapor in thermal equilibrium at temperature T, the number of atoms in the upper state is given by

$$N_j = N_0 \frac{g_j}{g_0} \exp -\frac{E_j}{\mathbf{k}T}$$

where

N_0 = number of atoms in the ground state,
N_j = number of atoms in the excited state,
E_j = energy of excitation,
g_0 and g_j = statistical weights.

For an idea of the values of the ratios N_j/N_0 for a series of elements at different temperatures, see Fig. 5–7. For typical flame temperatures in

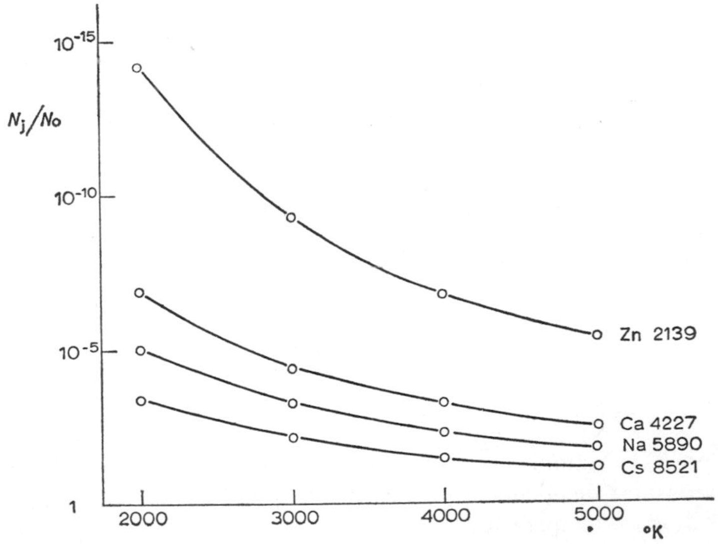

Fig. 5–7. Values of the ratios N_j/N_0 as a function of the temperature in °K for different metallic elements.

the range 2000–3000 °K, the number of atoms N_0 in the ground state is of the order of 10^4–10^{16} times N_j, depending on the element, N_j being the number of atoms in the lowest excited state for lines in the optical region of the spectrum.

Because T has an effect on N_j opposite to that of E_j, high temperatures are often sought in emission spectroscopy (this is not always true since consideration must be given to molecular spectra, ionization, background or interferences). The intensity of an emitted line corresponding to a transition from E_j to a lower state is proportional to N_j, and so, barring other effects such as ionization, an increase of temperature raises N_j, and therefore the intensity.

At the moderate temperature prevailing in flames, nearly all the atoms of an element are in the ground state[5], because N_j and all the N_i for more highly excited states, are very small compared with N_0; that is, N, the total number of free atoms, virtually equals N_0.

For this reason, the lines utilized in atomic-absorption flame photometry are nearly always those for which the lower state is the ground state (resonance lines). Because N_0/N is virtually 1 in flames, temperature scarcely affects this ratio, which is also unaffected by any other factor that alters the populations of the excited states[6].

The intensity of resonance lines is little affected by such factors as temperature, but these factors may, of course, affect the density (or partial pressure) of the atomic vapor and hence the intensity of the absorption lines. Thermal expansion is one such effect, and another is the dissociation of an oxide of the element. The degree of dissociation may rise rapidly with temperature, as in the case of aluminum, raising the intensities of the absorption lines correspondingly.

In emission flame photometry, on other hand, the lines utilized are any with whose upper states the flame is sufficiently well populated; these are not necessarily resonance lines. The N_i of interest, and hence the line intensities, depend very strongly on temperature, (except, sometimes, when excitation is due to chemiluminescence or is affected by other nonequilibrium phenomena).

Thus, atomic-absorption flame photometry enjoys the advantage over emission of relative insensitivity to fluctuations in flame temperature. In this respect, several authors have presented clear and instructive numerical examples (*615, 781*). For a given element, any factor in emission flame photometry which can produce a change of 20% in the number of excited atoms, immediately produces a 20% change in the intensity. But in ab-

[5] In elements with multiple "ground" states, possessing excited states close to the lowest state, the atoms may be extensively distributed among several states.

[6] Unless, again, there are excited states just above the ground state.

sorption, since the atoms in the ground state (about 99% of the total) play the vital role, any factor which produces a change of equal magnitude in the number of excited atoms, really produces a variation of only about ±0.2%. This effect is, in practice, essentially negligible.

2. QUANTITATIVE ASPECTS OF THE ABSORPTION PROCESS

In atomic-absorption flame photometry, the radiation beam passes through a carrier flame containing the absorbing atoms, forming in this way an absorbing medium of a definite thickness (fluctuations in the flame, in practice, produce small variations in the thickness). This absorbing medium acts as an *absorbing cell*[7].

Assuming that all the atoms considered in the atomic absorbing medium are in a neutral form and in the ground state, and also assuming that there are no scattering effects, if a practically parallel beam of light of intensity

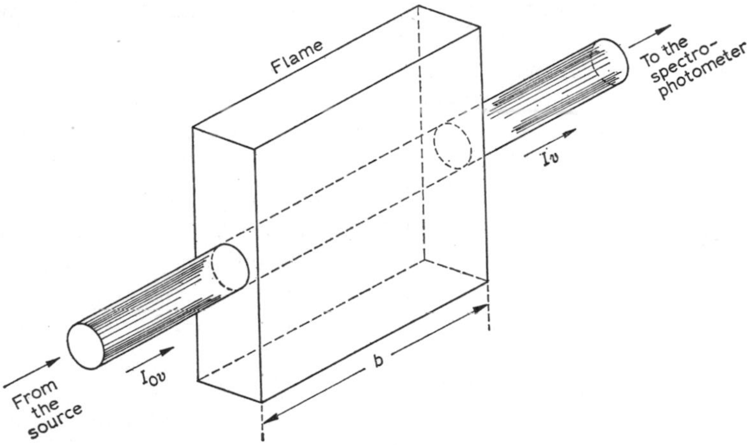

Fig. 5–8. Path length b of the absorption cell to be considered in a flame in atomic-absorption processes.

[7] The present discussion, based on the use of a flame as carrier of the absorbing atoms, may be extended to any other procedure that produces an atom population for absorption purposes.

$I_{0\nu}$ (at a frequency ν) passes through a pathlength b (Fig. 5–8), the emerging beam will have an intensity I_ν given by

$$I_\nu = I_{0\nu} \exp -K_\nu b$$

The absorption coefficient K_ν varies with the frequency, because the absorption line has a finite width. It will vary with all the factors that affect the width of the absorption line (temperature, pressure, nature of the atoms present in the absorbing medium, etc.).

According to the classical theory of dispersion, the integrated absorption

$$\int K_\nu \,\mathrm{d}\nu$$

is given by

$$\int K_\nu \,\mathrm{d}\nu = \frac{\pi \mathrm{e}^2}{\mathrm{mc}} N_\nu f$$

where

N_ν = number of atoms per unit of volume (cm^3) which absorb radiant energy between ν and $\nu + \mathrm{d}\nu$,
f = oscillator strength,
m = mass of the electron,
e = charge of the electron,
c = velocity of the light.

In a transition starting from the ground state (N_ν is practically equal to N_0, which is essentially equal to the total number of atoms), the integrated absorption is a linear function of the number of atoms, i.e. of the concentration of absorbing atoms in the medium. It should be noted that neither the temperature nor the excitation potential appears in this expression. In the last equation is included the value of the oscillator strength, which is the average number of electrons per atom which can be excited by the incident radiation.

2.1. Beer's law

The *Bouguer–Lambert–Beer–Bernard law*, frequently called Beer's law, is fundamental in the consideration of the quantitative aspects of the absorption process in atomic-absorption.

If the absorption cell has a thickness b, and contains a concentration of atoms c, the transmittance of the medium is given by

$$T = \exp -kbc$$

or, after the necessary transformations

$$T = 10^{-abc}$$

$$\log_{10}\frac{I_0}{I} = \log_{10}\frac{1}{T} = abc$$

This expression can be summarized in the form

$$A = abc$$

In this equation *a*, the coefficient of proportionality in this linear system, represents the value of the *absorbance A* per unit values of *c* and *b*. The coefficient *a* is known as *absorptivity* and has a characteristic value for each analytical system studied, i.e. for each analyte and for each set of instrumental parameters.

The absorbance values *A* are used in experimental work to represent variations of the quantitative variable measured (percentage of absorption) as a function of the concentration of the solutions.

A is calculated by means of the expression

$$A = \log \frac{100}{100-\%\ \text{Absn.}}$$

or, in other forms

$$A = 2-\log\,(100-\%\ \text{Absn.})$$

$$A = 2-\log T_{(\%)}$$

Values of *A* can be obtained from tables that give *A* corresponding to values of percentage of absorption (and of percentage of transmission) from 0 to 100 (see Table I in the Appendix).

In quantitative work a linear relationship is used which, in its simpler form, can be expressed as

$$A = mC$$

Sometimes this relationship is not linear and curves are used to represent the variations of *A* as a function of concentration values *C*.

This last equation in turn is based on the functional relationship

$$c = \varphi(C)$$

which relates the concentration of atoms in the absorbing medium to the concentration, C, of the analyte in the solution sprayed. This function is mainly governed by the efficiency achieved in the process of spraying and in the process of atomization.

2.2. *Significance of the width of lines in the absorption process*

In order to perform experimental readings, the instrument is set in such a way that it measures the intensity of the line emitted from the source. Absorptions produced on this line by the absorption line cause decreases in the intensity measured. Readings are expressed as percentage absorptions. The absorptions in percentage are converted into absorbances, and the absorbances are plotted on working curves (absorbances plotted versus concentrations of the solutions). If the source line were very broad, the decreases would be less noticeable. The halfwidth of the emission line coming from the source should be much smaller than the halfwidth of the absorption line.

The absorption lines have a natural width of about 10^{-4} Å, although in practice the actual width is increased by various factors. Even so the resolution of the usual instruments is not sufficient to measure the profile of such a line with the necessary accuracy[8]. These difficulties are avoided by using sharp line sources which produce very narrow lines.

The broadening is conditioned by the movement of the atoms (Doppler effect), by the collision of the atoms with atoms of a different gas (Lorentz effect), by the collision of atoms with atoms of the same kind (Holtsmark effect), by magnetic fields (Stark effect), and by other external factors such as electrical fields[9].

If the broadening of an absorption line can be wholly ascribed to the Doppler effect, the relationship between the absorption coefficient *at the center of the line* and the number of absorbing atoms N is given by

$$K_{\text{max.}} = \frac{2\lambda^2}{\Delta\lambda}\sqrt{\frac{\log_e 2}{\pi}}\,\frac{\pi e^2}{mc}\,Nf$$

[8] Even if the line is broadened to the order of 0.01 Å, the measurement of its profile would require a high resolution (about 500,000).

[9] See the discussion published by Rossi (*636*). Doppler, pressure, resonance, and self-absorption broadening, as well as Stark and Zeeman broadening, have been discussed extensively by Walsh (*800*), who also commented on hyperfine structure in the phenomena of atomic-absorption. The author recommends very strongly that the reader turn his full attention to the publications of Walsh, which contain a very complete theoretical treatment of these topics. The book by Mitchell and Zemansky (*503*) also provides an excellent discussion of many topics related to the theoretical study of the phenomena involved in atomic-absorption.

In this equation is included the oscillator strength of the corresponding transition, f, and a magnitude $\Delta\lambda$ which is the width of the line determined by the Doppler effect. This magnitude in its turn is expressed by

$$\Delta\lambda = 1.67 \frac{\lambda}{\mathbf{c}} \sqrt{\frac{2\mathbf{R}T}{M}}$$

which refers to a wavelength λ, including the universal constant **R**, the atomic weight (or molecular weight) M, and the absolute temperature T; e represents the electron charge and **c** the velocity of the light.

The relationship between $K_{\mathrm{max.}}$ and N is maintained only at low concentrations. At high concentrations the width may originate from factors different from the Doppler broadening.

Narrow emission lines are obtained by the use of hollow-cathode lamps. At the same time, the width of absorption lines is kept as small as possible by maintaining the minimum temperature, pressure and electrical fields. Under optimum conditions it is not necessary to look for slit-widths as narrow as the half-width of the absorption line. It will be sufficient if the spectrophotometer isolates the required emission line from other lines emitted by the source.

PART II

INSTRUMENTAL SYSTEMS

Chapter 6

Instrumental systems

In this Part, attention is turned to the subject of the instrumental systems needed for work in atomic-absorption spectroscopy. In Chapter 2, it was mentioned that the complete instrument is made of several individual systems to take case of emission, production of atomic vapor, optical selection, and measurement. These systems will be considered first, and then the equipment used by various authors and the commercial instrument available today will be discussed.

In every photometer intended for atomic-absorption, the following instrumental systems may be distinguished.

(a) *Emission system.* This system consists basically of a source of radiation which may be an emission spectrum of the analyte, the emitted radiation being directed towards the absorbing medium formed of the atoms of the analyte. The accessories needed to operate the source include power supplies for hollow-cathode lamps and similar but simpler power supplies for vapor lamps, housings, alignment mechanisms, rotating turrets, sliding lamp changers, warm-up mounts, auxiliary meters, and other devices. The chopper itself may be counted an integral part of the system since its principal function is to modulate the source light (chop the light beam by periodically interrupting it).

(b) *Absorption system.* The main component of this system is the atomic vapor which is to exercise its absorption on the beam of radiation from the source. The absorption system thus comprises all the instruments and accessories that are involved in generating the atomic vapor, starting with the means of introducing the sample; in these parts it is necessary to preserve a constant ratio between the concentration of the analyte in the sample and the concentration of the atomic vapor. In the case of photometers that use a flame, the absorption system consists of the flame, the burner that supports it, the sprayer (with or without spray chamber), capillaries, tubes or injection systems for introduction of the sample, regulators and manometers or flowmeters to control the gases, the gases themselves and their tanks or supply lines, turning mechanisms for rotating the burner, devices for adjusting the height of the burner, chimneys, and adaptors to provide long paths. In photometers that do not use a flame, flash-heating chambers, electrodes in spark-in-spray techniques, diverse

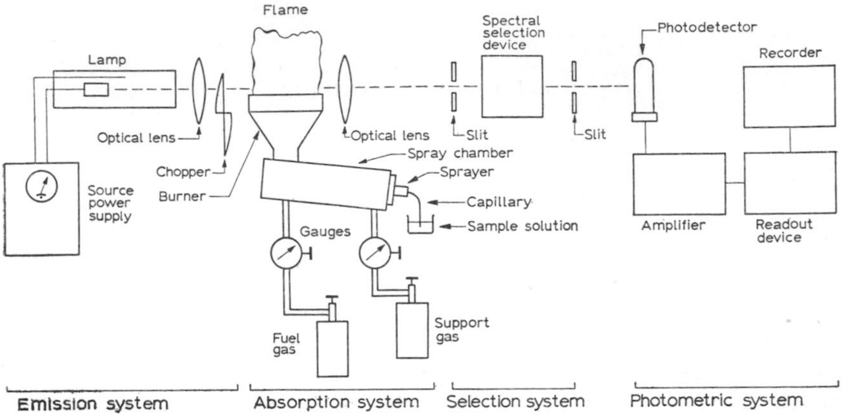

Fig. 6–1. General scheme of an atomic-absorption flame photometer, showing the different systems included.

chambers to generate the atomic vapor, supplies of inert gas, and the auxiliary electrical equipment. Also included in the absorption system are the auxiliary optical components such as lenses for collimating the beam, mirrors for the multi-path devices, and periscope couplings.

(c) *Selection system.* This refers only to the equipment for spectral selection. The system includes both the optical devices for spectral selection (filters, monochromators—with prism or grating) and mechanical accessories (slits, turning mechanisms, and means for reading wavelength settings and slit widths).

(d) *Photometric system.* This consists of systems for photodetection (non-multiplier photodetectors and photomultipliers) and for measurement. The photometric system includes all the electronic equipment necessary for supplying the photomultiplier, amplification, rectification, direct reading, scale expansion, and potentiometric recording. Digital reading devices and printers can also be included in this system.

Fig. 6–1 shows schematically a complete instrument that uses a flame in the absorption system. A comparison of this figure with one at the beginning of Part III of *Flame Photometry* (*125*) (Fig. III.1, p. 36) will reveal the differences between instruments intended for absorption and for emission flame photometry. Diagrams that show a variety of forms have been published by various authors. The diagram shown here is somewhat more complicated, but incorporates most of the instrumental components mentioned above.

Chapter 7

Emission system

It is best to establish at the start the important distinction between *continuous emitters* and *discrete emitters*. The first produce a *continuum* i.e., a continuous emission over a considerable range of the spectrum. The second are characterized by a *discrete spectrum*, that is an emission consisting of narrow, separated lines—a discontinuous spectrum[1]. Usually the spectrum consists of lines of only one element, the analyte, though it may consist of lines of two or more elements.

The discrete emitters best meet the requirements set down in preceding chapters. Greater efficiency is to be expected if the emission lines subjected to absorption are narrower than the absorption lines themselves. Winefordner (*841*) has made a detailed study of the effects of source linewidth on absorbance and has shown that high resolution is needed to measure line absorption when the source emits a continuum. Up to now, continuous emitters have been studied by several authors. Discrete emitters will be treated more extensively here since they have been the more widely used.

1. CONTINUOUS EMITTERS

In some publications, especially in the early ones, it has been stated that emitters of a continuous spectrum are not suitable as sources, because the absorption lines are very narrow and the brightness of the continuous sources is too low for satisfactory measurement of the absorption[2]. But more recently there have been some papers on the use of this type of emitter.

The use of a continuum was first mentioned by Alkemade and Milatz (*5*). A continuum has served as a background source for locating the lines most

---

[1] Continuum emitter and continuous emitter seem to be used indiscriminately in the literature. In comparing the two types, it would be consistent to say continuous and discrete emitters, or continuum and line emitters.

[2] Low brightness (radiance) of the continuous emitters available until recently makes measurement of absorption difficult primarily owing to limitations of noise. Most monochromators are not sufficiently luminous to provide an adequate photon flux with the narrow bandwidths required. Another disadvantage of low brightness is the greater interference from flame emission.

suitable for atomic-absorption (*15*), for studying the absorption spectra of various elements (*154, 228, 235, 264*), and for studying the effect of the monochromator on the shape of the working curves (*264*). For these purposes tungsten lamps, hydrogen lamps and high-pressure xenon-arc lamps have been used[3]. Spectrography has been used for selecting suitable absorption lines. For background corrections in long-path atomic-absorption spectrometry, Koirtyohann and Pickett have used the hydrogen lamp as a reference emitter (*409*).

One of the outstanding characteristics of continuous emitters is their stability. This helps to offset the loss of sensitivity resulting from the fact that even good monochromators do not provide narrow spectral bandwidth such as is offered by discrete emitters. The stability of the continuous emitter can improve sensitivity to the extent that sensitivity is limited by the signal-to-noise ratio. The greater stability then compensates for the ordinarily poorer resolution. No advantage will be found in those cases in which the loss of linearity with widening spectral bandwidth is more severe than the loss of sensitivity. If the stability is high, scale expansion can be used to read the small signals easily and to see if, under equal conditions, the fluctuational concentration limits are smaller than those obtained with less stable discrete emitters.

The paper presented by Fassel *et al.* (*236, 909*) on the evaluation of continua as primary sources is a very important contribution, as well as the papers by Kniseley (*399, 402*). Some of the results obtained are better than those with hollow-cathode lamps (see also references (*265, 458*)).

Ivanov and Kozireva have used a hydrogen arc continuum in combination with a quartz prism monochromator; with this instrument they studied the sensitivity of silver, copper, magnesium, manganese, iron, cobalt, lead, nickel, cadmium and zinc (*359*). The determination of magnesium in strontium nitrate has been reported also using a continuum as source (*359*). The determination of other elements, including rare earths, requires the use of fuel-rich flames, which has been examined by Fassel *et al.* (*236, 909*). Research on continuous source applications has also been reported by Ginzburg and Satarina (*282*), who used a DVS-25 hydrogen tube as a continuous spectrum source; their determinations show that higher sensitivities are obtained with a hollow-cathode lamp than with the hydrogen tube[4].

---

[3] The quartz iodine sources offer great potentialities.

[4] It is not surprising that working curves of smaller slope are obtained with continuous sources than with hollow-cathode lamp sources, and that a greater loss of linearity occurs when solutions of high concentration are measured. Nevertheless, an improvement can be expected in the coefficient of variation, especially at low absorption levels, if appropriate reading techniques are used.

So long as acceptable, sharp line sources for all the determinable elements are unavailable, and in spite of the fact that the development of satisfactory multi-element lamps promises to alleviate the difficulties of using several single-element lamps, the following advantageous characteristics of continuous sources may be pointed out.

(a) The lower cost of lamps, avoiding the capital investment in the purchase of single-element lamps or several multi-element lamps. This lower cost is in part compensated by the higher price of the monochromator required for continuous source work.

(b) No delay in the acquisition of new lamps when new elements are added to the analytical schedule or when worn out lamps need replacement.

(c) No time spent in changing and aligning the individual lamps.

(d) No time spent in a preliminary study of the best operating conditions of each individual lamp, especially looking for the best current.

(e) No delay in stabilizing multi-element lamps after changing the current for switching from one element to another.

(f) No repeated warm-up periods with single-element lamps.

(g) The stability of a continuous source is about the same for all wavelengths, and consequently for all the elements.

(h) The sensitivity and the shape of the working curve depend principally on the slit width.

(i) Scanning capabilities, with the inherent potentialities of performing qualitative and semi-quantitative analysis as in emission[5].

2. DISCRETE EMITTERS

Flames, vapor discharge lamps and hollow-cathode lamps are the principal discrete emitters, though some other sources are also mentioned below.

2.1. *The flame as a source*

The flame was considered as one possibility in the earliest work (*5, 6*); it is easy to produce and to maintain reproducibly, and yields a good intensity of emission. The flame is very versatile, and many elements can be excited in it to give an emission spectrum. But lines coming from a flame are less bright and wider than lines produced by other types of sources. With a system for introducing the sample—any of those commonly used in emission—the desired analyte can be excited in the source flame[6].

---

[5] Interesting scans were shown by Fassel *et al.* at the 1966 Pittsburgh Conference with clear peaks for several elements under the continuum signal level (*233*). Fassel also mentioned the possibilities of studying molecular absorption.

[6] For further information on the flame as a source of emission, consult *Flame Photometry* (*125*), Chapter V, p. 37.

Sawyer (*653*), who has made an extensive use of the flame as source, has indicated that this alternative should not be overlooked when adequate hollow-cathode lamps cannot be prepared. The flame as source has been replaced by the hollow-cathode lamp because of the many advantages of the latter. Regarding the recommendation by Hunt (*352*) of a more extensive use of flames as emitting sources, Walsh (*804*) raises the objection that the lines emitted by flames are much wider than those emitted by hollow-cathode lamps, so that there is a loss of sensitivity. Moreover, the intensity of the flame lines is inadequate in the ultraviolet region, where atomic-absorption has its greatest advantages.

The flame as a source has been used recently in isotopic analysis by atomic-absorption (*459, 678*) (see Chapter 19, p. 387).

The effect of a microwave field on flame emission, yielding an intense source of narrow spectral bandwidth, has been studied by Rosenthal and Eyer (*635*). They have studied the effect of this intense light source by applying a microwave field to a sodium-seeded oxygen–hydrogen flame. The waveguide is open at the end and has holes to permit the insertion of the flame with its axis perpendicular to the direction of the electric vector. The flame is practically confined inside a quartz tube containing a charge of small sodium chloride crystals. The instrument is placed in an exhaust cabinet and shielded against microwaves. The use of this notable bright source in atomic-absorption might be restricted because, as mentioned by the authors, the enhanced emission is limited to the vicinity of the resonance lines and shows rather extreme broadening with narrow reversal.

2.2. *Laboratory vapor-discharge lamps*

The characteristics commonly required of the sources employed in atomic-absorption are: (a) a wavelength characteristic of the analyte, (b) constancy of emission, and (c) small linewidth. These three requirements can be met by vapor-discharge lamps, hollow-cathode lamps, and high-frequency electrodeless discharge lamps. The first two have become the most popular for atomic-absorption flame photometry. This section will deal primarily with vapor-discharge lamps.

These lamps are made of a sealed tube of glass or silica containing oxide-coated electrodes; they contain one of the rare gases and a quantity of the metal whose spectrum is required. These lamps are very suitable for obtaining pure spectra of the alkali metals, mercury and other elements.

They can be run on alternating current, using a choke or a transformer. The use of an ammeter with a variable transformer is recommended because it is then very easy to study the instrumental responses obtained at different applied currents. The best efficiency is achieved with currents considerably lower than those recommended by the manufacturers. The lamps are underrun to avoid, or at least reduce, the effects of self-reversal. In this way greater sensitivity is achieved, but of course, if the current is reduced excessively, the measurements may become less accurate (*127*). Trent *et al.* (*774*) have studied particularly the influence of self-absorption in sodium arc discharge lamps on linearity and sensitivity. At present there are hollow-cathode lamps available for sodium and potassium, and a comparison between the results obtained with these lamps and the Osram vapor discharge lamps has been published by Manning *et al.* (*462*).

For details on the characteristics, construction and operation of vapor lamps, the paper by Elenbaas and Riemens (*208*) should be consulted.

Vapor lamps have been widely used in work with mercury (*238, 834*). Gilbert (*275*) mentions the possibility of using mercury lamps excited with microwaves to avoid self-reversal.

Vapor-discharge lamps are relatively cheap and are available for many elements (*335, 768*). Besides the Osram series[7], a wide selection of lamps is offered by Philips[8] including some with quartz envelopes (*768*)[9].

In commercial atomic-absorption spectrophotometers there are special sockets for vapor-discharge lamps, as they are recommended for alkali metals and mercury determinations. The use of the thallium lamp is becomming quite common; satisfactory results can be obtained for the determination of thallium with an Osram lamp at run low currents (*110*). The zinc and cadmium lamps, which were among the first vapor-discharge lamps, have been replaced by the corresponding hollow-cathode lamps.

Vapor lamps have the advantage of high intensity, which permits high signal-to-noise ratio. Recently they have been used for atomic-fluorescence flame spectrometry (see Chapter 4, p. 28). In this method a source illuminates a flame with a monochromatic radiation, but instead of the absorption of the light by the flame, the resonant-fluorescent radiation emitted by the flame is measured by the instrument. The source must be of sufficient intensity and must be modulated in order to distinguish the fluorescence from the radiations emitted by the flame.

2.3. *Hollow-cathode lamps*

Hollow-cathode lamps have long been familiar to spectroscopists as line sources yielding arc and spark spectra. They have also been offered by

[7] Osram G.m.b.H., Munich, Germany.
[8] Philips Gloeilampenfabriek N.V., Eindhoven, Netherlands.
[9] If the lamps have no quartz envelopes it is necessary to provide them with an exit hole which allows the use of short wavelength radiations.

commercial firms for some time. In 1964 Westinghouse Electronic Tube Division published a periodic table showing a series of lamps which cover most of the element determinable by atomic-absorption (*816*) (see Fig. 7–1). Their characteristics are given in references (*815, 817, 818*); the papers by Burger *et al.* (*119–121*) should also be consulted as well as references (*86, 102, 286, 387, 408, 705, 888, 899, 948, 950*).

Ideally, the hollow-cathode lamp used as a source should emit intense and stable light at only the wavelengths to be used for analysis. If proper conditions are chosen, the emission of a hollow-cathode lamp consists of a very steady, brilliant and clean spectrum showing very narrow lines of the element forming the cathode. The lamps now available fulfil these requirements satisfactorily.

The hollow-cathode lamp consists of a sealed tube containing an anode and a hollow cylindrical cathode. The hollow cathode is made of, or at least lined with, the metal whose spectrum is desired. The tube contains a rare gas at low pressure. The radiation exits from the tube through a window made of glass or quartz. The anode is usually made of tungsten; nickel anodes are also quite common.

When the lamp is connected to a suitable power supply, a discharge takes place, ionizing the rare gas. The ions bombard the cathode, knocking out atoms of the metal; this action is called *sputtering*. The atomic vapor of sputtered metal is in turn excited by collisions with atoms of the rare gas and emits its characteristic spectrum.

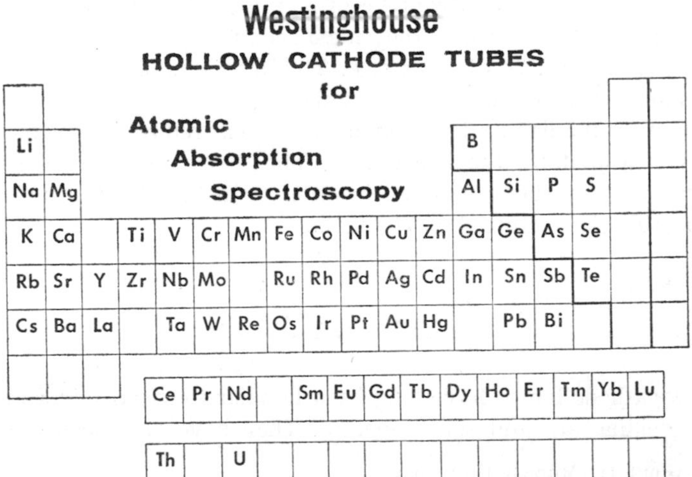

Fig. 7–1. Westinghouse hollow-cathode tubes for atomic-absorption purposes (by courtesy of Westinghouse Electric Corporation, Electronic Tube Division).

The resonance lines produced by hollow-cathode lamps are in most cases of smaller halfwidths (narrower) than the absorption lines. Thus it may be assumed that the effective band-pass of the whole instrument, conditioned by the width of the line coming from the hollow-cathode lamp, is so small that the absorption is really confined to the peak of the absorption line. Loss of linearity and sensitivity may be found if some Lorentz shift is produced. The effects observed on linearity and sensitivity are similar to those produced by Lorentz broadening (the absorption line at the flame shifts from slightly the position of the lamp line).

Since the vapor of the metal is more concentrated in the space inside the cathode, the most intense emission comes from there. Thus a glow discharge appears, whose emission may be utilized by letting it pass through a suitable window placed perpendicular to the axis of the hollow-cathode.

Normally the hollow-cathode lamps have circular cross-section cathodes (see Fig. 7–2). Since the distribution of the free atoms in the flame and

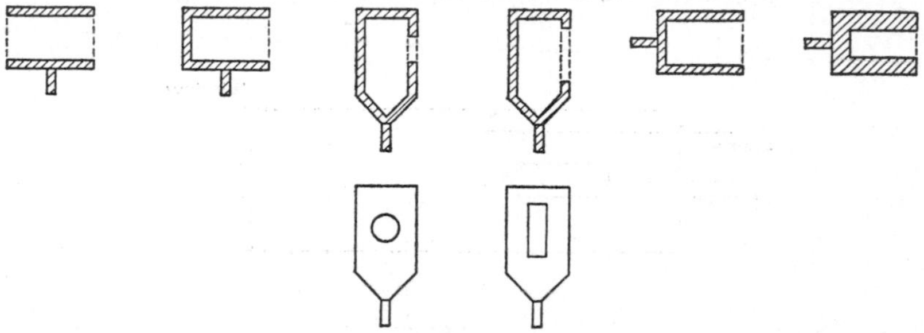

Fig. 7–2. Different shapes of cathodes for hollow-cathode lamps.

entrance slits of the monochromators has an elongated shape (vertical direction), Rann and Hambly (*605*) have suggested the use of an elongated spectral source (elongated cathode). The scheme is presented in Fig. 7–3. This would allow more light to enter the monochromator when it is focussed on the slit so that advantage could be taken of the low gradient of the distribution of the atoms in the flame in the vertical direction, and sensitivity could be increased. Rann and Hambly have confirmed their ideas by means of a copper machined cathode, vertically elongated[10].

The anodes are (a) simple wires adjacent to the cathode (Fig. 7–4),

[10] The light from inside the cathode is not strictly parallel, since the cathode is not narrow enough to do much collimating. Beyond the opening of the hollow-cathode there is a region where pure resonance radiation of the metal is emitted (*648*). It is a rather weak emission, and may be seen from the side, out of the range of the light from the interior of the cathode.

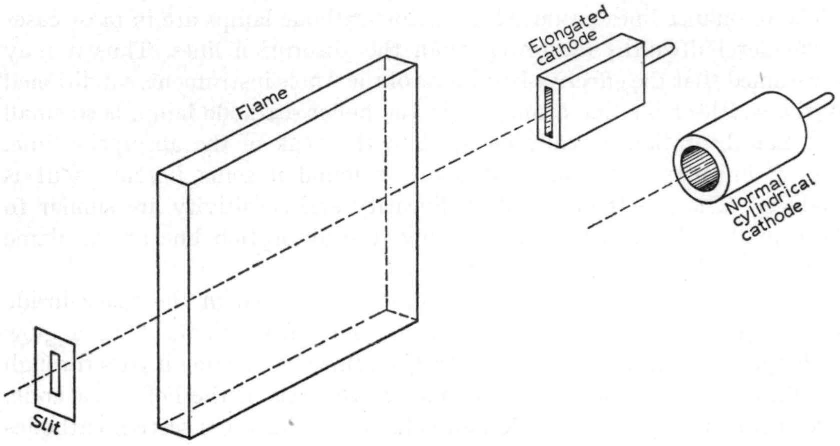

Fig. 7–3. Elongated cathode for hollow-cathode lamp.

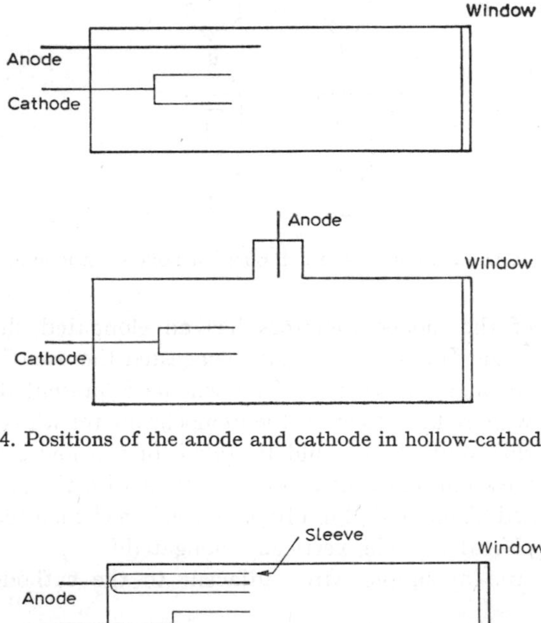

Fig. 7–4. Positions of the anode and cathode in hollow-cathode lamps.

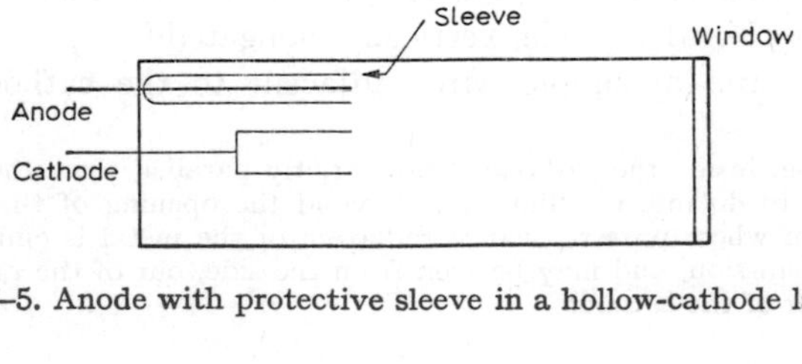

Fig. 7–5. Anode with protective sleeve in a hollow-cathode lamp.

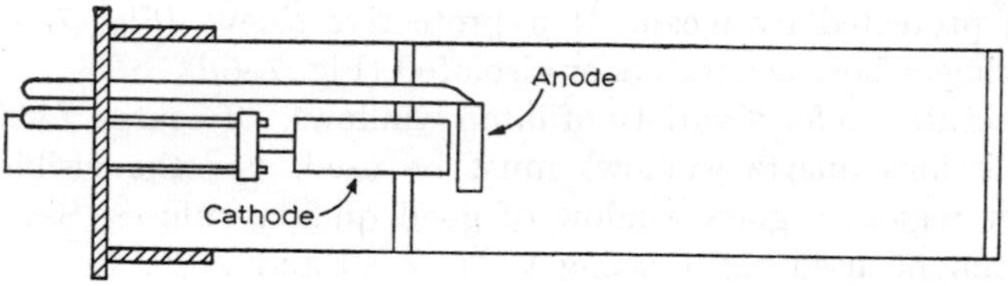

Fig. 7–6. Ring-shaped anode in a hollow-cathode lamp.

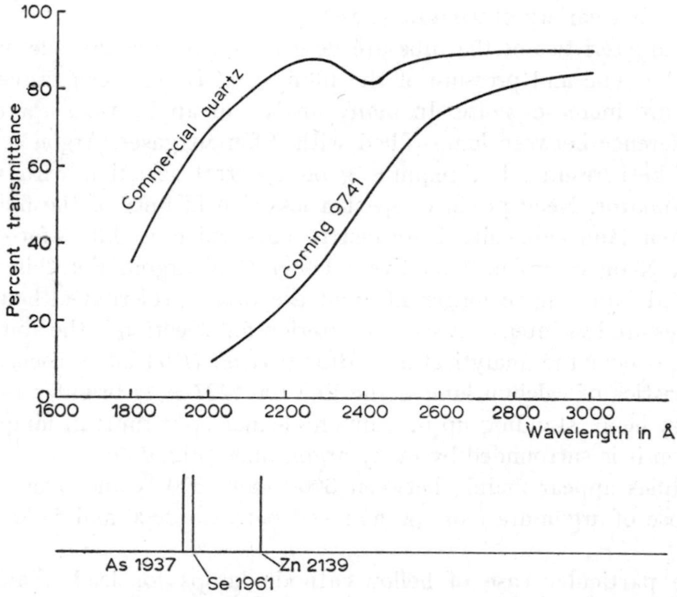

Fig. 7–7. Transmittance *vs.* wavelength curves of two different materials used in the preparation of the hollow-cathode lamp windows. See the position in the wavelength scale of the analytical lines of As, Se and Zn. (By courtesy of Westinghouse Electric Corporation, Electronic Tube Division).

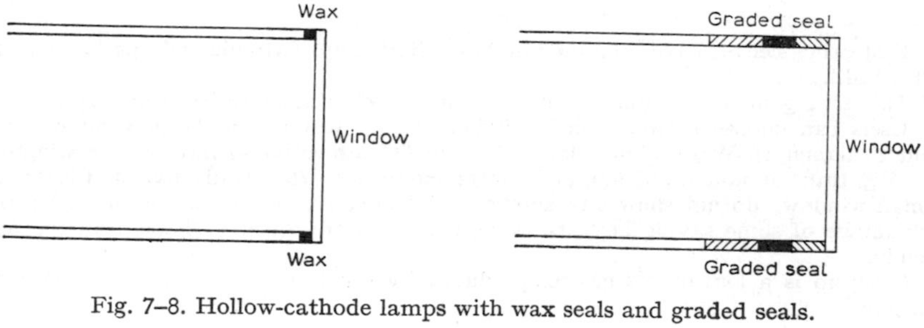

Fig. 7–8. Hollow-cathode lamps with wax seals and graded seals.

(b) wires protected by means of a protective sleeve (Fig. 7–5)[11], or (c) metallic rings whose connectors are isolated (Fig. 7–6)[12].

Manufacturers offer a variety of lamp windows. Of course, for the ultraviolet emissions quartz windows must be used. For the visible or near ultraviolet region, a glass window of good quality suffices. Several types of glass can be used e.g. Corning 9741, 7740 and 7720. In Fig. 7–7 are shown two curves for different materials used in the preparation of lamp windows. The window may be waxed or soldered; in some cases a graded seal may be needed to join the body of the lamp to the window (Fig. 7–8). There is also a variety of window sizes[13].

The characteristics of the tube are determined by the cathode material and by the type and pressure of the filling gas. It has been proved that gas pressure increases noise. In many analytical applications there is no great difference between lamps filled with different gases. Argon seems to give the best results, but requires good spectral selection with a good monochromator. Neon produces spectra less rich in lines of the filling gas so that neon lamps are suitable for instruments which use filters for spectral selection. Neon cleans up[14] relatively faster than argon. For this reason, argon-filled lamps have longer life and are often preferred although the metal lines are less intense. A second criterion for selection is the abundance of gas lines near the analytical line. Burger *et al.* (*121*) have discussed the characteristics of calcium lamps: the line Ca 4227 Å is brighter in lamps filled with neon, standing up in a much cleaner spectrum; in lamps filled with argon it is surrounded by many argon lines (Fig. 7–9).

Neon lines appear mainly between 3000 and 3800 Å and over 5000 Å, while those of argon are more pronounced between 3800 and 5100 Å (Fig. 7–10).

In the particular case of hollow-cathode lamps for lead, Slavin and Manning have found better performance with neon as filler gas than with the earlier argon-filled lamps (*704*).

Although helium has been tried, it is not very satisfactory for the following reasons: (a) it promotes spark lines, and (b) it is less effective in sputtering metallic atoms, since its atomic weight is lower than that of the other

---

[11] Protecting sleeves have been used in Australian lamps (Atomic and Spectral Lamps Pty. Ltd.).

[12] This arrangement is found in American lamps (Westinghouse Electric Corp.).

[13] Users can choose between small windows (1″ diameter) and large windows (1½″ and 2″ diameter). Westinghouse lamps (1″ and 1½″ respectively) have Pyrex windows (>70% transmission at 305 nm) and quartz windows (>75% transmission at 220 nm). Small windows do not show any appreciable decrease of performance, and offer the advantage of some saving in costs. Some examples are given in Table 2 in the Appendix.

[14] Clean-up is a loss of the gas fill produced by sorption by the sputtered cathode material.

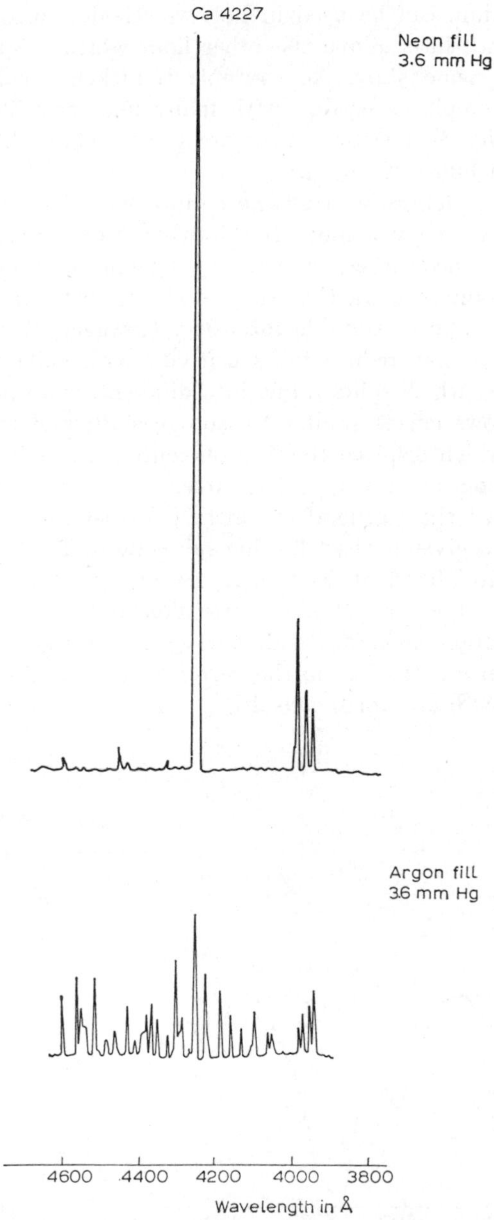

Fig. 7–9. Emission curves of two hollow-cathode lamps. Effect of neon and argon gas fill on spectral characteristics. Cathode Ca–Mg–Al. Current 20 mA in both. Recorded by means of a Beckman DU spectrophotometer (by courtesy of Westinghouse Electric Corporation, Electronic Tube Division).

rare gases. Helium can be used in hollow-cathode lamps to enhance the desired resonance lines above the other lines which are not absorbed by vapor in the ground state. An example is nickel, which, like iron and cobalt, emits complex spectrum with many lines near those used in absorption. In Fig. 7–11 some curves are presented to show the different behaviours of helium and argon.

Hollow-cathode lamps meet all the requirements for sources for atomic-absorption spectroscopy without the drawbacks of the continuous sources and flames mentioned earlier, and without the limitations of vapor discharge lamps. The discrete spectra that they emit are sharp and their lines sufficiently narrow and of suitable intensity. However, there are still some peculiarities that may reduce the sensitivity with hollow-cathode lamps: (a) isotope shift, which splits a line into different components, (b) nuclear spin, which shows effects similar to isotope shift, and (c) pressure shifts in the flame, which displace the line off-center. These inconveniences are not found if a continuum is used as source.

To supplement these general comments, further information on special types of lamps is given in the following subsections. The literature on lamps has become quite abundant, with many papers on the construction of new types, studies on the application of particular kinds of lamps and proposals for new demountable models. Besides the work of Burger *et al.* (*121*), which contains general information on the performance of hollow-cathode lamps, references (*74, 818*) are worth consulting.

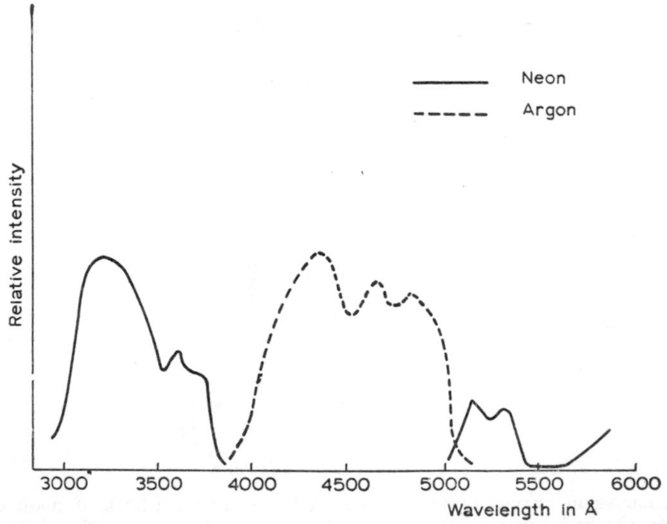

Fig. 7–10. Major regions of possible interference from fill gas lines. Reproduced from data published by Burger and Gillies (*119*) (by courtesy of Westinghouse Electric Corporation, Electronic Tube Division).

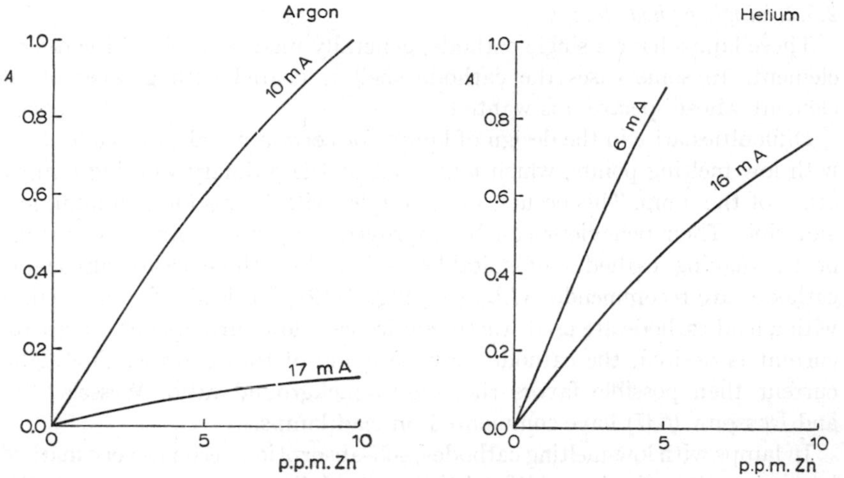

Fig. 7–11. Schematic representation of results obtainable with argon- and helium-filled hollow-cathode lamps for zinc at different currents.

2.3.1. *Classification of hollow-cathode lamps*

A simple classification of hollow-cathode lamps is difficult owing to the large number of varieties that exist. Depending on whether the heat produced during operation is eliminated or not, the lamps may be classified as *cooled* or *uncooled*. Most of them are made to function without forced cooling. In cooled lamps, the temperature in the vicinity of the cathode is kept low by circulation of water. Depending on the mode of closure, i.e. on whether the lamp is sealed or can be opened, especially for the interchange of cathodes, lamps may be classified as *sealed* or *demountable*.

A more important classification depends on the number of cathodes, grouping the lamps into *single-cathode lamps* and *multicathode lamps*. The distinction between *single-element lamps* and *multi-element lamps* will be treated later. This classification depends on whether the cathode is made of a single element or two or more elements.

Several companies manufacture and/or supply hollow-cathode lamps[15]. Some of these lamps have been described by several authors (see, e.g. references (*121*, *134*, *545–548*)).

[15] Listed below are some commercial firms that supply various models of hollow-cathode lamps: Atomic and Spectral Lamps Pty. Ltd., Melbourne, N. 5, Vic., Australia (formerly Ransley Glass Instruments); Beckman Instruments, Inc., Fullerton, Calif., U.S.A.; Carl Zeiss, Oberkochen, Germany; Hilger and Watts Ltd., London N.W. 1, England; Hitachi Ltd., Ibaraki, Japan; Micro-Tek Instruments, Inc., Baton Rouge, La., U.S.A.; Quartzlampen G.m.b.H. Hanau, Hanau, Germany; The Perkin-Elmer Corp. Norwalk, Conn., U.S.A.; Westinghouse Electric Corp., Electronic Tube Division, Elmira, N. Y., U.S.A. Most of these firms have representative offices in many countries.

2.3.2. Single-cathode lamps

These lamps have a single cathode, generally made entirely of the desired element. In some cases the cathode shell is coated with a layer of the element whose spectrum is wanted.

Difficulties arise in the design of lamps for certain metals, especially those with low melting points, which may melt at the ordinary working temperature of the lamp. This occurs, for example, with lamps for cadmium, lead and zinc. Their behaviour can be improved simply by using low currents or by making cathodes of suitable design. For these cases cup-shaped cathodes are recommended (*127*) (see Fig. 7–12). For lead, of course, lamps with a lead cathode are used; these require very low currents but if a greater current is desired, the cathode may be made of leaded brass. The higher current then possible favors the line-to-background ratio. Wessels (*813*) and Rossouw (*637*) have commented on lead lamps.

In lamps with low-melting cathodes, self-absorption becomes very marked, increasing the effective width of the emitted line, and in some cases the emission of the lamp rises rapidly with current. Many authors have published information on the variation of the emission intensity with the

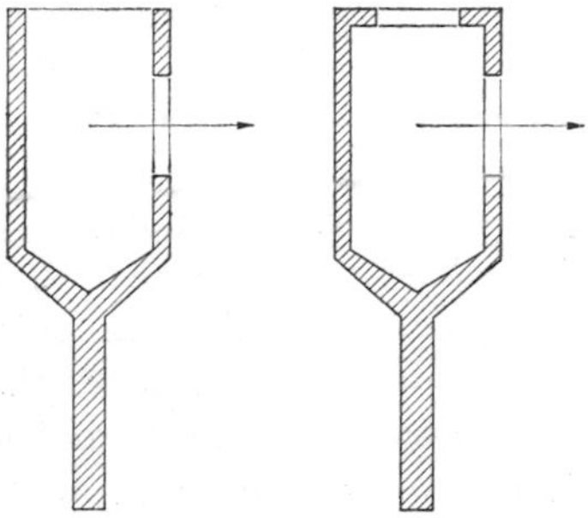

Fig. 7–12. Cup-shaped cathodes for hollow-cathode lamps.

current, and also on the shape of working curves at different currents used for the lamp. An example of these working curves is shown in Fig. 7–13; other typical curves can be found in the papers by Walsh (*800*) and by Butler (*127*).

Single-cathode sealed lamps have shapes similar to those shown in earlier figures in this chapter. The cathode is usually centered, and it is viewed by the rest of the instrument through its exit window. The distance from

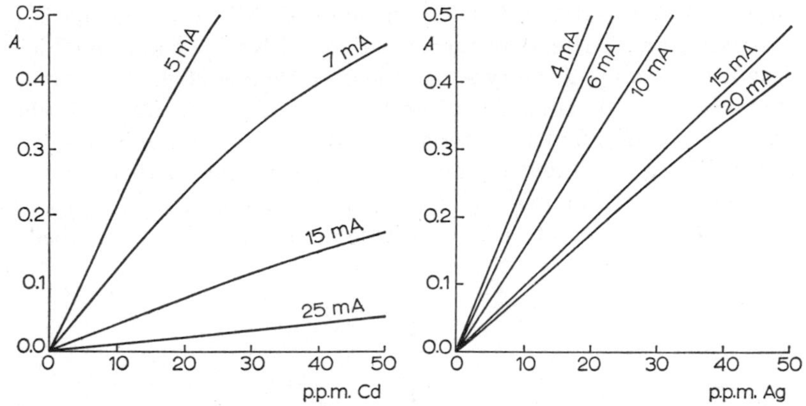

Fig. 7–13. Schematic representation of results obtainable for cadmium and silver by operating the lamps at different currents.

the cathode to the window and the size of the window limit the angular aperture of the optics.

2.3.2.1. Demountable lamps. These constitute a special case, since they are not completely sealed, the interior being connected through a valve to a gas handling and vacuum system. The lamp can be taken apart, permitting the cathode and anode to be demounted. Shternberg has described a suitable procedure for reloading and pumping such hollow-cathode lamps (*671*).

Demountable lamps lend themselves to the following versatile uses (see Fig. 7–14).

(a) The interior gases may be changed (and replaced in case they become excessively contaminated), and/or their pressure may be varied.

(b) The cathode may be replaced so that the lamp can be used for different metals. In some models the anode can also be changed.

Typical examples are described by Baker (*65*), Butler (*128*), Strasheim and Butler (*732, 733*) and Patterson (*546, 547*).

The lamp described by Strasheim and Butler can have a second tubulation with a lens instead of a simple plane window. With this the radiation of the one lamp can be focused on the *open-ended cathode* of a second lamp, with windows in both ends, so that the radiation from both lamps may reach the instrument for simultaneous determination of two or more elements. This arrangement is known as *tandem mounting* (Fig. 7–15).

In spite of the present availability of many types of sealed hollow-cathode lamps, some authors prefer to use demountable lamps, not only because of their versatility, but also because of their low contribution to total source costs. These were the objectives of Koirtyohann and Pickett (*409*) in using a lamp of the type described by Werner *et al.* (*812*).

The hollow-cathode lamp described by Eichhoff and Voigt (*205*) allows the introduction of different materials in a matter of three minutes. These authors used argon without circulation and recommended their lamps for work in emission and atomic-absorption, and for radioactive samples.

A laboratory model of hollow-cathode lamp has been described by

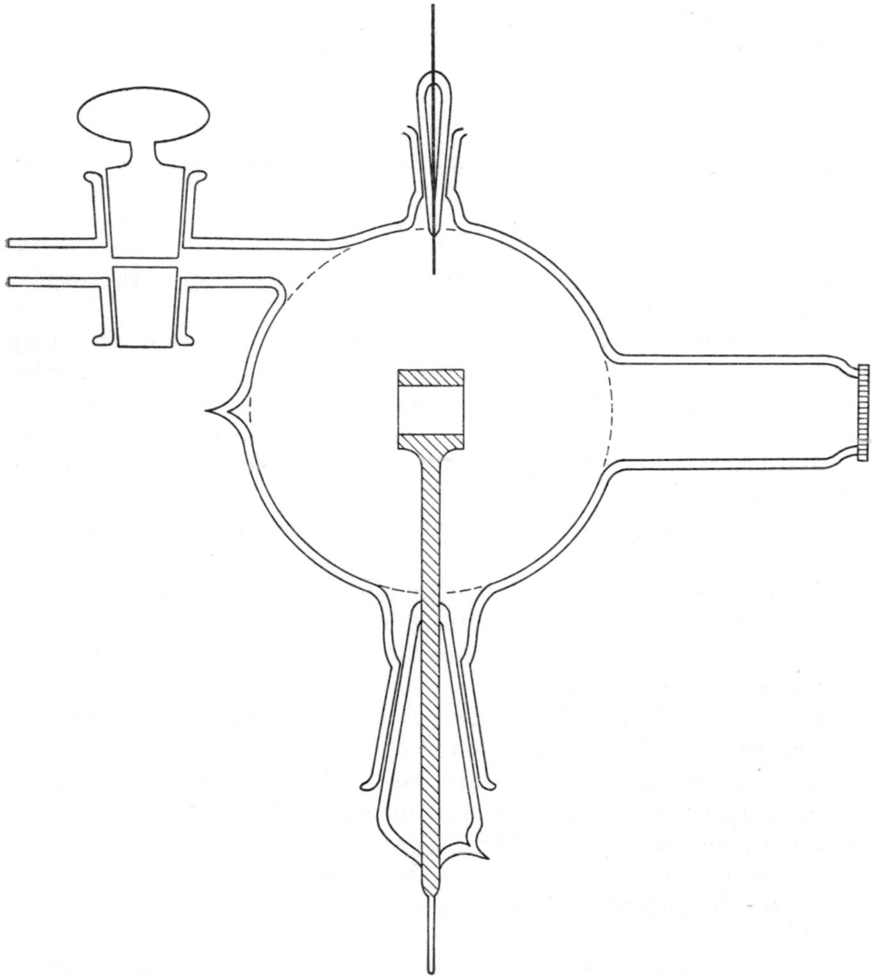

Fig. 7–14. Demountable hollow-cathode lamp.

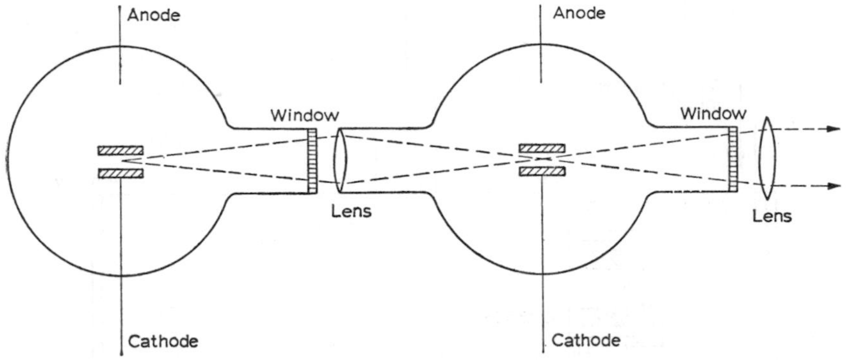

Fig. 7–15. Tandem mounting of two hollow-cathode lamps. The second lamp receives the emission from the first through a focusing lens.

Krasil'shchik, who also describes a vacuum circulation system. All parts are removable and fit on a ground molybdenum glass plug that supports molybdenum connecting wires (*413*).

2.3.2.2. *Lamps with cooling.* When cooling is necessary during operation, circulating water may be utilized. Examples of cooled lamps are those of Zeeman and Butler (*867, 868*) and of Baker and Garton (*66*). Cooling should be avoided whenever possible, to keep the instrument simple. As atomic-absorption spectroscopy is distinguished by its basic simplicity, efforts should be made to avoid additional complications, wherever possible.

Fig. 7–16 shows a schematic representation of a type of lamp using cooling.

2.3.2.3. *Single-cathode multi-element lamps.* These lamps have only one cathode, but they produce emissions from two or more elements. The use of cathodes of leaded brass for determining lead, to permit higher current, was mentioned above. This is not the only reason for which alloyed cathodes are used. The need to make several analyses simultaneously on the same sample led to putting several metals on the same cathode. One way of doing this is to use an alloy of the desired metals, since each of the constituents of the alloy will undergo sputtering from bombardment by the gas ions. It should be noted, however, that when the components of the alloy behave in different manners, the cathode may become enriched in one of them, if the other is preferentially sputtered out.

Coated cathodes sometimes emit the lines of the nominal element plus the lines of the element of the shell. Other ways of obtaining emissions from various elements, besides the use of alloys, are: (a) the utilization of compounds (e.g. tin telluride), and (b) the use of sintered powder compacts of mixed metals.

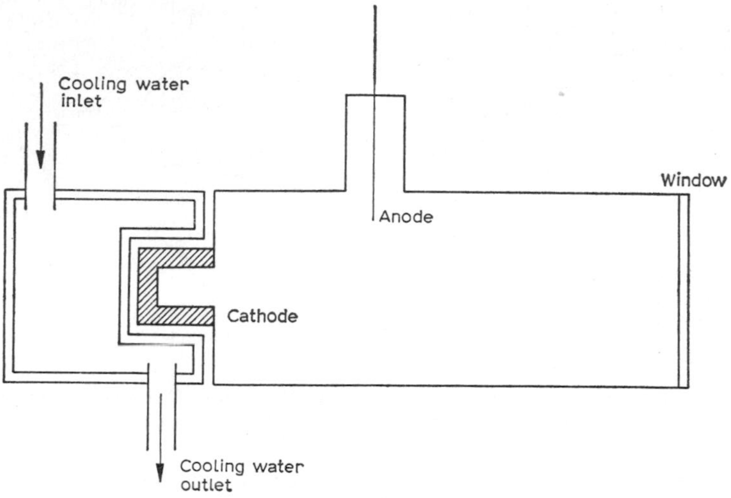

Fig. 7–16. Hollow-cathode lamp with cooling system.

Multi-element cathodes are tending to replace multicathode lamps in spite of the fact that the different rates of sputtering of the constituents may cause a drift of the emission of one or more of them.

Cathodes of Mn–Cu, Al–Mg, Cu–Zn (brass) and other alloys have long been used. In the case of the Al–Mg cathode, currents higher than those normally used with cathodes of unalloyed magnesium can be employed. Recently, the characteristics and performance of an improved Zn–Ca hollow-cathode lamp have been described by Vollmer *et al.* (*792*). They conclude that low dependence on lamp current, spectral intensity and spectral purity make this lamp superior to conventional zinc lamps; better performance is obtained when the lamp is filled with neon. Details on the performance of a Ca–Mg hollow-cathode lamp have been given by Manning, Trent and Vollmer (*463*), who present calibration curves for argon- and neon-filled lamps.

Spectral interference may result from the multiplicity of lines in the spectra of lamps containing too many elements. The main inter-element interference (*source* inter-element interference) results from failure of the spectral-selection system of the instrument to resolve two adjacent lines of different elements. If one belongs to the analyte and the other to an element not present in the sample, the unresolved line disturbs the reading, giving apparent results. In quantitative analysis, these errors may be compensated by calibration under the same conditions. The situation is different when both elements are present in the sample; both lines will be absorbed if they are capable of being absorbed, leading to a variable error. Finally, if both elements are present in the solution, and one absorbs that one of its lines which is received by the instrument, but the other does not (because its line is not a resonance line), then the situation reduces to the first case above, in which only the first element is present in the sample. In the second case, the most troublesome, the results depend on the concentration of the accompanying element; the errors are similar to those caused by inter-element interference *in the sample.*

More information on multi-element lamps can be found in the papers by Sebens *et al.* (*662, 663*) (see also ref. (*54*)). At present, a wide selection of multi-element lamps is available; some examples are given in Table 2 in the Appendix. Multi-element lamps are advantageous when routine analyses are limited to a few analytes, and they reduce the changeover time tremendously.

2.3.3. Multicathode lamps

Multicathode lamps provide another way of determining several elements with minimal adjustment of the instrument. Only the wavelength setting, and perhaps the conditions for producing the absorbing medium and the alignment of the proper cathode on the optical axis, need to be adjusted.

Fig. 7–17 shows several possible layouts of multicathode lamps. Lamps with two cathodes and no anode are special cases; by changing the polarity, either cathode can be utilized. These lamps can also be a.c.-powered and viewed independently (*372*).

The advantages of these lamps are debatable. And it is not easy to design a means of switching reliably from one cathode to the next.

A good solution is:

(a) Several concentric cathodes (*476, 477*) (Fig. 7–18).

(b) Multi-ring cathodes (*131, 132*) (Fig. 7–19).

Butler and Strasheim (*132*) describe multi-element cathodes of the ring type, that can be considered as real multicathode devices for multicathode lamps. For elements of high melting point, such as chromium, nickel, and iron, the cathode can have three separated rings pressed in a sheath of steel or copper. There is the possibility of varying the length of the rings according to the relative emission intensities. For elements with low melting point, such as zinc and lead, the cathode can have internal divisions, into which globules of the metals can be placed; it is necessary to run the lamps at currents which prevent melting of the globule.

2.3.4. Operation of hollow-cathode lamps

Two aspects are treated here: mechanical and electrical.

2.3.4.1. Mechanical aspects. The lamps must be perfectly aligned on the

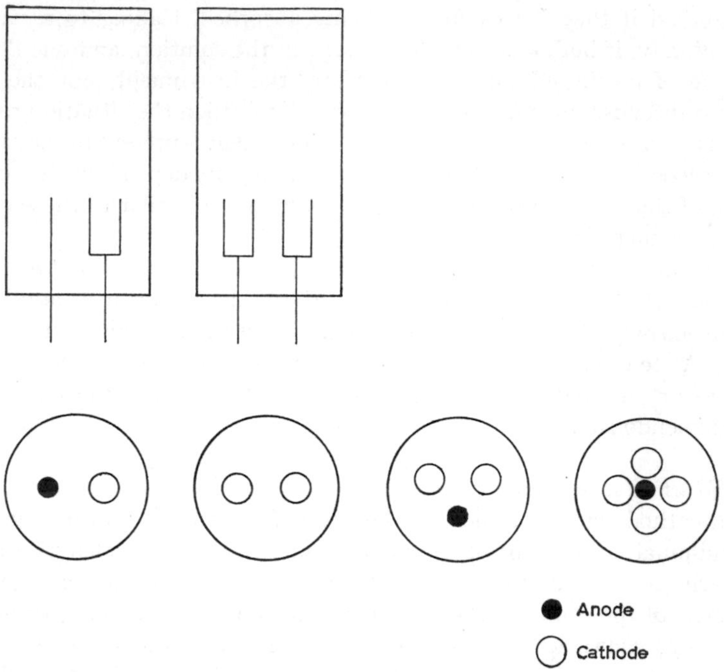

Fig. 7–17. Different possible layouts of hollow-cathode lamps. The second, third, and fourth types correspond to multicathode lamps.

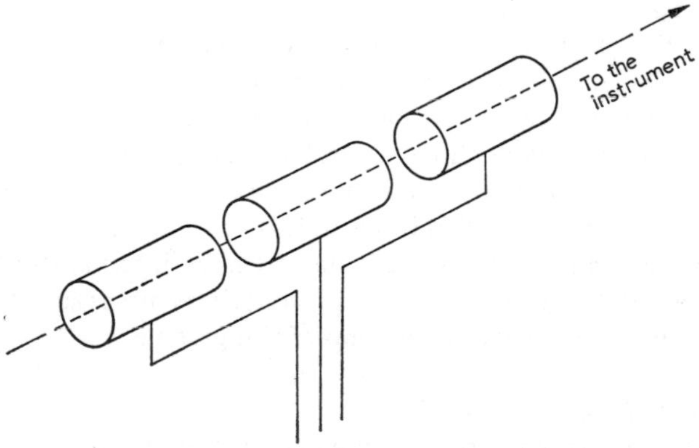

Fig. 7–18. Concentric cathodes.

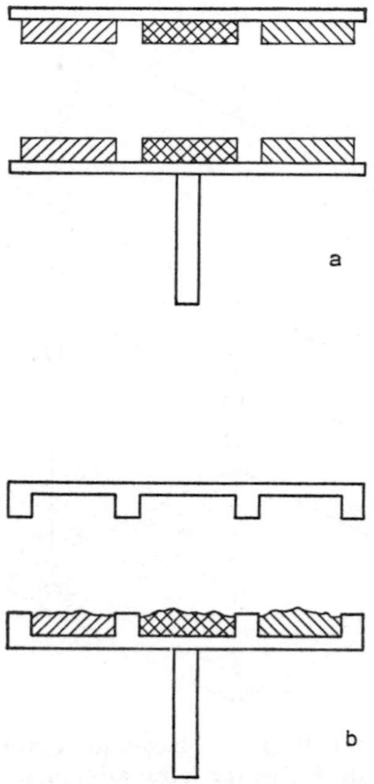

Fig. 7–19. Multi-ring cathodes: (a) for three elements with high melting point; (b) for three elements with low melting point.

optical axis of the instrument. If they are mounted on interchangeable bases (all of them of the same size, if prepared for lamps of equal size), requiring no adjustment of position, it is sufficient to change the base, once the correctness of the positioning has been verified in the accessory. The adjustable base used in Beckman instruments allows the use of a variety of cylindrical lamps; Fig. 7–20 shows a schematic representation of this type. If such bases are not available, the lamp must be realigned each time to give maximal instrumental response.

Most commercial lamps are supposed to have the cathode concentric with the envelope, but in aligning the instrument, it is advisable to test for excentricity by rotating the lamp about the optical axis to see whether the emission varies; the emission can then be optimized if necessary.

The lamps have to be warned up for several minutes to become stable (see Figs. 7–21 and 7–22). The various lamps that are to be used should therefore all be turned on at the start so that they will be stable when needed[16]. The lamps become too hot to handle comfortably, and devices

[16] The operator can plan a periodic switching on when a lamp has to be used for a long period of time (for instance, more than an hour).

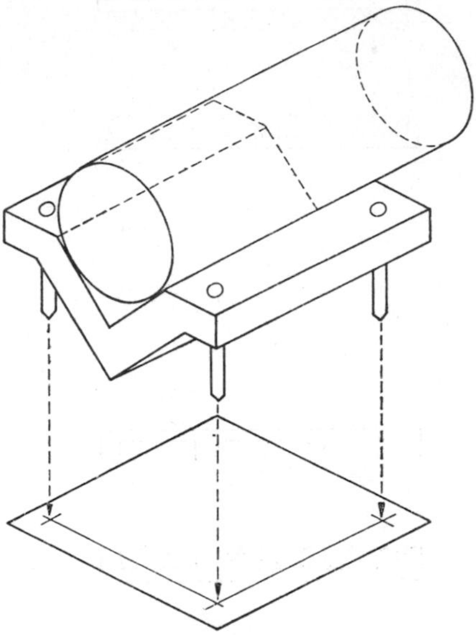

Fig. 7–20. Schematic view of the Beckman bases for cylindrical lamps. These bases are adjustable for lamp alignment.

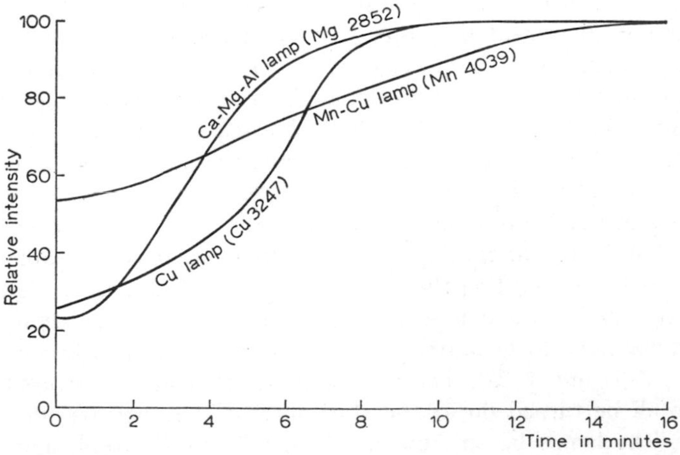

Fig. 7–21. Typical warm-up time for various cathode types (by courtesy of Westinghouse Electric Corporation, Electronic Tube Division).

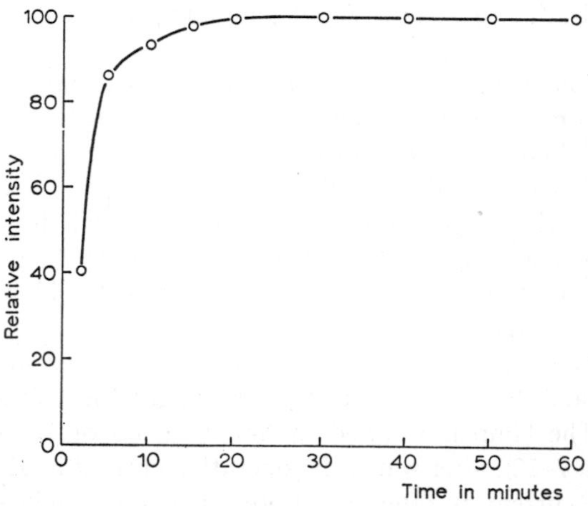

Fig. 7–22. Warm-up curve of a magnesium lamp. (Obtained by means of a Beckman DU-2 spectrophotometer with atomic-absorption accessory).

have been made to position the desired lamp in the instrument as required. These take the form of a revolving connector or turret. It might be possible to use also a sliding track or a magazine mount.

This saves time during working periods, but the operator must schedule his work so that only the needed lamps are kept warmed up, and these only as long as necessary. The lamps are warranted for a certain number of ampere-hours, and although the currents are often very low, any time consumed in warming up without use diminishes the effective life of the lamp.

2.3.4.2. Electrical aspects. Except in those cases in which the lamps are a.c.-powered, the lamp may be supplied with: (a) direct current, (b) alternating current with half-wave rectification, and (c) alternating current with full-wave rectification. In these cases it is customary to use a chopper to convert the emission to pulsating light which produces an alternating signal that can be amplified with an alternating-current amplifier tuned to the frequency of the signal. This scheme keeps the continuous (unmodulated) emission of the flame from affecting the reading. The chopper is simply a revolving sector disk that passes light half the time, driven by a synchronous motor (see Fig. 7–23). It must be noted that in some instruments the chopper, equipped with mirrors, has also another function: that of dividing the beam into two separate beams (double-beam systems).

When it is necessary to obtain more intense signals without the danger of damaging the lamp by long exposure to high currents, it is possible to work with pulsating short-time signals, avoiding the use of the conventional chopper.

The conditions for operating the lamp are critical. Special attention has therefore been given to the design of power supplies for these lamps. The need for careful control of the operating conditions is due to the fact that although a higher current intensifies the emission, it broadens the lines, thwarting the primary purpose of the source, which is to produce spectra of very narrow lines. Fig. 7–24 shows the variation of the relative intensity with lamp current. Care must also be taken to avoid overheating the cathode, which would shorten the life of the lamp.

To ignite the lamp, sufficient voltage must be supplied—for some models between 200 and 400 V—to start the discharge; the voltage should then be reduced. The lamp is warmed up for a period of 10–20 minutes (see Figs. 7–21 and 7–22), after which the operating current is adjusted suitably. The required current is often no more than a few milliamperes. Small adjustments of current do not need any waiting period for further stabilization, but if the current is drastically changed, it is advisable to wait for about 5 minutes until any drift disappears.

A proper adjustment of current can minimize the Doppler effect, and also improve the line: background ratio, in case there is some background emission from the lamp. But an unduly low current often makes the emission unstable and unduly diminishes its intensity. If the current is increased, the spectrum appears brighter, and this can overcome any interferences from flame emission, and from the emission of the filler gas of the hollow-cathode lamp.

Trials should be made to find the current that will produce the best

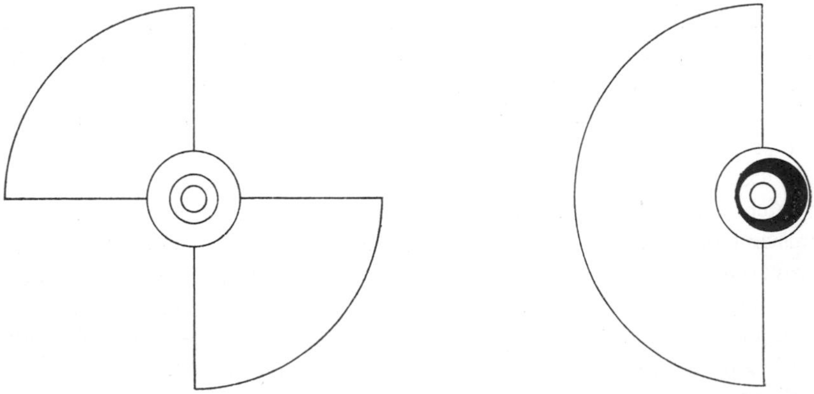

Fig. 7–23. Choppers.

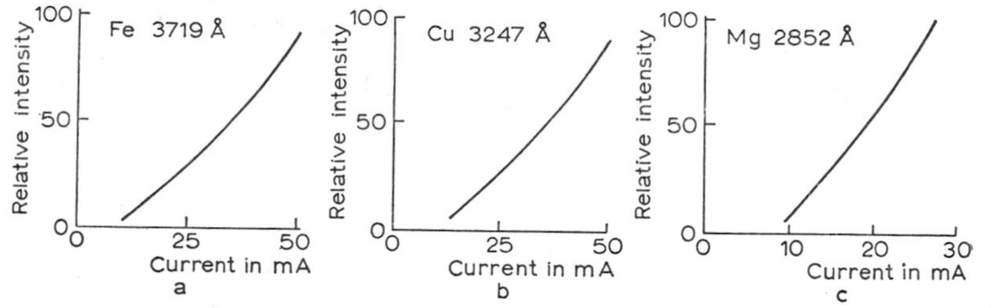

Fig. 7–24. Curves relative intensity *vs.* current in mA for several hollow-cathode lamps (D.C. current): (a) iron (neon) lamp; (b) copper (neon) lamp; (c) Ca–Mg–Al (argon) lamp (*119*) (by courtesy of Westinghouse Electric Corporation, Electronic Tube Division).

combination of the following: (a) sufficient intensity of emission, (b) sufficient analytical sensitivity, (c) sufficient stability to yield the required accuracy and precision. The effects of the lamp noise have been discussed by Devaney and Brech (*195*). If the noise contribution to the final total noise is considerable, it may reduce the sensitivity, specifically, the fluctuational sensitivity (see Chapter 13).

Current-stabilized power supplies help to obtain a stable emission. In Figs. 7–25, 7–26 and 7–27 a typical connection and two types of power supply are schematized. To some extent stabilization may be disregarded in double-beam instruments, which take advantage of the autocompensation of fluctuations by the double path traversed by light from the emitter. Commercial voltage stabilizers may be adequate for use in conjunction with the power supply for the lamp. The advantages of using a regulated power supply have been demonstrated by Kahn and Manning (*382*), who obtained much more stable recordings of the signal of the lamp emission vs. warm-up time in this way.

The stability is of special interest in dealing with elements, such as zinc, that show drastic changes of sensitivity as a function of the lamp current (see Fig. 7–28).

Most of the lamps have only two pins (anode and cathode). Care should be taken to avoid misconnecting the pins to the electrical circuit. Some lamps are provided with Jedec-type plug-in bases for easy changing during operation (see Fig. 7–29). Female sockets coded with identical key hole serve to avoid mistakes (see Fig. 7–30), or color-coded connectors are used.

2.3.5. Life of the lamp

In selecting lamps for use in atomic-absorption, one looks for (a) small spectral bandwidth (narrow lines), (b) high energy output, (c) low noise

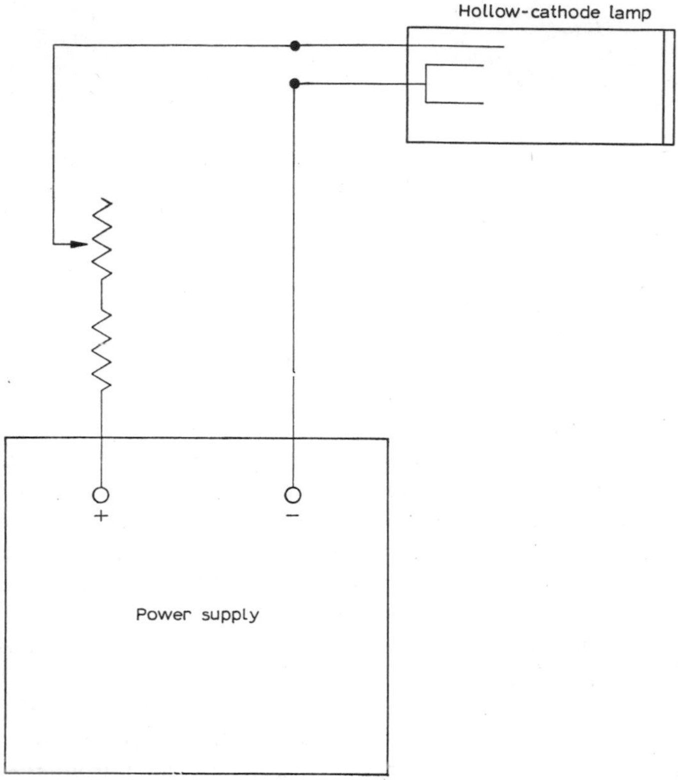

Fig. 7–25. Typical connection of a hollow-cathode lamp to a power supply.

level (low flicker—short term fluctuation), (d) constant light output (low drift—long term fluctuation), (e) fast warm-up, and (f) *long life.*

The lamps are among the most expensive auxiliary components of the entire instrument, and the cost is multiplied by the number of lamps that must be kept in reserve for the determination of different analytes.

Three main factors limit the life of the hollow-cathode lamps: (a) loss of the desired metal from the cathode, the metal being expelled from the surface of the cathode to form a cloud of atoms which are deposited eventually on the walls of the lamp (this partial diffusion of the metal gradually darkens the window, decreasing the efficiency of the lamp)[17]; (b) leakage of air into the tube due to a imperfect seal or cracks in the tube, a condition

[17] Robinson (*623*) mentions White's suggestion of using spherical-cavity cathodes with a small hole in one side, in which the vaporized metal would be redeposited within the spherical electrode. This led Robinson to use tubular cathodes closed at one end and with a restricted opening at the other end.

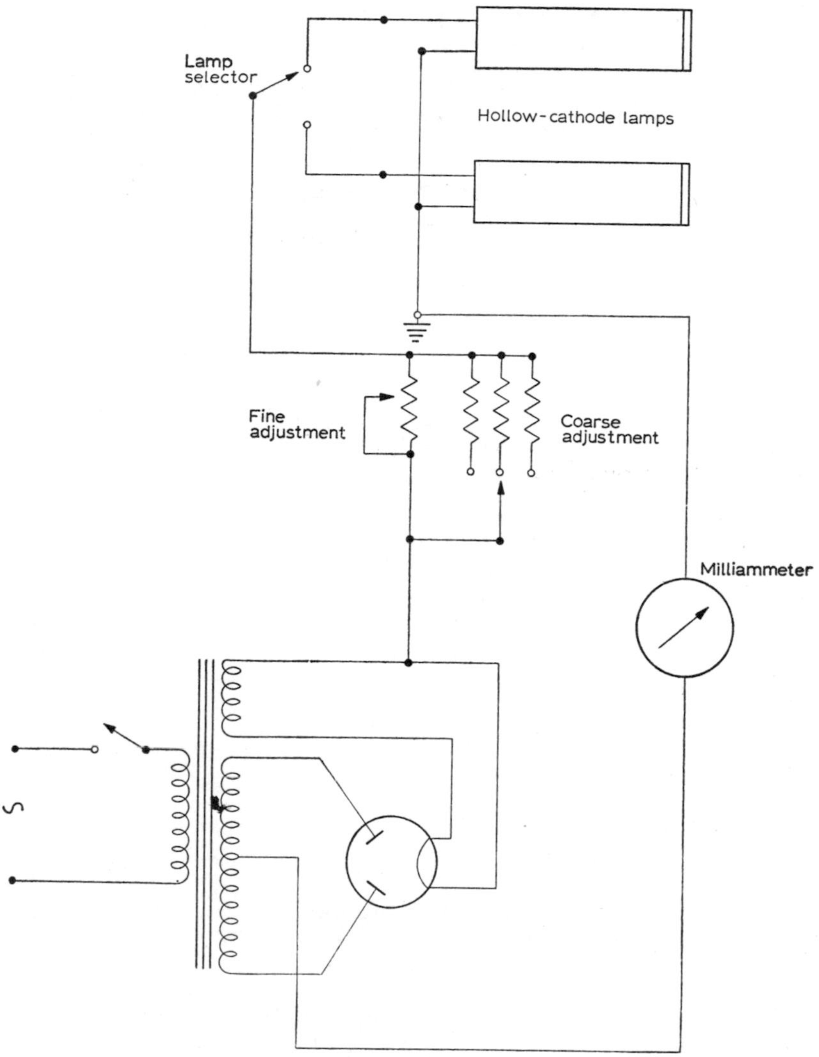

Fig. 7–26. Schematic representation of a power supply for two hollow-cathode lamps (for details on this type of circuit consult ref. (*109*)).

signaled by the appearance of the purple color characteristic of an electric discharge in air; (c) clean-up of the filler gas through entrapment by the metallic atoms or absorption on the glass surface of the lamp[18].

[18] See comments on this topic by Burger *et al.* (*121*).

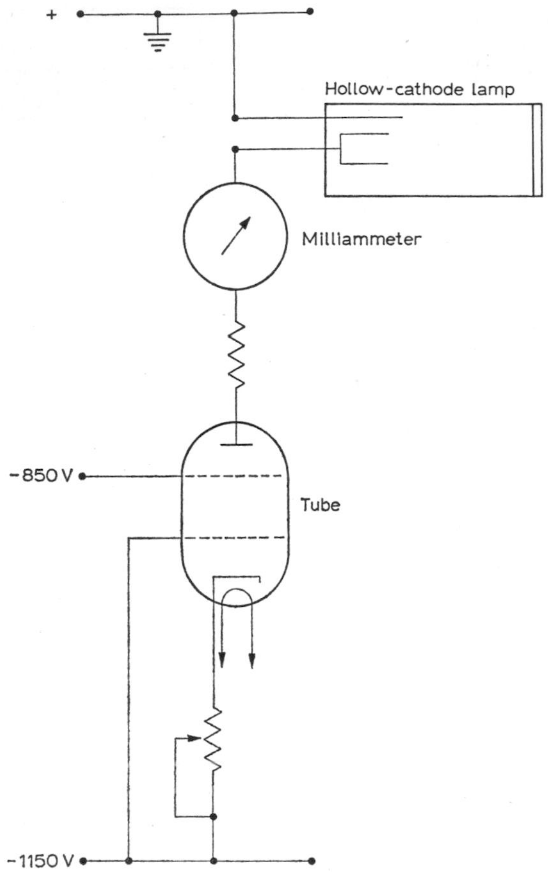

Fig. 7–27. Schematic representation of a current-control circuit for hollow-cathode lamps (for details on this type of circuit consult ref. (7)).

The lamp can also deteriorate owing to oxidation of the cathode, which makes its surface incapable of supplying atoms of the metal. Firing in these circumstances is quite difficult[19]. Regeneration by reversal of polarity is only temporary.

Lamp life seems to be limited much more by factor (c)—clean-up of the filler gas—than by the accumulation of impurities in the gas. Although completely sealed tubes are easier to handle in the laboratory, tubes with

---

[19] The author has successfully used a Tesla coil, approaching the electrode to the envelope of the lamp, for firing old lamps.

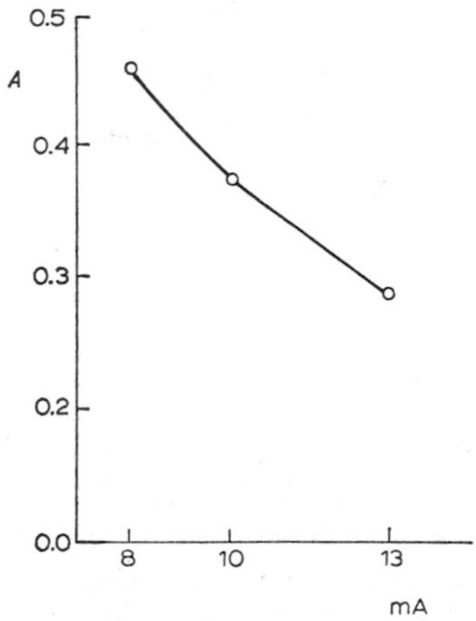

Fig. 7–28. Variation of the absorbance obtained with 0.5 p.p.m. of zinc (line Zn 2139) Å as a function of the lamp current (curve obtained by means of a Beckman DU-2 spectrophotometer with atomic-absorption accessory).

circulating gas have been used for the purpose of flushing out the impurities. Obviously the circulation system complicates the instrument and makes it considerably more expensive.

Efforts have also been made to use a chemical scavenger, i.e., a *getter*, inside the tube, which is intended to react with the impurities of the gas. For this activated uranium and zirconium may be used (see Fig. 7–31).

A lamp that has become useless owing to the deterioration of the filler gas, may be rejuvenated by filling it with flowing gas and running it with adequate current, connected to the vacuum line, until the emission becomes sufficiently stable and again consists of well-defined lines free from bands and background.

All these remarks apply to nearly all common single-cathode lamps. In multicathode lamps additional factors are involved. In these, there is a preferential sputtering among the different cathodes, as well as deposition of metal from one cathode upon other cathodes. Because of this, the life of a multicathode lamp is said to be about one-third that of a single-cathode lamp. This is why Massmann (*476*) built a multi-element lamp in which the cathode consisted of a set of coaxial cylinders or rings of different metals of equal diameter, longitudinally disposed along the axis of the cathode (see p. 65 and Fig. 7–18). The rings were separated by insulation and connected to individual power leads. An unidirectional flow of filler gas was passed through the lamp during operation.

Recently manufacturers have been studying not only these factors but

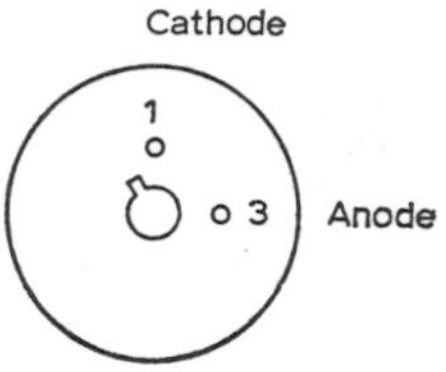

Fig. 7–29. Jedec-type plug-in base of a hollow-cathode lamp (octal 2-pin base).

also other factors of lamp design that contribute to better performance and longer life. New designs may contain such features as insulating diaphragms, circular anodes around the cathode, protective sleeves on the interior leads, and other details which help to make a more uniform glow that remains centered and does not wander about the cathode, and which also prevents back-glowing or discharge to the leads and the formation of a glow outside the cathode.

2.3.6. New lamps. High-intensity lamps

In this section are described some special types of new lamp which are intended to fulfil most of the requirements mentioned at the beginning of the preceding section. Some years ago, Jones and Walsh (*372*) mentioned lamps that could be used for up to 1000 hours in ordinary work (life-time of about 50 ampere-hours). This type of lamp accomplished the requirement

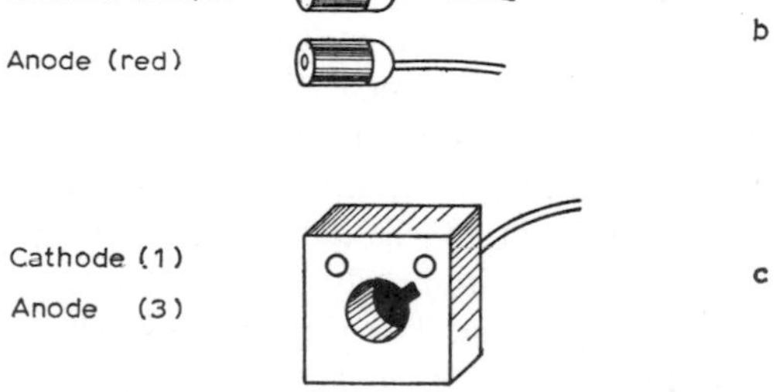

Fig. 7–30. Lamp connectors: (a) alligator-type color-coded connector; (b) female color-coded connector; (c) Key-hole female socket.

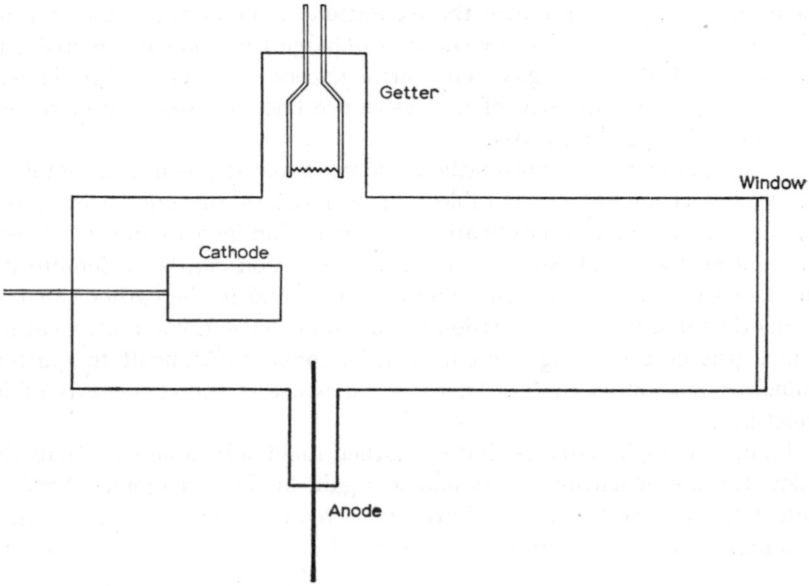

Fig. 7–31. Hollow-cathode lamp with getter device.

of long life, but more important is the requirement of high energy output.

Recently, Sullivan and Walsh (*746, 747*) described a new type of atomic spectral lamp capable, in some cases, of giving a hundred-fold increase in resonance-line intensity over conventional hollow-cathode lamps. These lamps give straighter working curves and make selection and detection possible by resonance fluorescence (see Chapter 9, Section 3).

The use of fuel-rich flames and sputtering chambers (see Chapter 8) (both of which can emit some radiation) requires high-intensity emission from the source, in order to compensate for the lowering of the signal-to-noise ratio.

Increasing the current to increase the emission in the conventional hollow-cathode lamps can cause a broadening of the line-width beyond the limits permissible in atomic-absorption work (widths of about 0.01 Å). On other hand, the current applied to a conventional hollow-cathode lamp creates a discharge that not only *produces* the atomic vapor but also *excites* this vapor. These facts have led Sullivan and Walsh (*746, 747*) to design a new type of lamp called a *high-intensity hollow-cathode lamp* or a *high-brightness lamp*. This new lamp uses two discharges: one to carry out the necessary cathodic sputtering and attainment of the optimum pressure of the atomic vapor, and a second (isolated electrically from the first one—

boosting discharge) to produce the excitation of the atomic vapor formed. The second discharge is a low-energy discharge that does not increase the excitation of the filler gas. This arrangement permits one to increase preferentially the intensity of the resonance lines without any increase in the line-width (see Fig. 7–32).

The high-intensity hollow-cathode lamps make it possible to obtain an intense spectrum with a notable enhancement of the lines arising from the unionized metallic analyte atoms because of an increase in the efficiency of exciting the metal being sputtered. This action can be a definite help in cases where the low melting point of the metal in the cathode severely limits the intensity of the emission produced in conventional hollow-cathode lamps (the need of using low current), by making it difficult to sputter a sufficient amount of metal. This is even worse if the element is of low volatility.

Lamps of high radiance have another main advantage in that they allow the use of narrower slits and less gain in the instrument. Narrower slits improve selectivity and lower gain reduces shot noise for a given reading, raising the fluctuational sensitivity for a given percentual sensitivity.

The high-intensity lamps have been described in some of the papers by Walsh (*805, 806*). They have been enthusiastically commented on and used in experimental work. David (*178*) emphasized the novelty of using an auxiliary discharge beyond the mouth of the cathode, thus raising the population of atoms in the upper levels of the resonance lines.

The lamps have been used by Capacho-Delgado and Manning (*139, 140, 901*) in determinations of tin. With these new lamps, the absorbance (and thus the sensitivity) is less dependent on the current applied, and higher signal-to-noise ratios are obtained in the measurements (which allows better precision).

Sullivan and Walsh (*747*) mention the improvement achieved in linearity, especially for nickel and cobalt, where the resonance line can be isolated without any severe interference from the adjacent lines (non-excited). The present author has found notable improvements for nickel when high-intensity hollow-cathode lamps are used; better linearity, better sensitivity and better signal-to-noise ratio are found (see Fig. 7–33) than with conventional lamps.

Sullivan and Walsh (*747*) have also compared the spectrograms obtained with high-intensity lamps and conventional lamps. The former produce a very clean spectrum (poor in lines); with a spectrograph, the resonance lines appear quite intense after a much shorter time of exposure.

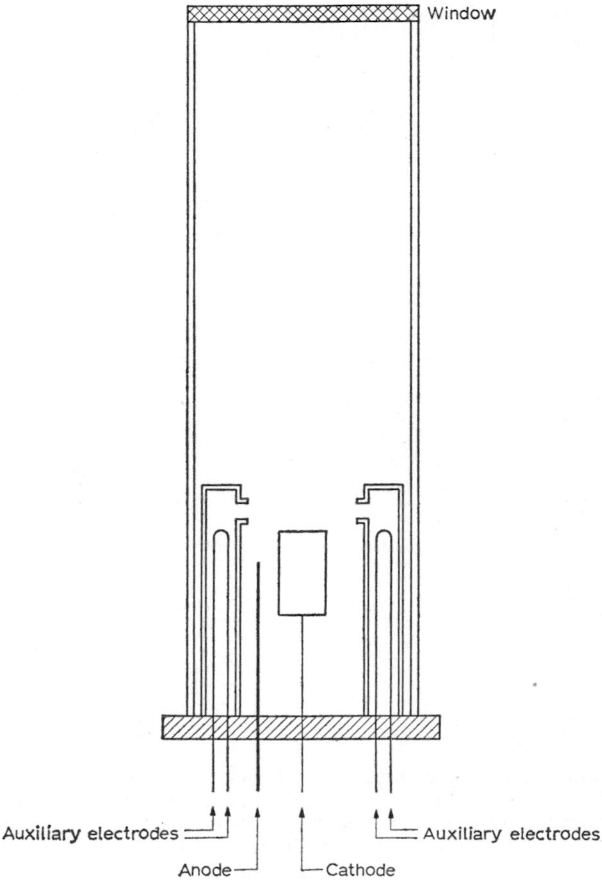

Fig. 7–32. Scheme of a high-intensity hollow-cathode lamp.

2.3.7. Lateral emission

Russell and Walsh (*648*) described an emission of pure resonance lines which can be seen from the side of the hollow-cathode lamps, e.g. at right angles to the axis of the cathode. This phenomenon permits easier selection of lines when the spectrum of the lamp is complex (*747*). The lateral radiation comes from the cloud extending from the cathode towards the anode.

2.3.8. Background

Sometimes a rather intense background is emitted from the cathode at the same time as the lines. This background is not absorbed by the free atoms existing in the flame and reaches the photometric system. The back-

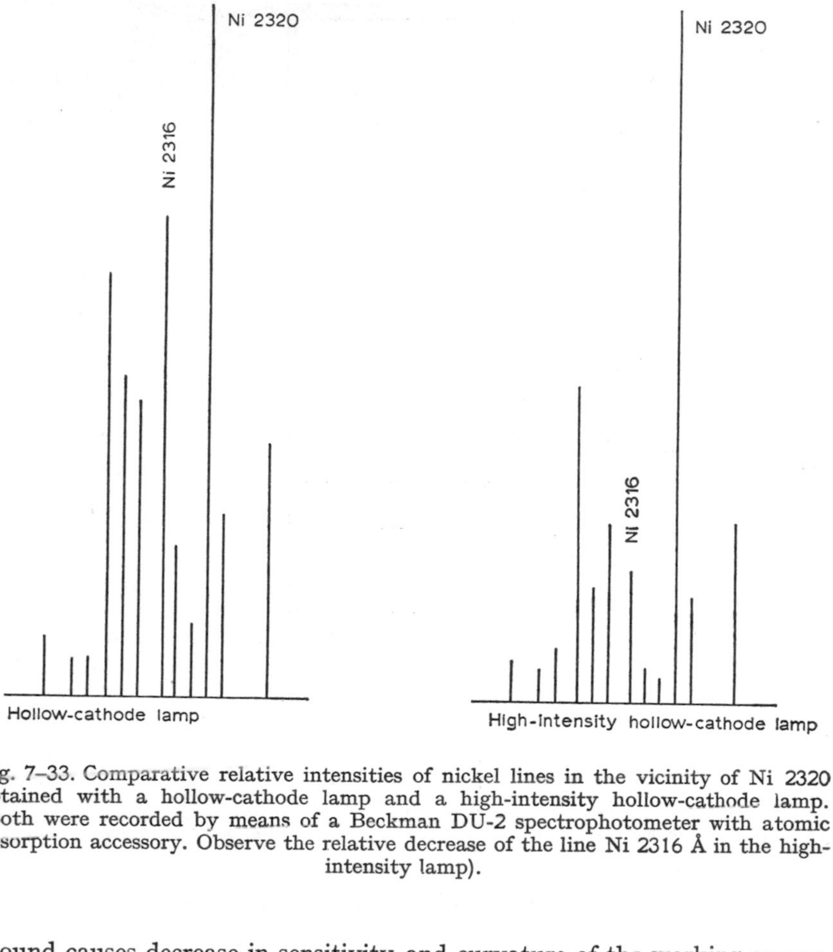

Fig. 7–33. Comparative relative intensities of nickel lines in the vicinity of Ni 2320 obtained with a hollow-cathode lamp and a high-intensity hollow-cathode lamp. (Both were recorded by means of a Beckman DU-2 spectrophotometer with atomic absorption accessory. Observe the relative decrease of the line Ni 2316 Å in the high-intensity lamp).

ground causes decrease in sensitivity and curvature of the working curves.

The presence of hydrogen in the lamp seems to be the cause of several difficulties, such as the production of background in the ultraviolet region and the reduction of the excitation energy, which in turn causes a decrease in the brightness of the source. The hydrogen comes from the hydrogen retained by the metals used in the configuration of the cathodes. Like the formation of oxide films in the inner part of the cathodes, the presence of hydrogen also makes it difficult to obtain sufficiently stable glows.

2.3.9. Emission curves

It is a good practice, if the instrument allows, to scan the source emission at different slits. By such tests it is easy to see how sharp and narrow emission lines can be obtained by improving resolution with narrower slits. Milazzo has described some peculiarities of hollow-cathode spectra and a technique for the study of the spectra of non-metallic elements (*499*).

The emission curve is no more than a representation of the relative intensities as a function of the wavelength. The values of the intensities should be considered as *relative* since they depend on the set of instrumental settings chosen for obtaining the corresponding readings. Figs. 7–34, 7–35, 7–36, 7–37 and 7–38 show several emission curves for different elements.

The emission curve provides a general view of the spectrum and also gives other interesting information, such as:

(a) the location of the resonance lines with respect to other non-absorbing lines and to lines of the filler gas,

(b) the source background in the region in which the resonance lines appear,

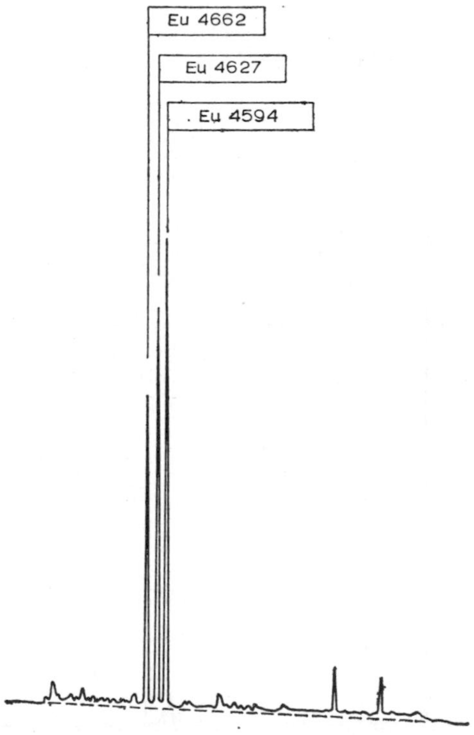

Fig. 7–34. Emission of a europium Westinghouse hollow-cathode lamp (neon) recorded by means of a Beckman DU spectrophotometer. 15 mA, 0.015-mm slit (by courtesy of Westinghouse Electric Corporation, Electronic Tube Division).

(c) the appearance and location of emission lines of other analytes (multi-element lamps) and of the shell metal in the proximity of the desired element. Efforts should be made to work with sufficient resolution to eliminate the disturbing lines by appropriate selection,

(d) the relative intensity of the resonance lines and signal-to-background ratio under each set of experimental settings.

This preliminary study becomes much more significant when multi-cathode lamps are employed, particularly old ones, where one looks for the presence of other analytes in observing each particular cathode.

Automatic scanning is of great help in obtaining these emission curves, because a graphic recording of the complete curve becomes available. It is even better if the scanning device allows the utilization of different scanning speeds. If the instrument has no facilities for obtaining automatic-scanned spectrograms, it is possible, of course, to obtain these curves manually, but the process is tedious and involves:

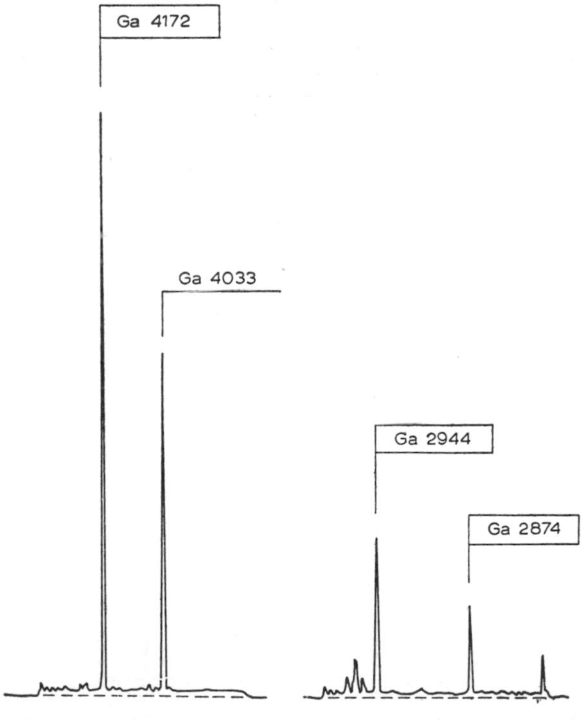

Fig. 7–35. Emission of a gallium Westinghouse hollow-cathode lamp (neon) recorder by means of a Beckman DU Spectrophotometer. 15 mA, 0.015-mm slit (by courtesy of Westinghouse Electric Corporation. Electronic Tube Division).

(a') reading and noting point by point the relative intensities (for each spectrum obtained under each set of experimental settings),

(b') setting manually the wavelength along the desired interval; an uncertainty in the abcissae plotting (wavelength scale) is inherent partly because of the deviation between the calibration curve of the monochro-

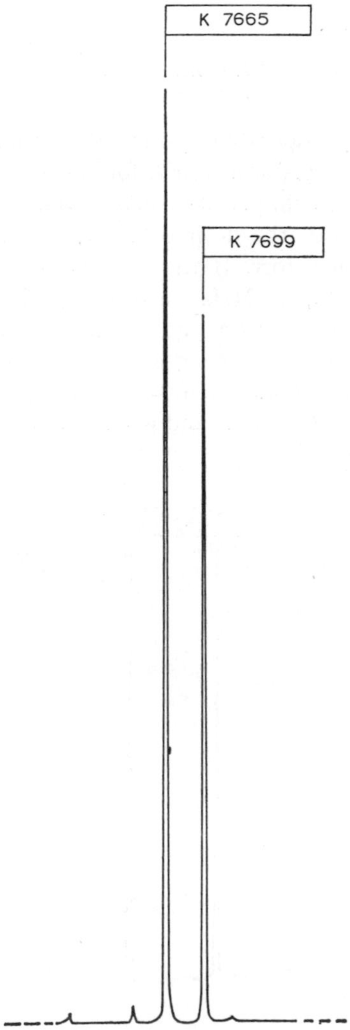

Fig. 7–36. Emission of a potassium Osram lamp recorded by means of a Beckman atomic-absorption spectrophotometer, No. 97900. 800 mA, 0.08-mm slit, 1P28-A photomultiplier (data obtained by M. Galassi).

mator and the ideal calibration curve, but also partly because of operator errors,

(c') plotting manually on graph paper the values read.

Manual scanning can easily mean that some minima and/or maxima situated between settings are missed; moreover, in many cases, only approximate curves are obtained where many narrow emissions appear distorted.

2.4. *Other Sources*

The *electrodeless lamps*, operated by means of radio-frequencies or micro-waves, can provide an adequate source for research in atomic-absorption. These lamps are made up simply of a small, sealed, quartz tube containing a small amount of metal (the desired analyte) and an inert gas at very low pressure—only a few torr. If the tube is placed in a high-frequency field (5–200 W and 1–10,000 MHz), a discharge is produced in the inert gas by the effect of the electrons activated by the field; these electrons then collide with the atoms of the gas, ionizing them and exciting them. When the metallic atoms intervene in the discharge a rather pure spectrum is emitted with very narrow lines and a minimum of Doppler broadening.

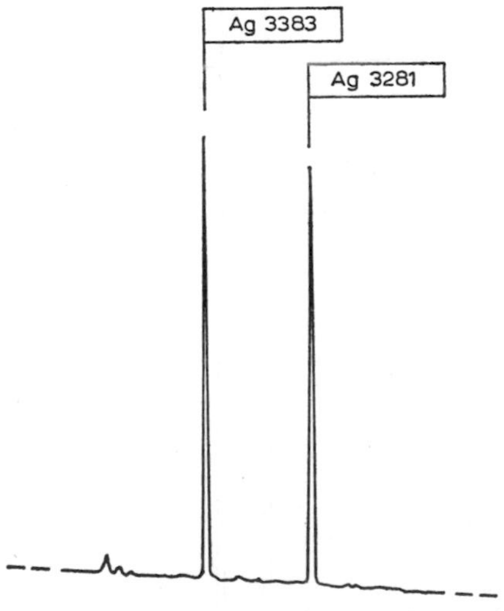

Fig. 7–37. Emission of a silver Westinghouse hollow-cathode lamp (argon) recorded by means of a Beckman DU spectrophotometer. 20 mA, 0.02-mm slit (by courtesy of Westinghouse Electric Corporation, Electronic Tube Division).

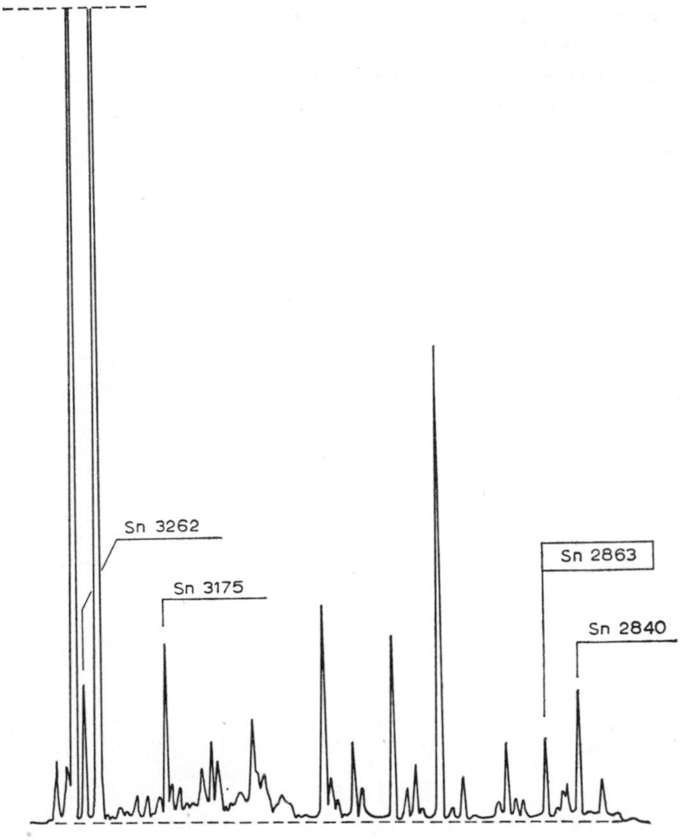

Fig. 7–38. Emission of a tin Westinghouse hollow-cathode lamp (argon) recorded by means of a Beckman DU spectrophotometer 20 mA, 0.04-mm slit (by courtesy of Westinghouse Electric Corporation, Electronic Tube Division).

Compared to the vapor lamps, electrodeless lamps have two objectionable characteristics: (a) they require a more complicated, and therefore more expensive, power supply, and (b) the emission of light is less stable.

For the determination of selenium, an electrodeless discharge tube, in which a vapor containing selenium was placed, has been tested as a source. Careful filling of the tube and good adjustment of the power supply discharge help in obtaining a self-reversal effect which is not great at the selected selenium line at 1961 Å.

Sharpline Spectro-source has announced a selection of electrodeless discharge tubes that can be used for atomic-absorption purposes (*665*).

Other possible sources for use in atomic-absorption are the *pulse spark time resolved sources* which, as Strasheim pointed out (*731*), can resolve lines emitted by ions and atoms; the *microwave-powered sources* described by Ham and Walsh (*304*); and the *Geissler tubes* (*213*).

Chapter 8

Absorption system

The absorption system is one of the most important parts of the instrument since the fundamental step of the absorption process takes place in it. The other systems are essential to the whole process, but in the absorption systems are produced the experimental variations of the quantitative variable. The absorption system is also the most complex system in the number and quality of its integral elements. It is extremely important with respect to the operating conditions, since the repeatability, accuracy and sensitivity of the total process depend largely on these characteristics of the absorption system. To reduce the enumeration of all its sections to the basic essentials, the *flame*, the *burner* and the *sprayer* are the most vital parts in the case of flame. Other parts, mechanical and optical, and even the instruments for the regulation of gases, play auxiliary roles in the proper functioning of the main sections.

The use of the flame is given most attention in this Chapter, because it is the most widely-accepted means of producing absorbing media. Other devices and procedures used in atomic-absorption are also mentioned.

1. THE FLAME

In Chapter 7, Section 2.1, reference was made to the use of the flame as a possible emitter in absorption research and even as a substitute for other conventional sources in some cases. Flames present some difficulties when used as emitters e.g. the difficulty in producing emission of lines corresponding to high potentials of excitation, the instability of emission, and the emission of broadened lines; but they offer many advantages when utilized in the absorption system.

Vaporization techniques involving the use of sputtering chambers and furnaces with reducing atmospheres are potentially perhaps the most suitable techniques for obtaining atomic vapors for atomic-absorption work, but the flame, with the spraying process, remains the simplest and cheapest way[1].

[1] The spraying process is still a limiting factor in the attainment of high sensitivities, and other procedures may present better atomization efficiency than the flame, being independent of the spraying efficiency.

1.1. Uses of the flame. Flame characteristics

Although it is common practice to speak simply of the flame *acting* in the instrumental analytical process, it is wise to point out that the flame plays two entirely different parts: (1) it is one of the sections which integrate the system—absorption system—, with its *pre-operative characteristics*, i.e. the products of the combustion of certain gases localized at the outlet of the burner; and (2) it plays an active role, receiving the sample as a spray, modifying the spray, contributing to the liberation of atoms and helping to maintain a population of free atoms during the process of absorption. Even when the analyte does not reach the flame (when the blank is being read or adjusted by spraying with blank solution, solvent or pure water), the flame develops an active role. When the instrument is zeroed—real or conventional 0% absorption—the flame is essential to the preliminary setting of the instrument. Thus the flame has two aspects, passive and active, but from the operational standpoint it is best to consider it as one entity. Consideration must be given jointly to the two active supplies which reach the flame: gases and sprayed sample.

A flame is characterized by the *gases involved*, the *temperature*, the *form in which the gases are mixed*, the *flow of the gases* (this determines the volume ratio) and its *shape* and *size*. All these aspects play essential roles in atomic-absorption processes.

1.1.1. Regulation

Most of the common combustible mixtures have been tried in flame research (emission and atomic-absorption). Efforts have been made in the case of atomic absorption to work with flames of different temperature, varying in each mixture the volume ratio and the mode of mixing (flames of premixed gases for laminar flames, and gases mixed at the top of the burner for turbulent flames), and many shapes and sizes have been tried. Once the qualitative composition of the flame and the method of mixing have been selected, the behaviour (and even dimensions) of the flame can be varied by appropriate regulation of the gases involved. At the moment of actually utilizing the flame, all variables must be fixed in order to achieve a flame as stable and as constant as possible. For this, the pressure and flow of each gas, as well as the flow ratio, must be kept as constant as possible during the aspiration of standards, samples and blanks.

This constancy is achieved in atomic-absorption instruments by the same type of devices as those used in emission flame photometers[2], with

---

[2] Consult Chapter 5, Section 4, p. 43 of *Flame Photometry* (*125*).

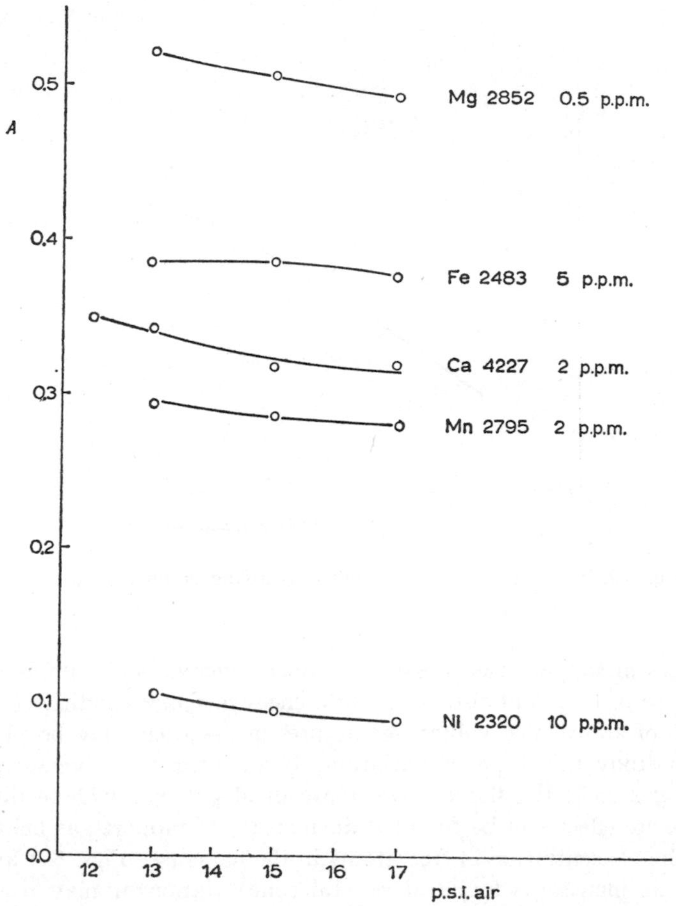

Fig. 8–1. Slight decreases of absorbance for several analytes with small increases of support gas pressure. Turbulent flow burner (Beckman DU-2 spectrophotometer with atomic-absorption accessory) with air and hydrogen-lean flame.

successive steps of regulation in the supply lines of the fuel gas and the support gas[3].

---

[3] The supporting gas helps to produce the spray, and afterwards accompanies the fuel gas towards or at the top of the burner. For many years air and oxygen have been used but other gases have recently been tested (nitrogen, nitrous oxide, enriched air (rich in oxygen), etc.). In reversed flames (as used in emission flame photometry) the fuel gas aspirates the sample solution; for details on reversed flames consult: H. F. Loken, J. S. Teal and E. Eisenberg, Flame spectrophotometry of calcium with reversed oxyacetylene flame. Application to serum and urine, *Anal. Chem.*, 35 (1963) 875.

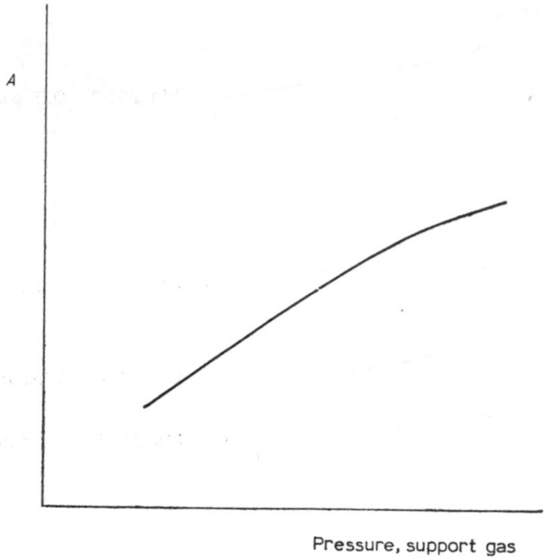

Fig. 8–2. Increase of absorbance with increasing support gas pressure.

Changes in support gas pressure produce differences in sample solution intake (see p. 127), and also some differences in flame conditions. Results in terms of absorbance values versus pressure settings may be plotted in order to study this type of variation. If an increase of pressure of the support gas cools the flame, a decrease of absorbance will be observed; the opposite effect will be found if an increase of support gas helps to increase the concentration of free atoms in the flame (see Figs. 8–1 and 8–2). If such an increase is found at several concentrations it may result in a progressive variation of the working curves, as shown in Fig. 8–3. Some caution is required in interpretation, however, because the variations observed at a fixed height of the burner may only be apparent, being caused by a variation in the distribution of the atoms in the flame.

If the temperature of the support gas changes, a change can be observed in the absorbance values (see Fig. 8–4).

Changes in fuel gas pressure should not notably affect the sample intake (more noticeable in turbulent flames) but they do drastically change the flame conditions. Increases of fuel pressure are convenient for some elements which need richer flames to achieve enough sensitivity (see p. 99). Results in terms of absorbance values *vs.* pressure settings can also be plotted for the fuel gas when the effects of these variations are checked in establishing new or better operating conditions (see Figs. 8–5 and 8–6).

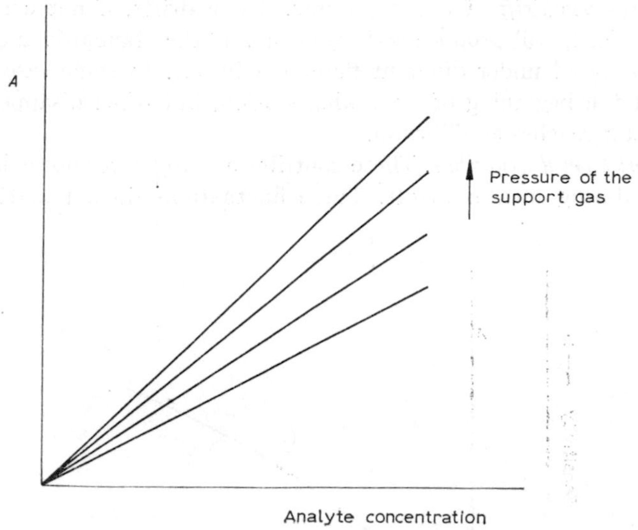

Fig. 8–3. Shape of working curves with increasing support gas pressure if the phenomenon represented in Fig. 8–2 is accomplished.

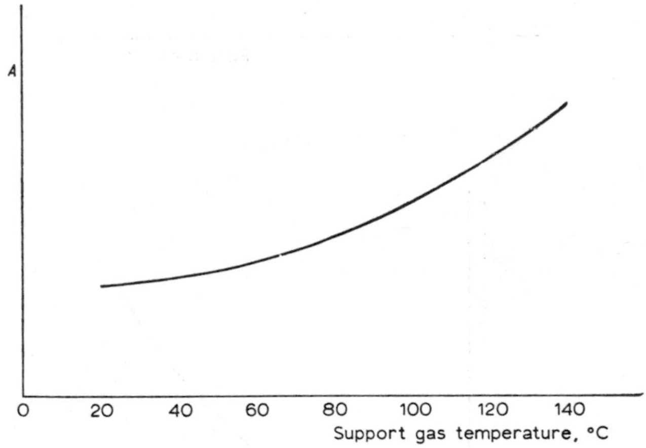

Fig. 8–4. Increase of absorbance when the support gas is heated above the ambient temperature.

Some attention should be paid to gas regulation during operation because there are two phenomena which can produce disturbances[4].

[4] Leakage is an accidental phenomenon. In any case, leakages should be tested for from time to time, and especially after the gas supply has been connected to the instrument for the first time. The use of Snoop® is advisable.

(a) *Long-term drift* of the regulators. These drifts, if not corrected as soon as noticed, will produce serious errors, as the standards and samples will be measured under different flame conditions. In some cases, drift is noticed at the beginning of a working session, but often disappears when the regulator reaches equilibrium.

(b) *Short-term fluctuations*. These contribute as regulator noise, increasing the noise during measurements. These fluctuations do not matter if the

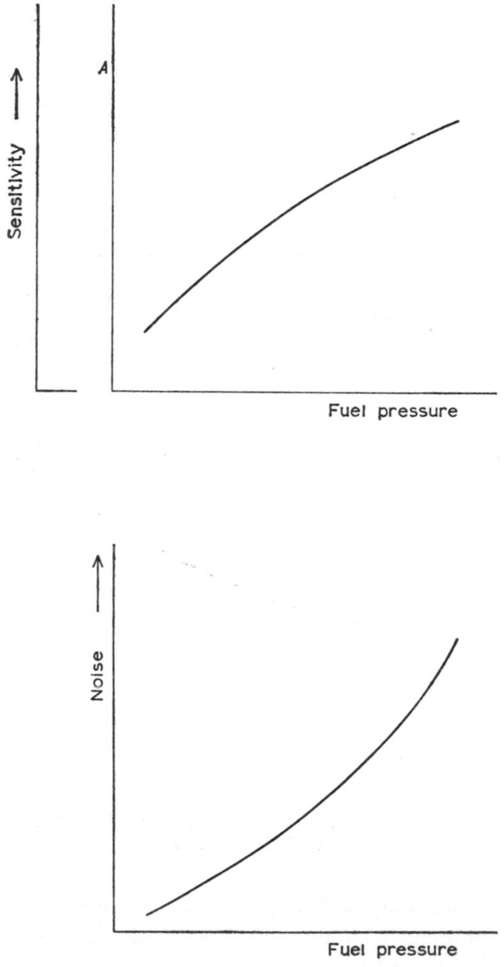

Fig. 8–5. Increase of absorbance (and sensitivity) with increasing fuel gas pressure (richer flame). The noise (see lower part) can increase, even at higher rate, under these circumstances.

noise is very small and if the average position of the needle on the gauge is perfectly stable. Attention is needed if the needle moves too much, or if the ball in flowmeters shows too much oscillation.

Although it is common practice to speak of adjusting the pressures of

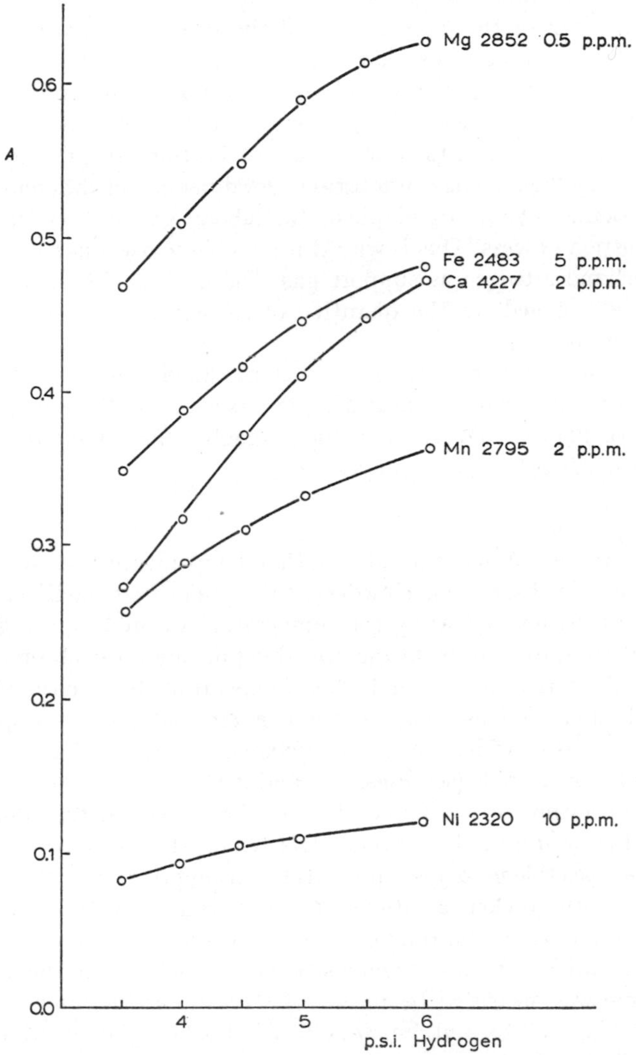

Fig. 8–6. Increase of absorbance for several analytes with increases of fuel gas pressure. Turbulent flow burner (Beckman DU-2 spectrophotometer with atomic-absorption accessory) with air and hydrogen.

the gases, it would be more correct to think in terms of measuring the real volumes per unit of time (flows) supplied to the burner. It is becoming quite common to use flowmeters along with other devices in the regulation section and the mano-reducers secured in the heads of the gas tanks. It is even possible to use flowmeters which are graduated in arbitrary units, which can be submitted to pre- or post-calibration.

The regulation of the gases is one of the most elastic variables at the disposal of the operator for changing the conditions of the flame, but it must be remembered that in each case the variation of conditions for the gases is subject to a series of limitations created by: the desired length of the flame, the characteristic velocity of combustion, and the temperature required in the flame. These limitations are different for different mixtures of gases. Besides the gases supplied, the laboratory air also intervenes in the combustion process. This is why it is possible to use a flame with hydrogen as fuel and nitrogen as support gas. The final conditions of the flame can also be changed by the quantity of solvent vapor that reaches the flame at any moment.

The necessity of maintaining a constant flame has inclined many investigators to favor flames which use pre-mixed gases; these produce much more stable flames, and are not too strongly affected on receiving the aerosol proceeding from the sprayer section.

1.1.2. Temperature

Some years ago it was considered that temperature was not a critical factor in atomic-absorption. However, this opinion was modified when the imperative need for increasing the temperature to produce a high enough concentration of free atoms in the absorbing medium was observed.

The result is that flames of higher temperature have been tested and extensively used, leaving cooler flames (e.g. air–coal gas, air–propane) only for certain cases in which an improvement in sensitivity has been experimentally demonstrated[5] (see Figs. 8–7 and 8–8).

The temperature of the flame changes depending on the solution flow rate and the nature of the solvent. The temperature of oxygen–hydrogen and oxygen–acetylene flames (in total consumption burners; turbulent flames) fed with aqueous solutions has been studied by Winefordner *et al.* (*847*). They measured the temperatures as a function of the solution flow rate for a variety of flame compositions and heights in the flame; the temperature was measured by means of the ratio of the intensities of two iron lines (Fe 3737.13 and Fe 3734.87 Å). Cooke (*155*) mentions his experiments in the determination of temperatures in dry flames and in flames

[5] Nevertheless, the use of Handigas, propane, etc. continues to be cited frequently.

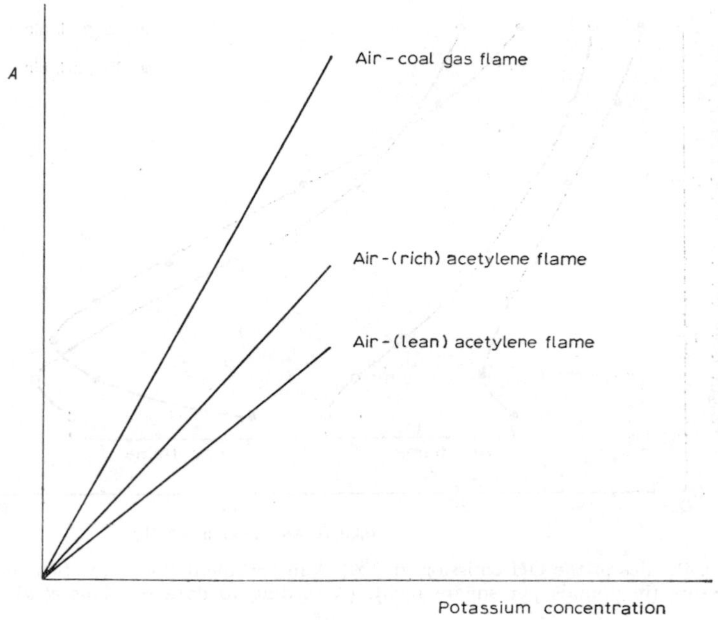

Fig. 8–7. Schematic representation of the relative situation of potassium working curves for different flame conditions.

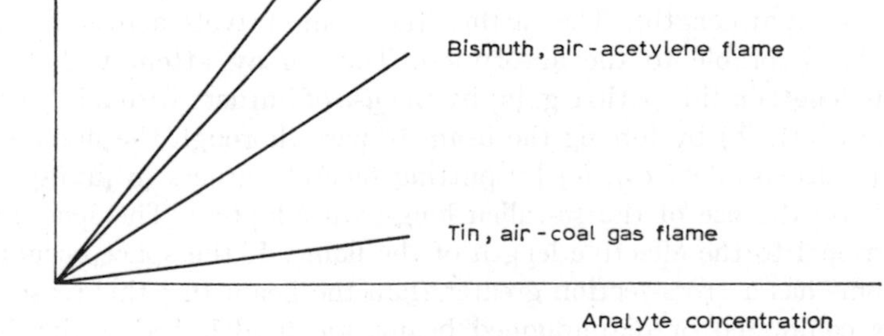

Fig. 8–8. Schematic representation of the relative situation of bismuth and tin working curves for different flame conditions.

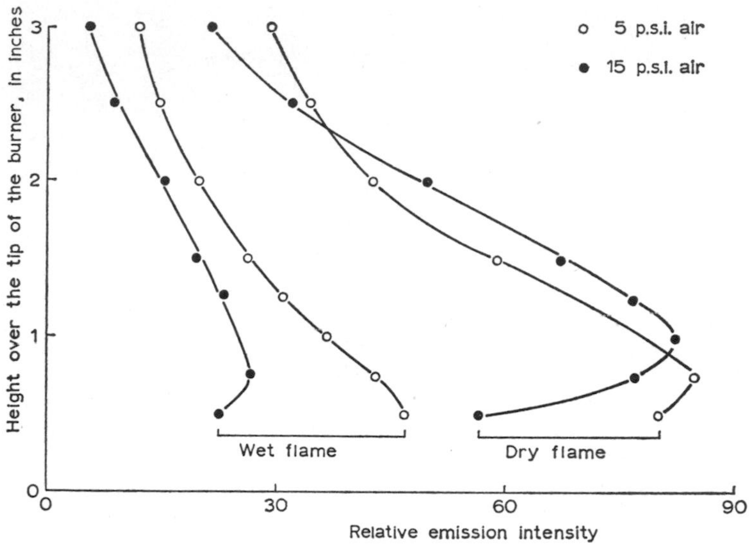

Fig. 8–9. Profiles of the OH emission at 3090 Å in turbulent flow burners at different air pressure (in pounds per square inch). (According to data of Claus *et al.* (*150*)).

fed with water and organic solvents; the introduction of water markedly reduces the temperature, whereas the introduction of acetone does not affect it.

There are many methods of measuring the temperature of the flame. In order to obtain an idea of the temperature changes at different heights above the top of the burner, measurement of the OH emission at 3090 Å can be used successfully; this was done recently by Claus *et al.* (*150*). Fig. 8–9 shows typical results.

1.1.3. Dimensions

The flame dimension of most interest in atomic-absorption is probably the length (pathlength). The farther the beam travels across the flame, the more favorable to the absorption. Thus many attempts have been made to lengthen this path, e.g. (a) by the use of burners with a longitudinal opening (slot), (b) by forcing the beam to pass thorough the flame several times (multipass devices), (c) by putting several burners in juxtaposition, and (d) by the use of the so-called long-path adapters. The sensitivity is proportional to the effective length of the flame. If the space occupied by the atoms has a cross-section greater than the beam (for this reason very narrow collimated or diaphragmed beams are used)[6], and if the density

[6] Diaphragms produce loss of energy.

remains constant in the cross-section, the absorbance is proportional to the length of the atom-filled space, i.e. to the product of the concentration of atoms and the optical path length (Beer's law).

The width is another important dimension. If the conditions of the sprayer remain constant, the concentration of atoms in the flame is inversely proportional to the horizontal cross-section of the flame. A reduction in this section can be achieved by reducing the practical width of the flame; this factor favors long-slot burners.

In the use of sprayer-burners, the small flame diameter presents difficulties in achieving good sensitivity with a single burner, although quite good results can be obtained by coupling several of them in one unit, and even better results if the beam is made to pass through the various flames several times by multipass devices.

The height of the flame is less critical. In many instruments the beam crosses the flame only a few millimeters above the top of the burner. When several passes are used—especially if they are situated in a vertical plane—the height is important if the beam is still to find atoms in the upper parts of the flame. The effective height of the flame can be varied more easily in turbulent flames. A method for testing the height of the flame involves aspirating a sodium solution of low concentration; the gas pressures are adjusted until the height of the yellow-colored flame exceeds the level at which the upper beam pass is located. This is only an approximate test, because one cannot assume that the free atoms of any element will occupy the same length at which the sodium emission was observed.

1.2. Different kinds of flames

Almost all conventional flames have been tested in atomic-absorption. For those elements that are easily vaporized in flames of low temperature, few advantages will be found in the use of oxygen–hydrogen, oxygen–acetylene, or oxygen–cyanogen flames. Moreover, the air–hydrogen flame is advantageous because of its meager emissive power. (The flame obtained with hydrogen as fuel and nitrogen as support gas is in fact an air–hydrogen flame, because the air around the burner helps to maintain the flame. This may help in the use of hydrogen in laminar flame burners designed for gases other than hydrogen).

The air–coal gas flame has been widely used and belongs to the low-temperature class, along with the air–propane flame. The latter has the advantage over the air–acetylene flame that it produces less background and lends itself more readily to non-critical designs of burners; owing to the lower velocity of this flame, the burner slots need not to be so narrow as those utilized for air–acetylene burners. It is not dangerous and is fully accepted by many safety regulations.

The air–coal gas flame is unsuitable when interference effects are found and the use of releasing agents is attempted. The utilization of releasing agents (see Chapter 18), such as proposed by Willis (*827*), e.g. the addition of strontium to minimize the effects of phosphate on calcium, is more effective with air–acetylene flames.

The use of oxygen instead of air increases the temperature of the flame, which is particularly useful for analytes that form undissociated compounds at low flame temperatures. In order to achieve higher temperature Robinson has studied the potentialities of oxygen–cyanogen flames.

The following list summarizes some references to different kinds of flames.

Flames	*Authors*	*References*
air–coal gas	Lockyer *et al.*	(*436*)
	Russell *et al.*	(*647*)
air–propane	Malmstadt *et al.*	(*451*)
air–acetylene	Allan	(*7*)
	David	(*161, 166*)
	Hell *et al.*	(*313, 314, 316*)
	Slavin	(*679*)
	Slavin *et al.*	(*708*)
	Willis	(*827, 828*)
air–hydrogen	Brace *et al.*	(*110*)
	Claus *et al.*	(*150*)
	Hell *et al.*	(*313, 314, 316*)
	Slavin *et al.*	(*708*)
oxygen–hydrogen	Robinson	(*620, 623, 624*)
	Warren	(*808*)
	Willis	(*827*)
oxygen–acetylene	Fassel *et al.*	(*225–235*)
	Gidley	(*268*)
	Hell *et al.*	(*316*)
	Trent and Manning	(*773*)
	Willis	(*827*)
oxygen–cyanogen	Robinson	(*617, 623*)
nitrous oxide–acetylene	Allan	(*14*)
	Capacho *et al.*	(*140, 900, 901*)
	Hell *et al.*	(*315*)
	Willis	(*838*)

If it is not strictly necessary (see p. 101), the operator should avoid the use of excessively bright flames whether he is working with instruments prepared for single beam or double-beam operation, or for d.c. or a.c.

operation. The luminous emission of the flame is received in the photodetector and may increase the shot noise, with a consequent decrease in the signal-to-noise ratio, and, therefore, with an effect on the values of the fluctuational (qualitative and quantitative) concentration limits. Of course, only an emission produced at or near the wavelength at which the instrument has been set, interferes. Flames colored e.g., by the presence of some high-emitting component (Na, Li) in the solution do not interfere despite the visual emission. The same may apply to water coming from some exhausted demineralizer and used by mistake in the preparation of a sample. However, attention should be given to components in excessive concentrations that can produce a continuous emission; this should be corrected by proper adjustment of the instrument.

For any flame, gases of good quality should be supplied. For long working periods in which several tanks are consumed, the same quality of gases should be selected for uniformity; it is a good practice to avoid using the first and last portions of a tank gas, particularly when acetylene is used, Laboratory pipe compressed air is much cheaper than compressed air in tanks, but a good filtering system is advisable to remove dust, oil residues and water vapor.

1.2.1. Fuel-rich flames

In this section the fuel-rich oxygen–acetylene and air–hydrogen flames are discussed.

1.2.1.1. Fuel-rich oxygen–acetylene flames. This name is given to flames which are produced with a high acetylene flow, so that the flame is very luminous, highly reducing, very calorific and rich in incandescent materials. Such flames are also known as *acetylene-rich flames*, *incandescent-acetylene flames* and *reducing flames*.

Although low-temperature flames (with low background and cool enough to avoid helping emission) have often been used, flames of greater calorific power are necessary to facilitate dissociation of some compounds. For example, Willis (*827*) favored the air–acetylene flame in the determination of calcium in blood serum, since calcium is a typical case of resistance to the liberation of atoms (see also refs. (*406, 618*)).

The experimental studies carried out by Fassel *et al.* (*200, 201, 225–235, 403, 404*) have formed the basis for present knowledge of the advantages and results of fuel-rich flames. A series of elements used to be considered impossible to detect and determine by flame procedures; a few years ago there were nearly 30 elements showing poor sensitivity, but this number has been reduced to about 10, thanks to the help of richer flames (*405*).

Fuel-rich flames produce a displacement of the dissociation equilibrium of the metallic oxides in favor of the concentration of the metal in atomic state. This effect, of course, produces an increase in sensitivity. This effect was first noted in atomic-absorption flame photometry by Allan (*7*) in the determination of magnesium. David (*165*) also indicated the possibility of using reducing flames in the case of molybdenum. The idea was then extended to the determination of elements such as chromium, ruthenium and tin. The possibility of determining vanadium by means of fuel-rich flames has aroused great interest (see Veillon (*788*)), and much research has been done in order to include vanadium, as well as aluminum, in the list of elements which can be determined by atomic-absorption.

Fuel-rich conditions seems to favor the process of dissociation rather than the actual volatilization of the solution components (temperature effects plus reducing effects). In this respect, David points out that even though molybdenum is more refractory than aluminum, it may be determined with fuel-rich flames (incandescent air–acetylene flame) which are relatively cold, whereas aluminum, which is more volatile as a metal, requires the high temperature and reducing conditions of the incandescent oxygen–acetylene flame (*176*).

The present author has found a notable increase in the sensitivity for molybdenum with rich-fuel air–acetylene flames (laminar flow burner); turbulent flow burner operation was necessary to detect and determine aluminum with fuel-rich oxygen–acetylene flames in conjunction with solutions containing much ethanol.

Most of the work with fuel-rich oxygen–acetylene flames carried out by Fassel *et al.* was performed with premix flames (Kniseley burner) (see p. 120). Manning has used a modified burner for aluminum, also with oxygen–acetylene flames (*456*).

The following list shows a few examples of elements which have been determined using fuel-rich flames.

Elements	*Authors*	*References*
Cr, Ru, Sn	Allan	(*15*)
Al	Chakrabarti *et al.*	(*146*)
Mo	David	(*165*)
Dy, Er, Eu, Gd, Ho, La, Lu, Nb, Nd, Pr, Re, Sc, Sm, Tb, Ti, Tm, V, Y, Yb	Fassel *et al.*	(*229, 230, 235*)
Sn	Gatehouse and Willis	(*258*)
Al, V	Hell *et al.*	(*313, 316*)
Al, B, Ge, Si, W	Manning	(*456*)
Dy, Er, Eu, Ho, Sm, Tm, Yb	Skogerboe and Woodriff	(*675*)
Al, Be, Re, Ti, V	Slavin, Manning *et al.*	(*461, 703*)

Since the temperature of the flame increases the number of atoms in excited states, these fuel-rich flames present high potentialities for emission work. However, they have an adverse effect in atomic-absorption for elements of low ionization potential.

The contribution of the inherent temperature effect in the dissociation chemical process, in favorable cases, leads to the absorption rate becoming indirectly dependent on the temperature. For cases where undissociable compounds are not formed, no notable improvement can be expected by changing from an oxidizing (or cold) flame to a reducing (hotter) flame.

The use of modulation (see p. 107, and also Chapter 9) permits the utilization, with fewer difficulties, of very luminous flames such as the fuel-rich flames. If modulation is not used (d.c. systems), a compensation must be made instrumentally for the luminous contribution of the flame.

Winefordner and Veillon (*850*) have studied the possibilities of reducing the background signal in the use of fuel-rich oxygen–acetylene flames by using light pipes; the determination of vanadium, tin and aluminum are improved in this way. Skogerboe and Woodriff (*675*) have used fuel-rich flames as a source in their studies on europium, thulium and yttrium.

Fassel *et al.* (*232*) have reported striking enhancements for many elements when the atomic-emission and atomic-absorption spectra are observed in the interconal zone of premixed fuel-rich oxygen–acetylene flames. The fuel-rich flames have also solved the problem of the determination of rhodium, as has been demonstrated by Schrenk *et al.* (*656*); a fluctuational concentration limit of 1–2 p.p.m. can be obtained. Under their working conditions, marked interferences were caused by calcium, magnesium, aluminum, and iron which decreased the sensitivity.

A 10-cm path burner head for fuel-rich oxygen–acetylene flames has been described by Bystroff (*135*), and used in studies of sensitivity and noise levels for beryllium, magnesium, calcium, barium, aluminum, yttrium, vanadium, tungsten, niobium, zirconium, gadolinium and holmium.

The present author has examined the behaviour of fuel-rich oxygen–acetylene flames with a turbulent flow burner (especially for the determination of aluminum and vanadium) (*316*). Determinations of aluminum (*199*), vanadium (*891*) and lanthanides (*510*) have been discussed.

1.2.1.2. Fuel-rich air–hydrogen flames. These flames are produced with a high hydrogen flow. They are not very luminous, but much more calorific than the corresponding lean air–hydrogen flame. It can also be called rich-hydrogen flame[7].

---

[7] The nomenclature shown in the heading of this subsection is preferred, as it shows clearly the kind of support gas involved in producing this type of flame.

Better sensitivities can be achieved for some elements in turbulent air–hydrogen flames when the hydrogen flow is increased (see Fig. 8–6). The sensitivity was especially improved for elements that tend to form non-dissociable compounds in the flame. It has been observed that the difficulty of converting such compounds to free atoms not only decreases sensitivity, but also restricts the distribution of the free atoms in the flame, as shown by testing different burner heights (*150*).

When the flow ratio of hydrogen to air is increased at different values of air flow, it may be possible to find a compromise between air flow and sample intake rate, as the percentual sensitivity is, to some extent, a function of the amount of analyte fed into the flame per unit of time. A summary of the behaviour of fuel-rich air–hydrogen flames (*150*) is given below.

(a) The fuel-rich air–hydrogen flame is practically colorless (absence of visible emissions), which means that no severe interferences would be expected in the visual region of the spectrum; this is in contrast to oxygen–acetylene flames fed with high acetylene flows[8].

(b) Excessively high sample intake may produce depression of signals by cooling effects; this has been demonstrated by measuring the intensity of the band emission at 3089 Å and also, in some cases, by an increase of the atom population at low air pressures, but at the same height over the burner (tin, chromium).

(c) Most of the elements studied show a progressive increase of absorption with increasing flow rates. Silver shows a maximum, but decreases afterwards.

(d) The fuel-rich air–hydrogen flames seem to reduce and thermally decompose the compounds formed in the flame. In the particular case of silver (long-life free atoms), a maximum appears sooner than any maxima for other elements, that do not appear in the graphs because of the flow-rate limits chosen.

(e) Fuel-rich flames of this type help to increase the sensitivity to some extent as shown below.

Some data obtained with fuel-rich air–hydrogen flames and a turbulent flow burner are shown below. The so-called lean flame was richer in hydrogen than the stoichiometric flame. Some curves obtained during this experimental work are mentioned on p. 108.

[8] This flame emission interference is visualized at the visual region of the spectrum, but it is extended towards the ultraviolet.

Analytes	Ratios $\frac{\text{Percentual Qual. Sensitivity Rich Flame}}{\text{Percentual Qual. Sensitivity Lean Flame}}$
As	2.90
Ba	1.70
Ca	1.78
Cr	11.7
Fe	1.50
Mg	1.47
Mn	1.55
Ni	1.47
Pb	10.5
Sn	7.93
Sr	2.43

Capacho-Delgado and Manning (*138, 139*) also have found an increase in sensitivity on switching from an air–acetylene flame to an air–hydrogen flame, and especially with a fuel-rich air–hydrogen flame. This allowed them to achieve a percentual concentration limit for tin of 1.3 p.p.m. (Sn 2863 Å) with a high-intensity hollow-cathode lamp. Claus *et al.* (*150*) obtained a percentual concentration limit of 5.3 p.p.m., but with only one burner and one light pass, a turbulent flame and a standard hollow-cathode tin lamp.

1.2.2. Enriched air–acetylene flame

In view of the need for hotter flames for the determination of some elements (hotter than the air–acetylene flame), Amos and Thomas have used an oxygen-enriched air–acetylene flame (*19*). A notable improvement in the sensitivity for aluminum was achieved with 50% air and 50% oxygen in a specially designed burner.

1.2.3. Nitrous oxide–acetylene flame

Willis (*838*) has described the use and potentialities of the nitrous oxide–acetylene flame, which appears to overcome several of the remaining difficulties in atomic-absorption work with low temperature flames. These difficulties were mainly:

(a) partial atomization found with analytes such as alkaline earths, chromium, molybdenum, tin, and also caused by chemical interferences.

(b) lack of atomization with analytes such as aluminum, beryllium, silicon, titanium, tungsten, vanadium.

Willis (*838*) evolved appropriate flame conditions for obtaining adequate sensitivity by means of a slot 4″ × 0.015″ (ca. 10 cm × 0.038 cm) in a non-cooled, thick stainless-steel head fitted directly on the spray chamber. He reported the percentual concentration limits shown below, as well as a practical disappearance of chemical interferences in systems such as P–Ca and Al–Mg.

Analyte	*Spectral line (Å)*	*Percentual concentration limit (p.p.m.)*
Al	3093	1
Be	2349	0.03
Si	2516	5
Ti	3643	4
W	2551	5
V	3184	1.5

The use of this type of flame has been discussed in several subsequent publications (see, e.g. refs. (*51, 56, 315, 806, 887*)). Manning has found that the results with nitrogen monoxide–acetylene flames are no better than those with the nitrous oxide–acetylene flame. The former was found more corrosive and more expensive to handle. Manning reported some fluctuational concentration limits obtained with the nitrous oxide–acetylene flame, but no percentual concentration limits were given (*453*).

Capacho-Delgado and Manning (*140, 901*) have described the application of the nitrous oxide–acetylene flame for vanadium determinations in oil and steel samples, but no percentual concentration limits were reported. Hell *et al.* (*315*) have also reported results with this new flame and a modified laminar flow burner.

The nitrous oxide–acetylene flame presents some phenomena of ionization interferences. The lanthanides seem to be very sensitive to alkali-earth ionization interference.

The new features of this flame are due to its high temperature and its relatively low flame speed. Fig. 8–10 shows a comparison of temperatures and flame speeds for several flames, as described by Willis (*838*).

1.3. Absorption phenomena produced by the flame itself

In atomic-absorption flame photometry the instruments are zeroed in the absence of analyte atoms in the absorbing cell. The zeroing may be done in the following ways:

(a) by aspirating the blank solution (I),
(b) by aspirating only the solvent (water in most cases) (I'),
(c) with the flame alone (I'').

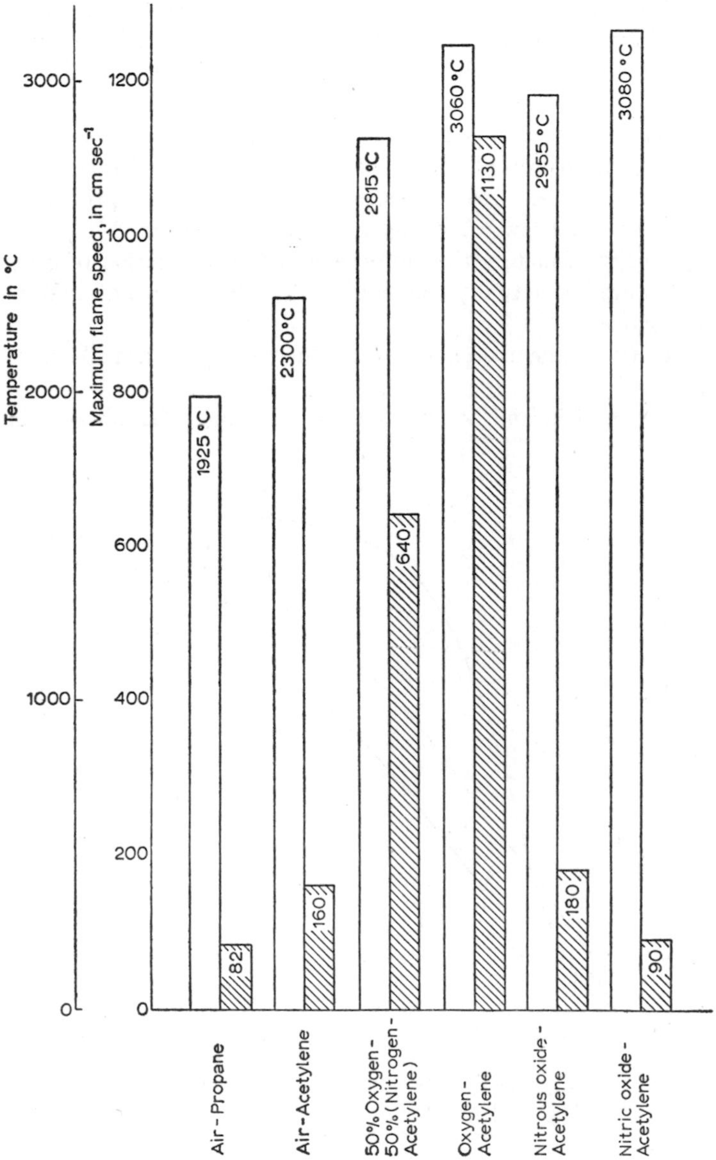

Fig. 8–10. Temperatures and maximum flame speeds for several types of flames. (From data published in ref. (*838*)) (by permission of J. B. Willis and *Nature*).

Here I, I' and I'' are the light intensities transmitted through the flame in each case. If significant absorptions are achieved only when atoms of the analyte are present in the flame, it could be assumed that $I \approx I' \approx I''$. In many cases, however, the blank solution and the solvent show some absorption in an instrument zeroed against the flame. If the instrument were zeroed *without flame* the absorption effects of the flame itself might be seen.

Gilbert has discussed this topic under the heading *Blank absorption in the flame* (*275*). In his recent studies of atomic-absorption flame photometry below 2000 Å, Allan reported interesting results on the absorptions produced by the flames at that low wavelength region (*17*) (see Fig. 8–11).

Below is a list of factors that intervene in the production of absorption effects which are not actually connected with the presence of analyte.

(a) The flame itself.

(a.1) Opacity of the flame, generally increasing toward shorter wavelengths.

(a.2) Presence of incandescent particles in luminous flames that increase

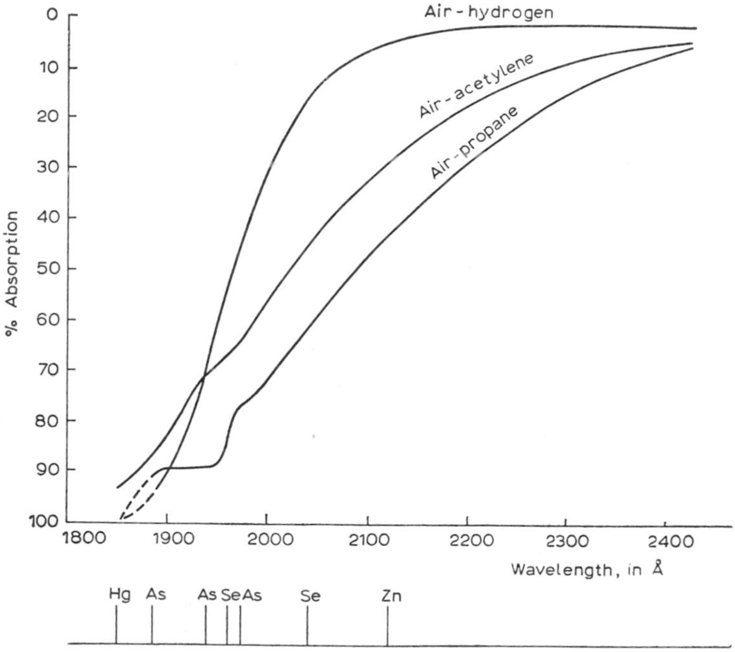

Fig. 8–11. Absorptions produced by different flames in the short wavelength region. (For more details consult ref. (*17*)).

opacity because of screening and scattering of the light coming from the source.

(b) Other causes originated at the flame section.

(b.1) Bands of variable intensity in which the solvent and other components of the solution intervene. A particular case is the absorption caused by mineral acids, especially halogen acids; this absorption is noticed even in spraying the blanks, if the blank has been corrected for the amount of acid to be found in the sample solutions. Another particular case is the absorption due to solvents which are not completely destroyed by combustion.

(b.2) Opacity due to salt particles proceeding from very concentrated standards, solutions and blanks (some light is scattered).

1.4. Modulation

Although the topic of modulation does not really belong to this chapter (see Chapter 10), a brief discussion seems appropriate at this point.

In instruments equipped with modulation, the flame may be considered as an uninterrupted emitter whose uninterrupted output cannot be seen by the photometric system, as this is tuned to the frequency of the emission system. Actually, it is difficult to eliminate completely the effect of any flame emission that may be present, even with the use of modulation, since the flame has a noise component which may be significant at the modulation frequency. This residual effect will result in a decrease of the sensitivity. Besides this, all the light selected at some short wavelength band by the selection system—unabsorbed light from the source and light emitted at that band by the flame—will be received in the photodetector.

The fraction of light emitted by the flame as re-emitted light depending on the light absorbed might increase the total emission of the flame. However, absorption occurs in a single direction (the passage of the beam across the flame) and the absorptions in the different points of the flame are integrated along its entire length; moreover, the light emitted by the flame, including the re-emitted light, is radiated *in all directions*. Accordingly, only the small fraction which happens to pass along the single important direction will penetrate the optical system and be selected. Except in the case of an excessive emission by the analyte in the flame (high-emitting elements) and of high-emitting flames (fuel-rich flames), very little emitted light enters the monochromator; in most cases it does not disturb the measurements. Several means of compensating for the effect are available: use of cooler flames, choice of appropriate heights over the burner, utilization of small slits, instrumental correction of the emission by careful adjustment of the 100% absorption end of the scale. In cases of excessive emission the use of modulation is, naturally, advisable.

1.5. Selected zone

The flame is not an uniform entity along its full length. As it rises from the burner, the flame varies in shape, temperature and composition[9].

Special emphasis is given in this section to variations in the composition. This variation is of importance and many studies have been devoted to measurements obtained at different heights above the tip of the burner, as has also been done in emission flame photometry. Atomic-absorption measurements have also been made above the natural limits of the flame, the exhaust gases of the flame being utilized (*869*).

From a consideration of the processes which occur in the flame after a sample is introduced (evaporation of droplets, drying of the solid particles, decomposition of the particles to free atoms, and subsequent recombination of atoms, or atoms and radicals, to form other products) it is clear that the life of the free atoms will be limited and their greatest concentration will be found at a certain height of the flame. The concentration of free atoms encountered by the beam in its passage through the flame will depend on the height of the burner with respect to the optical axis of the instrument (all the other parameters being constant).

If the height of the burner is varied so that the radiation coming from the source crosses different zones of the flame, a zone can be found which produces the greatest absorption effect and thus the greatest sensitivity. This zone is the *optimum* and is selected for subsequent measurements with the analyte studied. This justifies the names *selected zone* and *optimum zone*. As it is found by experimentally varying the height of the burner, it can also be called the *optimum height* or the *optimum height of the burner*.

Any test of this kind must be made by aspirating into the flame a solution containing the analyte at a given concentration while all other experimental parameters are kept constant. The optimum height varies with the concentration of the analyte. It is good practice to recheck the optimum height for a given analyte if determinations are required at two different concentrations intervals (low and high concentrations), especially when the sample solution is sandwiched between two standards, and the maximum sensitivity is essential in both cases.

The author has found that the optimum zone for atomic-absorption (working with turbulent flames) does not always coincide with the best zone for emission measurements (under the same flame conditions). This can be very favourable when an element with marked emission (alkali and

---

[9] See the information collected in Chapter 5 of the book *Flame Photometry* (*125*). The zones of the flame and the variation of the temperature according to height are shown there in Fig. 5.1, p. 40.

alkaline-earth metals) is determined by atomic-absorption, since a careful selection of the optimum height will minimize the emission.

Measurements made with the same element may show different optimum heights with water as solvent and with an organic solvent, because of the different mode of liberation of atoms. Optimum zones found experimentally for analytes in the absence of components that might form stable compounds with the analyte will not be the optimum when such components are present.

The study of the most suitable zone in the flame is almost obligatory in each new case. In some cases, e.g. in the determination of calcium with an air–coal gas flame, it is essential to go almost to the cone of the flame to find the zone for maximum response.

For the adjustment of the burner height with respect to the beam, a slow motion adjustment is very convenient. Some instruments are provided with a bar holding the burner, which slides in a support and may be affixed to it by a screw; others have a mechanical device to raise the burner by turning manually a knob in the control panel. The final position chosen can be referred to as the distance from the beam to the top of the burner or to the *blue cone* (sometimes this is mentioned in the literature as the height above the blue cone). With long-slot burners it is permissible to speak of the *blue zone* or the *blue edge*. In practice, it is useful to consider as zero position that height at which the beam is just "touched" by the burner (a slight decrease of the light intensity is noticed); if the burner is raised a little more it partially covers the beam. Naturally, it is possible to use as zero any conventional position of the burner vertical scale.

Some of the optical devices which have been recommended in the literature are designed to select the most suitable portion of the flame by means of a set of lenses and/or diaphragms. David (*168*) used a diaphragm arrangement at the exit of the lamp and also decreased the height of the slit. It is also possible to use simply a diaphragm on the emitter beam (*183*). The diaphragm reduces the fraction of the energy of the source that is normally picked up by the photometric system. In such cases a reduction of luminous energy by solid angle reduction at the beam might be possible. Various devices for selecting flame zones in emission work (*142*) have been described.

In general, a defective choice of the optimum height of the burner cause a loss of sensitivity, and in some cases curvature of the working curves.

The optimum height is not only different for different analytes, but may also differ for solutions containing different salts of a particular analyte. With a short-life free-atom analyte, the free atoms will be more abundant between the limits *a* and *b* shown in Fig. 8–12. The height of the line *a* above the top of the burner is conditioned by the temperature of the flame, the fineness of the sample mist and the streaming velocity of the gases used to produce the flame. The height of the line *b* depends also on the chemical properties of the analyte and its environment in the flame (oxidizing or reducing conditions). The distance between the lines will decrease for those analytes and those media with a tendency to form oxide-type compounds in the flame; some cases are shown in Fig. 8–13 and some practical examples are given in Fig. 8–14. Obviously, the selected zone should be situated, as far as possible, between the ideal lines.

Rann and Hambly (*604, 605*) have studied the distribution of atoms in atomic-absorption flames for a series of analytes (Cu, Mo, Mg, Cr, Ca, Ag, Sr, Ba, Na and Se) in rich and lean air–acetylene flames; their patient and valuable work is of great interest for the location of optimum zones, and also allows the history of the free atoms along the horizontal and vertical directions of the flame to be deduced. Their results also give a clear idea of recombination rates (e.g. in the cases of calcium, strontium, barium and molybdenum). Each pattern is presented as schematized in Fig. 8–15. Such patterns are obtained with an optical device (Fig. 8–16) which allows very narrow light beams to be used. A refraction pattern is scanned past the pinhole by movement of the flame (moving the position of the burner

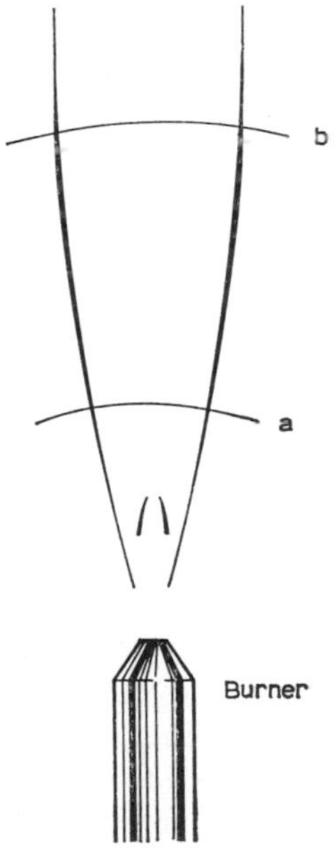

Fig. 8–12. Zone of higher concentration of free atoms of the analyte in the ground state.

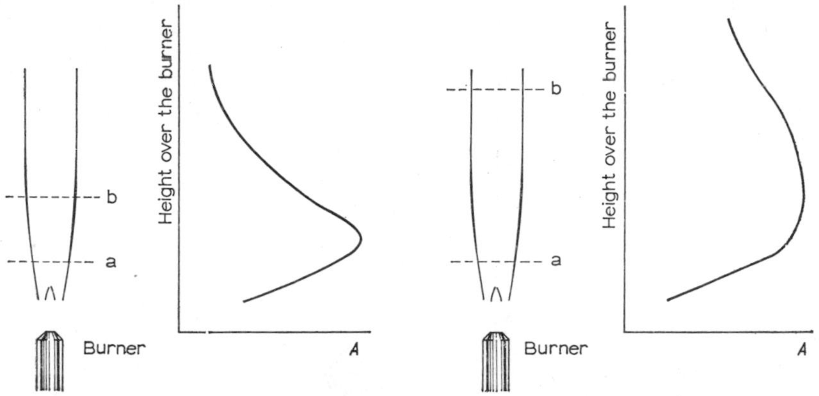

Fig. 8–13. Flame profiles for two cases of atom distribution.

by horizontal and vertical screws) and an absorbance reading is taken every 1 mm, the instrument being zeroed in each position by aspirating distilled water.

The same technique was used by Schrenk *et al.* (*656*) to obtain a complete flame pattern for rhenium.

The author has found that, in switching from one pass to three passes in multipass optical devices, with turbulent flames, the apparent atom distribution found in the case of three passes, is representative of the

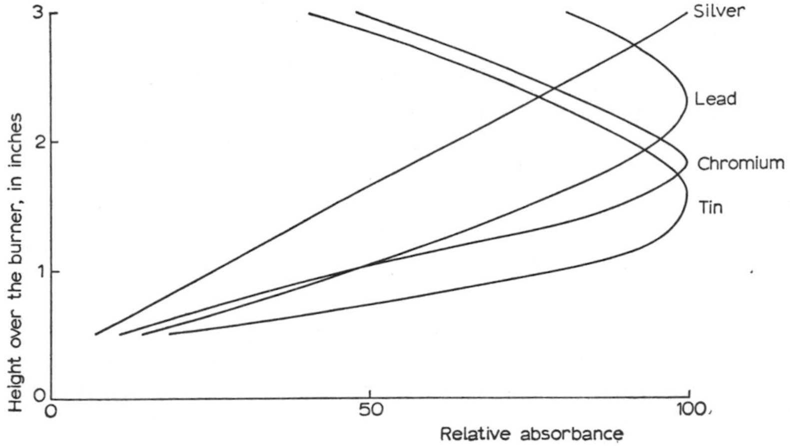

Fig. 8–14. Several flame profiles (expressed in terms of *relative absorbance*) obtained with turbulent flames (air–hydrogen) (*150*).

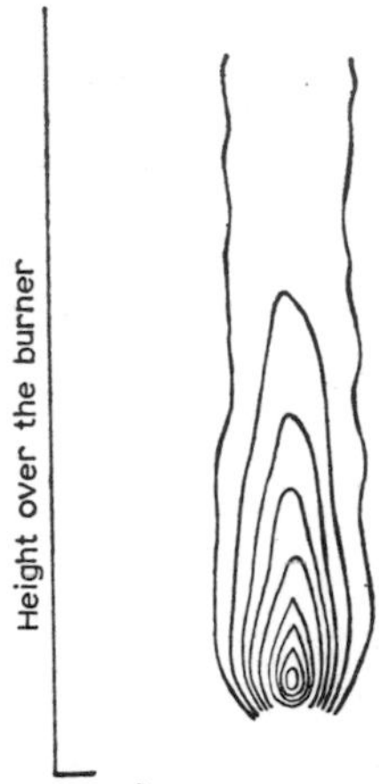

Fig. 8–15. Typical atom distribution pattern in the flame.

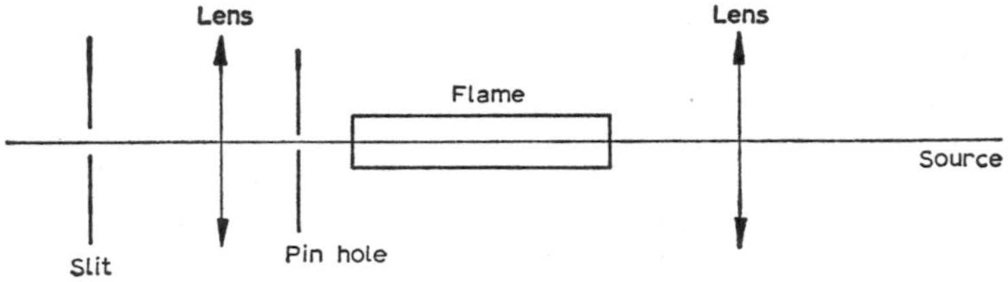

Fig. 8–16. Schematic representation of the optical device necessary to obtain the patterns shown in Fig. 8–15.

overlapping of three viewed zones. In such cases, after switching, the height of the burner should be re-adjusted.

In concluding this section it must be said that universal data cannot be given for the optimum burner height for each element, since in each case, besides the analyte, there are too many factors involved. Important factors are the nature of the flame used, the flow of gases, the state of the aerosol on arrival at the flame, the presence of non-aqueous solvents, other elements and anions, and the design of the burner. Other factors, outside the flame section, also intervene: optical devices, diaphragms, number of passes and their mode of crossing the flame, etc. The half-life[10] of the free atoms of each analyte will also vary for each set of experimental parameters.

[10] The half-life might be expressed in length units (distance above the top of the burner), instead of in time units, i.e., height over the burner at which the atom concentration is reduced to a 50% of the original maximum concentration observed.

2. THE BURNER

The role which the burner plays in atomic-absorption flame photometers is similar to its role in emission flame photometers. Fundamentally, it has two functions: (a) it is the ultimate instrumental part charged with introducing the sample solution into the flame, and (b) it conducts the gases which are to enter into combustion to produce the flame. It may receive the sample solution from the sprayer section, already in aerosol form, or it may take the sample solution up to the top, thus playing the double role of burner and sprayer (sprayer-burners). In the later case the sample usually enters the body of the burner by aspiration through a capillary submerged in the solution (or connected to the solution container with a tube), or it is administered by injection (forced feeding)[11].

There are three main tendencies in the utilization of the different burners: (a) the use of available burners which are already well-known for their satisfactory performance in emission (Lundegårdh, Beckman, Meker, Evans Electroselenium (EEL), etc.; (b) the modification of existing models to make them more suited to the atomic-absorption conditions; and (c) the design of new models (most of which are for laminar operation, especially equiped with a elongated perforated plate or a longitudinal slot, in both cases with the maximum dimension parallel to the luminous beam).

The tendency towards the use of the longitudinal opening (e.g. long slot) which provide a fish-tail flame is justifiable since it has been proved that the sensitivity increases with the length of the beam path across the flame (theoretically, a linear increase). It might be thought that the sensitivity could be increased indefinitely by increasing the length of the slot or upper plate of the burner, but, apart from the mechanical difficulties, strike-backs in the burner begin to be produced after a certain slot length (about 12 cm) has been reached, particularly if the burner is being fed with air and acetylene. If the slot is very long, an excessive fuel consumption is needed to produce a flame of sufficient height, and it must not be forgotten that when the length of the slot is increased considerably, the fluctuations also increase and therefore the precision and fluctuational sensitivity are reduced.

The use of burners with a slot of great length forces the aerosol, and fuel and support gases[12] to circulate from a narrow entrance to a zone which broadens too much in order to cover the effective length of the

[11] Chapter 6 of *Flame Photometry* (*125*) gives an ample description of non-spraying burners and sprayer-burners used in emission. Some of them, such as the Lundegårdh burner, Beckman Burner, and the Warren burner (with some modifications), have enjoyed wide application in atomic-absorption instruments.

[12] Fuel and support gases when the solution is not aspirated; fuel gas and aerosol during aspiration.

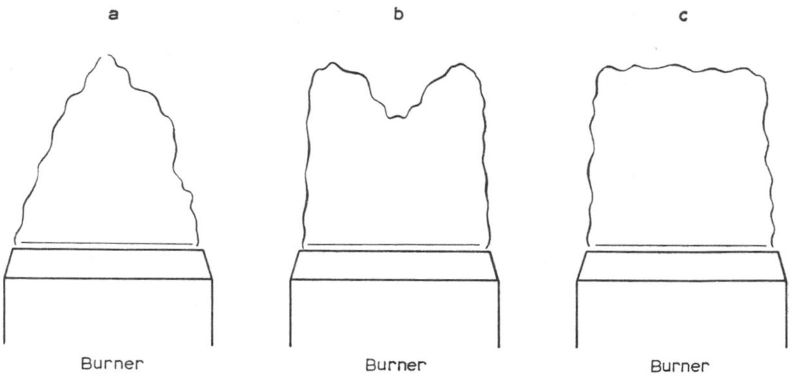

Fig. 8–17. Different shapes of laminar flames: (a) "A" shape; (b) "M" shape; (c) "Π" shape.

exit (danger of internal turbulence). The streaming velocity of gases can change too much from the center of the burner towards the ends. All this may produce an inequality in the form and composition of the flame along the length of the burner.

One might think that satisfactory results would be obtained, since the beam, in crossing the entire trajectory, participates in an integration of absorptions, even if the flame were not homogeneous; but if the gradient of temperature and/or composition is very pronounced, small variations in the height of the selected zone will be highly significant in the measurements.

The lack of uniformity in the longitudinal flames may be observed visually, since at times "A" or "M" shapes appear instead of the "Π" shapes which correspond to the more uniform distribution (see Fig. 8–17). If the distortion of the flame appears at a sufficient height above the burner, it probably will not have much effect on the uniformity of the temperature and composition of the flame in zones near the top of the burner. If the supplies of fuel gas do not change drastically the distribution of the aerosol over the burner, a visual observation of the aerosol *without flame* (observed with lateral illumination against a dark surface) may be useful.

It is easy to understand that the design of a new burner is a very difficult and complicated task. If all the factors involved are not carefully studied and the burner does not accomplish all its functions, a poor sensitivity will be obtained, as well as poor accuracy and precision.

2.1. Different kinds of burners

It is traditional in flame photometry to classify burners as *non-spraying burners* and *sprayer-burners*, but in the case of atomic-absorption it is more appropriate to distinguish between two large groups: (a) *burners which use premixed gases*, and (b) *burners which do not use premixed gases*. The manner in which the gases are introduced determines fundamentally the form of the flame.

2.1.1. Burners which use premixed gases

The gases are mixed before reaching the upper part of the burner. Thus the mixture of the gases is more uniform than in other types of burners. The sample travels towards the mixing chamber accompanied by one of the gases (generally the support gas).

Most of the burners mentioned in this section are characterized by a laminar flow pattern in the flame. In addition to the comments made on p. 118, a few more details are given here. The relatively low shearing velocity is only compatible with gas mixtures of slow burning velocity. The absence of turbulence requires premixing of fuel and oxidant and requires indirect aspiration of the sample solution (the Kniscley burner is an exception in this characteristic, because of the small distance between, and the concentric position of, the suction capillary and the mixing chamber; see Section 2.1.1.2 below). For this reason most of the *laminar flow burners* are equipped with spray chambers in which the sample solution mist is generated and mixed with the combustion gases. Because of the smaller burning velocity of the flame, the chances of accidental progression of the flame into the burner opening (flashback) are reduced; nevertheless the burner should be carefully designed. The conventional small circular openings of the turbulent burners are replaced by long narrow slots (the resulting long narrow flames are common to most laminar flow burners). The laminar flow burner with

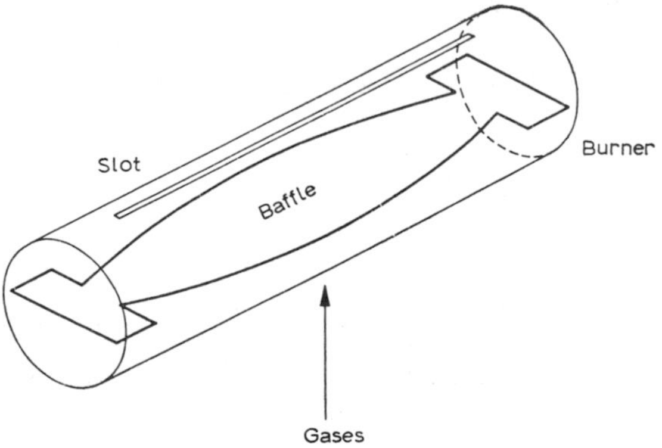

Fig. 8–18 Baffle placed inside a burner head.

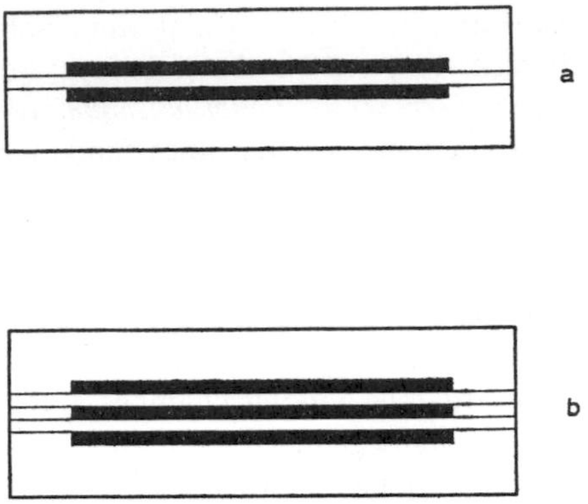

Fig. 8–19. Multi-slot burners: (a) double-slot burner head; (b) three-slot burner head.

its relatively cool and long flame is ideally suited to atomic-absorption work. The slow streaming velocity *increases the retention time of the atoms in the optical path area,* thus contributing a denser atom population and a stronger absorption. The low noise level is one of the most appreciated characteristics of this flame.

In some cases, laminar flow burners can show uneven distribution of the gases along the slot, with the consequent uneven distribution of the aspirated sample in the flame. Zettner and Seligson (*874, 875*) have prevented this effect by placing a baffle inside the burner head (see Fig. 8–18).

Strikeback can be prevented by the use of double-slot or three-slot burner heads (see Fig. 8–19).

2.1.1.1. Non-spraying burners. Some typical examples of these burners are mentioned below:

Burner described by Amos and Thomas (*19*). This burner is built with two pieces of stainless steel ca. 2.5 cm × 1.25 cm × 18 cm (1″ × 0.5″ × 6″) using steel spacers to leave a slot 0.45 mm × 30 mm. The head of the burner

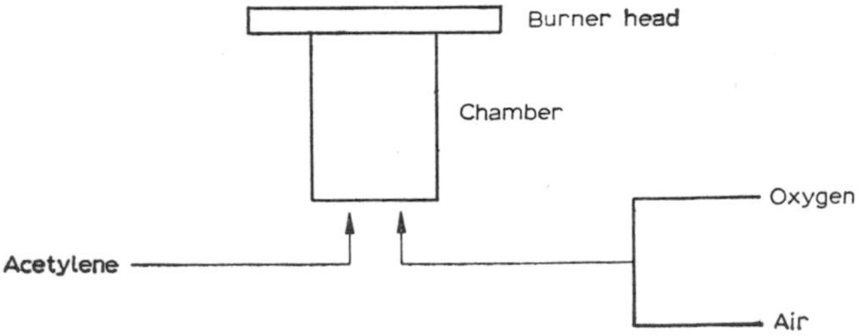

Fig. 8–20. Feeding a burner with acetylene and air–oxygen mixture.

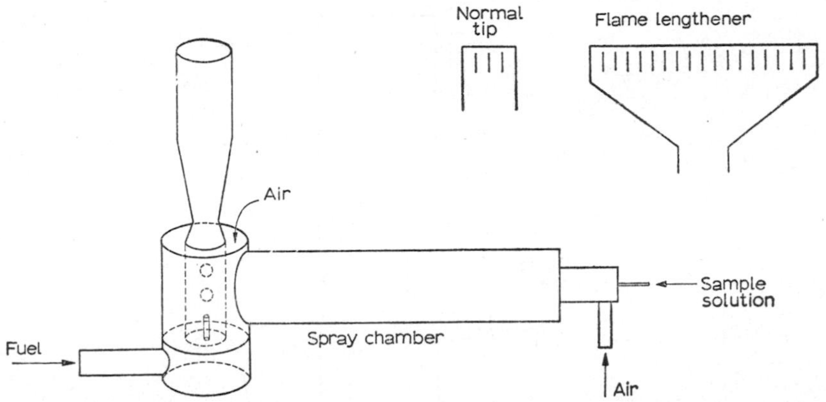

Fig. 8–21. Schematic view of the burner described by Baker and Garton (for complete details consult ref. (*66*)).

is not cooled and reaches an equilibrium of 130–150 °C which is quite safe for operation. The head is placed over the spray chamber, which receives the necessary gases (see Fig. 8–20) (refs. (*18, 20*) should also be consulted).

Burner described by Baker and Garton. Baker (*65*) and Baker and Garton (*66*) use a modified Meker burner to which they adapt a longitudinal flame lengthener (Fig. 8–21).

Burner described by Butler. This model is made of plastic (*129*). A multi-perforated plate and a plate with transverse slots are both used with cooling (Figs. 8–22 and 8–23). Butler mentions the fact that various types of burner tops can be fitted for different fuel gases. The burner can be rotated to decrease the sensitivity.

Burner described by Boling. The performance of this burner has been discussed by Sprague and Slavin (*725*). The burner has three slots, with the outer ones acting as protecting flame layers for the central one. The burner is said to show better stability than the single-slot burners, to be less critical with regard to mechanical positioning, and to enclose the light beam more fully.

Burner described by Clinton (*151*). This is a metallic burner with a longitudinal slot, cooled by water[13]. The burner can also be turned in order to decrease sensitivity (see Fig. 8–24).

Burner described by Hell (*311*). Hell has described a new type of laminar flow burner with a double-slot head. The burner is connected to the sprayer section (heated spray-chamber and a condensing chamber). The set can

---

[13] Cooling by water has been extensively used to reduce local heating in prolonged operations. Besides the models mentioned in this section, other models have been described by Finkelstein and Jansen (*241*) and Zeeman and Butler (*867*).

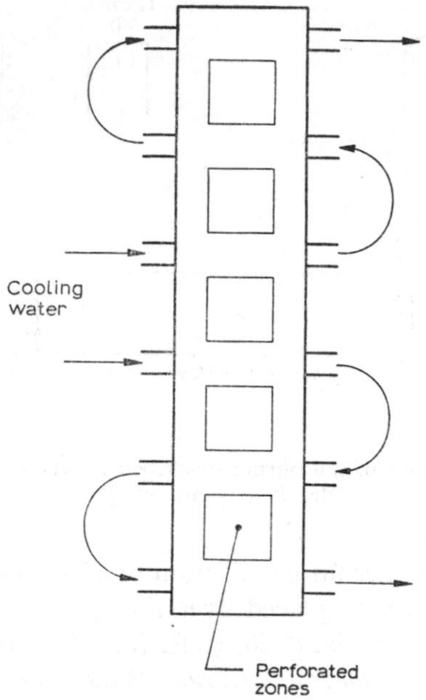

Fig. 8–22. Multiperforated plate and cooled burner head (*129*).

be used in hot and cold operation, and by changing the burner head it is possible to switch from air–acetylene flame to air–propane or air–natural gas flames. By taking advantage of the infrared-heated spray-chamber and solvent condenser, this model has been modified for use with nitrous oxide–

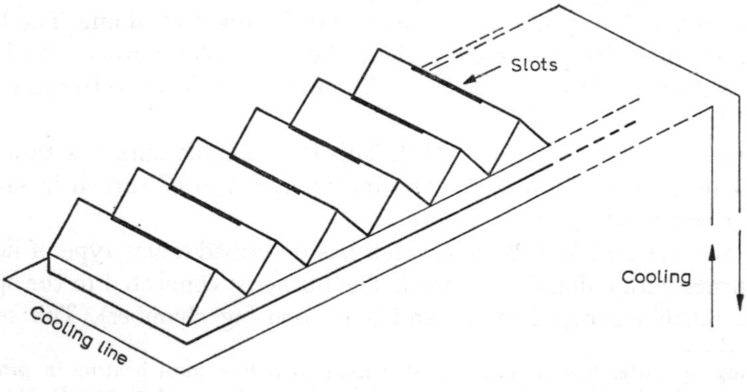

Fig. 8–23. Multi-slot and cooled burner head (*129*).

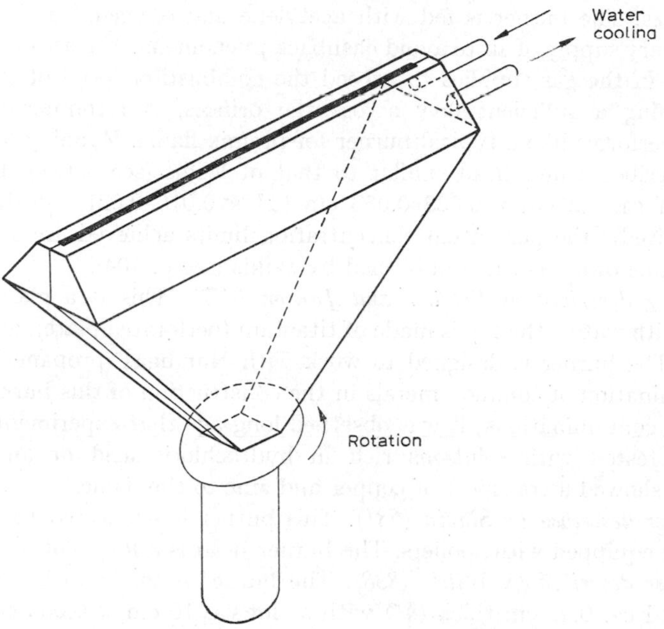

Fig. 8–24. Cooled and rotating burner (for detailed inside views of a burner of this type consult ref. (*151*)).

acetylene flames (*315*)[14]. The solvent condensation allows a relative concentration of the analyte in the aerosol before the aerosol reaches the flame. After the Hell burner had been described, Miklus and Menoski discussed a heated chamber coupled to a premix air–acetylene burner (*497, 498*).

Burner described by Hinson and Kitching (*345*). This burner is similar to the Hilger burner, but with a tubular passage under the top of the burner, which allows a lower light beam to pass through the burner to serve as reference signal.

Burner described by Lang and Herrmann (*419*). Among other characteristics, this burner offers the advantage of a great uniformity in the gas mixtures; the gas currents enter the chamber under the body of the burner in a tangential form.

Burners described by Manning (*456*). Manning has carried out tests with a burner designed to facilitate the determination of aluminum; the top has a series of small, aligned holes, and is equipped with cooling blocks on

[14] This type of burner has been used in a commercial laminar flow burner package (Beckman Instruments, Inc.); its performance has been discussed (*312–314, 316*).

both sides. The burner is fed with acetylene and oxygen, but it requires an auxiliary supply of air to avoid flashback phenomena. The use of sufficient pressure in the gas supplies to exceed the combustion speed of the gases, maintaining a sufficient flow across the orifices, is recommended. The burner performs like a typical burner for premix flame. Manning (*455, 457*) also describes a new head similar to that of Willis (see below), but with a slot of ca. 7.5 cm × 0.038–0.053 cm (3″ × 0.015–0.021″—width range investigated); the percentual concentration limits achieved are said to be of the same order as those published by Willis (see p. 104).

Burner described by Schüler and Jansen (*657*). This is a glass burner cooled with water; the top is made of titanium (perforated plate), also water cooled. The burner is designed to work with Handigas (propane–butane). The elimination of common metals in the construction of this burner tends to avoid contaminations; it was observed long ago that experimental brass burners tested with solutions rich in hydrochloric acid or ammonium chloride showed a transport of copper and zinc to the flame.

Burner described by Slavin (*681*). This burner is connected to a spray-chamber equipped with spoilers. The burner head is a long slot.

Burner described by Willis (*838*). The burner is made with a stainless steel head ca. 0.93 cm thick ($\frac{3}{8}$″) with a slot ca. 10 cm × 0.038 cm (4″ × 0.015″); there is no cooling, and the head is fitted directly to the spray chamber. This burner was designed for nitrous oxide–acetylene flame operation (see p. 103).

2.1.1.2. *Sprayer-burners.* These burners include the sprayer, but still produce a premixture of the gases before they reach the top of the burner. Special attention is given to them because of their extensive use in work with fuel-rich flames.

Burner described by Kniseley et al. (*404*). This burner is known as *Kniseley burner*. Kniseley *et al.* (*404*) have published details of the construction of a burner utilizing a Beckman burner No. 4030 to which they attach a copper cylinder which protects a perforated graphite cylinder. The tube is centered with the aid of several screws; the centering is critical. Some lateral orifices permit the entrance of some air, thus avoiding strikeback. Good results have been obtained with fuel-rich oxygen–acetylene flames without the production of deposits (which affect the flame background and reduce the efficiency of atomization). A low noise level is obtained, which contributes to obtaining good sensitivity values. Recently a cylinder of teflon with a central stainless steel tube has replaced the graphite tube (see Fig. 8–25).

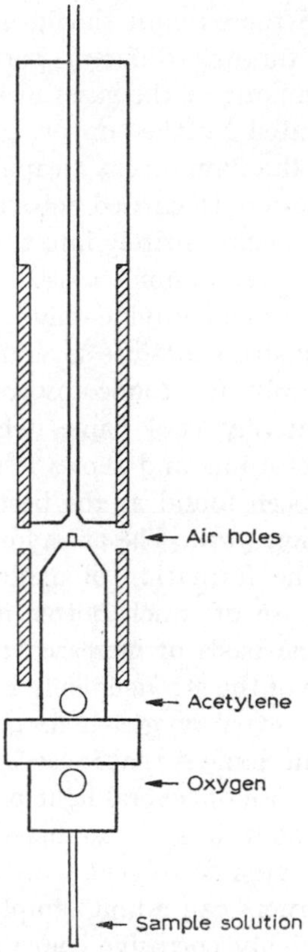

Fig. 8–25. Schematic internal view of the burner described by Kniseley *et al.* (*404*).

2.1.2. Burners which do not use premixed gases

All the burners mentioned in this section are sprayer-burners. They produce turbulent flames and are commonly known as *turbulent flow burners*. Such burners are used for combustible gas mixtures with high reaction velocity. In order to maintain a sufficiently stable flame the streaming velocity of the combustion gases at the burner tip has to be of the same order as the burning velocity. The high streaming velocity causes the *turbulence* in the flame[15]. This fast burning gas mixture is a real explosive

[15] Combustion in turbulent flames appears as a diffuse phenomenon, accomplished in a randomly-wrinkled, thin combustion wave. To obtain an idea of the shape of the combustion zone the flame may be fed with ammonium chloride smoke that disappears sharply at the combustion wave, revealing the structure of the flame. See photographs published by Karlovitz (*386*).

mixture and the fuel and the oxidant should not be mixed in the burner, but meet when exiting through different ports at the burner tip. The turbulence provides the mixing of the gases in the lower part of the flame. The Venturi effect generated by the support gas allows the aspiration of the sample solution into the flame from a capillary end at the burner tip. The sprayed sample solution is carried into the flame. Because all the solution is sprayed and brought entirely into the flame, this type of burner is also known as the *total consumption burner*.

The torch-like sprayer-burners provide only a relatively short absorption paths. This is why some instruments use several burners mounted in a row.

In general, the best results in atomic-absorption flame photometry can be obtained with a relatively cool flame, which efficiently decomposes chemical compounds into atoms and shows less flame emission. Thus the air–hydrogen flame has been found as the best general-purpose turbulent flame for atomic-absorption work. The air–hydrogen turbulent flame in its fuel-rich mode retards the formation of oxides of the analyte, showing advantages similar to those of much hotter flames; the atomic concentration is increased on the basis of increased thermal decomposition, but without the disadvantage of the stronger emission observed in hotter flames (e.g. oxygen–acetylene, or even oxygen–hydrogen). A further advantage of the air–hydrogen turbulent flame is that it can be adjusted to a considerable flame size; this allows the use of several light passes and high feeding rates (5 ml/min or more) without loss of atomization efficiency, either with aqueous solutions or with organic solvent solutions.

The turbulent flow burners can admit sample solutions containing high saline concentration or highly corrosive components (e.g., mineral acids); such solutions pose fewer problems than with more complicated burners.

Burner described by Lang et al. (*425*). This sprayer-burner uses three capillaries and offers high stability and versatility in flame work.

Oscillating burner described by Lang. Instead of the stationary burner which is generally used, Lang (*418*) has described a mobile, oscillating burner; this is comparable in operation to the double-beam systems[16].

Burner described by Robinson (*625, 632*). This model is quite different from the others, since it is a forced-feed burner. It is a concentric burner in which the sample solution is introduced into the gas current through a high pressure-drop orifice. The introduction of the solution at the rate of 5 ml/min is independent of the oxygen : hydrogen ratio used in the burner. A schematic view is shown in Fig. 8–26.

Burner described by Warren. Also known as the Warren burner. This is a modification of the burner utilized by Warren in emission flame photo-

---

[16] Lang uses differences of photocurrents corresponding to $I_0 - I = AI_0$.

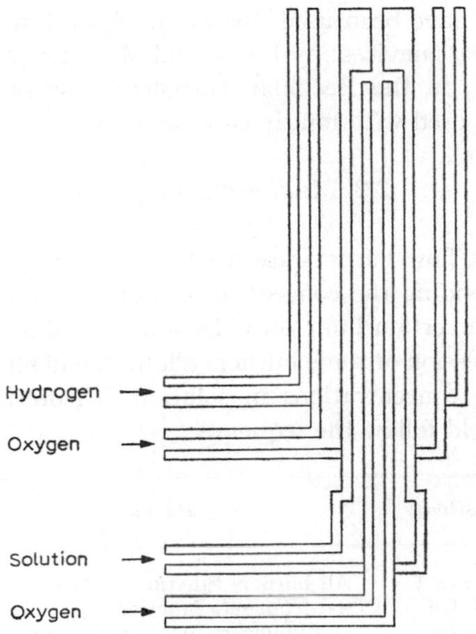

Fig. 8–26. Schematic internal view of the burner described by Robinson and Harris (*625, 632*).

metry (*808*). The burner may also be used with premixed gases (*808*), and has been modified by Baker and Garton (*66*).

2.1.3. Commercial burners

Several commercial burners have been offered for atomic-absorption flame photometry, and some of these have been used in home-made instruments:

Aztec burners. Available for several types of gas mixtures (*62, 63*)[17].

Beckman burners. Different types of turbulent flow single burners are available and also packages for turbulent or laminar flow operation (*75, 76*)[18].

Hilger burner. For laminar flow operation (*334*)[19].

Skinner burner. For laminar flow operation[20].

The Beckman burners have been widely used as single burners or by operating various burners at the same time[21]. Several Beckman burners,

---

17 Aztec Instruments, Inc., 2 Silverbrook Road, Westport, Conn., U.S.A.
18 Beckman Instruments, Inc., 2500 Harbor Boulevard, Fullerton, Calif., U.S.A.
19 Hilger and Watts Ltd., 98 St Pancras Way, Camden Road, London N.W.1, England.
20 S. R. Skinner Pty., Ltd. Malvern, Vic., Australia.
21 This burner was described on p. 59 of the book *Flame Photometry* (*125*).

coupled together, have been used, for example, in Jarrell-Ash instruments (*363*), with multipass devices; by Fassel and Mossotti (*235*), with horizontal multipass devices; in the Beckman turbulent flow burner package (*76*), which also can be used with multipass operation.

2.2. *Multiburner couplings*

When turbulent flow burners are used, multiburner couplings present a possibility of extending the concentration range. Increases in the number of burners up to a certain limit provides a means of increasing sensitivity. Progressive suppression of some burners allows the determination of a given analyte at higher concentrations in solution. Theoretically, the decrease of sensitivity should follow the sequence:

Sensitivity	*Burners*
$n/n = 1$	All burners functioning (n burners)
$n-1/n$	$n-1$ burners functioning
$n-2/n$	$n-2$ burners functioning, and so on.

In practice there is some deviation from the calculated figures owing to flame conditions, to the analyte itself, and to height of the group of burners. A similar sequence can be applied to the combination multiburner and multipass operation.

3. THE SPRAYER

As in emission flame photometry, the sprayer is a device used to form an aerosol by dispersion of the sample, standard, or blank solution in very small droplets with the help of a compressed gas (air, oxygen, nitrogen, nitrous oxide, etc.). Modern ultrasonic sprayers use ultrasonic dispersion of the solution.

The information given previously in *Flame Photometry* (*125*) (p. 61 ff.) on sprayers and the spraying process is relevant to the role of the sprayers in the atomic-absorption process. In the book mentioned, abundant information will also be found on spray chambers, i.e. chambers prepared to receive the spray formed at the sprayer, which is transformed to a fine aerosol before reaching the burner (by separating the big drops, producing a preliminary evaporation of the droplets, condensing the solvent to concentrate the analyte, etc.). An adjustable sprayer has been described (*179*).

A few years ago the spraying process was considered as a *simple mechanical complement* useful for carrying the liquid sample to the burner and the flame. Little attention was given to it, apart from ensuring sufficient stability of performance and smallness of drop size. However, more recently, increased attention has been given to this process; for, in fact, almost everything that may happen in the flame is fundamentally subject to the way in which the sprayer acts. Many of the studies in this area have been carried out primarily for emission flame photometry; in this field of spraying process, the work of Herrmann and Lang is outstanding (*318, 322, 325*). Useful comments on the subject are included in the publications of Gilbert (*275*) and Allan (*13*). Dunken *et al.* (*202*) have recommended the use of ultrasonic sprayers for introducing the solutions into plasma flames in emission work; this procedure might be successfully applied to some atomic-absorption problems.

If one accepts the close connection which exists between spraying in emission and absorption, it is not surprising that many of the sprayers used in emission have been applied to research in atomic-absorption flame photometry, such as the Lundegårdh sprayer (*7, 161*) and that of Evans Electroselenium Ltd. (EEL) with some modifications (*166, 827, 828*).

The sprayer is vital in the process of obtaining an aerosol of very fine droplets in which the following ratio is maintained constant: volume of sprayed solution : volume of aerosol. Moreover, the droplets must be fine enough to be easily converted to fine solid particles which are exposed to the thermal action of the flame.

It is customary to distinguish between *aerosol* and *spray*. Spray is the flow of drops issuing from the sprayer, at times with a great lack of homogeneity as regards drop size. Part of the spray is condensed, becoming a selection of drops. The fine drops remain in a suspension which is transported by the gaseous current. The equilibrated fraction of the spray reaching the burner is considered as aerosol (liquid–gas aerosol). When evaporation of the solvent takes place, the suspension is converted to a new type of aerosol in which solid particles are transported by the gaseous current (solid–gas aerosol). This suspension is sometimes called *clots* or *clotlets*. In a very short period of time (on occasions only hundredths of a second) the solid particles undergo a series of physical and chemical changes: complete calcination and/or fusion, decomposition and vaporization.

Menzies (*496*) gives special attention to the formation of the aerosol, especially to the phase in which the droplets, on undergoing evaporation, remain in the form of dispersed solid rather than dispersed liquid (drops). This dispersion, which Menzies calls *clots*, is subjected to the thermal effect of the flame, but within some limits conditioned by the concentration of the solution, and the velocity of the gases; therefore, only a small zone of the flame will be really effective in the process of liberation of atoms (cf. p. 108). There may be occasions in which only the actual surface of the particles of saline compounds will be effective in the thermal process, and this will be an index of the *efficiency of the aerosol in the flame.*

When solutions of high saline content are sprayed, the solid particles which are produced are so abundant that, when the aerosol reaches the flame, they cause a scattering of the luminous radiation coming from the source. The scattered intensity is proportional to the square of the volume of the solid particles.

The *total efficiency* achieved in the whole process will depend on the *efficiency of the sprayer* (represented by the fraction of the solution carried by the sprayer to the flame)[22] and on the *efficiency of the aerosol* (represented by the fraction of the aerosol that actually undergoes the processes at the flame).

Each of the solid particles, made up in most cases, of single salts or saline mixtures, acts independently in the flame. Menzies refers to the experiment of Gidley and Jones who passed aerosols of two solutions of two elements into the flame (Mg and Al; the aluminum produces interferences on the Mg), but separately. Interference was not produced since there was no chemical association between particles which were evaporated independently in the flame. This behaviour explains, of course, the mechanism of many chemical interferences, but it bears little relation to the practical problems found when the two elements—co-components—reach the flame from the same solution. The experiment also explains the effects of chelating agents, which inhibit the action of interfering components, even though the latter may form part of a particle in which the analyte exists; the analyte remains in the form of a chelate in the particle.

3.1. Optimum conditions of the sprayer

An ideal sprayer (considered as the whole *sprayer section* in the absorption system, i.e., including spray chamber, condensing chamber, spoilers, etc.) should fulfil the following conditions (cf. Lockyer and Hames (*438*)): (a) it should introduce the sample solution into the flame at a constant rate; (b) it should be not subject to clogging or blockage; (c) it should be easily cleaned; (d) it should be pre-set, or at least easily adjusted; and (e) it should be made of materials which are not susceptible to corrosion.

Condition (a) is basic in assuring the stability of the sprayer and consequently more stability in the readings[23].

---

[22] The *efficiency of the spray chamber* and the *efficiency of the condensing chamber* should also be considered if these other parts are included in the whole spraying section of the instrument.

[23] Andrew and Nichols (*22*) consider that stability may be increased by the installation of a "drip chamber", which simultaneously increases the efficiency.

Among the ideal conditions of a sprayer might be added the introduction of large amounts of solution into the flame. Actually there must be a compromise, since there is a danger of excessive cooling, which would attenuate the processes of dissociation and vaporization. If more solution is brought to the flame by means of an excessive pressure of the support gas, this can lead to a high velocity of the gases in the flame, which would diminish the effective concentration of the sample in the beam path.

The spraying process is, in fact, a very wasteful and inefficient process (in some sprayer sections, a great percentage of the solution goes to the drain). Efforts are constantly made to improve the efficiency of the sprayer, but also it is necessary to improve the efficiency of the aerosol formation for some types of solutions, and one cannot neglect the *efficiency of the burner* (expressed as the ratio between the number of milligrams of analyte converted into atoms capable of producing absorption, and *actually producing it*, and the number of milligrams of analyte which reaches the burner as an aerosol)[24]. The response obtained in the atomic-absorption photometer is directly related to the degree of conversion of the sample solution into a free-atom active vapor in the flame. Any inefficiency *in any step* in this conversion restrict the sensitivity.

3.2. Feed rate

The feed rate is the number of milliliters of solution aspirated by the sprayer per minute. It is also known by the terms *solution flow rate, consumption of sample, aspiration rate, sample intake* and *sample intake rate.* The feed rate is a predominant factor in the whole atomization process taking place in the absorption system. Increasing the feed rate increases the efficiency of the absorption system, but not indefinitely. Cooling effects may appear, though these may be obviated to some extent by adding organic solvents to the solution.

As the feed rate depends on the geometry and physical characteristics of the sprayer, there is another limit independent of the processes carried out in the flame. The operator cannot increase the feed rate indefinitely by increasing the pressure of the support gas. A maximum is obtained and then the feed rate decreases. Some examples studied by the author are given in Figs. 8–27 and 8–28.

If the sprayer allows only limited feed rates by simple aspiration, forced feeding by injection can be applied.

Very many studies have been done on feed-rate problems. Winefordner

---

[24] Number of milligrams reaching the burner = concentration of the analyte in the solution × number of ml of solution *in the form of an aerosol* which reaches the burner per unit of time.

and Latz (*845*) have studied the variation of the solution feed rates in relation to viscosity, surface tension, density, temperature, ionic strength, capillary radius, support gas flow, fuel gas flow and driving force. They found that the Poiseuille equation for capillary flow is followed only in cases of high viscosity and low solution flow rates.

All the factors mentioned in the preceding paragraph—including physical interferences—intervene in the spraying process in similar ways in both emission and atomic-absorption. In atomic-absorption very dilute solutions (and preferably simple aqueous solutions) are used wherever possible so that the physical properties of the sample solutions will be very similar to those of the pure water. Difficulties appear when the solutions contain high concentrations of acids, salts or organic matter; a clear example is the

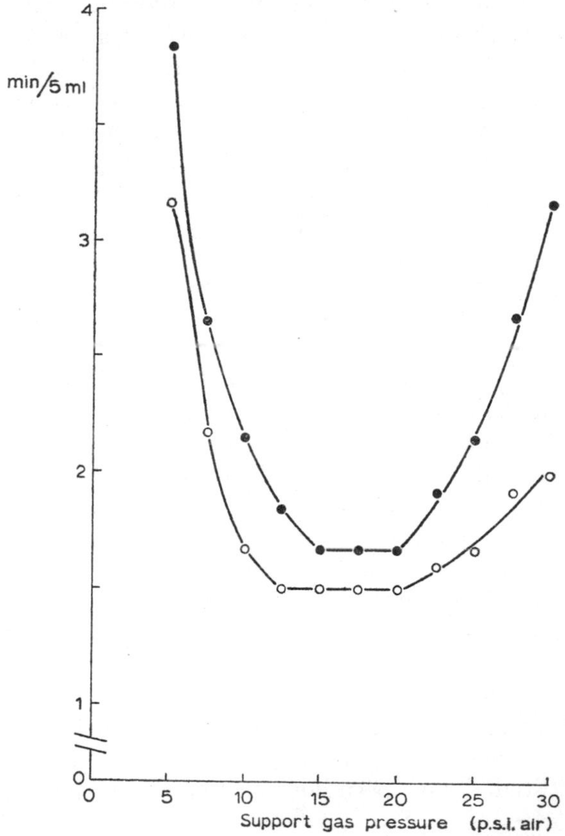

Fig. 8–27. Curves showing the time in minutes per given volume as functiona of air pressure for two sprayers.

case of the aspiration of undiluted—or only slightly diluted—biological fluids.

Lang and Herrmann (*421*) have studied the variations of feed rates with the pressure of the gas used in the spraying process (they used compressed air); they found that for the annular pneumatic sprayers used in flame photometry, the quantities of compressed air and sample solution flowing through the instrument can be expressed by a general flow equation as a function of the effective pressure of the compressed air.

A complete study of efficiency, and its variations as a function of the different factors involved, has been published by Winefordner *et al.* for the oxygen–hydrogen and oxygen–acetylene flames (*846*); the absorption of the radiation of a zinc source by zinc atoms in the flame was measured.

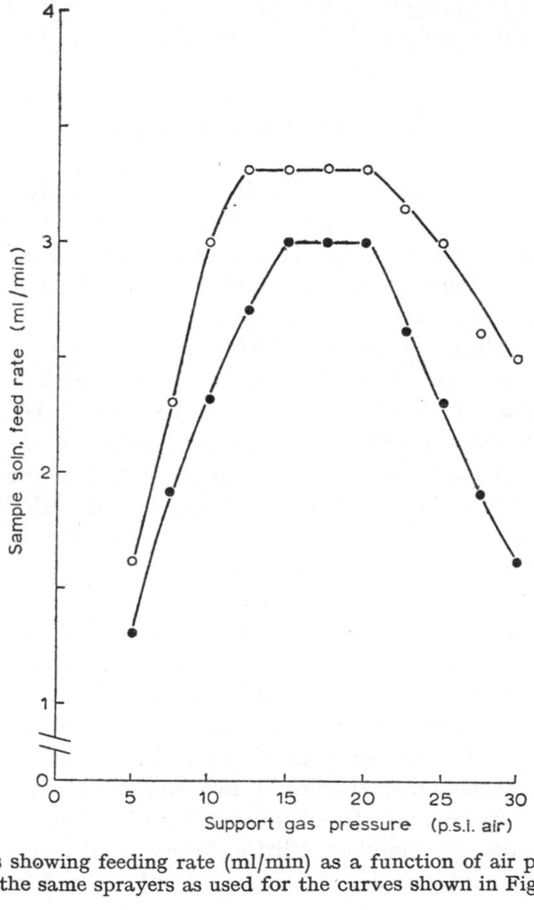

Fig. 8–28. Curves showing feeding rate (ml/min) as a function of air pressure for two sprayers (the same sprayers as used for the curves shown in Fig. 8–27).

They found that the efficiency is conditioned by the flow rate and height of the selected zone in the flame; in some cases the efficiency decreased with the flow rate and increased with the height in the oxygen–hydrogen flames, whereas it sometimes decreased with height for the oxygen–acetylene flame, and increased on addition of methanol. Claus *et al.* (*150*) obtained better sensitivity in some cases by decreasing the feed rate, i.e. by cutting down the support gas flow, for fuel-rich air–hydrogen flames.

Osterried and Preuss (*539, 570*) have studied the continuous change of flow rate of solutions aspirated in flame analysis. They presented a series of curves of absorption variations as a function of the flow rate.

An excessive feed rate can increase the noise associated with the signal, even if at normal feed rates the noise contribution of the sprayer is small.

In order to control the feed rate and overcome a lack of uniformity in the suction of the sprayer, some devices can be used: (a) motor-driven syringes, and (b) impellent piston pumps such as that described by Muny (*516*).

3.3. Heated spray chambers

Some authors have listed the disadvantages of heated spray chambers (see, e.g. Herrmann and Alkemade (*321*)), but others (*311, 313–316, 451*) have found satisfactory results with heated spray chambers in atomic-absorption work. Zeeman and Butler (*868*) have recommended pre-heating the air used as support gas; the efficiency is increased from 12 to 15%, with a corresponding increase in sensitivity.

Little efficiency can be expected from sprayers with a cold chamber. A very large part of the sample runs down the drain tube (approximately 90% of the aspirated solution) because the transfer of the mist from the sprayer to the flame is generally very inefficient. The transfer is greatly increased by using a heated spray chamber, in which the spray is transformed more completely to an aerosol. The aerosol particles, being so much lighter than the original droplets of the spray, are carried with the gas stream almost completely into the flame.

The gas stream leaving the spray chamber contains the aerosol and the vapor of the solvent. If this mixture were introduced into the flame, the vapor would overload the flame, reducing the burning velocity, and would simultaneously increase the streaming velocity at the top of the burner. These factors would make the flame very erratic. To avoid this disturbance, the heated spray chamber should be followed by a condensing chamber (water-cooled), where a selective condensation of the solvent occurs at the walls of the condensing chamber. A little of the solvent vapor will recondense on the aerosol particles, which will, however, retain the form of an uniform and very fine mist. The main fraction of the solvent (approximately 90%) is separated by condensation from the gas stream and is drained. Only the relatively enriched aerosol is carried toward the flame.

3.4. Tube feeding

This technique of transferring the solution into the sprayer has become very common. The solution is aspirated from a beaker or any container by means of a flexible plastic tube, connected to the capillary of the sprayer. Short tubes pose few problems (perhaps the formation of some bubbles). Long tubes produce decreases in the feed rate—the decreases observed would depend on the diameter of the tube—, which influence the sensitivity.

The author has also found static electricity effects in the tube during the passage of the solutions; the tube travels on the surface of new solutions to be aspirated by the instrument, and adheres to the beaker walls.

Care should be given to the metal–tubing connection in order to avoid damage, and thus loss of suction. A protective plastic collar (a tube of larger diameter, and about 1 cm long) avoids this type of mechanical damage.

4. MECHANICAL PARTS

In this section brief reference will be made to the mechanical parts which are used in the absorption system along with the fundamental sections already discussed in this chapter.

4.1. Auxiliary mechanisms of the burner

For the correct alignment of the burner (if it is not pre-aligned) and the choice of the most appropriate selected zone, two movements are necessary:

(a) Rotation around the vertical axis.
(b) Vertical displacement.

The rotation may be used to decrease sensitivity, by permitting the beam to cross a shorter horizontal length of the flame (see, e.g., p. 117).

Shortening the effective length crossed by the beam in the flame broadens the practical dynamic range of concentrations. When the rotation angle goes from 0° to 90°, solutions of high concentration will produce absorption signals similar to those of lower concentration (see Figs. 8–29 and 8–30). By varying the rotation angle, the path across the flame varies as a function of that angle. For narrow flame widths, practically, the path varies between *b* (horizontal length of the flame) and *w* (width of the flame) (see Fig. 8–31). For wide flames, at some angle—depending on the width of the flame—the path across the flame reaches a maximum (diagonal), and then decreases to reach the corresponding value *w* (see Fig. 8–32).

A good alignment of the burner with respect to the light beam is essential for proper operation. To achieve a good alignment with a minimum of attempts, and also to permit the manipulation to be done by a single person, Murie and Bourke (*517*) have described an *alignment plate* which may be placed over the burner and displaced along the slot during the tests.

Eickhoff and Sykes (*206*) have described the construction of a burner

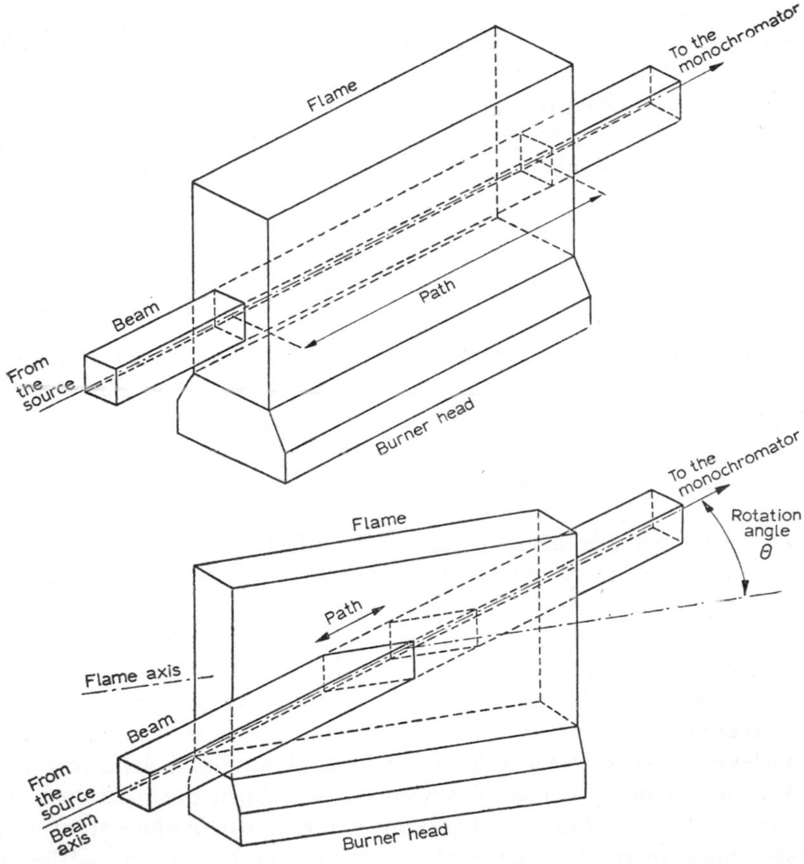

Fig. 8–29. Rotation of the burner. Variation of the path when the burner is rotated to an angle θ.

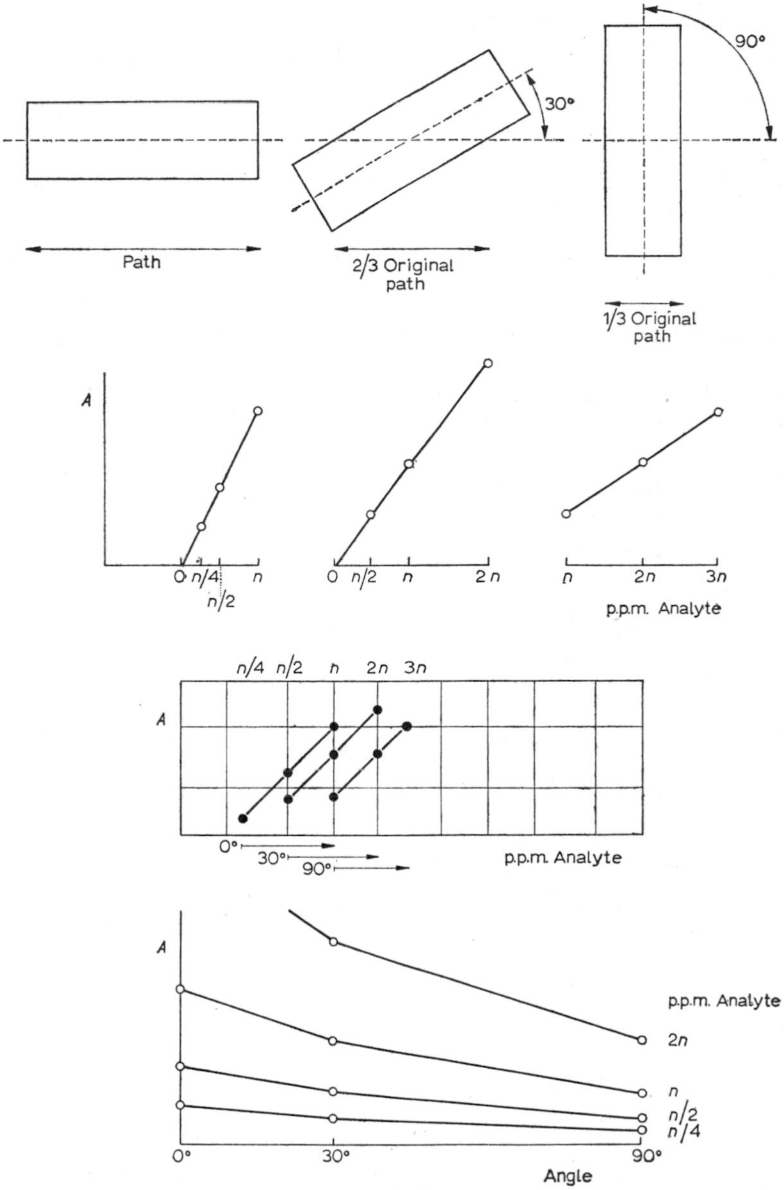

Fig. 8–30. Consequences of the rotation of the burner. At the top, the variations of the path are shown for angles of 0°, 30° and 90°. Underneath, the corresponding variations of sensitivity are detailed (see variation of slope of the graphs), around *n* p.p.m. of analyte. Concentration ranges covered are also shown on log–log representation (*A vs.* p.p.m. analyte). At the end, the graph shows the variations of *A* as a function of the angle for several concentrations.

mount with a micrometer screw movement for vertical and horizontal adjustments, which has also a screw adjustment for angular movements.

4.2. Long beam-path adapters

These are devices for lengthening the beam-path across the flame. Two versions are best known.

4.2.1. "T-form" adapters

These adapters, which have been mentioned by Robinson (*625*) and by Feldman and Dhumwad (*238*), are tubes in the form of a "T" which are

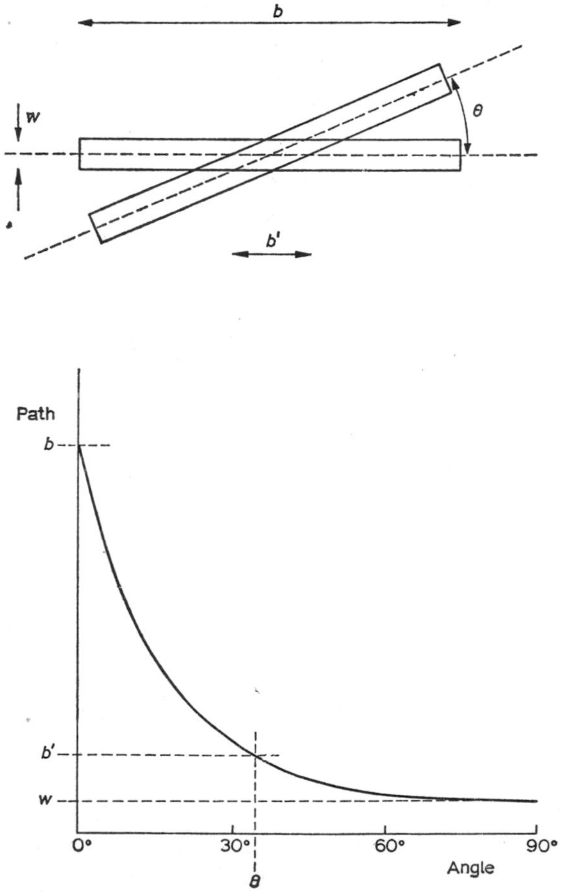

Fig. 8–31. Variation of the path from b down to w (width) as a function of the rotation angle.

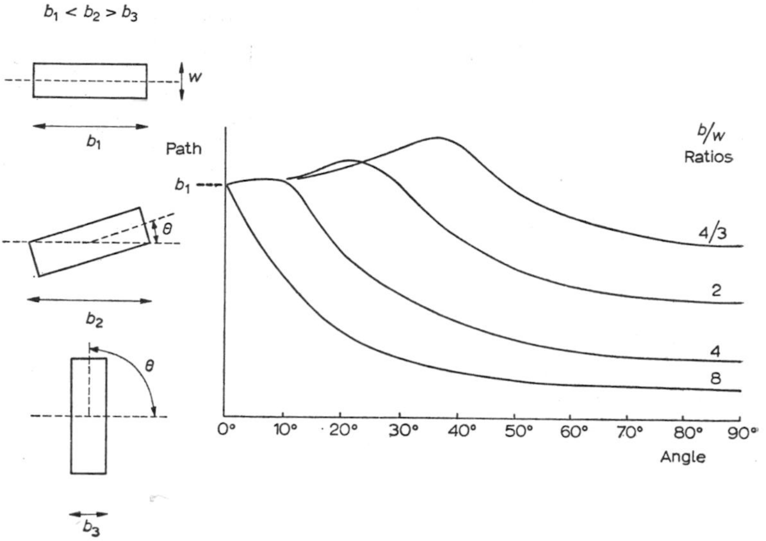

Fig. 8–32. Variation of the path for different ratios b/w (Path at angle zero/width). If w is significant with respect to the length of the flame, at certain angles the calculated path might increase from the starting value at angle zero.

coupled above the burner, forcing the flame to travel in the directions of the horizontal arms. They may improve the sensitivity in the determination of analytes with long-life free atoms. Fig. 8–33 shows a diagram of this type of adapter.

A T-shaped adapter (also called a *T-shaped combustion chamber*) made of silica was tested by Rann and Hambly (*606*) in their determinations of selenium. The tube (internal diameter 2.5 cm and length 15 cm) was centered with the optical axis of the instrument. Although a secondary air flow was provided, some small flames did appear at the ends of the horizontal tube. With this arrangement Rann and Hambly obtained a concentration limit of 1 p.p.m. of selenium with an air–propane flame.

4.2.2. Adapters in the form of an elongated horizontal tube

These adapters also force the flame to travel in the direction of its axis, which coincides with the axis of the instrument. The light beam travels across the tube. A turbulent flow burner is placed at the source end of the tube (see Fig. 8–34). Two air blasts are advisable, one of which cools the spot excessively heated by the flame, while the other prevents any damage to the monochromator. These tubes, which have been described by Fuwa and Vallee (*251*), are up to 90 cm long, and made of some material

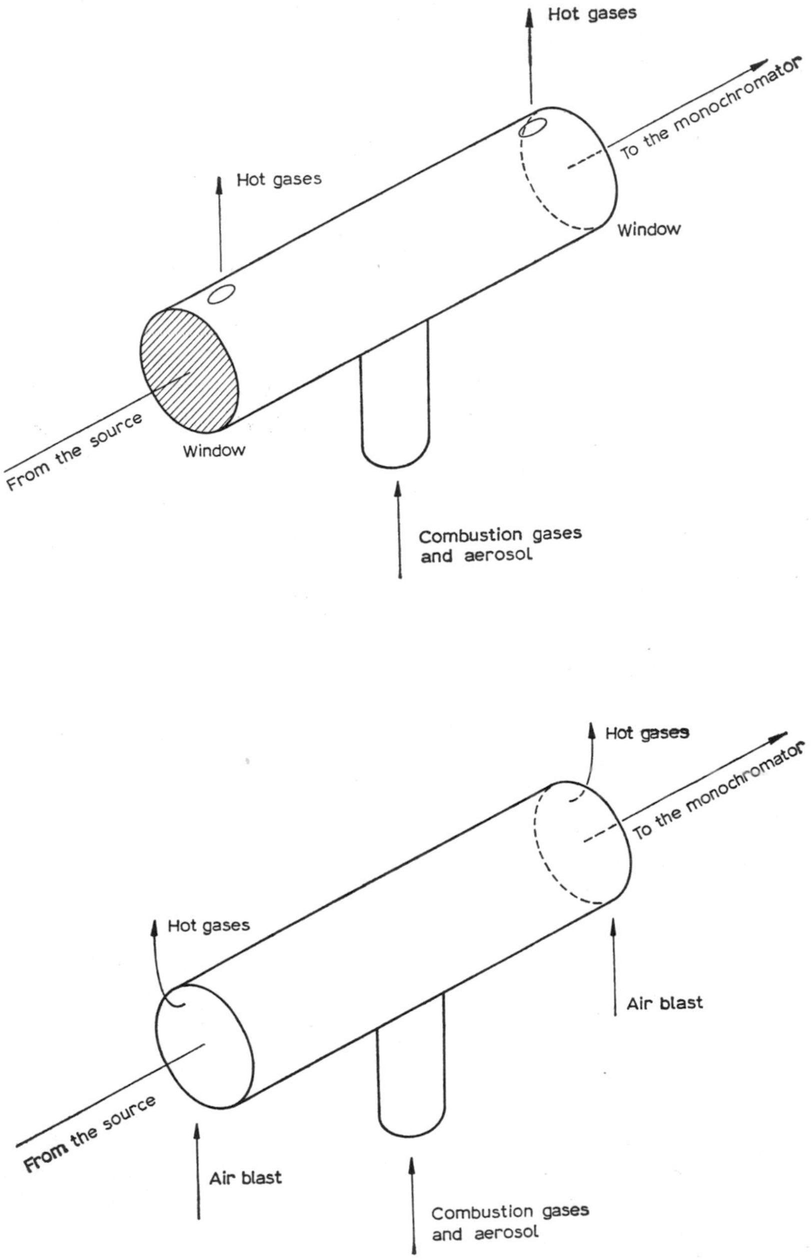

Fig. 8–33. Two types of "T-form" adapters.

which is resistant to high temperature (Vycor, silica, magnesia, etc.). The use of this device increases the sensitivity (percentual sensitivity) of the determinations—especially when analytes of long-life atoms are determined—, although once a certain limit has been reached (about 70 cm), little is gained in sensitivity. It is possible to prepare *long-tube flame profiles*, similar to common flame-profile curves, the absorbances being expressed as a function of the distance from the burner end of the tube (see Fig. 8–35).

The gain in percentual sensitivity is a function of the diameter of the tube (Fig. 8–36), and naturally it is also a function of the length (Fig. 8–37), for each analyte concentration.

These adapters must be cleaned from time to time, and are always exposed to breakage by devitrification, and must be replaced.

Minute quantities of zinc and tin have been determined by this procedure. Increments of sensitivity from 10 to 100 times can be expected in comparison with values obtained with burners without adapters. Allan (*17*) has achieved 10- to 50-fold increases in sensitivity depending on the element.

It does not seem appropriate to use a tube of great length for elements such as molybdenum, calcium and chromium which easily form oxides in the upper regions of the flame. However, for other metals which do not form oxides so easily, such as mercury, cadmium, lead and zinc, the use of the tube may prove very convenient.

The stability of the flame is one of the most significant variables, and Fuwa and Vallee (*253*) have improved this by means of a platinum burner

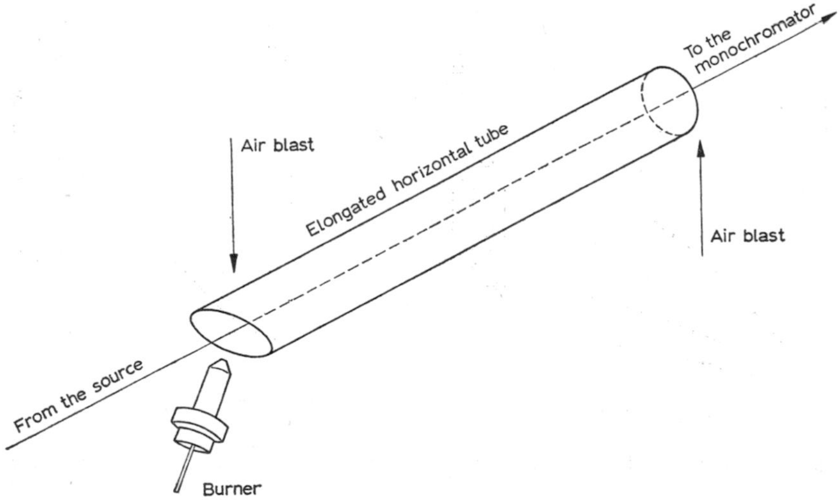

Fig. 8–34. Adapter in the form of elongated horizontal tube

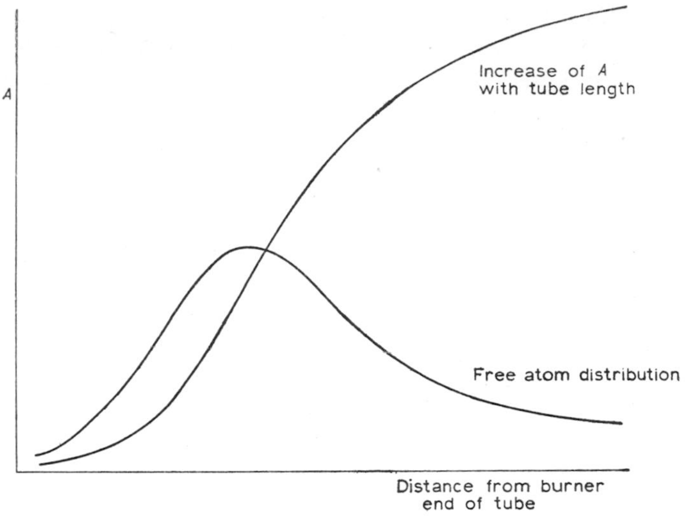

Fig. 8–35. Increase of *A* with tube length in adapters in the form of an elongated horizontal tube.

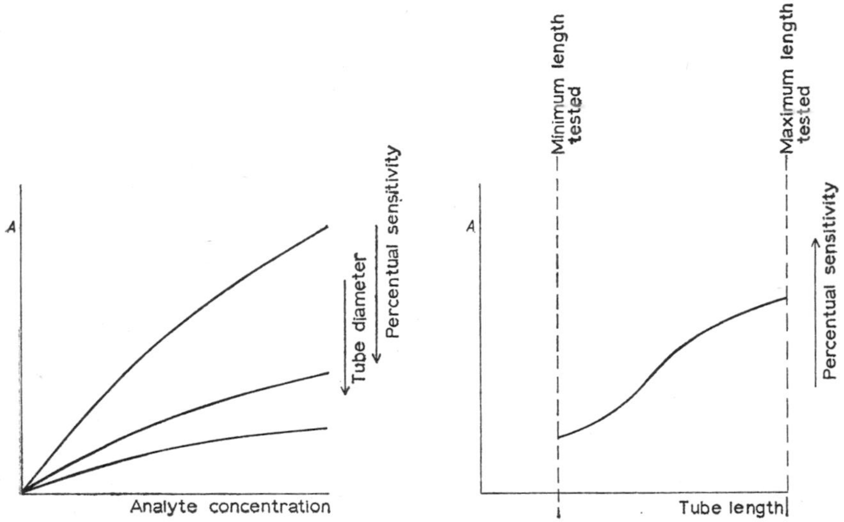

Fig. 8–36. Influence of tube diameter on percentual sensitivity with elongated horizontal tube adapters.

Fig. 8–37. Influence of tube length on percentual sensitivity with elongated horizontal tube adapters.

especially prepared for the long-tube procedure. This burner is said to eliminate any contamination that might appear from the materials of the burner. The burner allowed the sensitivity to be enhanced and previously inaccessible lines to be used. Fuwa and Vallee determined zinc, magnesium, cadmium and lead by this new approach, and considered this mode of operation to have great potentialities for other elements of biological interest.

The extensive use made by Fuwa *et al.* of the long-tube adapters justifies the frequently used name *Fuwa tube*. The long-tube adapter can also be called *long absorbing cell*.

There is a disadvantage in the use of the long-tube adapter, which is the emission from the hot tube. However, Koirtyohann and Pickett (*409*) have reported that in their adapter (40-cm long) the emission from the hot tube is not a serious problem, even though there is no electrical discrimination against it in their instrument. In fact, the energy emitted depends on the condition of the wall of the tube and on the wavelength used for measurement. Tubes that have been in prolonged use give some emission in work at wavelengths higher than 3000 Å. Compensation of 0% transmission (100% absorption) at shutter closed is enough to avoid the effects of this type of emission, if the adjustment of zero transmission is done while blank solution is aspirated under the same operating conditions as those used for sample solutions.

4.3. *Chimneys*

It is surprising that chimneys around the flame have not been recommended by many workers. In practise, the chimney prevents air currents which may produce variations in the flame, avoids accidental contaminations, and assists in the formation of *ascending* currents of air which help to achieve a greater stability of the flame. Of course, the chimney must be appropriately designed for the type of flame and characteristics of the burner. The use of side windows (silica windows) avoids damage to optical parts close to the chimney.

4.4. *Vents*

Vents placed at a reasonable height above the flame are recommended, especially when noxious elements are used. The intake current of the vent should be regulated so that it does not modify the form and stability of the flame. It is necessary to watch for particles coming from the vent and vent tubes (for instance, galvanized sheets used in the vent system may be common sources of zinc contamination).

4.5. Mechanisms for supplying the solutions

In this category may be classified all the mechanisms used in supplying the solution to the sprayer, whether it be by pumping—auxiliary feed pumps—or motor-driven syringes.

5. OPTICAL PARTS

Some optical accessories are generally used in the absorption system. They are briefly mentioned in the following sections.

5.1. Lenses

The simplest coupling of lenses used in atomic-absorption is that designed to convert a divergent light beam into a practically parallel beam during its passage thorough the flame, and to make it converge again when travelling to the selection system. The lenses should be of quartz and they require frequent cleaning so that occasional deposits will not decrease the light intensity that should arrive at, and emerge from, the flame. The lenses for this type of coupling should be, of course convergent, spherical. The use of sphero-cylindrical lenses to focus on the entrance slit (see Fig. 8–38) is another possibility.

It may be useful to make the beam converge through and in the flame with flames of relatively small diameter (see Fig. 8–39). The same applies to long flames (see Fig. 8–40). The focusing of narrow beams across the flame aids sensitivity, for if part of the light proceeding from the source passes outside the rather restricted optimal zone, there is a loss of efficiency in the absorption process.

5.2. Masking devices

Among the optical auxiliaries of the absorption system are all the possible devices for partial selection of the beam: pin holes, masking slits, masking diaphragms, etc. All these devices produce loss of light intensity (loss of energy).

5.3. Splitting devices and beam combiners

To a certain extent the splitting devices used for the division of the beam in double-beam systems belong to the absorption system. These are

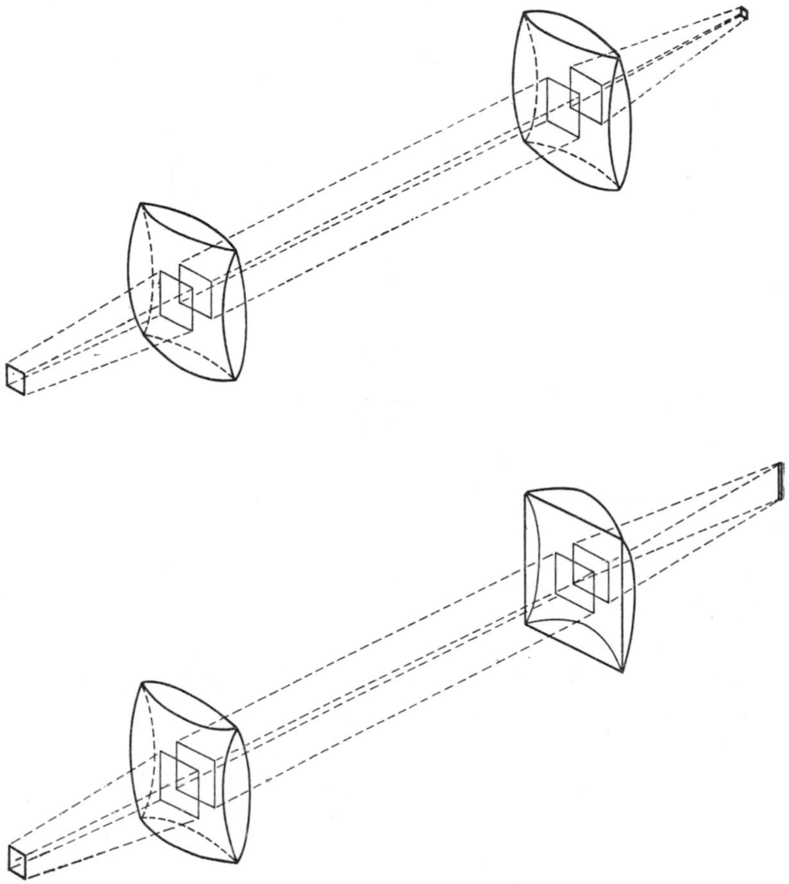

Fig. 8–38. Use of convergent lenses at both sides of the flame. It should be remembered that parallel beams may only be obtained from light coming from a point.

usually either semi-mirrors[25] or mirrors mounted in rotating split sectors (reflecting choppers). The beam combiners—generally semi-mirrors which are also used in double-beam instruments—also belong to the optical parts of the absorption system, if they are considered from the standpoint of their intervention in the formation of two independent beams, one of which suffers absorption, while the other does not (comparison beam or reference beam). See Fig. 8–41.

[25] Including polka-dot mirrors. Most of them consist of aluminum evaporated on a fused-silica substrate.

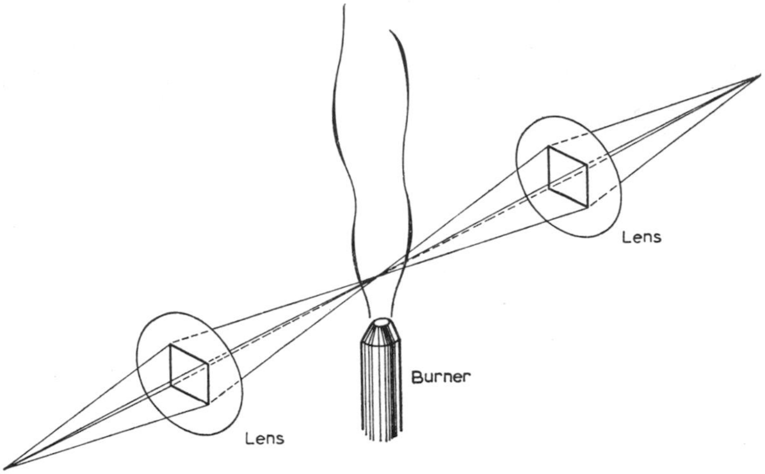

Fig. 8–39. Use of convergent lenses at both sides of a turbulent flame.

5.4. Optical multi-path devices

These devices serve to make the beam cross the flame or flames several times. The multiplicity of reflections is limited by the loss of energy in each

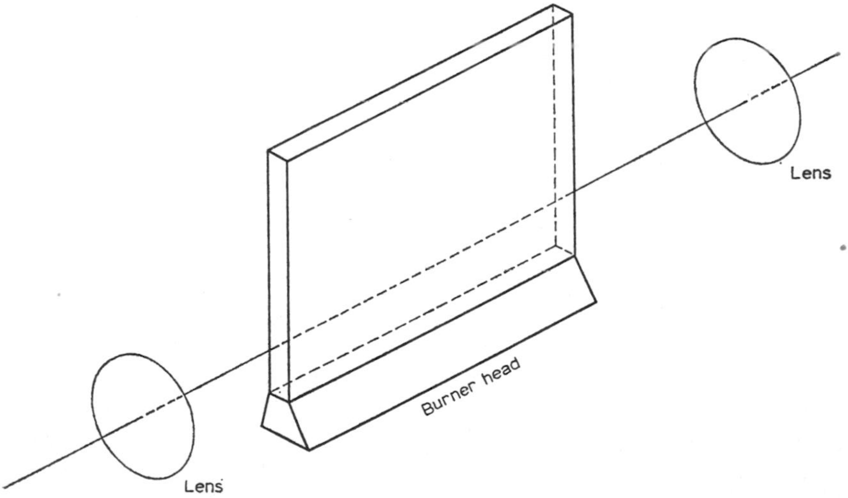

Fig. 8–40. Use of convergent lenses at both sides of a laminar flame. The situation is similar to that shown in Fig. 8–39, so that the beam might converge inside the flame.

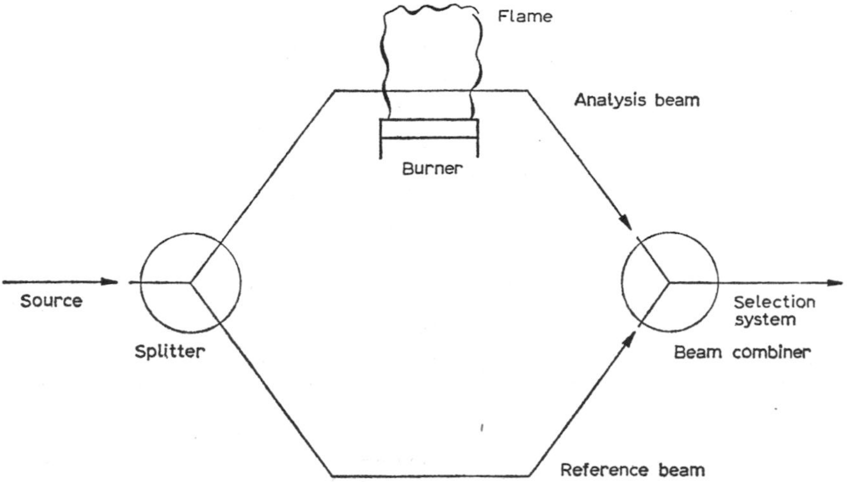

Fig. 8–41. Use of splitter and beam combiner for atomic-absorption flame photometric purposes.

mirror. It must not be forgotten that when the flame is crossed several times, it also plays a part in decreasing the intensity of the beam.

There are two basic types: angular-zigzag devices and circular devices.

The *angular-zigzag devices* are zigzag vertical arrangements such as the one described by Tabeling and Devaney (*756, 757*) and used by Jarrell-Ash Co. (*25*) (Fig. 8–42), and the triple-pass Beckman device (Figs. 8–43 and 8–44), as well as zigzag horizontal arrangements, such as that used by Fassel and Mossotti (*234*) (Fig. 8–45). Another arrangement has been described by Herrmann and Lang (*327*).

The arrangement described by Millikan (*501*) is a typical example of a *circular device* (Fig. 8–46). Eight mirrors with slightly decentered passages are used.

The ascending arrangement tried by Herrmann and Lang (*325*), in which the beam is made to cross the flame longitudinally upward, is not strictly a multi-path procedure, but rather a multi-layer path procedure, since the light crosses different horizontal layers of the flame. It is actually a derivation of the long-path devices. Herrmann and Lang have obtained improved results for sodium by this procedure. The same comments apply to the horizontal flame used by Baker and Garton (*66*).

The repeated passage of light through the flame is no doubt one of the best procedures for increasing the sensitivity in the sense of exposing the light from the source to the absorbing medium more times. It is an extension

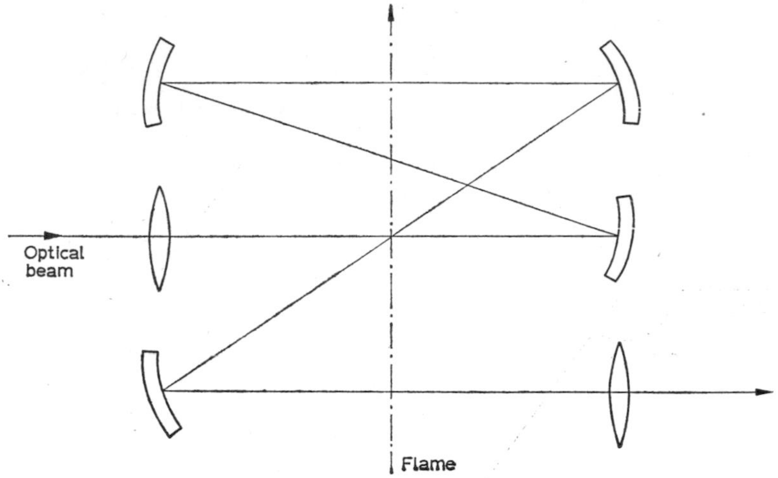

Fig. 8–42. Angular zig-zag multipass device (vertical). Side view.

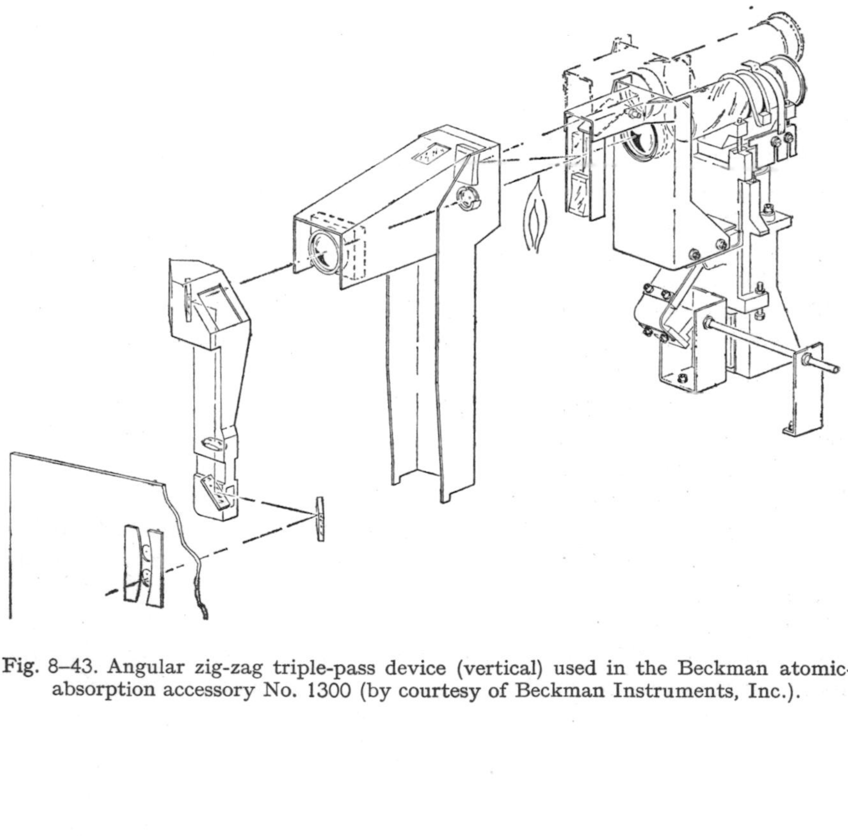

Fig. 8–43. Angular zig-zag triple-pass device (vertical) used in the Beckman atomic-absorption accessory No. 1300 (by courtesy of Beckman Instruments, Inc.).

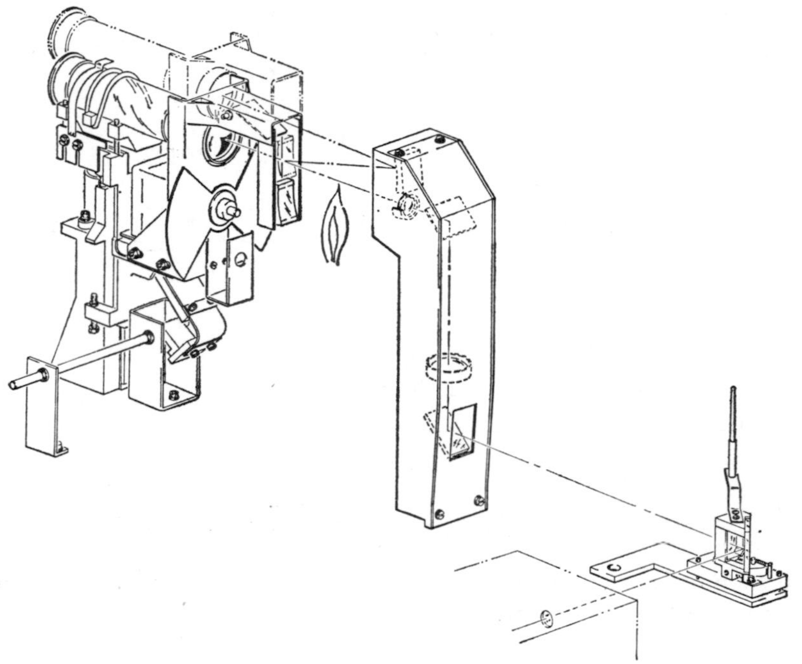

Fig. 8–44. Angular zig-zag triple-pass device (vertical) used in the Beckman atomic-absorption accessory No. 1301 (by courtesy of Beckman Instruments, Inc.).

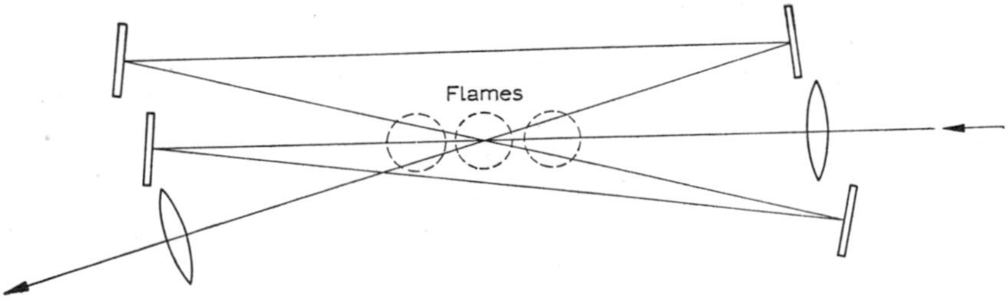

Fig. 8–45. Angular zig-zag multi-pass device (horizontal). Top view.

in atomic-absorption of the combinations of concave mirrors proposed some time ago by White (*819*). Russell *et al.* (*647*) have also reported good results with the multi-path devices.

The number of passes should be limited in those cases where the emission increases more rapidly than absorption, since the optical selector system sees the flame *absorbing and emitting* several times. The operating conditions

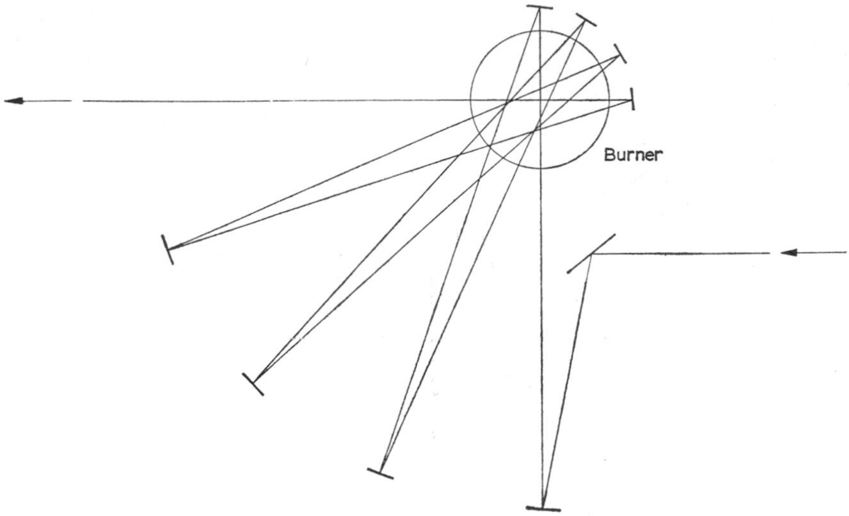

Fig. 8–46. Circular multi-pass device (horizontal). Top view.

used by Brace *et al.* (*110*) in the determination of high-emitting elements are of interest in this respect.

5.5. Periscope couplings

Whether they be horizontal or vertical, periscope couplings accommodate the entrance of the beam towards the selection system through the use of mirrors or prisms (total reflexion prisms). The mirrors are preferable because there is less loss of light in the external surface reflexions. Figs. 8–43 and 8–44 show two periscope couplings used in atomic-absorption.

5.6. Mirrors

Plane and concave mirrors are used as auxiliary optical parts in many instruments (for periscopes, and for double-beam and multi-pass operations). The positions of mirrors should be optimized for peak absorption. Any dust on mirrors should be avoided, but extreme care should be taken in cleaning the mirror surfaces in order not to cause scratches or other damage.

6. OTHER TECHNIQUES WHICH DO NOT INVOLVE THE USE OF CONVENTIONAL FLAMES

Grouped in this section are other instrumental techniques which do not involve the utilization of conventional flames and which are suitable for the attainment of the atomic population necessary for atomic-absorption purposes. The spectral absorption lines are narrow enough when the atomized analyte exists in the state of a free-atom vapor in a medium of *sufficiently low density*. Thus only gaseous media are suitable for atomic-absorption purposes. It is necessary to heat most substances to 2000–3000 °K in order to vaporize them and decompose them into free atoms. These conditions can be achieved by means of conventional flames and also by the techniques mentioned below:

(a) Laser volatilization.
(b) Plasmas.
(c) Spraying into a spark.
(d) Furnaces and hot tubes.
(e) Hollow-cathode sputtering.
(f) Flash vaporization.

6.1. Laser

David (*176*) recently mentioned the possibility of using a laser for the instantaneous volatilization of solid samples without the difficulties caused by selective volatilization. The laser is already being utilized in spectral analysis as a volatilization technique for local analysis. Hagenah *et al.* (*301*) and Brech (*113*) have discussed the possibilities of the use of laser in atomic-absorption.

6.2. Plasmas

Walsh indicated, at the 2nd Australian Spectroscopy Conference, that the plasma jet used as a spectral source—as described by Margoshes and Scribner (*474*)—may represent a new advance in the applications of atomic-absorption (*798*). Butler (*127*) mentions the possibility of using plasma jets as a means of vaporizing samples under *non-oxidizing conditions* at high temperature, which could help in the case of the analytes such as aluminum and silicon. Greenfield *et al.* (*294*), in discussing the production of d.c. arc and radiofrequency-induced plasmas as sources for spectrography and flame photometry underlined their *sensitivity*, their *independence from the effects of non-volatile substances* and their *stability*. Some of these characteristics would make them ideal for use in the absorption system of instruments prepared for atomic-absorption work. The research work by Wendt and Fassel (*949*) throws new light in this field. Wendt and Fassel have described the use of induction-coupled plasmas for atomic-absorption work, allowing the light beam to cross the plasma region three times before it reaches the monochromator. With this system, percentual concentration limits of 1 p.p.m. for aluminum, 0.6 p.p.m. for calcium, 0.1 p.p.m. for magnesium, and 3 p.p.m. for vanadium can be achieved, and also reasonable percentual concentration limits for niobium, rhenium, titanium, tungsten and yttrium. These are excellent sensitivities when one considers the small amount of aerosol passed through the plasma. Some other work (*249*) has also been done in this field.

6.3. Spark

Robinson (*625, 626*) has discussed the utilization of a spark, by means of the process called spark-in-spray, in which a spray containing aluminum is passed between the electrodes of an electrical discharge. In this way, up to 20% absorption was achieved (Al 3944 Å). A device has been described by Herrmann and Lang (*324*) in which a discharge is produced between two *sample electrodes*; the vapor obtained is carried to the flame by the support gas. Fig. 8–47 shows a schematic representation.

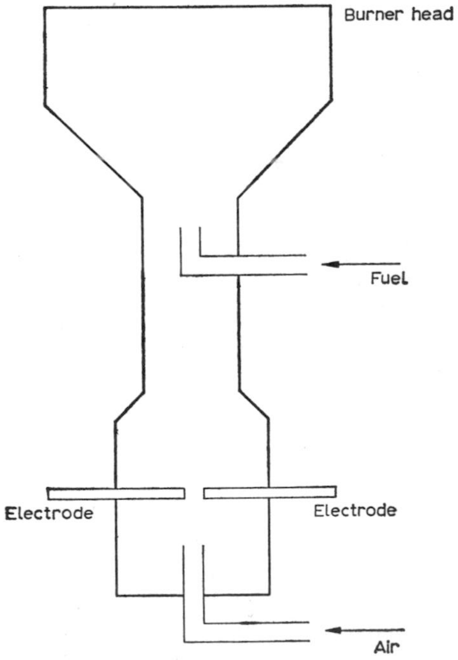

Fig. 8–47. Discharge between two sample electrodes.

6.4. L'vov furnace technique

L'vov prefers the use of the graphite crucible (King furnace) surrounded with a gas—argon—in order to avoid losses of metallic vapors. L'vov (*441, 443*) places the sample in solution form on a carbon electrode on which it is evaporated to dryness. This electrode is introduced into the graphite crucible, surrounded by argon. The device is electrically heated and under these conditions even the most refractory compounds—including oxides—are dissociated into their atoms. All this is enclosed within a box with quartz windows which permit the passage of the luminous beam. Photodetection is achieved by continuous recording, so that the absorption can be measured at the same moment as the sample is completely vaporized.

The flame offers a series of advantages over the graphite cell from the point of view of analytical measurements, but the graphite cell offers the highest absolute sensitivities, as about 100% of the atoms in the sample are utilized in the process. The sensitivity can be related to the concentration of atoms of the analyte in the gaseous phase (*444*). Calculated values are: 10^{-4}–10^{-6} for the graphite cell, 10^{-2}–10^{-4} for the flame, and about 10^{-6} % for the carbon arc in emission analysis. L'vov even considers it possible to increase the sensitivity (by one or two orders of magnitude) by combining the graphite-cell method with fractional vaporization.

Under the operating conditions of L'vov, the absence of chemical inter-

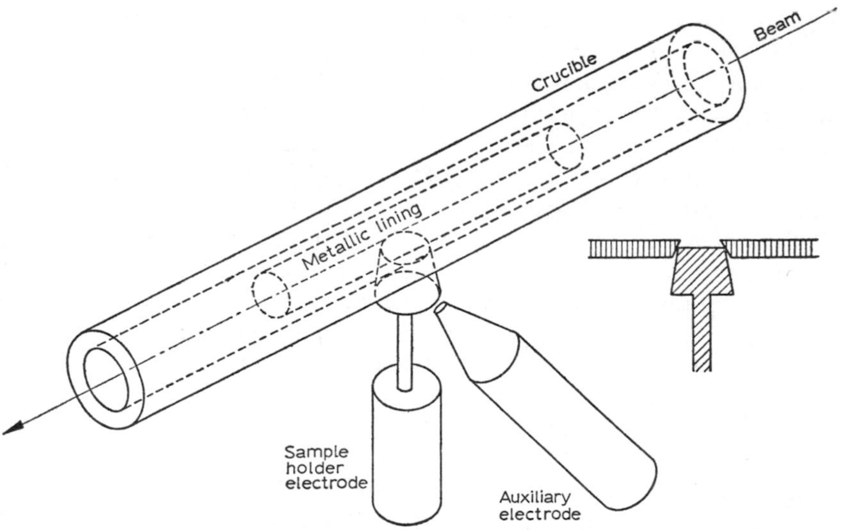

Fig. 8–48. Schematic view of a furnace for L'vov furnace technique.

ferences may be counted on. The experimental conditions are highly reducing, which explains their suitability for the dissociation of oxygenated compounds. Fig. 8–48 shows a schematic representation of his technique.

Nikolaev (*528*) describes a graphite cell internally coated with tantalum, which is used to evaporate zinc. He achieves absolute limits of $4 \cdot 10^{-9}$ g with Zn 3075.9 Å and 10^{-12} g with Zn 2138.6 Å. No interferences with 1000-fold excess of several accompanying elements (aluminum, iron, nickel, titanium, cobalt, copper, vanadium, magnesium, and silicon) were found.

6.5. *Vidale furnace technique*

Vidale has used the furnace technique for measuring, by atomic-absorption, the partial pressure of metallic vapors which are achieved by heating different compounds of the corresponding elements. The investigations of Vidale have been cited and discussed by Gilbert (*275*) and by Walsh (*801*). Vidale has studied the vapor pressure of sodium, the oscillator strength of the line Cu 3247 Å, the vaporization of sodium from glass, the standard enthalpy of formation of silicon carbide, and the oscillator strength of the line Si 2516 Å.

6.6. *Other furnace techniques*

Among the thermal procedures described for production of atomic vapor without the use of flame, consideration should be given to the method suggested by Mislan (*502*), who reported atomic-absorption measurements in which less than 10 p.p.b. of cadmium was detected by using the line Cd 2258 Å. The sample is heated in a quartz tube which acts as a tubular absorption cell. The tube is heated with a wire resistance furnace, reaching temperatures of 1250 °C. The instrument also has a spray chamber.

The absorption chamber used by Hudson (*349*) is made of stainless steel, with two water jackets at both ends. The furnace consists of two sets of windings of Nichrome wire on a cylindrical ceramic cover. This chamber was used to measure the atomic-absorption cross-section of sodium vapor.

The absorption spectra of silver vapor, using a furnace and a tube containing the metallic vapor, has been studied by Choong and Wang (*670*).

Solar furnaces also offer potentialities for atomic-absorption work (*500*).

6.7. *Cathodic sputtering technique*

This technique is also the hollow-cathode sputtering technique, and has been developed by Walsh *et al.* (*255, 257, 648*). It was first envisaged for the analysis of metals and alloys, since the sample is used in the form of a hollow cylinder which acts as a cathode in the discharge produced in the presence of a rare gas; the gas pressure is carefully adjusted so as to achieve the production of a discharge of the hollow-cathode type (Fig. 8–49). Under these conditions the tube which contains the sample hollow cylinder acts as the *sputtering chamber*. In the interior of the cathode, a sufficient concentration of atoms in the ground state accumulates.

The sputtering chamber is a chamber formed by a stainless steel tube, closed at both ends with silica windows. In the upper part, there is a hatch door through which the sample is placed on a support. The chamber is equipped with an anode and a take-off tube connected to a vacuum line. Once the sample has been placed in position, the chamber is closed and pumping is started, the chamber being kept in alignment with the optical axis of the instrument. During the production of the vacuum, the absorption is measured, since it increases to a maximum. The absorption then returns again to lower values, since sputtering of the metal becomes difficult as the vacuum increases. Carrying out the continuous measurement avoids the necessity of reproducing exactly the evacuation conditions for each analysis.

Walsh mentions (*804*) the results obtained by Sullivan with this technique (which is considered one of the most promising along with those of atomic-absorption flame photometry). Sullivan obtained linear working curves for phosphorus in copper, for silver in copper (up to 300 p.p.m.), and for silicon in aluminum and steel (up to about 2 p.p.m.) (cf. ref. (*145*)).

Besides the fact that it can be applied to elements which offer difficulties in conventional absorption procedures, this technique presents other notable characteristics. Chemical interferences are absent; it operates with a *large area of sample*, so that errors by accumulation or local absence are avoided since the sputtering effect counteracts any lack of homogeneity, achieving a homogeneous atomic atmosphere in the chamber; and, finally, it presents potentialities for extension to atomic-absorption spectroscopy in the vacuum ultraviolet region.

The technique has been extended to other metals, among which are sodium, calcium, magnesium and beryllium, all of which, along with silicon, have been studied by Goleb and Brody (*287*). These authors placed the samples in the cathode of a sputtering chamber, and achieved absorption even with minute quantities of analyte. Goleb has also published results for the analysis of uranium (*283*), and has recently mentioned again the use of hollow-cathode lamps as a means of introducing samples into the instrument (*288, 289*).

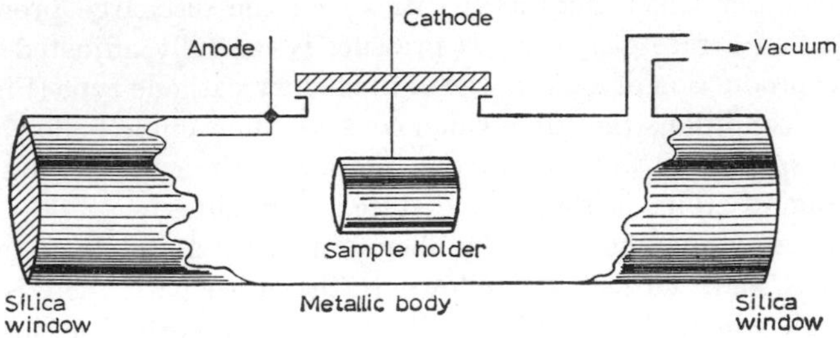

Fig. 8–49. Schematic view of a chamber for cathodic sputtering technique.

6.8. Flash heating technique

The samples, in the form of filaments, very thin wires or very thin metallic sheets are placed in silica frames. This arrangement is placed into a gas-purged chamber and flash heating is produced by means of a capacitor-discharge lamp. The instantaneous absorptions are recorded by making the luminous beam pass across the chamber. Information on this technique has been given by Kay *et al.* (*388*), Nelson (*519, 520*), and Nelson and Kuebler (*521–525*); the work of Nelson and Kuebler has been reviewed by Slavin (*679*).

Chapter 9

Selection system

The radiations coming from the absorption system are selected and then measured. The first of these functions is carried out by the selection system, which comprises all the necessary instrumental parts to achieve a sufficient *spectral selection*. The principal ones are discussed in the sections of this chapter.

1. FILTERS

The filters, whatever kind they may be—color or interference[1]—, are the first approach in attempting to perform spectral selection. The most suitable are, of course, those which are capable of selecting a sufficiently narrow wavelength band.

These selection devices, including simple color filters, suffice to select and isolate the line whose absorption is to be measured, when the required element emits very simple spectra with well-spaced lines, by means of conventional sources. For very easy cases in atomic-absorption methods, such as the analysis of solutions containing only alkali metals (sodium, potassium), monochromators are not really necessary, since filters—similar to those used in emission flame photometry—are sufficient. For potassium a red cut-off filter would be adequate. Fig. 9–1 shows the behaviour of two types of filters in the selection of radiation[2]. Malmstadt and Chambers (*451*) have used combinations of filters in the selection of lines for absorption purposes with sodium and potassium.

It is possible not to use any filters at all for the analysis of alkali metals—single analytes—, although it would be necessary in this case to modulate the lamp source and to use an alternating current amplifier.

For emission proceeding from the emitters, which are often free or almost free of background, the use of filters gives better results in atomic-absorption

---

[1] For further information on this subject, see Section 4, Chapter 6, p. 73 of *Flame Photometry* (*125*).

[2] Some of the figures inserted in this and next chapters do not represent the real physical behaviour of radiations and selectors, but are sufficiently illustrative for the present purpose.

than in emission flame photometry, where the filter would allow the passage not only of the desired radiation but also of the background emissions in the selected wavelenght band.

For other determinations it is considered essential to use a monochromator,

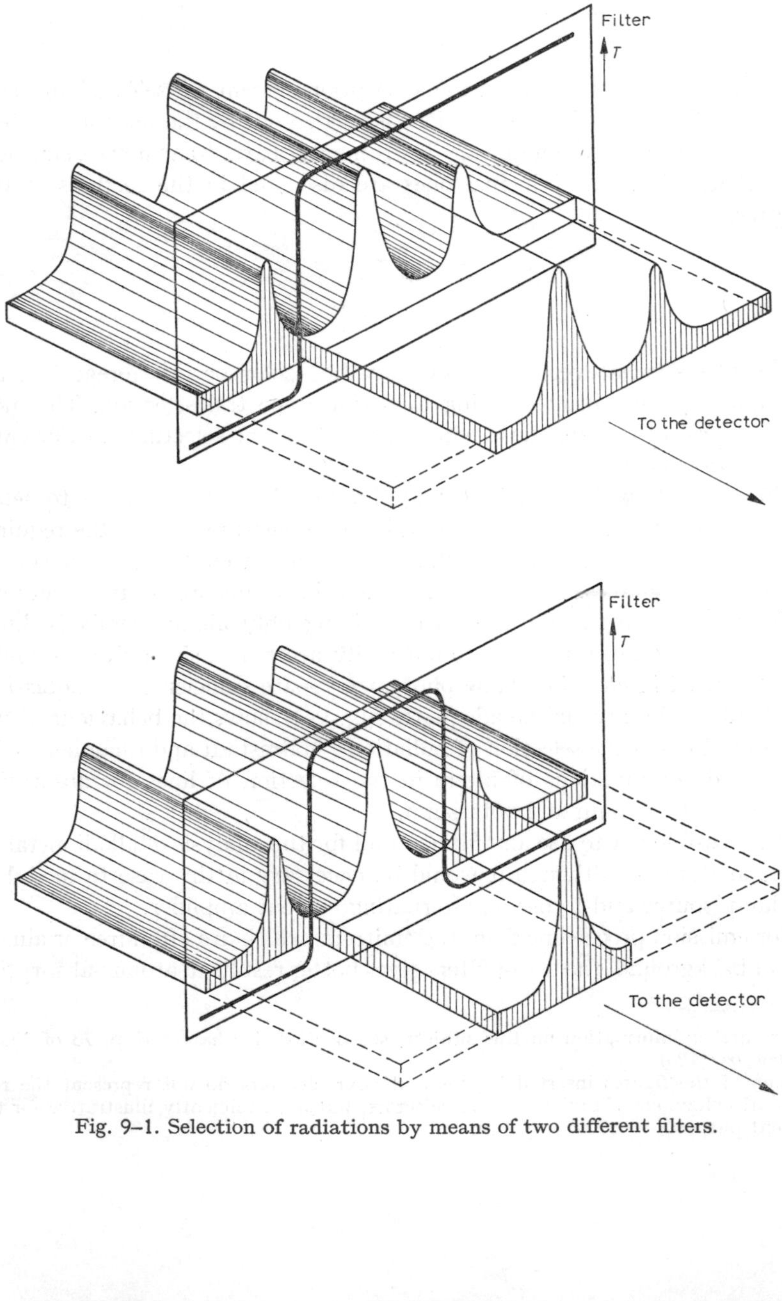

Fig. 9–1. Selection of radiations by means of two different filters.

especially with metals of a very complicated spectrum (noble metals, transition metals). In some cases a *high resolution* monochromator is imperative.

2. MONOCHROMATORS

Monochromators are widely used in flame photometry and as well as for atomic-absorption purposes[3].

In general, an atomic-absorption instrument is not limited by the quality of the monochromator as could be the case in emission work; for spectral discrimination in atomic-absorption is less critical than in emission. High resolution is necessary in emission to isolate the lines from other neighboring lines and to free them, as far as possible, from the effects of background. In atomic-absorption the monochromator plays a more circumscribed role, since there is a first selective step imposed by the narrow absorption line acting on a line emitted at the source which is even narrower. The monochromator then functions to isolate the resonance line from other lines which may be emitted in its vicinity by the source (see Fig. 9–2). The

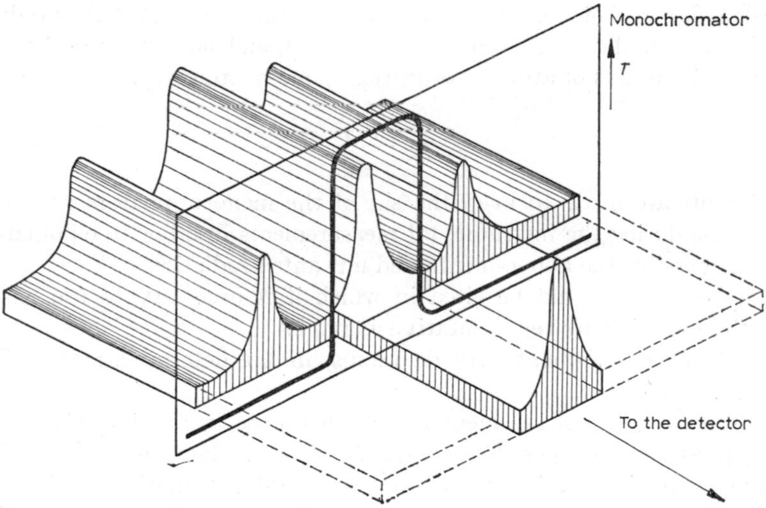

Fig. 9–2. Selection of radiations by means of a monochromator.

[3] Beckman, Hilger, Jarrell-Ash, Optica, Perkin-Elmer and Carl Zeiss monochromators are widely used.

monochromator in atomic-absorption also serves to prevent the admission of too much background radiation from the source (background from the source causes curvature on the working curves). In this double role, it attempts not to admit any unabsorbed light which does not correspond to the absorbed peak.

In atomic-absorption *background radiations* can be understood in two senses: (a) *background radiation from the source* (unabsorbed radiation), and (b) *flame background radiations* (radiation emitted from the flame, due to the presence of emitting elements or due to the flame itself).

If some unabsorbed radiation penetrates across the selection system and reaches the detector, this radiation as well as the radiation characteristic of the analyte are measured. If the unabsorbed radiation comes from a modulated source, even when a tuned amplifier is used, the unwanted radiation will also be measured. The results obtained in both cases are erroneous. This unwanted radiations may be: (a) some unabsorbed sharp line of very close wavelength—from the cathode metals or from the filler gas—, or (b) a continuous emission beneath the sharp analytical line.

The selection achieved by atomic-absorption methods has solved cases which are impracticable by emission. Allan (7) shows how the determination of magnesium in soil extracts obtained with solutions of sodium acetate—a very widely used extractant in agricultural chemistry—is impossible by emission flame photometry because the sodium (Na 2852.8 Å) produces interference on the magnesium (Mg 2852.1 Å), and how this problem can be solved by means of atomic-absorption flame photometry.

2.1. Slit

Attempts are made to keep the slit of the monochromators as narrow as possible during the instrumental measurements in order to eliminate as much as possible the above-mentioned unwanted radiation.

Many examples could be cited in which it is necessary to use narrow slits; the following are representative examples.

(a) With mono-element cathode lamps, in the determinations of iron, cobalt, nickel, etc.

(b) With bi- or multi-element lamps, in the determination of selenium in the presence of copper (if the cathode of the Se-lamp is prepared from a copper cathode containing selenium); in the determination of zinc with the line Zn 2139 Å, in order to separate it from the adjacent copper lines if a lamp with a brass cathode is used.

Reducing the slit as much as possible also helps to eliminate background radiation from the flame; while the signal coming from the source—spectral line—is reduced proportionately as the slit is closed, the signal from the flame background is reduced in proportion to the square of the decrease of the width of the slit[4].

2.1.1. Focusing on the slit

In the use of auxiliary lenses, the second lens (monochromator-side lens) can be adjusted to focus the beam on the monochromator slit. If in this arrangement the beam crosses the flame in the form of a practically parallel beam of light, the emissions produced in the flame are actually defocused on the slit, and this is considered to alleviate the flame effects.

2.1.2. Variations of sensitivity as a function of the slit width

When the source lines are very isolated and the source background is minimal, little is gained in sensitivity by narrowing the slit. In other cases, some increase in sensitivity is noticed; an example is shown in Fig. 9–3 for the case of iron. If unabsorbed close source lines are not eliminated the absorption coefficient apparently decreases. Robinson has published a table in which he shows the spectral slit width (in Å) for a series of slit settings (in mm), giving the concentrations (in p.p.m.) necessary to obtain a signal of two divisions of the scale ($I_0 - I = 2$ div.), which he found for Ni 3414 Å (*625*). The concentrations required increase with the slit width.

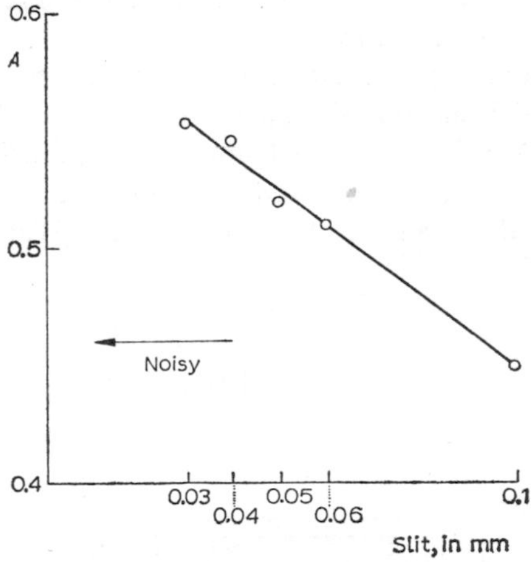

Fig. 9–3. Increase of the absorbance values (increase of sensitivity) on decreasing the slit width. Values obtained for 5 p.p.m. Fe with a Beckman DU-2 spectrophotometer and a Beckman atomic-absorption accessory.

[4] As in emission flame photometry work, for emission lines the energy increases with the first power of the slit width, while continuous background radiation increases with its square.

In cases in which additional sensitivity can be achieved by closing the slit, it is necessary to use higher gain. If the increase of gain is accompanied by more noise, then one obtains an increase in percentual sensitivity, but the fluctuational sensitivity remains the same or even decreases, if the noise grows more rapidly than the slope of the working curves.

A drop in sensitivity as the slit is closed, may be due to mistakes in selecting the peak emission of the source with larger slits, or to asymmetry of the slit.

3. USE OF THE RESONANCE RADIATION

The use of resonance radiation phenomena used to be restricted to those elements which show a considerable vapor pressure at low temperatures, and has also been limited by the weakness of the sources used. An atomic resonance radiation can be obtained by illuminating a hollow-cathode lamp with an atomic spectral lamp (Fig. 9–4). The atomic resonance radiation can be observed from the side; a shield around the cathode prevents excessive radiation produced in the lamp from being observed through the lateral window (*748*).

However, the new high intensity lamps (see Chapter 6, Section 2.3.6) make it more advantagous to utilize these phenomena, by using them as atomic spectral sources to illuminate a conventional hollow-cathode lamp such as that shown in Fig. 9–4 (*748*); both lamps contain the same element. The resonance radiation seen through the lateral window (detected with a photomultiplier) consists of a spectrum, which is much simpler than that obtained when the lamp is observed in the direction of its optical axis. Fig. 9–5 shows the data published by Sullivan and Walsh (*748*).

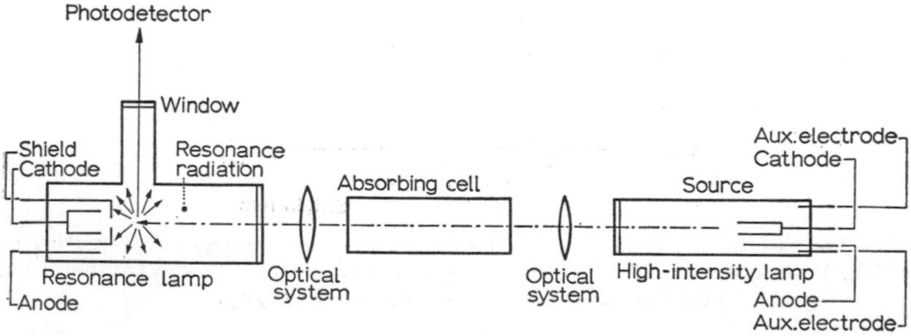

Fig. 9–4. Schematic view of an atomic-absorption spectrophotometer bases on resonance radiation phenomena. If the source is modulated and tuned with the detection system, the effects from the flame can be eliminated.

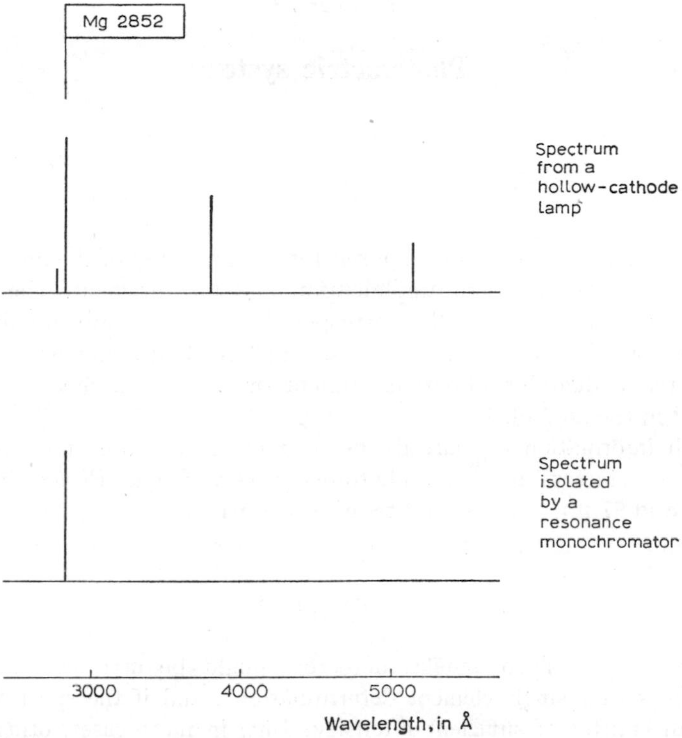

Fig. 9–5. Magnesium spectrum isolated by a resonance monochromator in comparison with the spectrum obtained from a magnesium hollow-cathode lamp.

Sullivan and Walsh (*748*) described a simple instrument based on these principles. This device leads to a simplification of atomic-absorption photometers, the monochromator being replaced by a resonance detector. Simultaneous multi-element determinations are possible. Residual radiation coming from the lamp used as a detector can be avoided if the power supply for the high-intensity lamp is modulated and tuned to the a.c. photodetector system, and the detector lamp is left unmodulated. Various additional information on this new approach to atomic-absorption has been published (*56, 176, 648, 806*).

Chapter 10

Photometric system

The photometric system is required for the final step of the instrumental operation: photodetection, amplification and measurement. The selected radiation is detected and the corresponding impulses are amplified and then measured, either by means of a direct reading meter or a recorder. A printer, a digital read-out instrument or a tape puncher can also be utilized in the final phase.

Much information has already been given on the use and function of common detectors in flame photometry (see *Flame Photometry* (*125*), pp. 89 and 97 ff.), and does not require repetition.

1. DETECTION

Barrier-type cells or similar detectors might be used in very simple instruments for single element determinations, and if the spectral source were an emitter of sufficient intensity. But, in most cases, other photodetectors and photomultipliers are needed, as in emission flame photometry. The time-consuming, photographic procedure is not generally used as a means of detection and measurement, though it is useful in preliminary tests for selection of lines and it would perhaps be one of the surest methods of achieving proper corrections for background effects. Fassel *et al.* have used photographic procedures in some of their atomic-absorption studies.

Photomultipliers of the type which is traditional in emission flame photometry are also very suitable for the detection of emissions corresponding to wavelengths in the visible and ultraviolet spectrum. For the red region of the visible spectrum and in the near infrared, it is more convenient to use phototubes and photomultipliers sensitive to these wavelengths.

The familiar 1P28 photomultipliers have given very good results in atomic-absorption; the same is true of the 1P22 detector. The possibility of using Hamamatsu photomultipliers in the red and near infrared regions has been examined in special cases (*46*).

There are many instruments which incorporate only one detector. Others need more than one detector (simultaneously) during measurements:

(a) Double-beam instruments, in which each beam is received by a separated detector (see p. 170).

(b) Multichannel instruments, in which radiations from two or more instruments are detected at the same time (see p. 172). The radiations belonging to each element are separated by the monochromator and are received through exit slits by the respective detectors.

(c) Instruments utilizing the technique described by Menzies (*496*) and Robinson (*625*), which requires the use of two detectors; one receives the radiation which undergoes absorption and other receives another radiation which, although it comes from the same source, does not undergo absorption (reference). The ratio of these two radiations from the source must not vary even if some variations are produced in the emission system. During determinations, the ratio of the responses of the two detectors is correlated with the concentration of the analyte in the solution aspirated at the absorption system. Robinson has discussed tests made with 27 iron lines in comparison with the line Fe 3719 Å; 22 of these lines showed no variation even with large changes in the feed voltage of the source, while 5 showed notable variations.

Instruments equipped to use only one detector at a time, can have more installed if different detectors are needed for different regions of the spectrum.

2. AMPLIFICATION

As in emission, the direct coupling of the detectors to the meters is not suitable for cases of very weak radiations, and an amplifier is needed between the detector and the measuring device. In atomic-absorption d.c. or a.c. amplifiers can be utilized.

3. MEASUREMENT

The signals from the detector, once amplified, are converted to a visual signal: a deflection of a needle in a meter, a digital result in a printer or read-out device, a recording on a strip-chart, etc.

The readings may represent absorption percentages or absorbances, depending on the type of scale, which are related to concentrations; or the scales or read-out devices can be prepared to provide the operator with direct concentration readings. In any case the final reading will be *real* or *apparent* according to the luminous signal (selected by the selection system) which reaches the detector.

Under ideal conditions, the complete process should be as represented in Fig. 10–1. The detector receives only the characteristic emission of the analyte coming from the source, partially absorbed in the absorption system, and isolated from other radiations of different wavelengths by the selection system. The final reading will *really* represent certain absorption (not distorted) depending on the concentration of the analyte in the tested solution.

Under other conditions, the final reading will be *apparent* (distorted). Some typical examples are given below.

The source contributes some background emission. The process follows the pattern represented in Fig. 10–2. After selection, the detector receives the partially absorbed line emission plus a part of the background passing through the selection system. This contribution from the source causes curvature of the working curves.

The flame contributes some background emission. This case is represented in Fig. 10–3. The detector receives the partially absorbed line emission from the source and a part of the background emission of the flame. The absorptions measured are apparently smaller.

The analyte contributes with some emission. This case is typical of the determination of high-emitting elements. The partially absorbed line e-

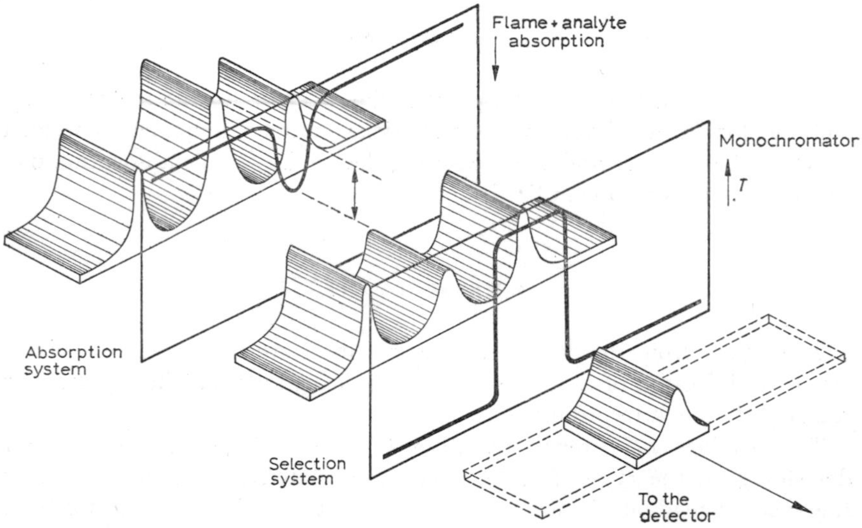

Fig. 10–1. Representation of the complete process of absorption and selection of radiations in an atomic-absorption flame photometer. The radiations coming from the source are selectively absorbed and then selected by the monochromator. The selected radiation is conducted to the detector.

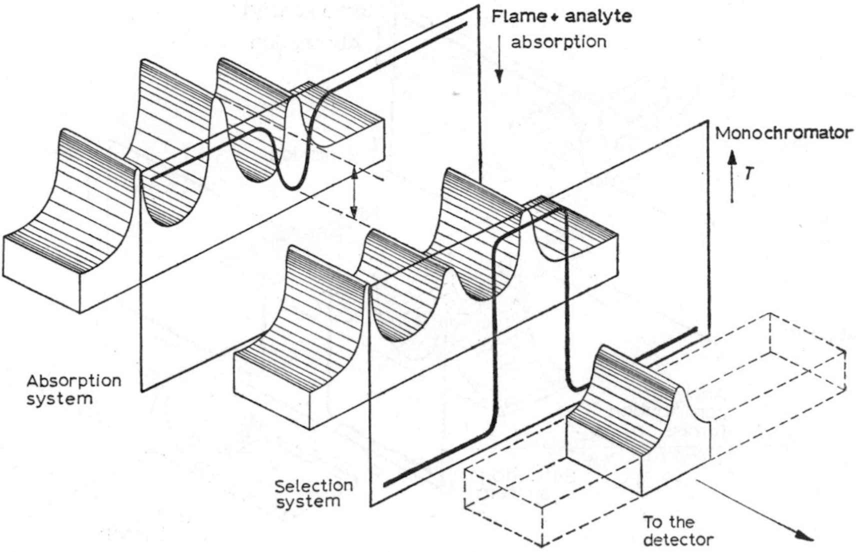

Fig. 10–2. Representation of the same process as in Fig. 10–1, but when the source contributes with some background emission.

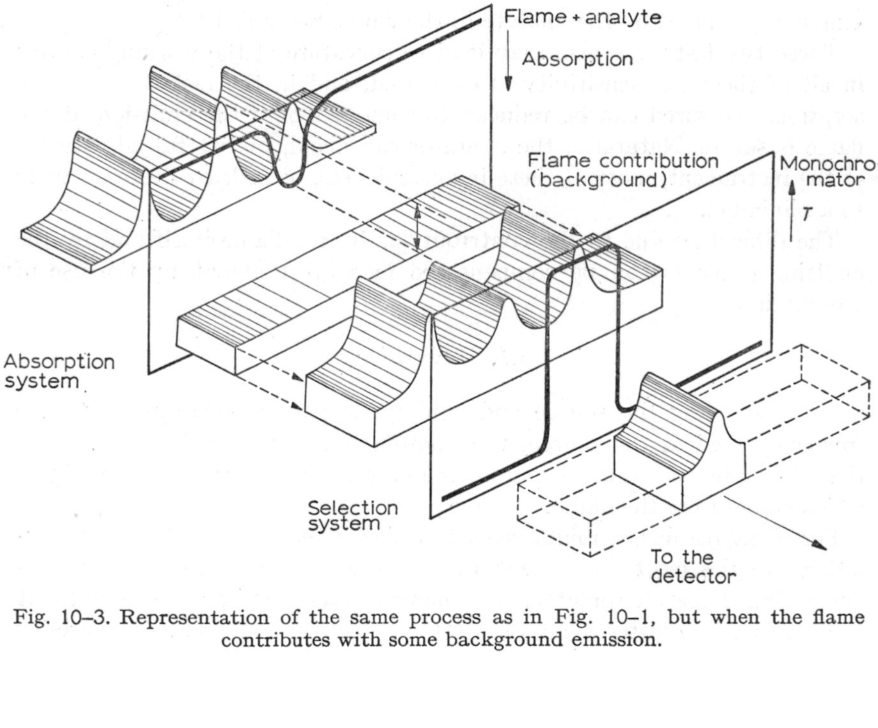

Fig. 10–3. Representation of the same process as in Fig. 10–1, but when the flame contributes with some background emission.

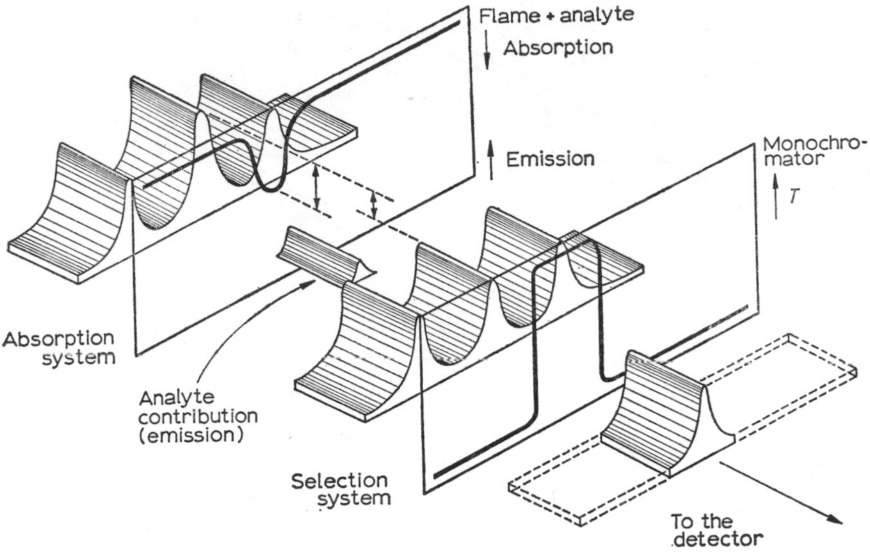

Fig. 10–4. Representation of the same process as in Fig. 10–1, but when the analyte contributes with some emission.

mission from the source is enhanced *at the same wavelength* with some emission produced by the analyte in the flame. See Fig. 10–4.

These two last cases also may lead to curvature of the working curves; in all of them the sensitivity is decreased, and in the last case the absorptions measured can be reduced to some extent if the emission at the flame is severe. Naturally, the operator can avoid, by careful adjustment of the instrument, most of these inconveniences, or at least decrease them to a minimum.

The difficulties due to the contributions by the flame itself and by the emitting elements can be compensated in a great extent by the use of modulation.

3.1. Modulation

By modulating the source and tuning the photometric system to the frequency used at the source, the photometric system will measure only the interrupted signal coming from the source, and not the constant signal which comes from the flame.

For many reasons, it might seem that instruments equipped with modulation are the most convenient in the practical application of atomic-absorption flame photometry, but many workers prefer systems without modulation. The latter type permit the attainment of greater sensitivity by taking advantage of all the light input of the source, and make less noisy operation possible. These are also the reasons given by many workers who prefer single-beam to double-beam operation.

Modulation and tuning may be disregarded for determinations in which lines below 2800 Å are measured; in that zone of the spectrum, the common flames produce very little emission.

Modulation may be achieved: (a) by feeding the source with d.c., and inserting a chopper in the path of the radiations, at the exit of the source; or (b) by feeding the source with a.c.[1].

Then, tuning can be done: (a') by tuning the photometric system with the chopper; or (b') by using a.c. operation and tuning the photometric system to the frequency of the hollow-cathode source signal.

In a.c. operation with a chopper, it is advisable to examine the chopper to ensure its proper working before measurements are taken. If the chopper fails, the light coming from the source is not chopped out and the signals which are received in the photometric system, if any, are completely abnormal.

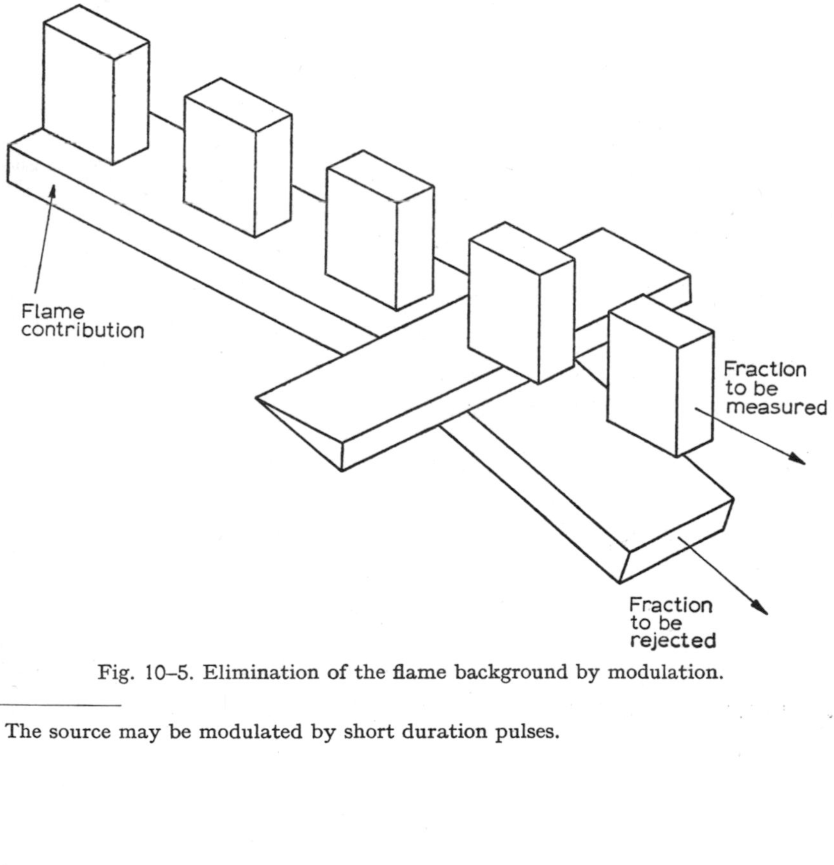

Fig. 10–5. Elimination of the flame background by modulation.

[1] The source may be modulated by short duration pulses.

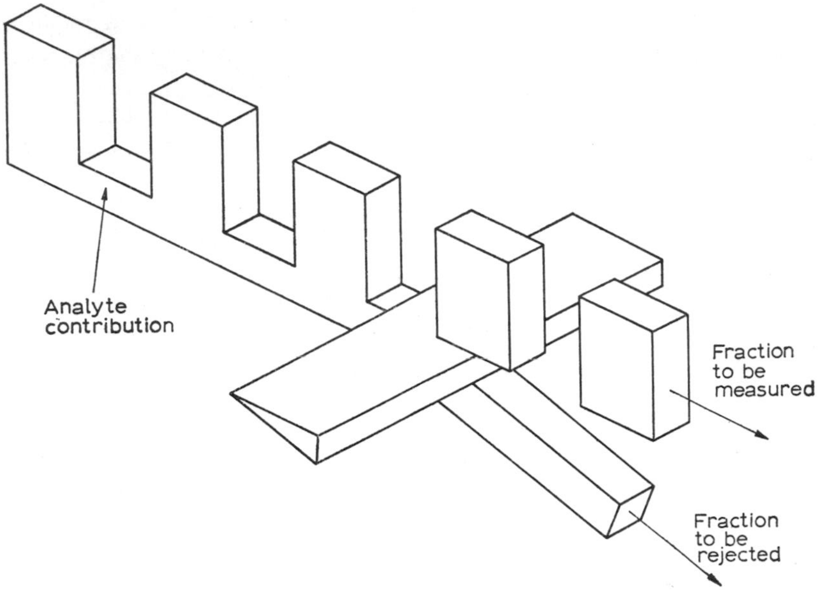

Fig. 10–6. Elimination of the analyte emission by modulation.

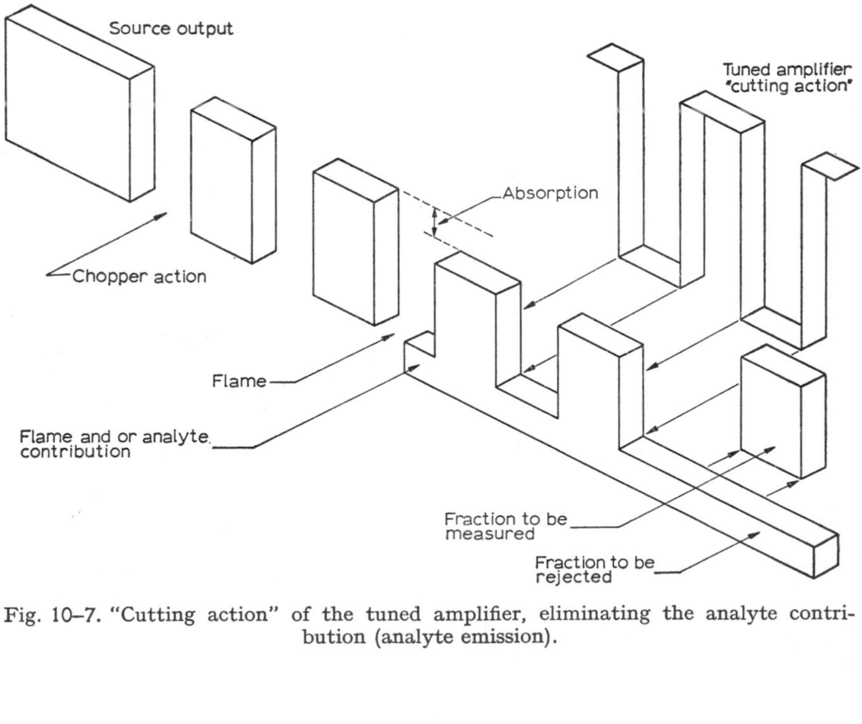

Fig. 10–7. "Cutting action" of the tuned amplifier, eliminating the analyte contribution (analyte emission).

When it is stated that a tuned detector is tuned, this implies that all the photometric system is tuned. The amplified signals may be rectified before being admitted to the meter or other read-out device.

Fig. 10–5 shows a case in which the background from the flame is eliminated by modulation and a tuned photometric system. In Fig. 10–6 the radiation (non-chopped) emitted from the flame (in the case of emitting elements) is eliminated. The action of the tuned photometric system can be understood as a separation by "cutting action", as represented in Fig. 10–7.

Modulation procedures can also be applied to work without the use of flames: Bowman *et al.* (*107*) use modulation, when the atomic-vapor is produced in a sputtering cell.

Other methods of modulation have also been described in the literature. To modulate the flame-photometric signals without using a chopper, Herrmann *et al.* (*328, 329*) introduce the sample into the flame periodically (*intermittent spraying*). These authors consider this *intermittent feeding* as especially advantageous in atomic-absorption work (see also Herrmann (*320*)).

3.2. *Noise*

In the measurement step, some noise is noticed, which comes mainly from fluctuations of the source and of the absorption system[2], and from noise contributions by the photometric system.

A.c. modulation does not eliminate the contributions coming from the flame, since noise level depends on the total light incident on the photodetector.

Shot noise limitations appear less frequently in atomic-absorption than in emission flame photometry (these limitations appear in emission work at very low light intensity levels). On other hand, the instrumental equipment is very rarely limited by the sensitivity of the photodetector, since in most cases enough light intensity reaches the detector to provide a reading usable for analytical purposes, even when narrow slits and/or instruments of low aperture ratio are used.

Continual attempts have been made to achieve better signal-to-noise ratios in atomic-absorption, since noise can limit seriously the analytical precision and fluctuational sensitivity. Increasing the time needed to reach a given level of analytical precision undoubtedly leads to better analytical results, but under these conditions, the amount of sample solution consumed

---

[2] Including fluctuations due to the flame, the sprayer noise and the regulation section (gas regulators), as well as the fluctuations to be expected in the atomization process.

is larger. The operator must balance the volume of solution required and the precision desired, in those cases in which the sample size is limited.

Lang and Herrmann (*423*) have published an equation for signal-to-noise ratios in atomic-absorption flame photometry. In order to be able to operate at low noise level, Boling (*104, 105*) describes an integrating analog computer that uses integraters for data collection (they act by increasing the signal-to-noise ratio) and voltage dividers to compute the signal-to-noise ratios. The Beer law is solved by means of a nonlinear potentiometer and a second servo-driven divider to give concentration directly in digital form.

3.3. Recording

Strip chart recorders are a useful complement to the photometric system, in providing permanent recordings of readings. Recorders are particularly useful in studies of operational stability as a function of time, and of the effects of flushing, contamination and memory. The recording of noise for the purposes of calculating fluctuational sensitivity and fluctuational concentration limits is another application.

Recorders, though not essential, offer several advantages:

(a) A recorded file of data becomes available and can be consulted at need.

(b) More confident reading of signals is possible.

(c) A history of the recorded signal along the variable time is available.

(d) Recording is very useful in the calculation and use of noise values at the top of signals and at the blank solution level. The operator can perform visual integration of variable signals.

(e) Time constants can be studied and decisions on the use of condensers to modify the time constant and noise are simplified.

In the final step of measurement damping can be used (damped recorder), but it makes the experimental reading stage more tedious. A condenser of appropriate capacity across the terminals of the recorder will increase the time constant, and the recorded signals and zero line (0% absorption level) will present less noise than those obtained without the condenser. Too much damping makes the recording operation too sluggish.

3.4. Scale expansion

The need of measuring absorption in very dilute solutions, with very low values of absorption, has brought about the use of scale expansion in absorption work. Scale expansion allows one to work more conveniently in the region 0–20% absorption.

Information on scale expansion has been given by many workers (*26,*

165, 170, 173, 175, 375); detailed descriptions have been given by Andrew and Nichols (*22*), Belcher and Brooks (*81*), Kahn (*378*) and Trent and Slavin (*778*). Attention has been given to the improvement in readability when scale expansion is used, and some examples in determinations of barium and mercury have been discussed (*937*).

Scale expansion is especially recommended when the source and photometric system are very stable. Little is gained in noisy readings if expansion is not accompanied by some damping. If sensitivities (or other parameters) are measured by signals obtained with scale expansion, it is, of course, essential to divide the results by a number equal to the magnitude of the expansion.

Lang and Herrmann (*422*) have described two procedures for scale expansion; one of these is similar to the conventional procedure, and the other uses peak rectification of the a.c. signal and simultaneous increase of sensitivity of the measuring device.

3.5. Measuring procedure described by Lang

Lang (*417*) has described an electrical differentiation procedure, which is said to offer a series of advantages: (a) elimination of flame background in some cases; (b) elimination of null point drift with d.c. amplifiers; (c) better spectral resolution; (d) improvement of the signal-to-noise ratio by means of a supplementary integration which makes it possible to achieve greater sensitivity; (e) elimination of the defective measurements caused accidentally; (f) measurements with microliter samples; and (g) determinations below 0.3% absorption.

3.6. Measuring procedure described by Warren

Warren (*808*) has applied *short interval wavelength scanning*. The source mirror used under normal conditions of operation is replaced by a hollow-cathode lamp (Hilger copper–zinc lamp). The light intensities which reach the photodetector over a short wavelength interval centering on the analytical line of the analyte are recorded. The interval is 10–20 Å, corresponding to a time period of 5–10 sec. The sample consumption is about 0.1–0.2 ml under these conditions.

3.7. Other measuring procedures

A digital voltmeter which gives direct concentration readings has been described by Keats (*390, 391*). The integration of signals and their conversion to absorbances through a logarithmic analog computer circuit and the use of printers has been mentioned by Boling (*104*).

4. DOUBLE-BEAM OPERATION

Although double-beam operations are partially connected with the absorption system, the topic is dealt with in this chapter because this type of operation needs special arrangements in the photometric system. The two signals must be separated of suitable compensations made (null-point circuits) or the ratio between the two signals measured (for instance, ratio recorders).

One of the main limiting factors for accuracy, precision and fluctuational sensitivity in atomic-absorption is the fluctuation of the light source, hence the increasing popularity of double-beam operation[3], which attenuates the influence of those fluctuations and also of the emitter drifts, can be readily understood. However, as Gidley has said (*269*), the use of instruments based on double-beam principles eliminates errors due to primary source intensity variations, but does not control other sources of error. Actually the fluctuations of the final signal depend only in part on the instability of the source.

A double-beam optical device, and its related electronics, is solely designed to divide the beam from the source into two beams (analysis beam and reference beam), only one of which crosses the absorption medium; both beams are then recombined before entering the selection system. The double-beam systems do not require very stable power supplies for the hollow-cathode lamps, since any small variations produced during the operation are automatically compensated. Thus a power supply of lower price and of less critical characteristics may be used. Double-beam instruments are restricted in the same way as single-beam instruments in regard to spectral scanning.

Baker (*65*) states that double-beam instruments are preferable because not only is the need for an extreme source stability eliminated, but an extreme detector sensitivity is also unnecessary. Shelton and Walsh (*667*) do not consider that the use of double-beam operation is essential, since with the use of a regulated power supply for the source and photomultiplier, the assembly can be sufficiently stable, and a simplification of the apparatus can be achieved.

---

[3] Instrumental systems prepared for double-beam operation are also known as *double-beam systems*. See Chapter 8, Section 5.3 and Fig. 8–41.

5. OTHER MEASUREMENT PROCEDURES INVOLVING COMPARISON OF TWO LIGHT SIGNALS

Herrmann *et al.* (*329*) have clained a series of advantages by means of *alternating aspiration of blank solution and sample solution* (see Fig. 10–8). Shorter times are required and greater accuracy is achieved. The method gives the same advantages as the double-beam instruments, but with single-beam instruments. The effects of both matrix and emitting elements are eliminated. Finally, local scanning, which shows only the lines of the source which are absorbed in the flame, is possible.

Koirtyohann and Pickett (*409*) have demonstrated, by a very careful study, that a *background absorption* which depends on the composition of the sample solution, is inherent in atomic-absorption determinations. The various elemental absorptions are superimposed on this background absorption. It is difficult to measure this background absorption because the hollow-cathode lamp producing monochromatic emission cannot be used to scan along the wavelength scale in the proximity of the analytical line when one wishes to make a correction for background absorption. At the same time, the absorptions due to the matrix and to an impurity of the analyte in the matrix cannot be distinguished without scanning. These

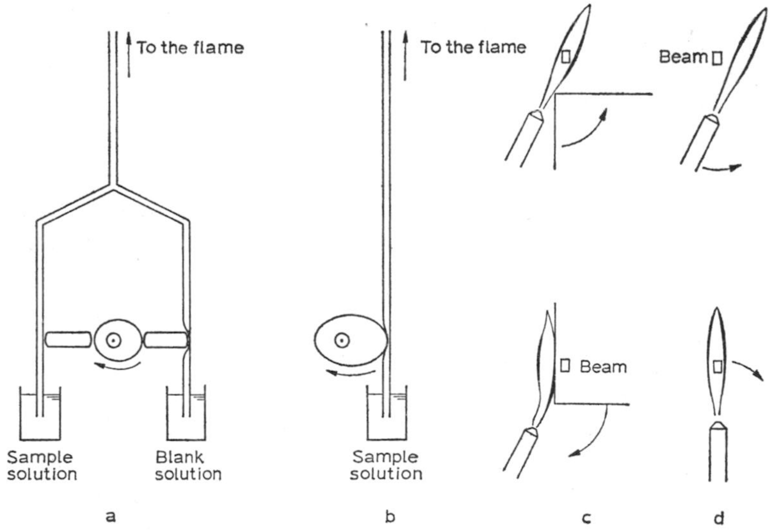

Fig. 10–8. Diverse possibilities for measuring procedures involving comparison of two light signals: (a) and (b) by alternating aspiration of the sample solution; (c) by blocking the flame out of the beam; (d) by swinging the burner and flame. For more details consult ref. (*320*).

authors have made it possible to correct this type of interference by using *two different light sources*: (a) a hollow-cathode lamp that aids in measuring the total absorption (elemental absorption plus background absorption) at the analytical wavelength, and (b) a hydrogen lamp that is used in measuring the background absorption at adjacent wavelengths. A swinging mechanism allows the use of both types of light beams.

Under this heading of procedures involving the comparison of two light signals can be mentioned those procedures that involve the measurement of two lines proceeding from the same source. The lines (one of which undergoes absorption, while the other does not) act virtually as if they belonged to two beams of different behaviour but superimposed. Actually, it is a single-beam operation. These procedures compensate for variations in the source.

6. MULTI-ELEMENT MEASUREMENT

This type of operation corresponds to the so-called *multi-element instruments*, which allow simultaneous measurement of several elements. The necessary emission proceeds from different emitters[4]. If the radiations of two or more hollow-cathode lamps are combined (combined double- or multiple-beam), then they are separated in the selector system and measured separately (*127, 184, 478*). Such instruments do not compensate for source variations.

7. INTERNAL STANDARD OPERATION

If the sample solution contains an internal standard[5] and the analyte and the internal standard are measured simultaneously, some of the experimental fluctuations can be compensated as in emission[6].

The instrument compares the behaviour of the combined (superimposed) radiations of both elements (analyte and internal standard) which participate in all the phenomena in the analytical beam. It is implied that the internal standard also undergoes absorption. If the instrument is also prepared to measure a non-absorbing line, this line is called *non-resonant monitor line*.

Butler and Strasheim (*131, 132*) have made use of their simultaneous

[4] It is possible to use a single multi-element hollow-cathode lamp.

[5] A metallic element whose concentration is constant and previously known. The element used as internal standard should behave similarly to the analyte.

[6] Consult Chapter 14, p. 236 of *Flame Phototmery* (*125*).

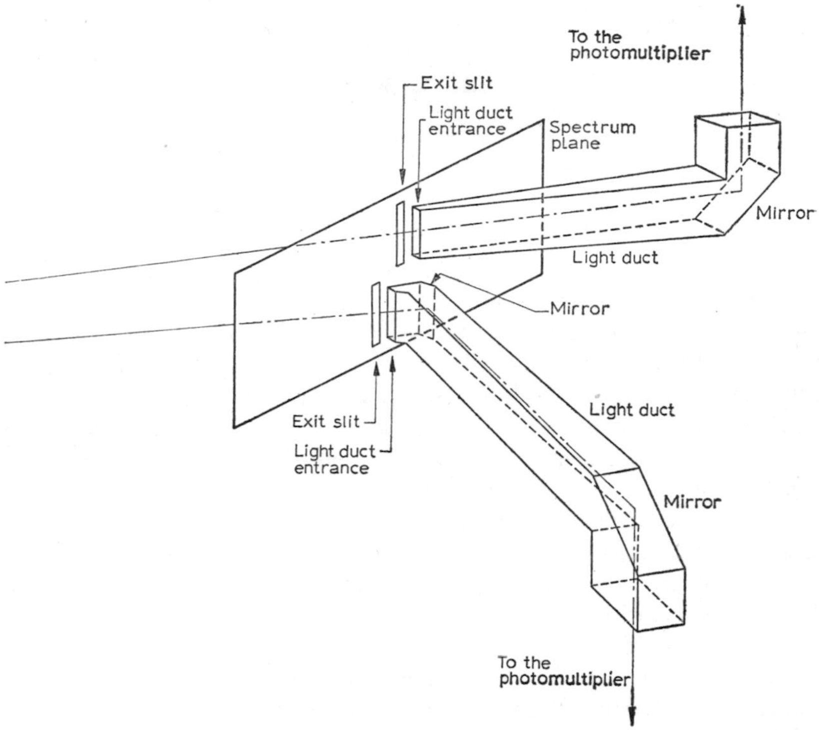

Fig. 10–9. Light ducts to allow the measurement of two lines very close on the spectrum.

multi-element instrument to measure copper with gold as internal standard. The spectral line Cu 3247 Å is used as the analytical line, Au 2428 Å as the internal standard line, and Au 3122 Å as the non-resonant monitor line. For this purpose a single hollow-cathode lamp with a ring cathode containing copper, gold and silver is used. Favorable results, especially in precision, can be achieved by means of monitor line ratios (the monitor line being affected only by changes in the refractive index of the flame), and also by internal standard line ratios (this line also being affected by the concentration of gold atoms in the flame during the determinations). By selecting the radiations at two different levels (two different exit slits), it is possible to measure lines very close on the spectrum (Fig. 10–9).

Chapter 11

Instruments

An attempt has been made in this chapter to reduce to a minimum the description of instruments, both home-made and commercial. In certain cases only some distinctive characteristics are mentioned. Most attention is given to instruments designed for atomic-absorption flame photometry. Instruments which use techniques other than flame have already been mentioned in Chapter 8. The compilation is not exhaustive but an attempt has been made to present a series of representative instruments.

The equipment constitutes an *instrumental system* which is to be applied to an *analytical system* to obtain *analytical information*. The instrumental system must be correctly designed in order to take proper advantage of the *information sources*, through the necessary *data processing links* and *control links* in order to produce *readable* or *stored information*. This final information should be a close image of the reality; i.e., a close image of the chemical composition of the original samples studied. Because of their eminently quantitative character, atomic-absorption instruments will normally only give information on the *quantitative composition of samples*.

Two principal aspects must therefor be considered when the performance of an instrument is evaluated: *physical performance*, which corresponds to the behaviour of the physical instrument itself and its ability to deal with physically evaluated information from the sources[1], and the *analytico-chemical performance*.

To achieve an ideal analytico-chemical performance, the instrument would have to fulfil all the following criteria which are considered fundamental in atomic-absorption work.

---

[1] It should be understood here that these paragraphs refer to *information sources*, and not to the emission sources commonly used in the instruments. The atomic-absorption instrument is, like any other instrument, *a device for communicating information*. If the instrument uses a recorder, the 60-cycle line voltage—which acts as a time signal—, the electrical response of the detector, and the reference voltages act as *information sources*; the amplifier and the slidewire potentiometer act as *data processing links*; the chart drive motor and the pen drive motor, as *control links*. The *information storage* takes place in the strip chart of the recorder. The flow of information is directed in the atomic absorption instrument in a direction leading to a refinement of information. The instrument does not create this information. The signal is conduced by means of transducers that help to transform it into other forms which should be capable of being represented and stored.

(a) A *concentration range* which is sufficiently extensive to permit its application to a large variety of samples of the same or of different origin, but all containing the analyte at different concentration levels.

(b) A good *repeatability*, a characteristic which is immediately related to the precision of the analyses. It is important to consider and study the repeatability in *short term* and *long term* sets of experiments and observations.

(c) A good *linearity* along the different ranges of concentration, as far as the nature of the analyte and available sources permit. This characteristic offers the opportunity of obtaining a linear response along an extended concentration range without a loss of percentual sensitivity. In the cases in which linearity is lost, the percentual sensitivity decreases as a function of the concentration.

(d) An adequate *accuracy* made possible through a *short number* of repeated determinations; i.e., under the usual conditions of most analyses.

(e) A good *sensitivity* which makes it possible to determine analytes in very low concentrations, in original samples and/or prepared solutions. It is important to achieve a good *response* : *stimulus* ratio—a ratio which constantly defines the slope of the calibration curves.

1. HOME-MADE INSTRUMENTS

A great diversity of instruments which often differ from each other in their emission, absorption, selection and photometric systems, has been described in the literature. Although most instruments are based on the same absorption system (the flame) and the same selection system (a monochromator), the great variety of burners, sprayers, types of monochromator, and measurement procedures makes any simple classification according to operational or instrumental characteristics impossible. The following brief descriptions of the different modifications are therefore given in alphabetical order[2].

Instrument described by Agazzi (*2*). This instrument uses a modulated hollow-cathode lamp focused on the entrance of a long-path adapter (absorption tubular-cell), a Jarrell-Ash monochromator, and a photomultiplier as the detector. The output of the photomultiplier is amplified by means of an a.c. amplifier. The instrument is used with a recorder. A large-bore Beckman burner is fed by means of a glass syringe and teflon tubing. The long-path adapter is a quartz tube 30-cm long and 9 mm in diameter, with two cooling air blasts, one near the entrance and the other at the exit, between the tube and the monochromator.

[2] For descriptions of other instruments and attachments see references (*350, 426, 448, 651, 666, 758, 885, 886*).

Instrument described by Allan. Allan (*9*) has described a single-channel direct-reading attachment adapted to a Hilger medium spectrograph along with a modified Lundegårdh burner. The use of this selection system allowed Allan to achieve good results in the analysis of iron and manganese in vegetable matter (with the lines Fe 2483.3 Å and Mn 2794.8 Å). For the production of the flame, burners of a design similar to the burner described by Clinton with a modified Lundegårdh sprayer have also been used (*12*).

Instrument described by Amos and Thomas (*19*). These authors have described an instrument equipped with a Zeiss M4QIII monochromator, a modulated power supply and a broad-band a.c. amplifier. The spray chamber is designed to be connected with a flat plate multi-hole burner, using a standard type (EEL) sprayer. Three gas supplies (acetylene, nitrogen and oxygen) can be used and are measured by three flowmeters. With this instrument aluminum can be determined in aqueous solutions with high sensitivity and precision.

Instrument described by Andrew and Nichols (*22*). In this instrument commercial equipment is modified in order to achieve greater precision and sensitivity. A Hilger apparatus with its atomic-absorption attachment is used. The amplifier circuit is connected to a 10-mV Honeywell-Brown recorder, with an opposing voltage in order to utilize more advantage ously the zone from 100 to 50%, since the sweep range of the detector is about 20 mV.

Instrument described by Baker and Garton. Baker (*65*) and Baker and Garton (*66*) describe the use of a Meker burner and the burner described by Warren with hollow-cathode lamps which are continuously pumped and fed at 500 V, d.c., with a regulated current between 10 and 50 mA. A large quartz Littrow spectrograph is used as monochromator and the photomultiplier faces the exit slit. Synchronization of signals is achieved through iron segments in the sector and pick-up coils. The amplified signal is adjusted to zero by utilizing a beam attenuate calibrated directly in % transmittance.

Instrument described by Belcher and Bray (*80*). This instrument includes a Hilger large quartz E 492 spectrograph as a monochromator.

Instrument described by Box and Walsh (*109*). This instrument is a typical example of one that may be converted, at need, to an emission flame photometer. The instrument has an EEL burner (fed with air and coal gas, or with air and acetylene), a Beckman monochromator and a photomultiplier.

Instrument described by Butler and Strasheim (*132*). The reasons that Butler and Strasheim point out for the infrequent utilization of multiple element determinations are: the great difficulty of directing the light from different sources (for different elements) along the optical axis of the absorbing cell with enough efficiency, the inflexibility of some of the available direct-reading spectrophotometers, and the limited number and close proximity of useful spectral lines for atomic-absorption. For these reasons, Butler and Strasheim have used a Hilger medium quartz spectrograph with exit slits prepared at two different levels, so that two close lines can be measured, and even two simultaneous measurements can be done on the same line. The slit is mounted in a light duct that conveys the light to a moving photomultiplier housing. These authors have used four photomultipliers in this type of mounting[3]. The photomultipliers can be moved with two-speed planetary gearboxes with anti-backlash devices (coarse 1:1 ratio, and fine 150:1 ratio). The positions of the exit slits are read on four scales projected onto a screen. The scales are divided in wavelength units. A 13-stage photomultiplier is used in each housing, and the readings can be taken by a micro-ammeter or by integration. The electronic system is of the d.c. type, with a non-modulated light source. Tandem mounting of the hollow-cathode lamps (see Chapter 7, Section 2.3.2.1) is used and the lamps have multi-element cathodes in concentric metallic rings. The use of the internal standard method (Chapter 10, Section 7) is simple, because it is possible to measure two or more different elements simultaneously.

Instrument described by Chambers. Chambers (*147*) and also Malmstadt and Chambers (*451*) describe and use an apparatus with null-point measurement. Malmstadt and Chambers describe the use of filters and two flames (one of them as reference). Increasing amounts of blank solution are added until equalization of absorptions is achieved (null-point). They consider that a precision up to 0.1% may be achieved.

Instrument described by Davey (*160*). The instrument is designed to allow rapid interconversion.

Instrument described by David (*170*). David has described two single-beam instruments, one for the determination of elements in low concentration and the other for macro-components. The former has a burner with a longitudinal slit, a Hilger monochromator and scale expansion. The latter has a burner with a small slit, a medium Hilger spectrograph (quartz optics) and a photomultiplier in front of the exit slit.

Instrument described by Dawson and Ellis (*184*). This is an automatic, multichannel, high-speed scanning spectrophotometer based on an Optica

---

[3] Butler and Strasheim (*132*) mention that though a four spectral channel was available, a mounting for six channels was preferable for those cases in which five or six lines should be read simultaneously. A four-channel direct-reading head for the medium spectrograph has been announced by Hilger and Watts Ltd. (*341*).

CF4 monochromator, with double-beam operation[4]. The voltages built up in the integrators are measured in a digital voltmeter, and its output is fed to an electric typewriter.

Instrument described by Doerffel et al. (*197*). The instrument is designed for sodium determinations; a sodium vapor lamp is used as source.

Instrument described by Fabricand et al. (*223*). A Perkin-Elmer Model 13 apparatus is modified by replacing the source with Westinghouse lamps.

Instrument described by Gatehouse and Willis (*258*). This instrument is similar to that of Box and Walsh. It is equipped with Techtron power pack and amplifier.

Instrument described by Herrmann and Lang (*325*). The instrument is equipped with a high pressure sprayer, a water-cooled Meker burner, a baffle plate to spread the flame, and a multipass device with several mirrors. Herrmann and Lang have also used other instrumental systems.

Instrument described by Hinson and Kitching (*345*). This actually behaves like a double-beam apparatus. Beam-splitting prisms and half-silvered mirrors are avoided, since they were found troublesome in previous work; a chopper allows the light to pass alternately through two light channels (upper and lower channel) with a frequency of 12 pulses/sec in each channel. The lower channel passes *under the flame*. The two channels are recombined by means of a lens before entering the monochromator. The channel separator is operated by contacts moved by a cam mounted in the chopper.

Instrument described by Koirtyohann and Pickett (*409*). See Chapter 10, Section 5, where the most important features are mentioned.

Instrument described by Malmstadt et al. (*450*). These authors describe a multipurpose high-precision recording photometer. For atomic-absorption work, a burner and an Optica sprayer are attached to a Beckman Model DU spectrophotometer. Versatility can be achieved by the use of multi-element hollow-cathode lamps (Ca–Mg–Al).

Instrument described by Menzies (*496*). Menzies describes the coupling of the lamp, the flame and a line-operated power pack to a Uvispek spectrophotometer. He uses single-beam operation, but with characteristics of double-beam operation, following the principle of homologous pairs with two lines of the same element, with constant rates of intensity (in order to compensate changes in the emitter). The two lines are separated in the selection system and measured in a dual-channel direct reader simultaneously, either with immediate reading or by integration with condensers[5].

---

[4] The instrument is based on principles described by R. K. Brehm and V. A. Fassel, *J. Opt. Soc. Am.*, 43 (1953) 866.

[5] This procedure was mentioned briefly by Menzies at the XVth International Congress of the IUPAC, in Lisbon, in 1956 (*492*).

Instrument described by Perkins (*554*). Perkins uses a sodium vapor lamp and an oxygen–hydrogen flame.

Instrument described by Poluéktov and Grinzaid (*562*). The source is a detachable hollow-cathode lamp, with a graphite cathode, for elements of low melting point. The readings are made on a recorder.

Instrument described by Poluéktov and Vitkun (*564*). This is equipped with a cadmium vapor lamp, a flame of air–propane–butane and a SF-4 spectrophotometer. A similar apparatus has been used for determinations of mercury (*565*).

Instrument described by Priest (*572*). This author has described an apparatus for multichannel operation.

Instrument described by Rawling et al. (*608–610*). This instrument has an EEL sprayer and spray chamber and a standard Beckman DU spectrophotometer. Greaves (private communication) has stated that silver can be determined in the presence of very large amounts of other elements without any interference effects using this equipment.

Instrument described by Rechnitz (*611*). This is a very simple double-beam instrument and contains two cells with a compensation circuit. Filters are used.

Instrument described by Robinson (*615*). A Perkin-Elmer model 13 instrument is modified by means of a Bausch and Lomb grating (1800 lines/mm) and photomultiplier detection. This author has used other instrumental systems.

Instrument described by Schüller and Jansen (*657*). A burner is coupled to an EEL sprayer, and a Hilger atomic-absorption unit, a Zeiss M4QII monochromator and a Zeiss PMQII unit are used.

Instrument described by Shelton and Walsh (*667*). These investigators have described a double-beam instrument in which the light beam is divided into two beams, one of which is chopped at twice the frequency of the other, so that a dephasing of 90° is achieved. A Meker burner and a Beckman instrument as monochromator are used; the latter is so arranged that the slit remains horizontal. In the exit slit a 1P28 detector is placed. The two signals corresponding to the two beams are recorded with a ratio recorder, the ratio between the intensities of the two beams being read directly[6].

Instrument described by Skogerboe (*674*). This is equipped with a constant-current power supply for the emission system, a Beckman burner, a Beckman DU spectrophotometer as monochromator and a photomultiplier as

[6] See also the description published by Russell *et al.* (*647*).

TABLE 11-1
COMMERCIAL INSTRUMENTS

INSTRUMENT CHARACTERISTICS				100-AA & Electronics Corp. (Natl. Instruments Labs., Inc.)	Beckman Instruments, Inc. No. 97900 (Model 979)	Beckman Instruments, Inc. AAA + DU-2 (or DU)	Beckman Instruments, Inc. AAA + DB	Beckman Instruments, Inc. AAA + DB-G	FA-2-Carl Zeiss	140-Evans Electroselenium Limited	H. 1150-AAII-Hilger and Watts Limited	139-0420-Hitachi Limited	Jarrell-Ash Company 82500	Jarrell-Ash Company 82600	Jarrell-Ash Company 82700	Jobin-Yvon	Densatomic - Optica S.p.A.	Perkin-Elmer Corp. 303	Perkin-Elmer Corp. 290	Research and Control Instruments	Techtron Pty. Limited A-100	Techtron Pty. Limited AA-3	Unicam Instruments Limited SP 90	Unicam Instruments Limited SP900A
BENCH INSTALLATION	*Compact*			x	x					x				x	x		x	x	x	x	x		x	x
	Aggregated units					0	0	0	0		x	0	x			x						x		
	Attachment					x	x	x	x			x												
EMISSION SYSTEM	*Power supply*	Lamp channels	Single channel							x			x		x		x						x	x
			Multichannel		x	x	x	x			x			x		x				x	x	x		
			Stand-by		x	x	x	x																
		Stabilization	Stab. current		x	x	x	x	x	x	x		x	x	x	x	x	x			x	x	x	x
			Stab. voltage																x					
		Modulation	Chopper		x		x	x	x		0		x				x							x
			Chopper + mirrors															x						
			Lamp modulation	x						x	x		0	x	x				x		x	x	x	
	Source	Hollow-cathode lamps		x	x	x	x	x	x	x	x	x	x	x	x	x	x	x	x		x	x	x	x
		Vapor discharge lamps			x	x	x	x									x	x	x		x	x		
		Exchange devices	Turret								x		x										x	
		Prealigned	(lamp or holder)		x	x	x	x	x	x	x		x	x	x	x	x	x	x		x	x	x	x

ABSORPTION SYSTEM	*Sprayer and burner*	Separated (laminar)			x	x	x	x	x	x	x	x	0			x	x	x	x	x	x	x	x	x
		Combined	Single sprayer-burner	x									x	x	x									
			Multiple sprayer-burner		0	0	0	0																
		Heated spr. chamber			x	x	x	x																
		Cooled head									x					x								
		Prealigned			x	x	x	x	x	x	x			x	x								x	x
		Adjustments	Alignment		x	x	x	x					x				x	x	x		x	x		
			Rotation		x	x	x	x		x	x		x					x	x		x	x	x	
			Height		x	x	x	x			x		x	x	x		x	x	x		x	x	x	x
		Feeding	Direct	x	x	x	x	x		x			x	x										
			Tubing		0	0	0	0	x		x	x			x		x	x	x		x	x	x	x
			Forced														0							
		Sheath			0	0	0	0																
	Gases	Fuel	Acetylene		x	x	x	x	x	x	x	x	x	x		x		x	x		x	x	x	x
			Hydrogen		x	x	x	x	x				0	x	x			x	x		x	x		
			Propane		x	x	x	x	x		x					x		0	0		x	x	x	x
			Natural gas		x	x	x	x										0	0					
			Coal gas																		x	x		
			Liq. petroleum gas															x	x					
		Support	Oxygen		0	0	0	0					0	x										
			Air		x	x	x	x	x	x	x	x	x	x	x			x	x		x	x	x	x
			N_2O		0	0	0	0					0	0				0	0		0	0	0	0
		Auxiliary	Oxygen		0	0	0	0																
			Air		0	0	0	0	x									x	x					
		Flow meters							x		x	x		x	x		x				x	x	x	
		Safety valves			x	x	x	x	x				x				x				x	x	x	x
		Gauges (pressure)			x	x	x	x		x		x					x				x	x		x
	Light passes	Single pass			0	0	0	0		x	x	x	0				x	x	x		x	x	x	x
		Multiple passes			x	x	x	x	x				x	x	x					x				
SELECTOR SYSTEM	*Monochromator*	Silica prism				x	x				x												x	x
		Quartz prism							x															
		Diffraction grating		x	x			x	0	x		x	x	x	x	x	x	x	x		x	x		
	Operation	Single channel		x	x	x	x	x	x	x	x	x	x		x		x				x	x	x	x
		Multichannel												x						x				
PHOTOMETRIC SYSTEM	*Detector*	Photomultiplier			x	x	x	x	x	x	x	x	x	x	x	x	x	x	x	x	x	x	x	x
		Red sensitive phototube				x																		
		Red sensitive photomultiplier			0	0	0	0	0															
	Amplifier	D.c.		x		x																		
		A.c.			x		x	x	x	x	x		x	x	x	x	x	x	x		x	x	x	x
	Operation	Single-beam		x	x	x	x	x	x	x	x	x	x	x	x	x	x		x		x	x	x	x
		Double-beam																x		x				
	Read-out	Meter		x	x		x	x		x	x	x	x	x	x		x		x		x	x	x	
		Null-balance				x												x		x				
		Galvanometer							x															x
		Recorder (or other)			0	0	0	0	0	0	0		0	0	0	x	0	0	0		0	0	0	0
	Scale expansion	Available							x		x		x				x	x	x				x	0
		Only with recorder			x	x	x	x					0		x						0			
	Damping				0	0	0	0	x		x		x		x		x	0	0				x	x
	Internal standard													x										

x applicable
0 also applicable

the detector. The light beam is modulated with a chopper and the a.c. amplifier is tuned to the same frequency.

Instrument described by Sullivan and Walsh. See details in Chapter 9, Section 3.

Instrument described by Thilliez (*769*). An air–butane flame is used but can be replaced by an air–acetylene flame for greater sensitivity. Background emission is eliminated by coating the inner surface of the hollow-cathode lamp with a thin film of magnesium (volatilized by heating the cathode). The width of the incident beam can be adjusted so that the image is focused completely inside the flame. Thilliez has used this instrument to measure magnesium in zinc chloride, high-purity molybdenum and chromium, fertilizers and phosphates; calcium, chromium, manganese, cobalt, nickel, copper and zinc in zincblende and in catalysts for methanol production; rhodium in platinum–rhodium alloys; silver, cadmium, platinum and gold; lead in gas–line and in the air of lead fabrication plants.

Instrument described by Warren (*808*). The instrument has a modified sprayer-burner described by Warren and a Littrow system as a monochromator.

2. COMMERCIAL INSTRUMENTS

Many of the home-made instruments have been built from existing commercial instruments, particularly monochromators, sprayers and burners; the use of Beckman, Evans Electroselenium, Hilger and Zeiss equipment has been mentioned in many publications. A simple instrument, the Si-ro-spec instrument, designed solely for sodium and potassium analysis, was described some years ago (*108*).

At present a variety of commercial instruments are available. Some summarized information about them is included in this section.

Atomic-Absorption and Electronics Corporation. This company has announced an instrument known as *Atomic-Absorption Spectrophotometer Model 100,* distributed by National Instrument Laboratories, Inc.[7]. Details are given in Tables 11–1 and 11–2.

Beckman Instruments, Inc. This company[8] manufactures an *Atomic-Absorption Accessory* for Ultraviolet Spectrophotometers, in two models (Nos. 1300 and 1301) respectively for Beckman DU and DU-2 spectro-

[7] Atomic-Absorption and Electronics Corporation. 50 Broadway, New York 4, N. Y., U.S.A.; National Instrument Laboratories, Inc., 12 300 Parklawn Drive, Rockville, Md., U.S.A. See reference (*58*).

[8] Beckman Instruments, Inc., 2500 Harbor Boulevard, Fullerton, Calif., U.S.A.

TABLE 11-2
COMMERCIAL INSTRUMENTS.
ATOMIC ABSORPTION AND ELECTRONICS CORPORATION
(NATIONAL INSTRUMENTS LABORATORIES, INC.) MODEL 100

EMISSION SYSTEM	*Power supply*	Type	A.c.
		Modulation	Pulsating d.c.
		Current range	0–100 mA RMS
	Lamps	Type	Hollow-cathode lamps
		Operation	
ABSORPTION SYSTEM	*Sprayer and burner*	Type	Total consumption
		Operation	
		Slot dimensions	
		Adjustment	
	Gases (see Table 11-1)		
	Light passes		
SELECTION SYSTEM		Type	Grating monochromator 600 line/mm
		Range	2000–9000 Å
		Band pass	
		Slit	30–2000 microns
		Operation	Single beam Single channel
PHOTOMETRIC SYSTEM	*Detectors*		
	Read-out scale		Full scale Zero suppression
	Accessories		
EMISSION FLAME PHOTOMETRY			

TABLE 11-3 COMMERCIAL INSTRUMENTS

MODEL			MODEL 979 ATOMIC ABSORPTION SPECTROPHOTOMETER (97900)	
EMISSION SYSTEM	*Power supply*	Type	Current stabilized Three channels	
		Modulation	Chopper	
		Current range	4–40 mA	
	Lamps	Type	Beckman or any cylindrical hollow cathode lamps Vapor discharge lamps	
		Operation	Two lamps in stand-by Pre-aligned holders	
ABSORPTION SYSTEM	*Sprayer and burner*	Type	Turbulent flow burner Direct feeding	Laminar flow burner Direct feeding
		Operation	Can be used with oxygen or air sheath. 1–3 burners	Heated chamber cold or hot operation Solvent condenser
		Slot dimensions		10 cm
		Adjustment	Pre-aligned Precision height adjustment	
	Gases (see Table 11-1)		Air–hydrogen Air–acetylene Oxygen–hydrogen Oxygen–acetylene	Air–acetylene Air–propane Air–nat. gas N_2O–acetylene
	Light passes		Single or triple pass	
SELECTION SYSTEM		Type	Diffraction grating 1200 line mm, blazed at 2500 Å	
		Range	1900–7700 Å **	
		Band pass	2.5 Å for all wavelengths (at 0.1 mm slit)	
		Slit	Continuously variable up to 2 mm	
		Operation	Single beam Single channel	
PHOTOMETRIC SYSTEM	*Detectors*		RCA 1P28-A	
	Read-out scale		Linear transmission Functional absorbance	
	Accessories		Recorder Can be connected to digital read-out or printer	
EMISSION FLAME PHOTOMETRY			It can be switched to emission. Built-in motor driven scanning of spectra	

* According to information kindly supplied by Beckman Instruments Inc.
** Up to 8521 Å with optional red sensitive photomultiplier.

ECKMAN INSTRUMENTS, INC.*

IODEL 1300, WITH DU OR DU-2 TOMIC-ABSORPTION ACCESSORY		MODEL 1301, WITH DB OR DB-G ATOMIC-ABSORPTION ACCESSORY	
urrent stabilized hree channels		Current stabilized Three channels	
one		Chopper	
-40 mA		4–40 mA	
eckman or any cylindrical hollow cathode lamps apor discharge lamps		Beckman or any cylindrical hollow cathode lamps. Vapor discharge lamps	
wo lamps in stand-by re-aligned holders		Two lamps in stand-by Pre-aligned holders	
urbulent flow burner irect feeding	Laminar flow burner Direct feeding	Turbulent flow burner Direct feeding	Laminar flow burner Direct feeding
an be used with oxygen or air sheath. 1–3 burners	Heated chamber, cold or hot operation Solvent condenser	Can be used with oxygen or air sheath. 1–3 burners	Heated chamber, cold or hot operation Solvent condenser
	10 cm		10 cm
re-aligned recision height adjustment		Pre-aligned Precision height adjustment.	
ir–hydrogen ir–acetylene xygen–hydrogen xygen–acetylene	Air–acetylene Air–propane Air–nat. gas N_2O–acetylene	Air–hydrogen Air–acetylene Oxygen–hydrogen Oxygen–acetylene	Air–acetylene Air–propane Air–nat. gas N_2O–acetylene
ngle or triple pass		Single or triple pass	
lica prism		DB: Silica prism. DB-G: Diffraction grating 1200 line/mm. blazed at 2500 Å	
00–10000 Å		DB: 2050–7700 Å DB-G: 1900–7700 Å**	
bout 3 Å (1250 to 3250 Å) bout 10 Å (3250 to 7900 Å) (at 0.1 mm slit)		DB: About 5 Å (2050 to 3250 Å) About 15 Å (3250 to 8500 Å) DB-G: 2.5 Å for all wavelengths (at 0.1 mm slit)	
ontinuously variable up to 2 mm		Continuously variable up to 2 mm	
ngle beam ngle channel		Single beam Single channel	
CA 1P28 Photomultiplier ed phototube. R-136 Red sensitive photomultiplier (Optional)		RCA 1P28-A Photomultiplier R-136 Red sensitive photomultiplier (optional)	
near transmission unctional absorbance		Linear transmission Functional aborbance	
corder CRA an be connected to digital readout or printer.		Recorder Can be connected to digital readout or printer	
can be switched to emission.		It can be switched to emission. Some models with built-in motor driven scanning of spectra..	

TABLE 11-4
COMMERCIAL INSTRUMENTS.
CARL ZEISS* FA-2 AND EVANS ELECTROSELENIUM LTD. ** 140

MODEL			MODEL FA-2 WITH PMQII	MODEL 140
EMISSION SYSTEM	*Power supply*	Type	D.c. Current stabilized Single channel	Current stabilized Single channel
		Modulation	Chopper	Half wave rectification
		Current range	4–70 mA	0–30 mA
	Lamps	Type	Carl Zeiss or Westinghouse HC lamps	EEL or any cylindrical lamp
		Operation	Prealigned sockets Preset position with magnetic stops	Self-centering spring-loaded holders
ABSORPTION SYSTEM	*Sprayer and burner*	Type	Laminar flow burner Array of canulae, each 1.2 mm dia.	Laminar flow burner
		Operation	Tube feeding	Direct feeding
		Slot dimensions	Array 50 mm long	4" x 0.015"
		Adjustment	Preset	Only rotation Preset height
	Gases (see Table 11-1)		Acetylene, hydrogen, or propane and air or nitrous oxide	Air–acetylene
	Light passes		Triple pass	Single pass

SELECTION SYSTEM	Type	Quartz prism or grating (600 line/mm)	Diffraction grating (576 line/mm)
	Range	1850–25000 Å	2000–10000 Å
	Band pass		7 Å at 0.1 mm
	Slit	0.01–2.0 mm	Adjustable from 0.1 mm
	Operation	Single beam Single channel	Single beam Single channel
PHOTOMETRIC SYSTEM	*Detectors*	RCA 1P28 or HTV–R136	Photomultiplier
	Read-out scale	Linear transmission	Logarithmic circular scale
	Accessories	Recorder	Recorder Built in damping Can be connected to digital read-out
EMISSION FLAME PHOTOMETRY		It can be switched to emission	

* According to information kindly supplied by Carl Zeiss.
** According to information kindly supplied by Evans Electroselenium Ltd.

TABLE 11-5
COMMERCIAL INSTRUMENTS.
HILGER AND WATTS LTD.* H 1150 AND HITACHI LTD. 139

MODEL			H 1150 Model AAII	Model 139-0420 with 139
EMISSION SYSTEM	*Power supply*	Type	Single or multiple channel Stabilized	A.c.
		Modulation	400 cps	
		Current range	5–30 mA	
	Lamps	Type	Hilger and Watts or other	Hollow-cathode lamps
		Operation	Turret Two co-ordinate alignments	
ABSORPTION SYSTEM	*Sprayer and burner*	Type	Laminar flow burner	Laminar flow burner
		Operation	Tube feeding Cooled head	
		Slot dimensions	0.020" x 4.75"	
		Adjustment	Pre-aligned Rotation and height adjustment	
	Gases (see Table 11-1)		Air–propane Air–acetylene	Air–acetylene
	Light passes		Single pass	Single pass

SELECTION SYSTEM		Type	30° Littrow fused silica prism	139 Hitachi spectrophotometer
		Range	1850–8500 Å	
		Band pass	Selectable	
		Slit		
		Operation	Single beam Single channel	Single beam Single channel
PHOTOMETRIC SYSTEM	*Detectors*		EMI Photomultiplier 6256	Photomultiplier
	Read-out scale		Linear absorption	
	Accessories		Recorder	
EMISSION FLAME PHOTOMETRY			Attachment	

* According to information kindly supplied by Hilger and Watts Ltd.

TABLE 11-6
COMMERCIAL INSTRUMENTS
JARREL-ASH COMPANY

MODEL			MODEL 82500		MODEL 82600	MODEL 82700
EMISSION SYSTEM	*Power supply*	Type	Single channel Stabilized		Four channel Stabilized	Single channel Stabilized
		Modulation	Rectified (chopper) or pulsed		Pulsed	Pulsed
		Current range	0–25 mA		0–25 A	0–25 mA
	Lamps	Type	Westinghouse		Westinghouse	Westinghouse
		Operation	Turret		Preset lamps	Pre-aligned sockets
ABSORPTION SYSTEM	*Sprayer and burner*	Type	Laminar flow burner	Turbulent flow burner	Turbulent flow burner	Turbulent flow burner
		Operation	Direct feeding	Direct feeding	Direct feeding	Tube feeding
		Slot dimensions	0.020" x 10cm or 0.020" x 5cm for N_2O			
		Adjustment	Alignment, rotation, height	Height	Height	Height
	Gases (see Table 11-1)		Air–acetylene N_2O–acetylene	Air or oxygen and acetylene or hydrogen	Air or oxygen and acetylene or hydrogen	Air–oxygen
	Light passes		Single	5 Passes	5 Passes	4 Passes

SELECTION SYSTEM	Type	Half meter Eber grating spectrometer	3/4 meter Eagle concave polychromator	1/4 meter Czerny Turner grating spectrometer
	Range	1900–6700 Å With two gratings: 1900–8000 Å	1900–4300 Å (2nd order) 3800–8600 Å (1st order).	2900–8000 Å
	Band pass	2 Å	0.5 Å (2nd order) 1 Å (1st order)	4 Å
	Slit	Interchangeable fixed slits	75 microns entrance 100 microns exit	100 micron fixed slit
	Operation	Single beam Single channel	Two tandem by-pass systems. Internal standard compensation	Single beam Single channel
PHOTOMETRIC SYSTEM	*Detectors*	9 Dynode photomultiplier	Individual photomultiplier	9 Dynode photomultiplier
	Read-out scale	6'' meter	Individual 8'' projection meter	6'' meter
	Accessories	Recorder Direct conc.reader printer	Digital voltmeter Direct concentration reader and print-out	Recorder Direct concentration reader and printer
EMISSION FLAME PHOTOMETRY		It can be switched to emission	Used as standard for alkalies and other sensitive elements to emission	Used as standard for alkalies and other sensitive elements to emission

* According to information kindly supplied by Jarrel-Ash Company.

TABLE 11-7
COMMERCIAL INSTRUMENTS.
JOBIN-YVON* AND OPTICA S.p.A. ** DENSATOMIC

MODEL				Densatomic
EMISSION SYSTEM	*Power supply*	Type	Stabilized Multichannel	Stabilized Single channel
		Modulation		Chopper
		Current range		5–40 mA
	Lamps	Type	Hollow-cathode lamps	Fivre-Optica water cooled lamps or any other hollow-cathode lamp
		Operation		Vapor discharge lamps Auto aligned
ABSORPTION SYSTEM	*Sprayer and burner*	Type	Laminar flow burner Cooled head	Laminar flow burner
		Operation		Tube or forced feeding
		Slot dimensions		50 mm
		Adjustment		Adjustable Height adjustment
	Gases (see Table 11-1)		Acetylene or propane	Any conventional combination
	Light passes			Single pass

SELECTION SYSTEM		Type	Grating monochromator	Stigmatic plane grating monochromator
		Range	1850–8000 Å	2000–10000 Å
		Band pass		0.2–1.0 mμ approx.
		Slit	Variable	Continously adjustable
		Operation	Single beam	Single beam Single channel
PHOTOMETRIC SYSTEM	*Detectors*		Photomultiplier	Photomultiplier
	Read-out scale			Laminar absorbance circular scale
	Accessories		Recorder	Recorder Digital printer Direct concentration reader
EMISSION FLAME PHOTMETRY			It can be used for emission	It can be switched to emission

* According to information kindly supplied by Jobin-Yvon.
** According to information kindly supplied by Optica S.p.A.

TABLE 11-8
COMMERCIAL INSTRUMENTS.
PERKIN-ELMER CORPORATION (THE)*

MODEL			MODEL 303	MODEL 290
EMISSION SYSTEM	*Power supply*	Type	Single channel Current stabilized	Single channel Voltage stabilized
		Modulation	Rotating chopper with mirror	A.c. lamp current
		Current range	0–50 mA	0–25 mA
	Lamps	Type	P–E, ASL, Westinghouse Vapor discharge lamps	P–E, ASL, Westinghouse Vapor discharge lamps
		Operation	Pre-aligned holders	Pre-aligned holders Standby oper. for 3 lamps
ABSORPTION SYSTEM	*Sprayer and burner*	Type	Laminar flow burner	Laminar flow burner
		Operation	Tube feeding	Tube feeding
		Slot dimensions	Up to 10 cm	Up to 10 cm
		Adjustment	Adjustable alignment and height	Adjustable alignment and height
	Gases (see Table 11-1)		Acetylene, hydrogen or LPG and air or N_2O	Acetylene, hydrogen or LPG and air or N_2O
	Light passes		Single pass	Single pass

SELECTION SYSTEM		Type	Grating monochromator	Grating monochromator
		Range	1900–8521 Å	2000–8500 Å
		Band pass	0.7–40 Å	2–40 Å
		Slit	Adjustable	
		Operation	Double beam Single channel	Single beam Single channel
PHOTOMETRIC SYSTEM	*Detectors*		EMI 9529P photomultiplier	RCA 1P28 photomultiplier
	Read-out scale		Linear absorption	Linear absorbance
	Accessories		Recorder	Direct concentration scales
EMISSION FLAME PHOTOMETRY			Attachment	

* According to information kindly supplied by The Perkin-Elmer Corporation.

photometers and for Beckman DB and DB-G spectrophotometers[9]. Details are given in Tables 11–1 and 11–3. This company also manufactures the *Model 979 Atomic Absorption Spectrophotometer.*

Carl Zeiss. This company[10] manufactures the *Flame Spectrophotometer* Model PQM II - FA 2. Details are given in Tables 11–1 and 11–4.

Evans Electroselenium Ltd. The *Atomic-Absorption Spectrophotometer* Model 140 is manufactured by Evans Electroselenium Limited[11]. Details are given in Tables 11–1 and 11–4.

Hilger and Watts, Ltd. Hilger and Watts Ltd.[12] manufactures the instrument H. 1150 Model AAII. Details are given in Tables 11–1 and 11–5.

Hitachi Ltd. Hitachi Ltd. manufactures the attachment No. 139-0420 for the spectrophotometer model No. 139[13]. Details are given in Tables 11–1 and 11–5.

Jarrell-Ash Company. Three instruments are manufactured by the Jarrell-Ash Company[14]: *Maximum versatility Atomic-Absorption Unit,* Model 82-500; *Multi-element Atomic-Absorption Flame Emission Spectrometer,* Model 82-600; and *Control Atomic-Absorption Unit,* Model 82-700. See details in Tables 11–1 and 11–6.

Jobin-Yvon. Jobin-Yvon[15] have in production an *Atomic-Absorption Instrument.* Some preliminary information on this unit is included in Tables 11–1 and 11–7.

Optica S. p. A. A compact instrument was offered by Optica, the Model AT-6 (*537*), and also an attachment to the CF-4 Optica grating spectrophotometer (Optica ATA atomic-absorption accessory). At present, Optica produces the *Densatomic - Atomic-Absorption and Flame Analysis Spectro-*

---

[9] The general characteristics of Beckman equipment and of one of the Perkin-Elmer instruments have been discussed briefly in the pages of *Analytical Chemistry* (*55*). The new models of Beckman, Perkin-Elmer, Jarrell-Ash, Techtron, and Hilger and Watts have been discussed in an article published in *Chemical and Engineering News* (*883*)—the same journal had also published comments on commercial instruments in 1960 (*24*). A description of Beckman's atomic-absorption accessory and of the two burner systems which are offered (laminar flow burner and turbulent flow burner) is included in reference (71). Hell *et al.* (*313–316*), Manning (*464, 465*), and Ulrich and Shifrin (*784*) have published data on the physical and analytico-chemical performance of the Beckman instruments; the laminar flow burner, along with characteristic performance data, has been discussed in detail by Hell (*311*). See also references (*71–76, 540, 668, 884, 892*).

[10] Carl Zeiss, Oberkochen, Württemberg, Germany. See references (*903, 930*).

[11] Evans Electroselenium Ltd. St. Andrews Works, Halstead, Essex, England. See references (*33, 152, 219, 220, 881*).

[12] Hilger and Watts Ltd. 98 St. Pancras Way, London, N. W. 1, England. See references (*50, 333–343*).

[13] Hitachi Ltd., New Marunouchi Building. 4, 1-Chome, Marunouchi. Chiyoda-ku, Tokyo, Japan. See references (*889, 916*).

[14] Jarrell-Ash Company. 590 Lincoln Street, at Route 128, Waltham, Mass., U.S.A. Abundant information on the Jarrell-Ash instruments can be found in the publications by Brech (*112–114*). See also references (*362–366, 533, 755, 898*).

[15] Jobin-Yvon, 26 rue Berthollet, Arcueil (Seine), France.

TABLE 11-9
COMMERCIAL INSTRUMENTS.
RESEARCH AND CONTROL INSTRUMENTS

MISSION SYSTEM	*Power supply*	Type	Multichannel
		Modulation	
		Current range	
	Lamps	Type	Several H.C. lamps positioned
		Operation	
BSORPTION SYSTEM	*Sprayer and burner*	Type	Laminar flow burner
		Operation	
		Slot dimensions	
		Adjustment	
	Gases (see Table 11-1)		
	Light passes		Double pass
ELECTION SYSTEM		Type	Grating monochromator 1 meter 36000 lines/inch
		Range	
		Band pass	
		Slit	
		Operation	Double beam Multichannel
HOTOMETRIC SYSTEM	*Detectors*		Photomultiplier
	Read-out scale		Linear transmission
	Accessories		
MISSION FLAME PHOTOMETRY			

TABLE 11-10
COMMERCIAL INSTRUMENTS.
TECHTRON PTY. LTD*

MODEL			MODEL A-100	MODEL AA-3
EMISSION SYSTEM	*Power supply*	Type	Stabilized Multiple channel	Stabilized Multiple channel
		Modulation	Modulated lamp current	Modulated lamp current
		Current range	0–12.5 mA	0–25 mA
	Lamps	Type	ASL Wotan vapor discharge lamps	ASL Wotan vapor discharge lamps
		Operation	Pre-aligned	Pre-aligned
ABSORPTION SYSTEM	*Sprayer and burner*	Type	Laminar flow burner	Laminar flow burner
		Operation	Tube feeding	Tube feeding
		Slot dimensions	4" x 0.02" 4" x 0.06" 2" x 0.018"	4" x 0.02" 4" x 0.06" 2" x 0.018"
		Adjustment	Adjustable, alignment, rotation, height	Adjustable, alignment, rotation height
	Gases (see Table 11-1)		Acetylene, hydrogen, propane or coal gas and air or N_2O	Acetylene, hydrogen, propane or coal gas and air or N_2O
	Light passes		Single pass	Single pass

SELECTION SYSTEM	Type	Grating monochromator 638 l/min 0.25 meter Ebert	Grating monochromator 638 l/min 0.5 meter Ebert
	Range	1860–10000 Å	1860–10000 Å
	Band pass		0.3–9.9 Å
	Slit	Fixed	Variable
	Operation	Single beam Single channel	Single beam Single channel
PHOTOMETRIC SYSTEM	*Detectors*	Photomultiplier	Photomultiplier
	Read-out scale	Linear intensity	Linear intensity
	Accessories	Recorder	Recorder
EMISSION FLAME PHOTOMETRY			Attachment

*According to information kindly supplied by Techtron Pty. Ltd.

TABLE 11-11
COMMERCIAL INSTRUMENTS.
UNICAM INSTRUMENTS LTD.*

MODEL			MODEL SP 90	MODEL SP 900A
EMISSION SYSTEM	*Power supply*	Type	Stabilized Single channel	Stabilized Single channel
		Modulation	Modulated at line frequency by an interrupted d.c. supply	Chopper
		Current range	0–25 mA	0–25 mA
	Lamps	Type	Unicam, ASL	Unicam, ASL
		Operation	Pre-aligned turret for 3 lamps	
ABSORPTION SYSTEM	*Sprayer and burner*	Type	Laminar flow burner	Laminar flow burner
		Operation	Tube feeding	Tube feeding
		Slot dimensions	10 cm (Meker head for emission)	7 cm (Meker head for emission)
		Adjustment	Adjustable, rotation, height	Adjustable, height
	Gases (see Table 11-1)		Air–propane or Air–acetylene or N_2O–acetylene	Air–propane or Air–acetylene or N_2O–acetylene
	Light passes		Single pass	Single pass

SELECTION SYSTEM		Type	Prism monochromator	Prism monochromator
		Range	2100–7700 Å	2000–8500 Å
		Band pass	6Å at 2500 Å, 45Å at 4500 Å, 125Å at 6500 Å } 0.1 mm slit	4Å at 2500 Å, 30Å at 4500 Å, 85Å at 6500 Å } 0.1 mm slit
		Slit	Variable 0–2 mm	Variable 0–2 mm
		Operation	Single beam Single channel	Single beam Single channel
PHOTOMETRIC SYSTEM	*Detectors*		Photomultiplier	Photomultiplier
	Read-out scale		Linear intensity	Linear intensity
	Accessories		Recorder Sample changer	Recorder
EMISSION FLAME PHOTOMETRY			Built in as standard	Emission is standard mode of operation; wavelength-drive motor for scanning spectra

* According to information kindly supplied by Unicam Instruments Ltd.

photometer[16]. Details are given in Tables 11–1 and 11–7.

Perkin-Elmer. The Perkin-Elmer Corporation[17] produced the Perkin-Elmer atomic-absorption spectrophotometer Model 214[18]. At present this company manufactures two *Atomic-Absorption Spectrophotometers*, Models 303 and 290. Details are given in Tables 11–1 and 11–8.

Research and Control Instruments, Inc. Details of the *Atomic-Absorption Spectrophotometer* developed by this company[19] are given in Tables 11–1 and 11–9.

Techtron Pty. Ltd. This firm[20] initially sold their atomic-absorption spectrophotometer Model M 1. At present, it manufactures two *Atomic-Absorption Spectrophotometers*, Models AA100 and AA3, details of which are given in Tables 11–1 and 11–10.

Unicam Instruments Ltd. Two *Atomic-Absorption/Flame Emission Spectrophotometers* Models SP90 and SP900A are manufactured[21]. Details are given in Tables 11–1 and 11–11.

---

16 Optica S. p. A. Via Gargano, 21, Milan, Italy. See references (*117, 536*).

17 The Perkin-Elmer Corporation, Norwalk, Conn., U.S.A. For description on performance and operation of these instruments and their accessories, consult references (*29, 41, 52, 53, 85, 89, 259, 374, 376, 383, 385, 458, 550–553, 711, 893, 918, 943, 944*).

18 The Model 214 has been described in detail in the book by Mavrodineanu and Boiteux (*479*). See also ref. (*549*).

19 Research and Control Instruments, Inc. Woburn, Mass., U.S.A. (A subsidiary of Epsco Inc., Westwood, Mass., U.S.A.). This instrument has been described in the book by Mavrodineanu and Boiteux (*479*).

20 Techtron Pty. Ltd. 271 Huntingdale Road, East Oakleigh, S. E. 12, Vic., Australia. See references (*60, 61, 766, 880*).

21 Unicam Instruments Inc. York Street, Cambridge, England. See references (*571, 785*).

PART III

RANGE AND LIMITATIONS OF ATOMIC-ABSORPTION METHODS

Chapter 12

Determinable elements. Choice of lines

The range of elements (mostly metals) which can be determined by the atomic-absorption process is quite wide. As long as the element, in the form of an atomic vapor, produces a measurable absorption, the atomic-absorption process can generally be utilized as a *direct* determination[1].

Chemical species which cannot be measured directly, can be determined if they act in some way to *inhibit* or enhance quantitatively the response of an element for which a direct method of measurement is available. An example would be the determination of an anionic radical which produces an insoluble precipitate with a determinable metal. With a constant quantity of metallic element, the anion would precipitate a fraction of that element, and the excess could be determined in the supernatant solution after centrifuging. Sulfates, with barium as background element, and chlorides, bromides, and iodides with silver are typical examples of *indirect* procedures in atomic-absorption. These procedures involving precipitation can be considered as cases of inhibition (inhibition by precipitation). There are also cases of inhibition in which a compound resistant to dissociation in the flame is formed.

1. DETERMINABLE ELEMENTS

The number of elements which can be determined by atomic-absorption has grown in the last few years. Although the method was initially confined to a few elements, the availability of adequate sources and of procedures for achieving conversion into free atoms has notably enlarged the list of elements that can be determined.

Table 12–1 lists the elements which at present are considered as suitable for atomic-absorption measurements. Some of these elements may present

---

[1] The methods are readily seen as *direct* if only the *absorptions* (percent of absorption) are considered, since the absorption *increases* as the concentration of the analyte increases; moreover, the concentration of the analyte is measured *directly by its immediate effects*.

The word *indirect* should be used when the analyte does not intervene in the process of absorption, its effects being measured by its action on a determinable element.

TABLE 12-1
ELEMENTS SUITABLE FOR DIRECT ATOMIC-ABSORPTION MEASUREMENT

	Ia	*IIa*	*IIIb*	*IVb*	*Vb*	*VIb*	*VIIb*	*VIII*			*Ib*	*IIb*	*IIIa*	*IVa*	*Va*	*VIa*	*VIIa*	*Inert Gases*
1	H																	He
2	Li	Be											B	C	N	O	F	Ne
3	Na	Mg											Al	Si	P	S	Cl	Ar
4	K	Ca	Sc	Ti	V	Cr	Mn	Fe	Co	Ni	Cu	Zn	Ga	Ge	As	Se	Br	Kr
5	Rb	Sr	Y	Zr	Nb	Mo	Tc	Ru	Rh	Pd	Ag	Cd	In	Sn	Sb	Te	I	Xe
6	Cs	Ba	La	Hf	Ta	W	Re	Os	Ir	Pt	Au	Hg	Tl	Pb	Bi	Po	At	Rn
7	Fr	Ra	Ac															
R.E.				Ce	Pr	Nd	Pm	Sm	Eu	Gd	Tb	Dy	Ho	Er	Tm	Yb	Lu	
A.E.				Th	Pa	U	Np	Pu	Am	Cm	Bk	Cf	Es	Fm	Md	No	Lw	

TABLE 12-2
ELEMENTS WHICH PRESENT CHARACTERISTICS
SUITABLE FOR EMISSION FLAME PHOTOMETRY

	Ia	*IIa*	*IIIb*	*IVb*	*Vb*	*VIb*	*VIIb*	*VIII*			*Ib*	*IIb*	*IIIa*	*IVa*	*Va*	*VIa*	*VIIa*	*Inert Gases*
1	H																	He
2	Li	Be											B	C	N	O	F	Ne
3	Na	Mg											Al	Si	P	S	Cl	Ar
4	K	Ca	Sc	Ti	V	Cr	Mn	Fe	Co	Ni	Cu	Zn	Ga	Ge	As	Se	Br	Kr
5	Rb	Sr	Y	Zr	Nb	Mo	Tc	Ru	Rh	Pd	Ag	Cd	In	Sn	Sb	Te	I	Xe
6	Cs	Ba	La	Hf	Ta	W	Re	Os	Ir	Pt	Au	Hg	Tl	Pb	Bi	Po	At	Rn
7	Fr	Ra	Ac															
R.E.				Ce	Pr	Nd	Pm	Sm	Eu	Gd	Tb	Dy	Ho	Er	Tm	Yb	Lu	
A.E.				Th	Pa	U	Np	Pu	Am	Cm	Bk	Cf	Es	Fm	Md	No	Lw	

difficulties with some instruments because of limited wavelength intervals.

Table 12–1 should be compared with Table 12–2, in which are included those elements that can be determined by emission flame photometry.

2. CHOICE OF LINES

Several criteria have been followed for the choice of lines for atomic-absorption work.

(a) Resonance lines should be studied from two points of view: (1) whether these analyte lines show the greatest absorption effects (compared with other lines of the same analyte), and (2) whether they are affected by interferences.

(b) Choice of those lines which are the most intense in emission. This is not always the best way. In the case of the alkali metals, for instance, the greatest absorption is obtained for the lines which offer the greatest sensitivity in emission. However, for elements with a more complicated spectrum, the line which responds best in atomic-absorption is not necessarily the same one that presents the greatest emission intensity.

In this respect Allan (*10*) has found that the nickel and cobalt lines, Ni 2320.0 Å and Co 2407.2 Å, produce more intense absorptions than the lines Ni 3414.8 Å and Co 3528 Å which are of maximum intensity in emission[2]. This example has also been discussed by David (*176*). Another typical example is given by the two copper lines Cu 3247.5 Å and Cu 3274.0 Å. Except in air–hydrogen flames, their intensities in emission are quite similar, but they behave quite differently in atomic-absorption. Allan (*15*) observed a two-fold increase in sensitivity for the line Cu 3247.5 Å (a concentration limit of 0.11 p.p.m. compared to 0.22 p.p.m. for the other line). Herrmann and Lang (*324*), measuring the emission of a hollow-cathode lamp (lamp spectrum), found greater intensity for the line Cu 3247.5 Å; and this copper line absorbed the radiations more strongly than the other. The results obtained by the present author with a Westinghouse multi-element lamp—Cu, Fe, Mn, Zn—, for the copper lines during spraying of a solution containing 1 p.p.m. Cu are shown in Fig. 12–1. The opposite effect was observed when the test was repeated for silver (Fig. 12–2); of the silver lines Ag 3280.7 Å and Ag 3382.9 Å from the lamp, the latter is more intense—as commonly observed in emission flame photometry—but the line Ag 3280.7 Å present stronger absorption.

---

[2] Comparative data on intensity of spectral lines in emission flame photometry is given by P. T. Gilbert in *Flame Spectra of the Elements* (2nd Ed.) Beckman Bulletin 753-A (1961) 28 p. The values of intensity given in the tables can easily be converted into conventional fluctuational concentration limits in p.p.m.

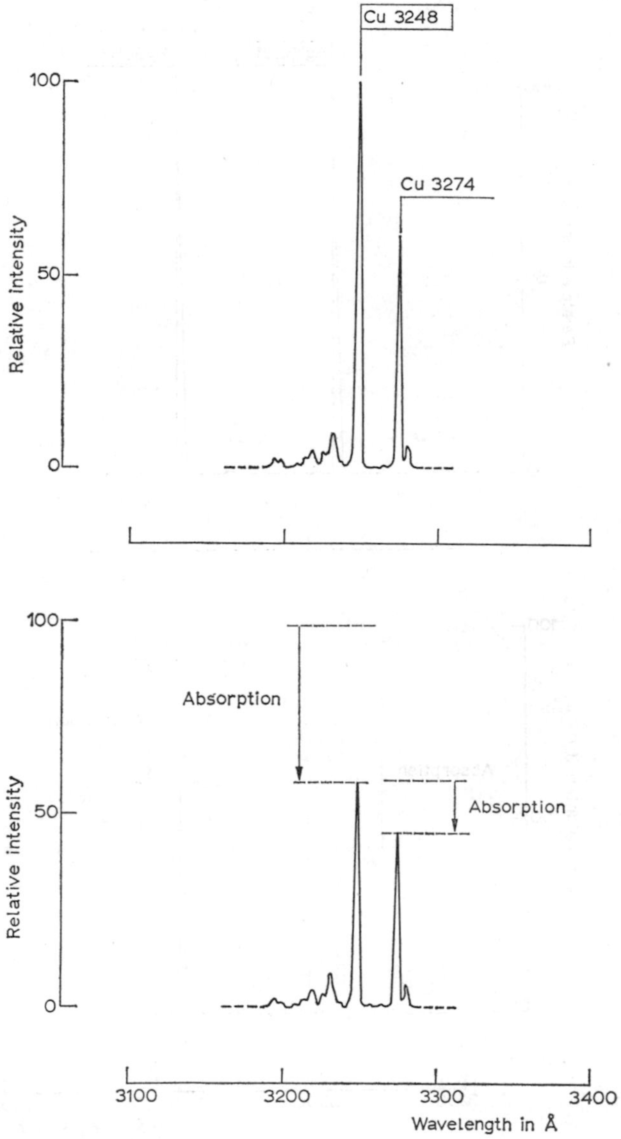

Fig. 12–1. Absorption of copper lines by aspiration of 1 p.p.m. Cu (BeckmanModel 979 atomic absorption spectrophotometer, 0.01-mm slit width; 10 mA).

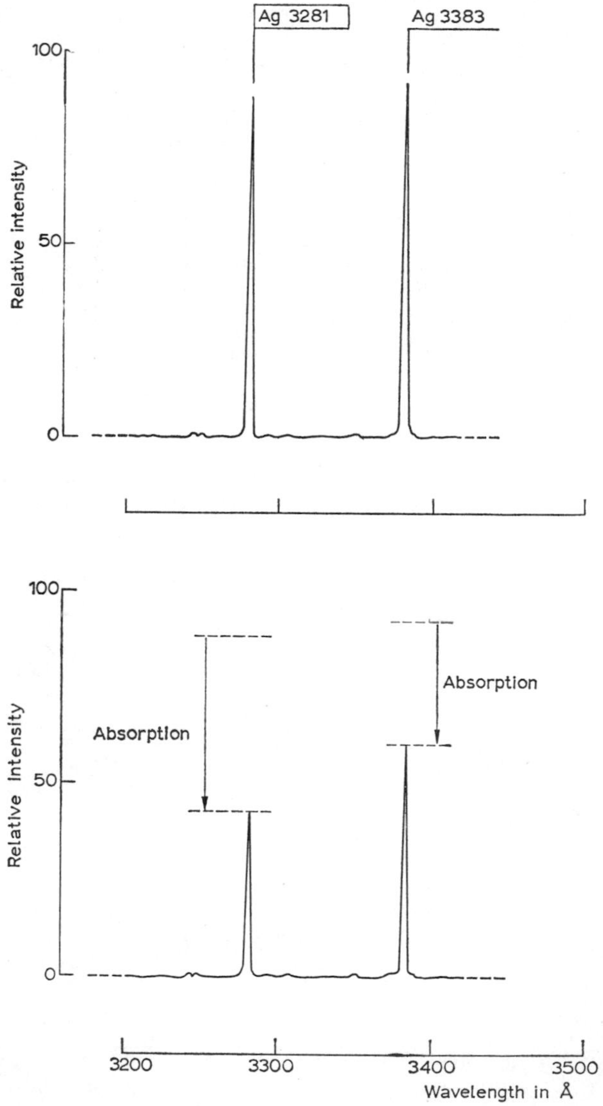

Fig. 12–2. Absorption of silver lines for aspiration of 1 p.p.m. Ag (Beckman Model 979 atomic-absorption spectrophotometer, 0.01-mm slit width, 10 mA).

(c) A study of the behaviour of the entire spectrum of the emitter. This is necessary to indicate the coincidence of other lines showing less or no absorption; serious difficulties may arise in isotopic analysis due to overlapping. This procedure is long and requires great care, but it provides definitive experimental data of great value in studying any new or unfamiliar problem. It is necessary to scan the emission spectrum of the emission source. Once this is known, a sample containing only the analyte is introduced into the atomic-absorption flame spectrophotometer and the experimental absorption for each analyte line is recorded. For these trials it may be necessary to work with solutions of fairly high concentration, and to use solutions of different concentrations, if the absorptions of the different lines differ too much.

Allan (*9*) recommends photographic recording (spectrographic inspection) of the complete spectrum—or at least an extensive portion of the spectrum within the interval of interest—determination of the absorptions by densitometric measurement.

The citeria mentioned above are particularly useful for home-made instruments. For commercial instruments recommendations on appropriate working conditions, sufficiently tested in advance, are normally available. However, these possibilities should be kept in mind for testing different conditions (for example, in looking for less sensitive lines in order to extend the range of concentrations).

2.1. Lines in the far ultraviolet

Some lines suitable for absorption appear in the far ultraviolet, but certain difficulties may prevent their use. Factors that can intervene, are (a) absorption by air, (b) absorption by the flame itself, (c) lack of an appropriate source, and (d) lack of transparency in the optical parts.

Factor (c) is due to the fact that in this region lines are emitted by elements for which it is difficult to use hollow-cathode lamps, either because the element is very volatile or because it melts at ordinary research temperatures. All these difficulties have been taken into account by Allan (*17*). He mentioned purging with nitrogen[3] and studied the transmission of different flames (hydrogen, acetylene, propane) in order to establish, in the region beyond 2000 Å, the flame most suitable for detecting the absorptions (absorptions due to the analytes in the fraction of light transmitted

[3] Kahn and Slavin (*384*) point out that elimination of the absorbing atmosphere by purging with nitrogen or argon falicitates the investigation of elements such as phosphorus and iodine, which have their resonance lines beyond 1950 Å. In addition, if the vacuum ultraviolet is reached, the analysis of molecular entities and non-metallic elements which have their resonance lines there, might be possible.

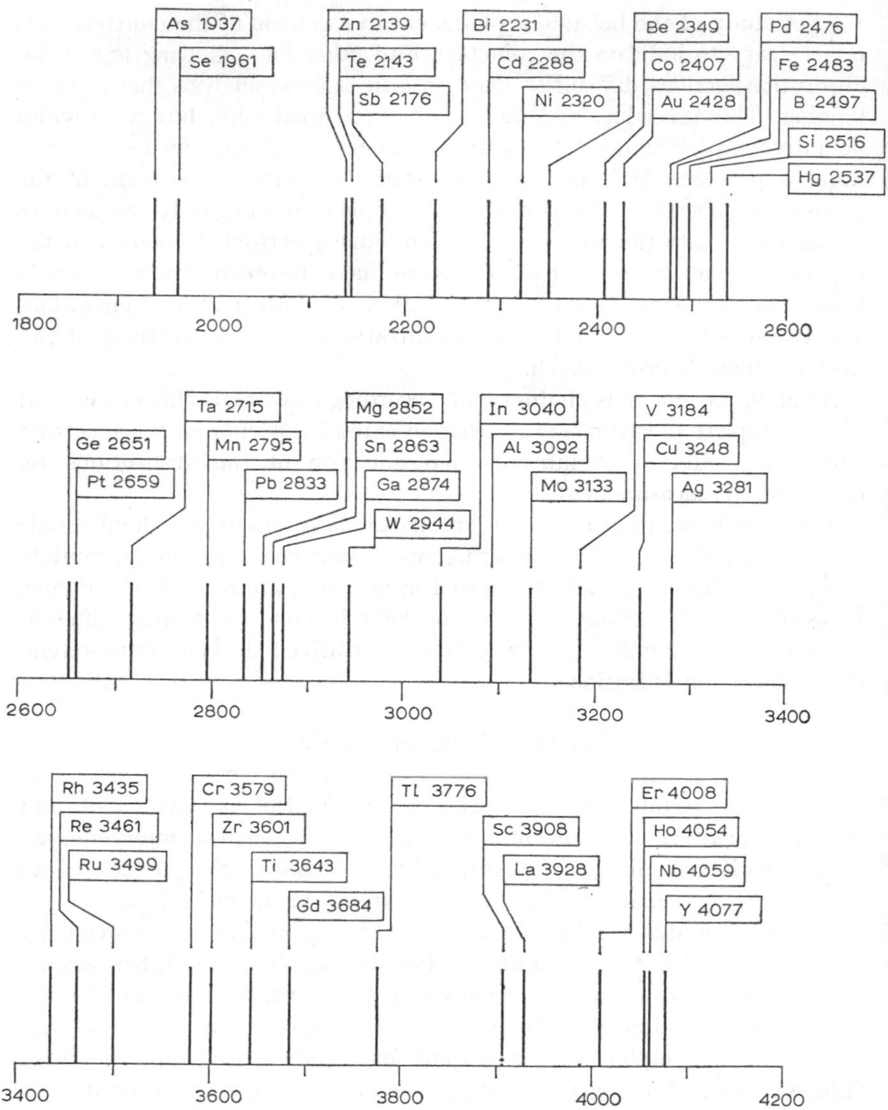

Fig. 12–3,I. Lines utilized in atomic-absorption (1800–4200 Å)[a].

---

[a] For other lines of the elements shown in these figures consult Tables 13-4 and 13-5, and data included in the Appendix.

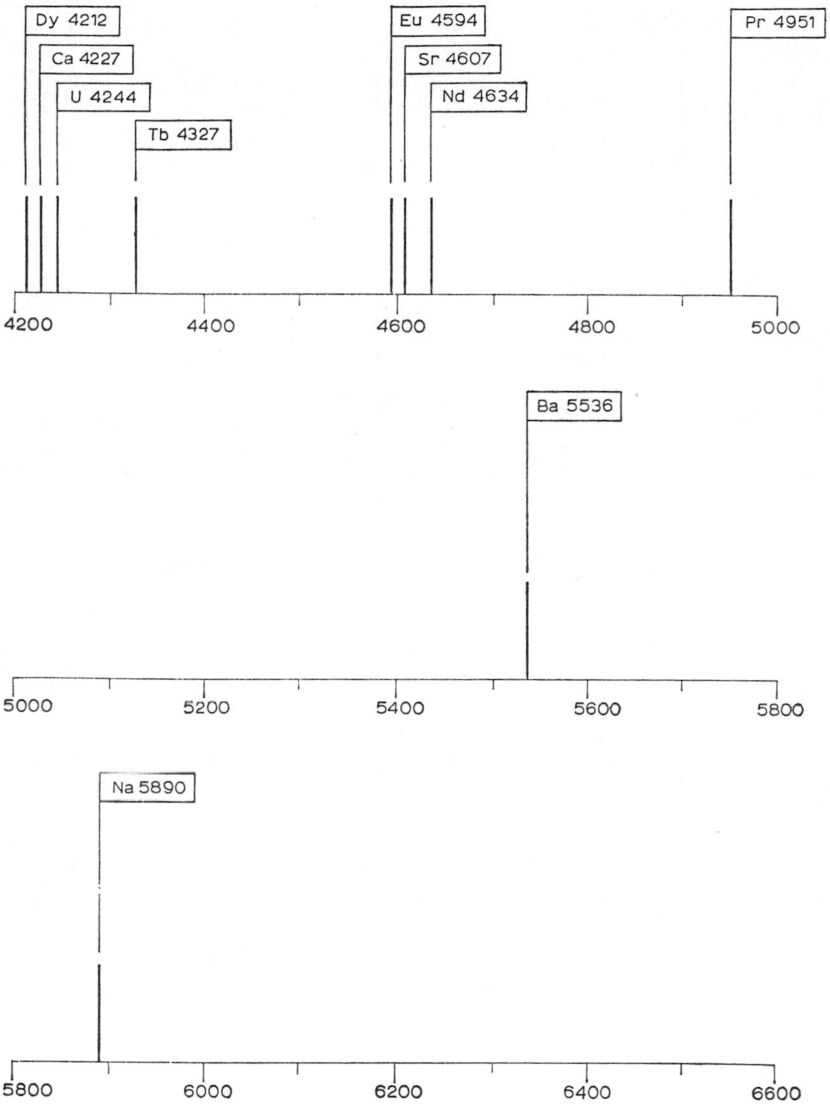

Fig. 12–3,II. Lines utilized in atomic-absorption (4200–6600 Å)[4].

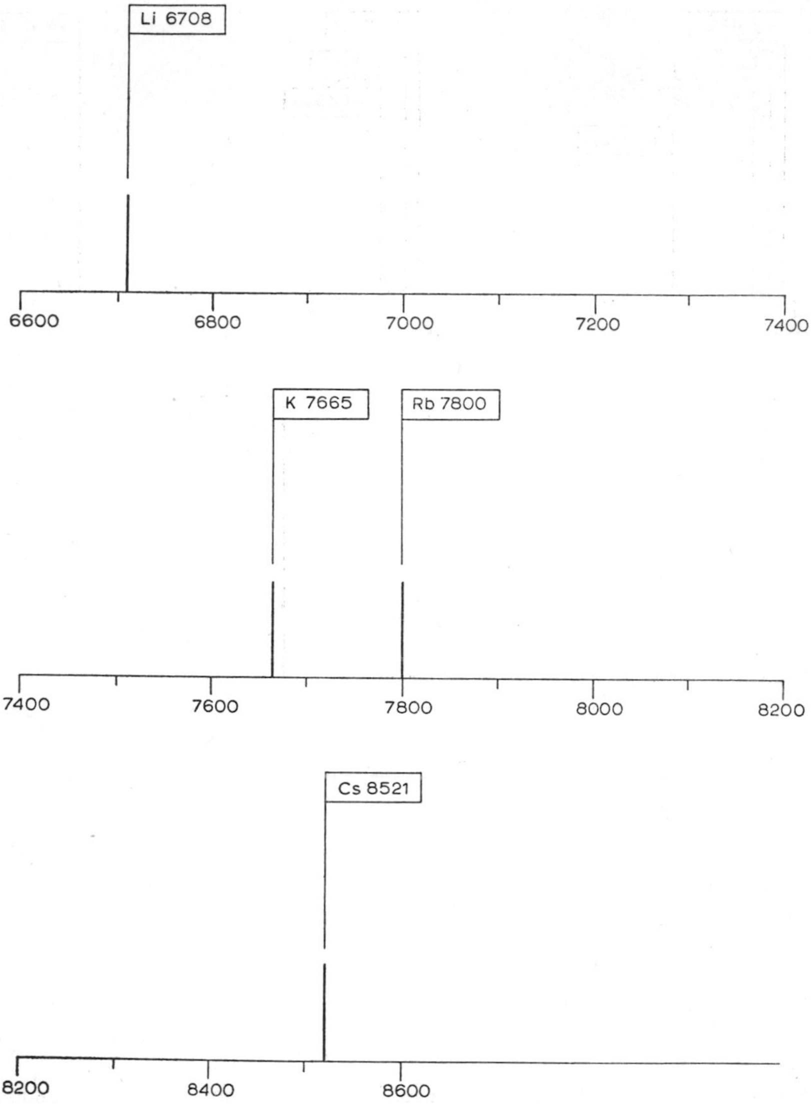

Fig. 12–3,III. Lines utilized in atomic-absorption (6600–8600 Å).

across the flame). Allan had to prepare special emitters (lamps with compounds of selenium, arsenic and mercury)[5] and achieved concentration limits of 0.4–0.5 p.p.m. for selenium and 1 p.p.m. for arsenic. A greater sensitivities could be obtained by means of long-path adapters; when the flame of a Beckman sprayer-burner was introduced into a tube (60 × 1 cm), PCL values of 0.015 p.p.m. for selenium (Se 1960 Å), 0.035 p.p.m. for arsenic (As 1970 Å) and 0.09 p.p.m. for mercury (Hg 2537 Å) were achieved. Allan indicated serious difficulties in the utilization of the line Hg 1849 Å, which would be expected to offer better possibilities than the line Hg 2537 Å, owing to its greater oscillator strength. Kaye (*389*) has published an interesting spectrum of mercury (mercury vapor), in which two absorption maxima can be clearly seen, the most intense being the farther into the ultraviolet.

2.2. *Bands*

Although some studies in molecular absorption have been made (*368, 519, 521–523*), no analytical applications have been proposed. A theoretical study of the absorption of discrete emission by molecular bands has been done by Plass (*556*). Walsh (*804*) considers the use of bands in atomic-absorption flame photometry of little attraction because of their poor selectivity and sensitivity.

3. MEASUREMENT OF LINE PROFILES

Atomic-absorption methods have provided an opportunity for studying the profiles of absorption lines. Moreover, a knowledge of the profiles of the resonance lines is considered as basic information in atomic-absorption. Interesting contributions on this topic have been made by Isaak (*357*), Hercus (*317*), Shimazu and Hashimoto (*669*) and Yasudo and Matsudaira (*857*).

4. LINES UTILIZED IN ATOMIC-ABSORPTION

Fig. 12–3 has been included to give the reader an idea of the distribution of the lines used in atomic-absorption in the spectral scale (see also Table 13–4). It may be useful to compare this figure with a similar one prepared for emission (see Fig. 8.1, p. 147 of *Flame Photometry* (*125*).

---

[5] Consult the data published for arsenic in emission (*189*).

Chapter 13

Sensitivity

Sensitivity is one of the analytical characteristics which has been most discussed in extolling the potentialities of atomic-absorption methods, particularly when compared to emission methods. Therefore, it is proper to give special attention to the various aspects included in the problem of sensitivity. This chapter contains discussions of concepts, correlations between different forms of expressing sensitivity and the methods of calculating sensitivities and limits; finally, some paragraphs are devoted to factors which influence the sensitivity achieved or achievable through atomic-absorption[1]. Symbols used in this Chapter are listed in Table 13–1.

1. DEFINITION OF SENSITIVITY

Any definition of sensitivity in the atomic-absorption flame photometric field must be based on the accepted concepts of sensitivity in analytical chemistry. Sensitivity has been defined in terms of *limits* (minimum and maximum), under *absolute concepts* (absolute amounts) or under *relative concepts* (concentrations and dilutions). These concepts are applicable to the *qualitative* or *quantitative* aspects as indicated below.

	Absolute concepts	*Relative concepts*	
	Minimum limits	*Minimum limits*	*Maximum limits*
Qualitative sensitivity	Minimum quantity of analyte which can be identified.	Minimum concentration of the analyte which can be identified.	Maximum dilution of the analyte at which it can be identified.
Quantitative sensitivity	Minimum quantity of analyte which can be determined.	Minimum concentration of the analyte which can be determined[2].	Maximum dilution of the analyte at which it can be determined.

[1] Some of the topics dealt with in this chapter have been discussed in a general paper on sensitivity in flame photometry (*600*). Any material presented in this book that coincides with parts of that paper have been reproduced by permission of the Editor of *Talanta* (Pergamon Press Ltd.).

[2] The minimum determinable concentration determines the lower limit of the useful range (also called dynamic range) in the concentration scale.

The sensitivity varies according to variations of concentration, dilution, and absolute amount of the analyte, and may be *good or bad, low or high,* as indicated in the following scheme.

Sensitivity

⟶

bad (worse) — good (better)

Sensitivity values

⟶

low (lower) — high (higher)

Amounts detectable or determinable

⟵

high — low

Concentrations detectable or determinable

⟵

high — low

Dilution ratios (1:n)

⟵

high — low

Dilution values (n times)

⟶

low — high

A good sensitivity (high sensitivity values) will be obtained when the limits attainable are low for the amount of analyte, low for the concentration limit, low for the dilution ratio limit, and high for the dilution limit.

Although qualitative sensitivity does not have the same practical meaning in atomic-absorption methods as in other analytical methods, the important quantitative sensitivity is closely connected with qualitative sensitivity. An analyte to be instrumentally determined needs to be also qualitatively "seen" (identified) by the instrument. Identification is used in a broad sense, with the meaning of an identifiable (detectable) signal, i.e., a signal with a measurable magnitude and a *statistical* probability of being due to the analyte, as well as the *unequivocal* and specific identification in the scale of the qualitative variable of the analytical system (wavelength scale). In atomic-absorption the qualitative variable is, as in emission flame photometry, the wavelength (*125*).

TABLE 13–1

SYMBOLS

A	Absorbance
C, C_1, C_2, C_3, C_4	Concentrations
$\Delta A, \Delta A_1$	Increments of absorbance corresponding to percentual and fluctuational concentration limits, respectively
$\Delta C, \Delta C_1$	Increments of concentration corresponding to percentual and fluctuational concentration limits, respectively
D	Dilution ratio
D'	Dilution
F	Feed rate (ml/min)
m	Mass
m	Slope of calibration curves
M	Percentual minimum amount of analyte detectable
M'	Fluctuational minimum amount of analyte detectable
p, p'	Conversion factors
$\mathrm{p}C$	$-\log C$
$\mathrm{p}D$	$-\log D$
$\mathrm{p}D'$	$-\log D'$
p%	$-\log$ percentage
$\sigma, \sigma_{\mathrm{B}}, \sigma_{\mathrm{S}}$	Standard deviations
t	Feed time (seconds)
V	Volume

The limits given in terms of maximum dilution are the inverse values of the limits given as minimum concentration ($D' = 1/C$). Of the six concepts listed at the beginning of this section, only two are considered fundamental in atomic-absorption: the absolute minimum quantitative limit and the relative minimum quantitative limit. These two concepts will be defined in this chapter after some others of a qualitative nature have been considered.

In the particular case of emission flame photometry, and since some instruments can scan rapidly for qualitative analysis, the qualitative sensitivity has a practical meaning, as a definite emission may be seen on the recorded spectrum and the corresponding analyte thus identified. To attain sufficient certainty regarding the presence of the analyte, the signal seen should be of a magnitude equal to or larger than, some multiple of the standard deviation of the background recorded at the corresponding wavelength (corresponding to a given *confidence level*). The identification in this case is made in the region of *positive response*, over the actual zone of uncertainty that may be considered in all qualitative identification.

1.1. Diverse units used to express limits

Different units may be used:

(1) For *absolute limits* the gram, or submultiples of the gram for very small amounts of analyte.

(2) For *relative limits* the gram per milliliter (g/ml), or submultiples of the gram and multiples of the milliliter (e.g. μg/ml or mg/l). The expressions: part per million (p.p.m.), part per billion (p.p.b.), and part per trillion (p.p.t.)[3] can also be used. Practically 1 p.p.m. $= 1 \times 10^{-6}$ g/ml $=$ 1 mg/l $=$ 1 μg/ml.

It is advisable to use g/ml because it is an expression of concentration (mass/volume) by rationing two units homogeneous in order of magnitude. For very dilute aqueous solutions it is supposed that 1 g of solution corresponds to 1 ml of solution. For solvents other than water, this identity cannot always be maintained.

The values of concentration in g/ml, C, may also be given as pC:

$$\mathrm{p}C = -\log C$$

Then 1 p.p.m. corresponds to p$C = 6$. Sensitivity values, as limits, have been given as well as p% in atomic-absorption (*275*). These values can be transformed into p.p.m. or pC. With the pC values, the corresponding symbol pD can be used for the dilution ratios related to the concentration limits. For instance, for 1 p.p.m. (concentration limit):

Concentration limit (C, concentration)

$$1 \times 10^{-6}\ \mathrm{g/ml} \quad \text{and} \quad \mathrm{p}C = 6$$

Dilution ratio limit (D, dilution ratio)

$$1{:}10^{6}\ (1\ \mathrm{g\ diluted\ to}\ 10^{6}\ \mathrm{ml}) \quad \text{and} \quad \mathrm{p}D = 6$$

Dilution limit (D', dilution)

$$10^{6}\ (\text{Analyte diluted } 10^{6} \text{ times}) \quad \text{and} \quad \mathrm{p}D' = -6$$

The concentration values, as limits, have been used to express detectabilities, and therefore the limits are called detection limits[4]. Never-

---

[3] Here 1 billion $= 10^{3}$ millions, and 1 trillion $= 10^{6}$ millions. In some countries 1 billion $= 10^{12}$.

[4] Beckman Instruments Inc. has published a periodic table which presents detectabilities of elements by emission and by absorption and indicates those elements which present detectabilities below or above 1 p.p.m. (expressed in terms of fluctuational concentration limits) (*73*).

theless it would seem more realistic to express the detectability using sensitivity instead of limits, since the detectability increases in the same way as the sensitivity.

1.2. Factors governing the absolute sensitivity

Absolute *quantitative* sensitivity—the minimum amount of analyte determinable—is conditioned in practice by a series of different factors:

(1) *Magnitude of the relative sensitivity*, as far as the analyte is usually studied under definite operating conditions that produce a given relative sensitivity.

(2) *Minimum volume of solution available* depending on the sample size.

(3) *Minimum sample size available.* If the sample has to be dissolved, (2) and (3) are related by the dilution factor $F = C/C'$.

(4) *Minimum volume of solution required.*

(5) *Minimum time required* by the instrument in order to be able to measure the measurable signal and to convert it into a recorded or visualized signal. This time depends on the damping used.

All these conditions converge to those corresponding to (1) and (4). If the concentration limit is known correlated to the relative sensitivity and the minimum volume required (V, given as a function of the feed rate and the reading time), the minimum amount is calculated by the formula $m = CV$ (m in g, and V in ml, as C in g/ml).

In analytical chemistry it is not really meaningful to say that a certain small amount may be determined, if the concentration values are not added (but the absolute values have great significance when accompanied by the relative value, concentration). Absolute values help in calculating the minimum sample size required if the content of analyte—or content range—in the samples is known.

1.3. Different definitions of relative sensitivity

In atomic-absorption the quantitative variable of the analytical system is the measurable absorption. The absorption is measured as *percentage of absorption*. Absorbance values are later calculated from these values:

$$\text{Absorbance} = \log \frac{100}{100 - \%\ \text{absorption}}$$

Sensitivity definitions have to be related to this experimental quantity. In emission there are many ways of defining and interpreting sensitivity (*125*). In absorption, definitions for relative sensitivity are confined to only two aspects: (a) *as a function of an arbitrary signal* (% absorption), and (b) *as a function of the experimental fluctuations* (noise) at the zero percent absorption level.

The first way of interpreting sensitivity refers to the term *analytical sensitivity*. The second way utilizes the same basis of the expression *relative detection limit*. Interesting comments on these two expressions have been published (*697, 709*). According to Slavin *et al.* (*709*), following Australian and New Zealand publications, the analytical sensitivity is defined as *the concentration* in μg/ml of analyte (p.p.m.) that produces an absorption of 1%. The relative detection limit is defined by them as *the concentration* that produces an absorption equivalent to *twice* the magnitude of the fluctuation in the background (0% absorption). Later, Gidley (*269*) referred to this definition, considering the sensitivity *also as a concentration*[5].

Both terms are correlated to *analytical sensitivity*, and involve concentration limits, so that both are *relative limits*. Many other names are found in the literature to express concentration limits[6]. The real distinction between the two terms is the functional dependence on a *limiting and arbitrary instrumental condition* imposed in the first case, and the dependence on the *experimental fluctuations* in the second case. Both are correlated to *minimum relative limits* (concentration limits), i.e. determined points in the concentration scale.

1.4. Qualitative sensitivity and qualitative limits

1.4.1. Sensitivity conditioned by an arbitrary absorption

In the atomic-absorption literature, an absorption of 1% has been traditionally fixed. There are many reasons for having chosen this particular absorption, among which are the following: (a) 1% absorption is the unit in the 0 to 100% absorption scale; (b) 1% absorption is within the interval of linearity of percentage of absorption with respect to concentration; (c) 1% absorption, even in curved systems (curved working curves of absorbance–concentration), is close enough to the origin of the curve to calculate the slope of the tangent at that point; (d) for working curves that present a linear portion, and after a clear curvature it is more realistic to refer concentration values to a low absorption percentage, than to use

---

[5] The contents of the Conference in which the Gidley's paper was presented have been discussed by Smith (*713*).

[6] For instance, in an abstract published in *Chem. Abstr.* (*C.A.*, 63 (1965) 12307E) referring to the paper by Rigault (*613*), the percentual qualitative concentration limit is mentioned as the *limit of resolution* (defined as *number of γ/ml for 1% absorption effect*). In the paper by Jones (*370*) values are published as *reciprocal sensitivity* (defined as p.p.m./% *A*).

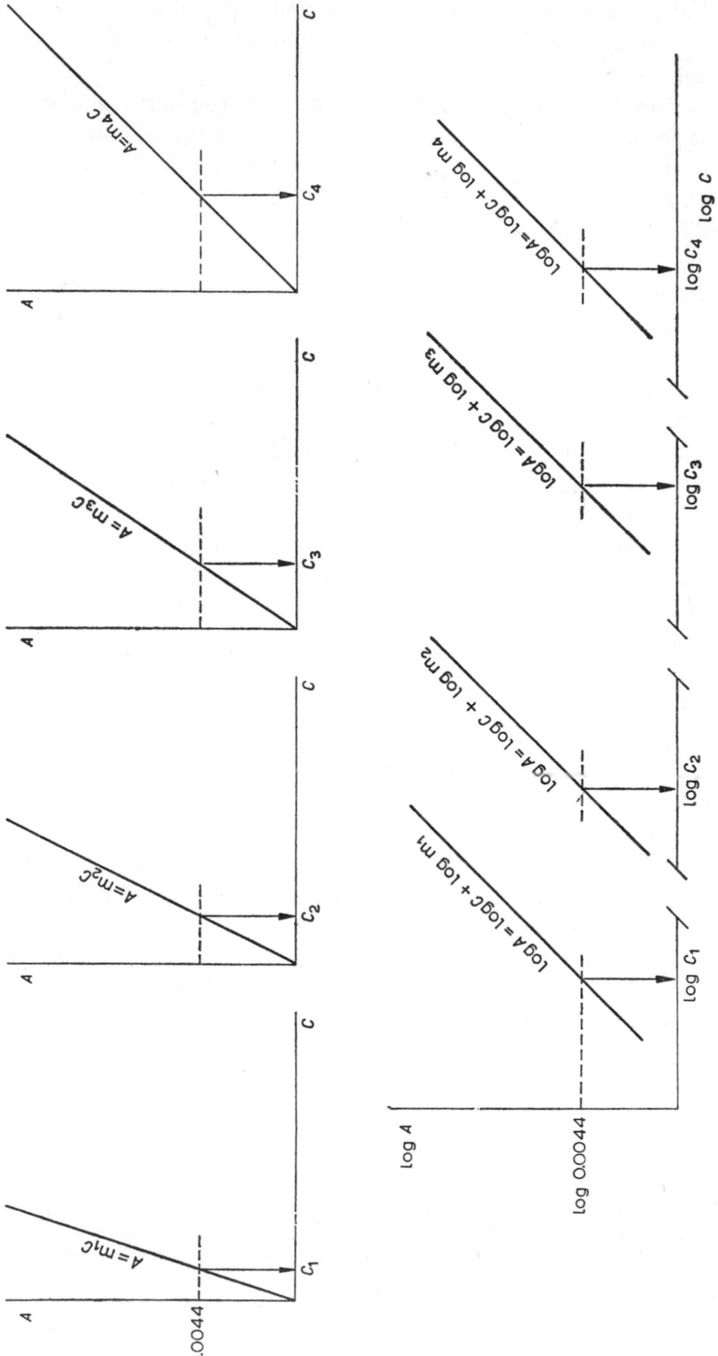

Fig. 13–1. Ordinary working curves and their corresponding log–log curves.

bigger signal values, out of linearity; (e) under 10% the relationship between percentage of absorption and absorbance is practically linear.

Sensitivity, as *relative sensitivity*, can thus be measured by means of a correlation between a signal and the concentration of analyte necessary to produce that signal. If linear response is obtained at low concentrations, there is a proportional relation between absorbance and concentration of the analyte in the solutions:

$$A = \mathrm{m}C$$

This means that when several elements are studied, once an arbitrary absorbance has been fixed, each element has to be in concentrations C_1, C_2, etc., to produce that absorbance. The absorbance fixed is $A = 0.0044$, corresponding to 1% absorption. Then, each analyte involves a different value of m: m_1, m_2, etc. This linear functional dependence explains why in log–log coordinates, tracing different absorbance–concentration curves (one curve for each analyte: $\log A$ *vs.* $\log C$), the parallel traced at absorbance 0.0044 cuts these curves at *different concentrations*. These concentrations read on the graph represent *concentration limits*. This is one of the practical methods of finding these limits from experimental values. Fig. 13–1 shows several ordinary working cuvers and the corresponding log–log curves. In fact, from $A = \mathrm{m}C$,

$$\log A = \log C + \log \mathrm{m}$$

For different elements a family of curves can be obtained, all of which are theoretically straight and parallel (theoretically equal slopes of value 1, but with different ordinates at the origin). Concentration limits are here *abcissae at the arbitrary absorbance origin.*

With m as the slope value of the absorbance–concentration curve, this slope may be represented by the ratio

$$\Delta A/\Delta C = \mathrm{m}$$

When ΔA has a value equal to the arbitrary absorbance value fixed to determine concentration limits, this is

$$\Delta A = 0.0044$$

then

$$\mathrm{m} = 0.0044/\text{concentration limit}$$

Fig. 13–2, where ΔA has been situated at the value 0.0044 absorbance, illustrates the above points.

In this case this concentration limit is conditioned by a *percentage* of absorption (1% absorption) and may be called *relative percentual concentration limit*[7]. It does not seem sufficient to say *relative percentual detection limit*, because *detection limit* is a general term that may mean a concentration limit, a dilution ratio limit, or a dilution limit.

In atomic-absorption spectroscopy it is usual, and more useful, to give these values in concentrations. The three above expressions apply to *relative* detection limits, so that it would suffice to use the term *percentual concentration limit*.

According to the value of m:

$$\text{Relative percentual concentration limit} = 0.0044/\text{m}$$

In those cases in which the relative percentual concentration limit is 1 p.p.m.

$$\text{m} = 0.0044$$

For each analytical system *sensitivity values* may be calculated dividing the slope by 0.0044:

$$\text{Relative percentual sensitivity} = \text{m}/0.0044 = 229\ \text{m}$$

These concentration limits and sensitivity values can be utilized to describe the behaviour of each element and as comparative terms. They do not involve yet any relationship with determination ranges, and can be called respectively *relative percentual qualitative concentration limits* and *relative percentual qualitative sensitivities*, or just *percentual qualitative concentration limits* and *percentual qualitative sensitivities*.

Percentual qualitative sensitivities are the inverse values of the corresponding percentual qualitative concentration limits.

The value m itself measures in other units the percentual qualitative

---

[7] The following nomenclature was suggested to the author by P. T. Gilbert, corresponding to the Spanish nomenclature used by the author:

$$\left.\begin{array}{l}\text{Absolute}\\ \text{Relative}\end{array}\right\}\left\{\begin{array}{l}\text{percentual}\\ \text{fluctuational}\end{array}\right\}\left\{\begin{array}{l}\text{detection}\\ \text{determination}\end{array}\right\}\left\{\begin{array}{l}\text{limit}\\ \text{sensitivity}\end{array}\right.$$

This includes the adjectives *percentual* and *fluctuational* (in Spanish *percentual* and *fluctuacional*) in order to distinguish sensitivities and limits defined by a percentage of absorption and by fluctuations found in the experimental work.

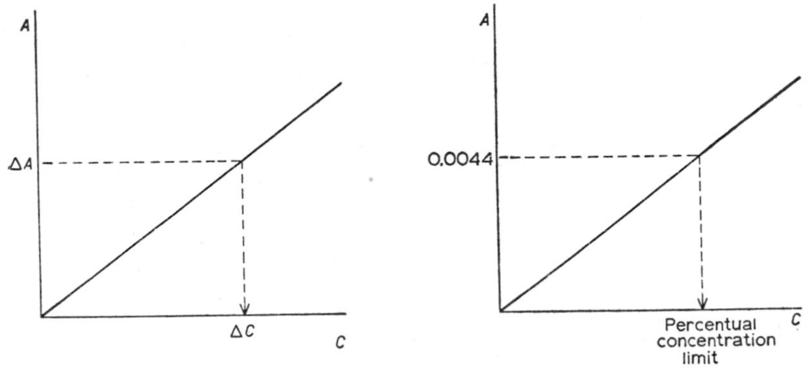

Fig. 13–2. Percentual concentration limit.

sensitivity as well (in slope values). The value m may be calculated at different absorbance levels:

(1) by dividing the absorbance 0.0044 by the concentration in p.p.m. necessary to obtain this absorbance (percentual qualitative concentration limit in p.p.m.),

(2) by the ratio of an absorbance and the concentration in p.p.m. producing it (at any absorbance level along the straight line portion of the absorbance–concentration curves),

(3) by calculating the inverse of the concentration giving an absorbance equal to 1.0000 (assuming that at that level the straight-line response is still conserved).

In Fig. 13–3 a particular case is represented in which 1 p.p.m. produces 1% absorption.

The slope m really corresponds to a *specific* value. It is specific for a definite analyte, and also specific for a set of experimental conditions. For this reason, different authors may find different sensitivities for an element, because the operating conditions are different. Thus, by means of some preparative procedure or some instrumental device, it is possible *to increase the sensitivity* or *to lower the concentration limit*. Both percentual and fluctuational sensitivities depends on m (see later). This value m also acts in the same way as a sensitivity coefficient, because for any given concentration, larger signals will be obtained if m is increased. Like most of the variable coefficients, it will remain constant for a given analytical system if a series of parameters is also kept constant.

The limits indicated by Skogerboe (*674*) as p.p.m. per 5% absorption are really percentual qualitative concentration limits based on conditions which give results 5 times greater than those expressed as described in this chapter (1% absorption).

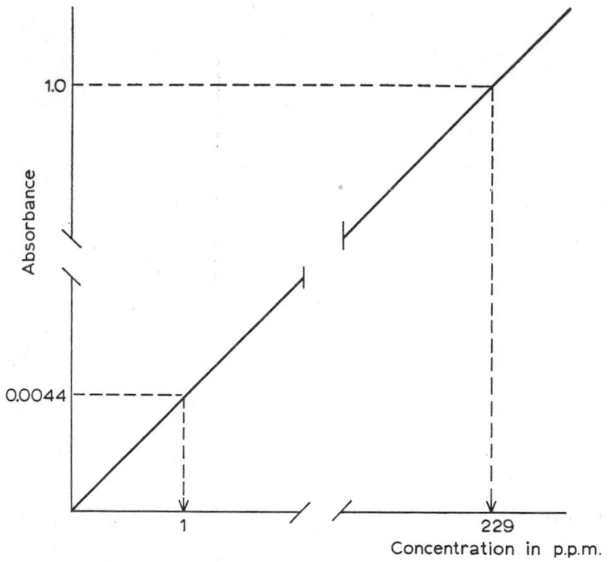

Fig. 13–3. Percentual concentration limit equal to 1 p.p.m.

1.4.2. Sensitivity conditioned by experimental fluctuations

For obtaining experimental measurements, the instrument is zeroed at the position known as *zero percent absorption*. In this condition, the instrument works as if $I = I_0$, which corresponds to $A = 0.0000$. Small concentrations of the analyte will produce slight decreases of the intensity I,

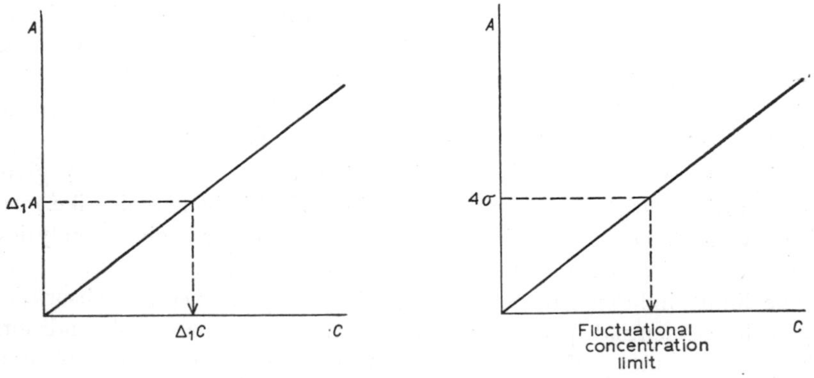

Fig. 13–4. Fluctuational concentration limit.

becoming smaller than I_0. At the percentual qualitative concentration limit, according to the concepts given in the preceding section, I becomes 99.0 (absorbance 0.0044) for $I_0 = 100.0$, i.e. there is 1% absorption.

If instrumental fluctuations cause variations at the zero percent absorption level, with the peak-to-peak noise reaching a value equivalent to a signal $\Delta_1 A$ (this can be measured in absorbance units), then it is possible to calculate the slope of the curve by the ratio

$$\Delta_1 A / \Delta_1 C = \mathrm{m}$$

A new condition is included here (see Fig. 13–4), the value of the absorbance $\Delta_1 A$, and a new concentration limit is introduced. Now the

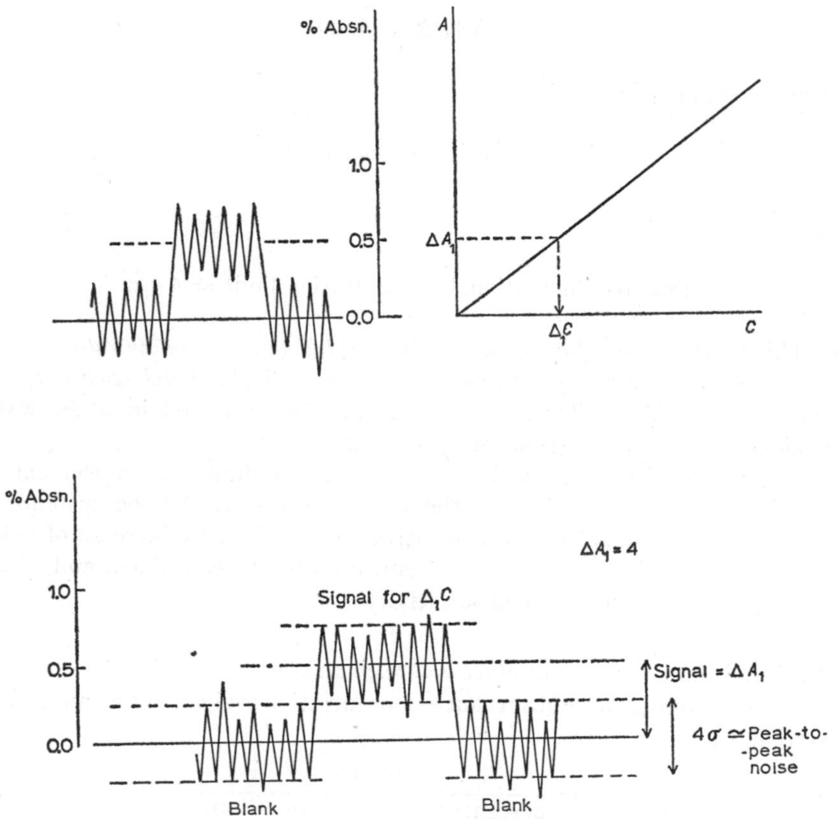

Fig. 13–5. Signal corresponding to the fluctuational concentration limit. In the lower part, situation of that signal over the blank signal.

concentration limit is calculated at the absorbance level $\Delta_1 A$, according to the fluctuations encountered.

A clear understanding of *fluctuations* is necessary here. If a standard deviation σ may be calculated from deviations at both sides of the average, the spread of values, for a reasonable certainty in single trials, may be about $4\,\sigma$ ($\Delta_1 A = 4\,\sigma$). For definition purposes $4\,\sigma$ may be taken as measured at zero percent absorption level. It is still questionable if the same value may be obtained by measuring the noise with the blank or with an absorbing solution containing the analyte at very low concentration.

In Fig. 13–5 is shown the signal that might correspond to a concentration ΔC_1 and to an absorbance ΔA_1. Observe that the signal appears just over the top of the noise.

The equation

$$\Delta A_1/\Delta C_1 = \mathrm{m}$$

may be expressed as

$$4\,\sigma/\text{relative fluctuational concentration limit} = \mathrm{m}$$

hence:

$$\text{Relative fluctuational concentration limit} = 4\,\sigma/\mathrm{m}$$

This limit can also be called simply the *fluctuational concentration limit.* The inverse value $\mathrm{m}/4\,\sigma$ represents the *relative fluctuational sensitivity*, or the *fluctuational sensitivity*. This term can be expressed in other ways analogously to the percentual sensitivity (see above).

The value of the fluctuational concentration limit for an element is conditioned by the stability of the systems involved. All the systems of the instrument should be both sensitive and stable. Any increase of noise will produce an increase in the concentration limit determined, and, thus, a decrease of the fluctuational sensitivity.

1.4.3. Relation between percentual and fluctuational sensitivities

The slope of the curve absorbance–concentration is given, for an analytical system, by

$$\mathrm{m} = \frac{0.0044}{\text{percentual concentration limit}}$$

and also by

$$m = \frac{4\,\sigma}{\text{fluctuational concentration limit}}$$

Thus, the two limits can be related by

$$\text{fluctuational concentration limit} = \frac{\sigma}{0.0011} \times \text{percentual concentration limit}$$

For comparative purposes between different analytical methods that can be applied for the determination of the same analyte, use may be made of the *instrumental sensitivity*[8] which is defined by the slope of the calibration curve ($\Delta A/\Delta C$) divided by the standard deviation:

$$\text{instrumental sensitivity} = \frac{\Delta A/\Delta C}{\sigma} = \frac{m}{\sigma}$$

When this concept is applied to atomic-absorption (on the basis of the absorbance–concentration curves), the values obtained are closely related to the values of the percentual and fluctuational sensitivities previously discussed. In fact:

$$\text{instrumental sensitivity} = \frac{0.0044}{\sigma} \times \text{percentual qualitative sensitivity}$$

and also

$$\text{instrumental sensitivity} = 4 \times \text{fluctuational qualitative sensitivity.}$$

The use of the slope values is one of the easiest ways of comparing numerically and graphically the results obtained for several elements, under constant or different operating conditions, because of the specificity of the slope for each analytical system. In some cases, the slopes may turn out to be equal for more than one element, so that the percentual qualitative sensitivities will also be equal for those elements.

The slopes, converted to percentual qualitative sensitivities and concentration limits, help to produce figures of more analytical meaning. The

---

[8] This concept of sensitivity has been discussed by the author (*581*) on the basis of the publication of Stiehler and Mandel (*946*), who state, inter alia, that "Sensitivity is a measure of performance useful in the evaluation of methods of test. Its application to analytical chemistry can be pictured in terms of an analogy with a radio receiver. Thus, an analytical method receives a signal in the form of a sample, and noise in the form of experimental error. The method detects and amplifies the desired signal (component to be determined) and yields a message in the form of a measured value. Sensitivity, in terms of this analogy, is a measure that increases directly with amplification and inversely with noise".

fluctuational sensitivity expresses more practical values when information about noise level is needed, and is valuable in studies of operating conditions; it is also useful in studies of the effects of chemical composition of samples in the presence of components giving rise to chemical interferences and so decreasing precision. Finally, the relative fluctuational qualitative sensitivity clearly shows variations of sensitivity due to variations of noise, even if the slope is virtually constant.

Although fluctuations should be measured at zero percent absorption level for calculating sensitivities and fluctuational limits, it is permissible to measure them at different absorbance levels (as is done when *instrumental sensitivity* is used for comparative purposes). This allows variations in sensitivity along the calibration graphs to be determined, e.g. in the curvature zones of calibration graphs.

One of the reasons that the noise is often more intense in the proximity of the 0% absorption level is that the luminous intensity reaching the photodetector is greater under those conditions. If the appearance of noise is especially due to the shot noise of the detector, the noise will gradually decrease as the absorption signals become greater. It should be recalled that the shot noise increases with the square root of the luminous intensity of the radiations which reach the photodetector.

If the effect is the reverse, i.e., if the noise appears as the absorption signals increase, then one must consider the participation of the sample and the flame (flame flickering). This phenomenon also appears if the burner is not in good alignment. The influence of the electrometer noise on the sensitivity has been discussed from a theoretical point of view by Winefordner and Veillon (*851*).

1.4.4. Absolute sensitivities and absolute limits

Absolute limits can be calculated as qualitative limits from the corresponding concentration limits, multiplying them by the *required volume* V. These absolute limits are:

M = percentual minimum amount detectable
M' = fluctuational minimum amount detectable

Their values are given in Table 13–2. Absolute sensitivities may also be calculated by introducing the volume V as also shown in the same table. Absolute quantitative sensitivities and limits are mentioned later in this chapter. The volume required, the relative concentration limits and the absolute limits can be correlated graphically as shown in Fig. 13–6.

The concepts, calculations and factors involved in the use of absolute limits and absolute sensitivities in atomic-absorption work have been

TABLE 13–2

SENSITIVITIES AND LIMITS

Criteria	*Sensitivities*		*Limits*	
	Qualitative (Detection sensitivity)	*Quantitative (Determination sensitivity)*	*Qualitative (Detection limits)*	*Quantitative (Determination limits)*
Absolute				
Percentual	$\frac{m}{0.0044V}$	$\frac{m}{0.0044Vp}$	*Percentual minimum amount detectable*[10] $M = V\frac{0.0044}{m}$	*Percentual minimum amount determinable*[10] Mp
Fluctuational	$\frac{m}{4\sigma V}$	$\frac{m}{0.0044Vp}$	*Fluctuational minimum amount detectable*[10] $M' = V\frac{4\sigma}{m}$	*Fluctuational minimum amount determinable*[10] $M'p'$
Relative[9]				
Percentual	$\frac{m}{0.0044}$	$\frac{m}{0.0044p}$	*Percentual qualitative concentration limit*[11] $\frac{0.0044}{m}$	*Percentual quantitative concentration limit*[11] $\frac{0.0044p}{m}$
Fluctuational	$\frac{m}{4G}$	$\frac{m}{4\sigma p'}$	*Fluctuational qualitative concentration limit*[11] $\frac{4\sigma}{m}$	*Fluctuational quantitative concentration limit*[11] $\frac{4\sigma}{m}p'$

reviewed in detail, with practical examples and graphs that correlate absolute limits and other analytical variables (*936*).

1.4.4.1. Volume factor. The volume factor V (volume required in ml to perform an adequate reading) can be calculated as a function of the feed rate, F (measured in ml/min) and feed time, t (measured in seconds):

$$V = \frac{t \cdot F}{60}$$

[9] The adjective *relative* may be deleted when dealing with qualitative or quantitative *limits*, as they are always given in relative values (concentrations, dilutions, percentages).

[10] Given in μg if concentrations are calculated in p.p.m. and V is given in ml. These four values (M, M', Mp, and $M'p'$) correspond to the *absolute* (percentual and fluctuational) *detection limits.*

[11] Similar formulae may be used for dilution ratios. Real dilution values require inverse ratios: $D' = 1/C$. If the dilutions are expressed in ml/g, it is necessary to use the conversion factor when concentrations are given in p.p.m.

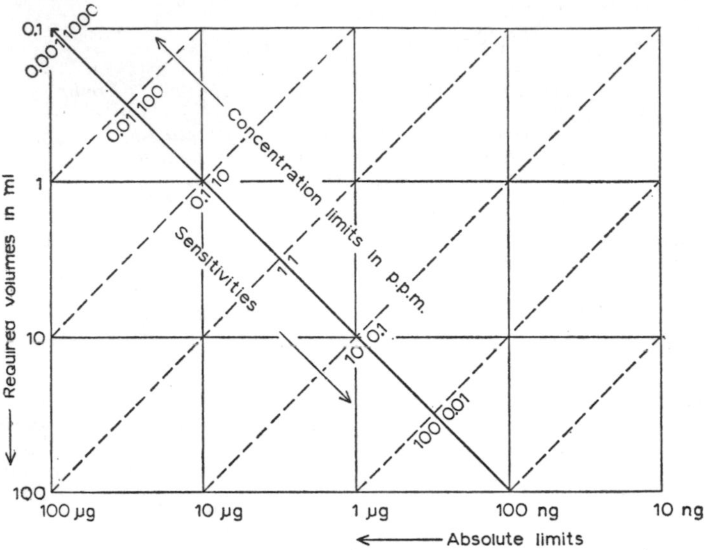

Fig. 13–6. Correlation between required volumes, concentration limits, sensitivities and absolute limits.

1.5. Quantitative sensitivities and quantitative limits

Limits of a quantitative nature are of more significance than qualitative limits in establishing determination ranges, but quantitative limits must be calculated from qualitative limits, the fluctuational concentration limit being particularly important.

As the lower limit of the determination range will depend on the precision desired, which in most cases should be better than that attainable at the extreme detection limit, a factor p' may be calculated as follows:

$$p' = \frac{\text{precision attainable at the fluctuational concentration limit}}{\text{precision desired}}$$

In this equation, both precisions are expressed as coefficients of variation. This factor p' may be applied to the fluctuational qualitative concentration limit, directly, and inversely to the fluctuational qualitative sensitivity (see Table 13–2). It can also be applied to the absolute fluctuational sensitivities and absolute fluctuational limits.

For some purposes, it is useful to define two quantitative concentration limits for an analytical system:

(a) *Fluctuational*: Minimum concentration necessary in order to carry out determinations with coefficient of variation not greater than a given value.

(b) *Percentual*: Minimum concentration necessary in order to carry out determinations at absorbance not lower than a given value.

For the latter case a new factor p may be calculated as follows:

$$p = \frac{\text{absorbance desired as minimum}}{0.0044}$$

The factor p has been used for transformation purposes in Table 13–2. In other cases only one quantitative concentration limit will be used (the fluctuational quantitative concentration limit), with the precision being the most important conditioning variable. In such cases the factor p must be calculated as a function of factor p'. The factor p' cannot be greater than a certain value delimited by the best precision attainable in the method.

At low concentrations the two factors are related by:

$$p = p' \times \frac{\text{fluctuational qualitative concentration limit}}{\text{percentual qualitative concentration limit}}$$

and also by

$$p = \frac{\text{fluctuational quantitative concentration limit}}{\text{percentual qualitative concentration limit}}$$

If p is calculated as mentioned above, the percentual and fluctuational quantitative limits have the same values:

$$Mp = M'p'$$

and

$$\frac{0.0044}{\mathrm{m}}\,p = \frac{4\,\sigma}{\mathrm{m}}\,p'$$

It is more convenient to calculate p' (fluctuational correction factor), its value being directly correlated with the fluctuational qualitative concentration limit. At the blank level (blank zeroed to zero percent absorption) a standard deviation σ_B is calculated. For a low concentration giving a small signal over the blank level, another standard deviation σ_S is calculated.

The standard deviation of the measurable differences between blank and sample signals will be

$$\sigma_D = \sqrt{\sigma_B{}^2 + \sigma_S{}^2}$$

It can be assumed that $\sigma_B = \sigma_S = \sigma$, as in practical work no significant changes are introduced by the contribution of the analyte sprayed into the flame and atomized in the flame; then

$$\sigma_D = \sigma\sqrt{2}$$

From a practical point of view, one must multiply σ_D by a quantity q so that the resultant value corresponds to a signal having a measurable magnitude and *some given statistical probability of being due to the analyte.* In this manner a quantitative value is related to the realistic situation of detecting. Thus

$$q\,\sigma_D = q\sigma\sqrt{2}$$

where

$$q\sqrt{2} = 4$$

Then

$$q = 4/\sqrt{2} = 2.83$$

At the fluctuational *qualitative* concentration limit level, measurements of signals of magnitude equal to 4 σ are made with a precision corresponding to a coefficient of variation of

$$\frac{100}{q} = 100\,\frac{\sqrt{2}}{4} = 35.3\%$$

The factor p' should have the value

$$p' = \frac{35.3}{\text{precision desired expressed as coefficient of variation}}$$

The factor p' cannot have all possible values for two reasons:

(a) The precision cannot be better than some limiting value; i.e., the coefficient of variation cannot be made infinitely small.

(b) The preceding expression for p' is valid only for concentration values close to the fluctuational qualitative concentration limit.

If the peak-to-peak fluctuation values are known, the factor p can be calculated from p'. If signals are not very noisy, then $p<p'$, but for very noisy signals, $p>p'$. Also, $p = p'$ if the noise has a peak-to-peak value of about 1% absorption ($A = 0.0044$). Under these conditions $\sigma \approx 0.0011$.

To achieve coefficients of variation in the range 3–5% at low concentration values, the factor p' should have values between 7 and 12.

This means that determinations should be performed with concentrations 7–12 times the relative fluctuational qualitative concentration limit (see Fig. 13–7). Choosing convenient concentrations in terms of the limit enables the analyst to work in the regions of best precision and accuracy of the working curves. In some cases, experimental values lead to coefficients of variation different from those desired, because of collateral experimental factors.

For a complete discussion on quantitative sensitivity and quantitative limits in atomic-absorption, the reader should consult the paper by Ramírez-Muñoz *et al.* (*602*) (see also ref. (*416*)). The definitions of some of the terms included in this chapter are summarized in Table 13–3.

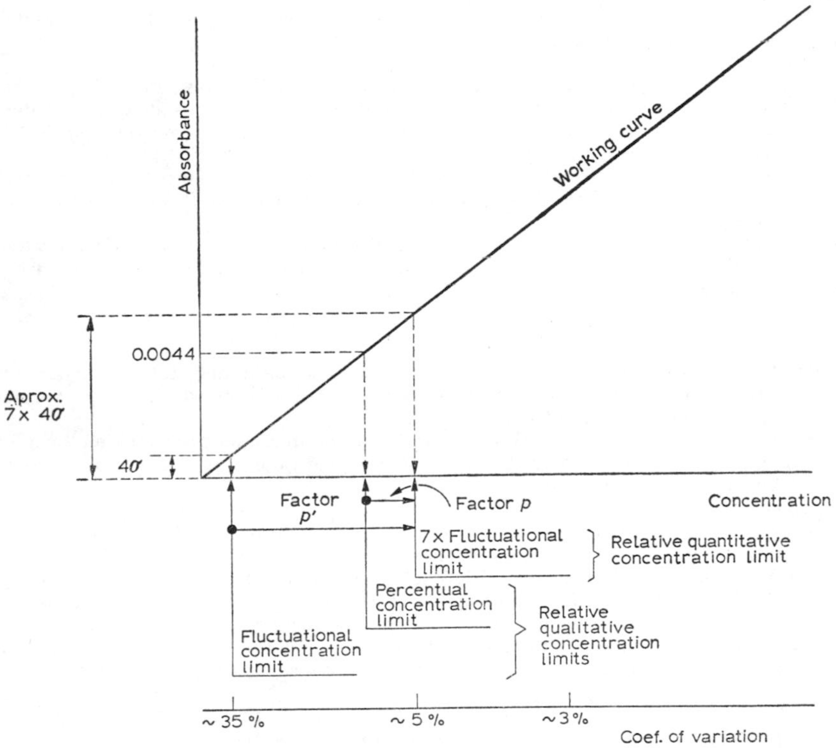

Fig. 13–7. Significance of factors p and p' in connection with qualitative and quantitative concentration limits.

TABLE 13–3

DEFINITIONS

RELATIVE LIMITS

Percentual qualitative concentration limit. Concentration in p.p.m. of analyte giving a signal corresponding to 1% absorption under given operating conditions.

Its value is equivalent to the *minimum concentration required* if the instrument is operated at maximum instrumental sensitivity.

This limit is frequently symbolized by PCL. It is equivalent to the "sensitivity" expressed in the literature as p.p.m./1% absorption.

Fluctuational qualitative concentration limit. Concentration in p.p.m. of analyte giving a signal corresponding to the magnitude of the peak-to-peak noise measured at 0% absorption level (blank or solvent adjusted at 0% absorption) under given operating conditions.

It is necessary to express clearly the scale expansion and *time constant* conditions used for its determination in order to be able to derive real information from figures published.

Its value should be equivalent to the *minimum concentration required* if the instrument is operated at maximum instrumental sensitivity and at the lowest possible noise conditions.

This limit is frequently symbolized by FCL. It is comparable to "detection limits" expressed in the literature, if they are obtained at *the same time constant* and scale expansion conditions.

Percentual quantitative concentration limit. Concentration in p.p.m. of analyte necessary in order to perform determinations at absorbance not lower than a given value.

For a given absorbance value, it should be the *minimum concentration required* if the instrument is operated at maximum instrumental sensitivity.

Fluctuational quantitative concentration limit. Concentration in p.p.m. of analyte necessary in order to perform determinations with coefficients of variation not greater than a given value.

For a given value of coefficient of variation, it should be the *minimum concentration required* if the instrument is operated at maximum instrumental sensitivity and at the lowest possible noise conditions.

ABSOLUTE LIMITS

Percentual qualitative limit (Percentual minimum amount detectable). Amount of analyte in grams detectable in the experimental conditions at which the percentual qualitative concentration limit is calculated.

Fluctuational qualitative limit (Fluctuational minimum amount detectable). Amount of analyte in grams detectable in the experimental conditions at which the fluctuational qualitative concentration limit is calculated.

Percentual quantitative limit (Percentual minimum amount determinable). Amount of analyte in grams determinable in the experimental conditions at which the percentual quantitative concentration limit is calculated.

Fluctuational quantitative limit (Fluctuational minimum amount determinable). Amount of analyte in grams determinable in the experimental conditions at which the fluctuational quantitative concentration limit is calculated.

For all absolute limits it is necessary to calculate first the volume required by the instrument, as a function of the feeding rate and the feeding time.

SENSITIVITIES

In all cases the sensitivities are the reciprocal values of the corresponding limit (relative or absolute, percentual or fluctuational, or qualitative or quantitative).

2. SOME ADVANTAGES IN THE USE OF SENSITIVITY VALUES

Apart from the convenience of using a magnitude that increases when the instrumental system allows smaller amounts of the analyte to be detected and/or determined, sensitivity values permit easy comparisons between results attainable by different instrumental procedures. The use of logarithmic scales makes it possible to calculate graphically the ratio between the sensitivities of the cases compared. Comparisons are presented in Figs. 13–8 and 13–9.

The sensitivity values allow the presentation of a logical sequence of data when an increase in sensitivity by modification of experimental parameters is studied. Many authors describe the experimental variations found when instrumental parameters are varied (length of the optical trajectory across the flame, width of the slit, fuel gas pressure, etc.). These experimental variations may be expressed as variations of (the directly read) percentage absorption, or as variations of absorbance (calculated

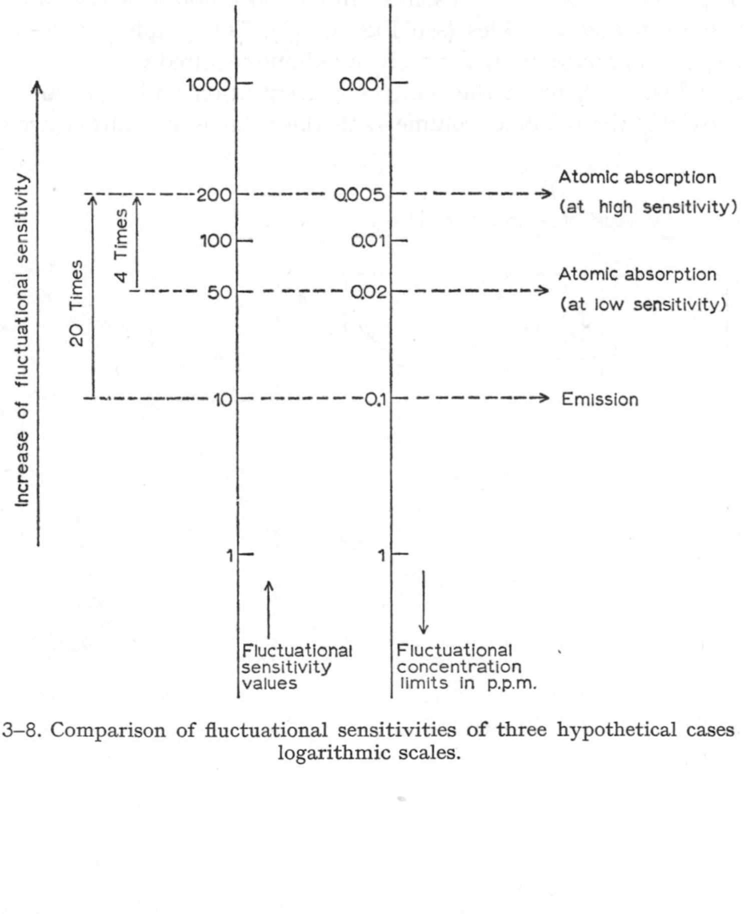

Fig. 13–8. Comparison of fluctuational sensitivities of three hypothetical cases using logarithmic scales.

from the former); but if any of these variations is accompanied, as almost always happens, by a change in the slope of the calibration curves, it is then very simple to calculate the corresponding sensitivities and to present them, in tables or graphs, as a function of the parameter modified.

When increase ratios are to be tabulated, it is easier to calculate ratios of sensitivities, by *direct* ratioing of values (instead of *indirect* ratioing of concentration limits).

Sensitivities may be easily calculated from pC values or from p% values found in tables in the literature, and compared, if the logarithm of the sensitivity values are used for this purpose. It is possible to use the following equations:

$$\log \text{sensitivity} = pC - 6$$
$$\log \text{sensitivity} = p\% - 4$$

In these cases it is convenient to express pC from C values given in g/ml. The correspondence of logarithmic scales is shown in Fig. 13–10.

It is possible to correlate absolute limits and absolute sensitivities with other experimental variables (see Fig. 13–11). This graph permits one to calculate the absolute limits for a given volume required by the instrument (see also Fig. 13–6) when the relative concentration limits are known. It also correlates the required volume with the volume of solution necessary

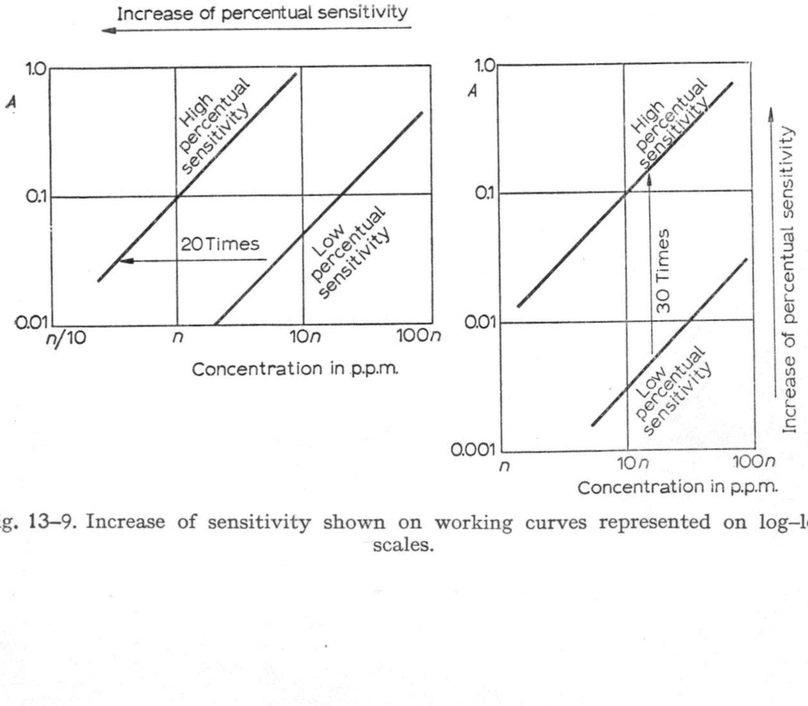

Fig. 13–9. Increase of sensitivity shown on working curves represented on log–log scales.

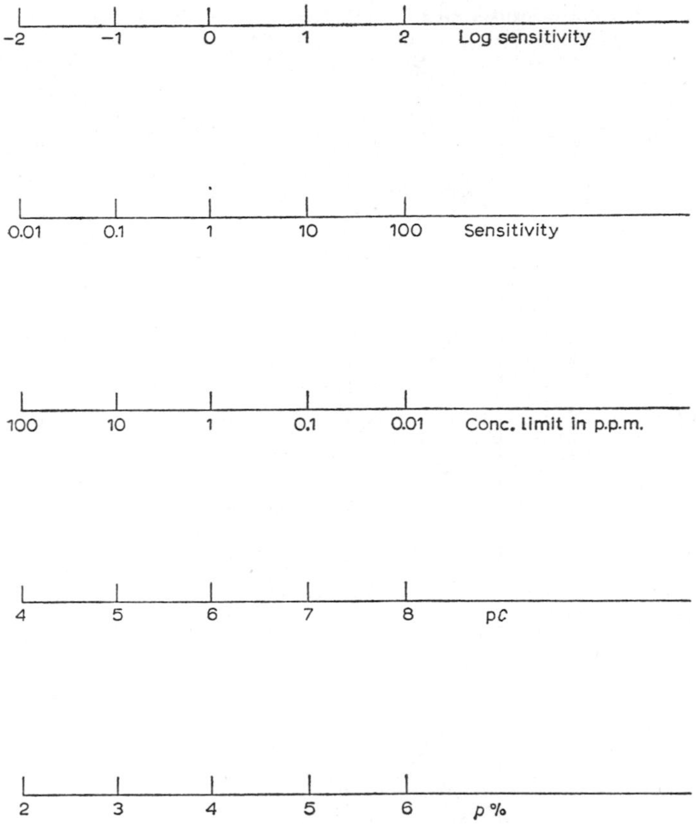

Fig. 13–10. Correlation between log sensitivity, sensitivity, concentration limit, p*C* and p%.

and the size of the sample. Inverse problems can also be solved graphically.

Absolute sensitivity will decrease as the volume of the prepared solution required by the instrument increases. While an increase in the feed rate may increase the percentual relative qualitative sensitivity, at the same time it decreases the absolute sensitivity. Samples which are excessively small and cannot be diluted to a large extent before being sprayed will require that a sufficiently small absolute sensitivity be achieved.

Because of the sufficiently large percentual relative qualitative sensitivity of atomic-absorption methods for some elements, the absolute quantities of analyte required for a determination (minimum feed time and duplicate or triplicate reading) is reduced to a small fraction of a gram.

For instruments that need a high feed rate, if the concentration of the

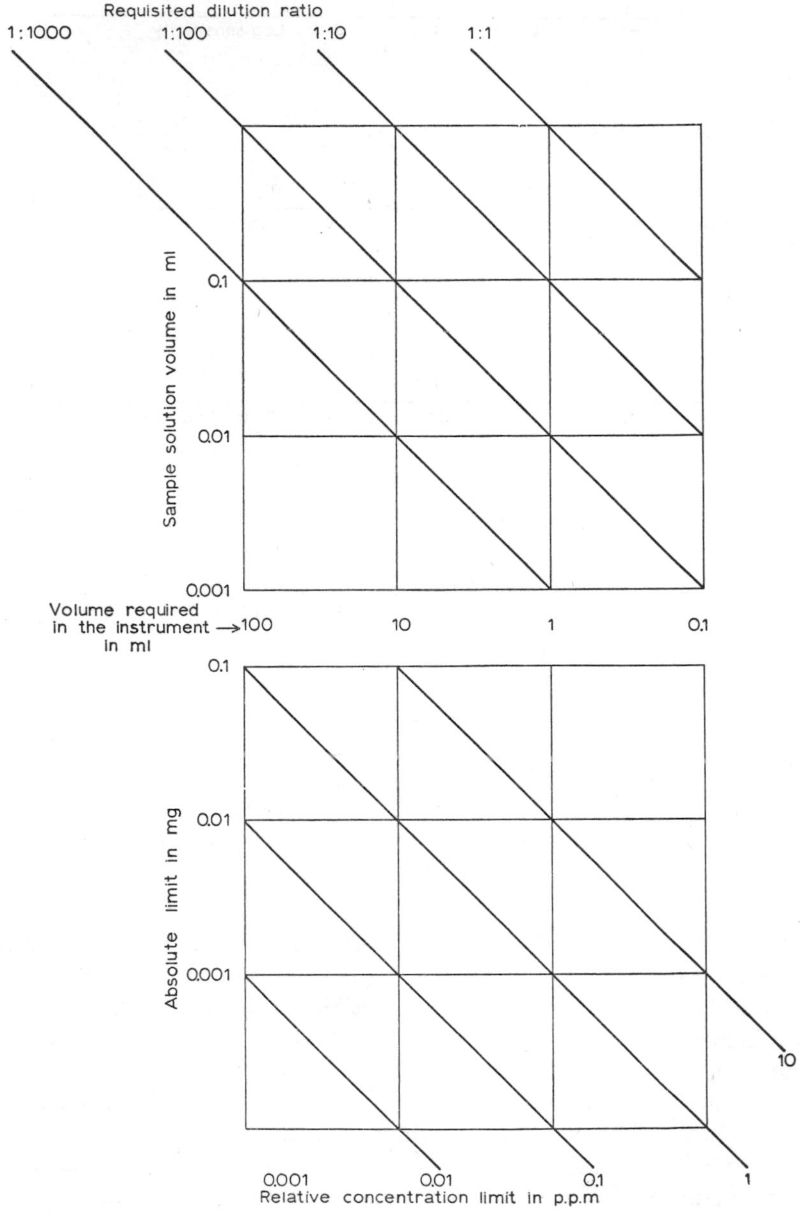

Fig. 13–11. Correlation of several quantities used in sensitivity and limit calculation (see text). The values for the volume required serve as a link between the two section of the graph.

analyte in the original sample and the percentual relative qualitative sensitivity allow, sufficiently large solutions may be prepared to assure the required consumption of sample, even in multiple readings on the same solution. Naturally, under such circumstances the fluctuational relative quantitative sensitivity should be taken into account.

Some comments have been published (*931*) on the practical use of concentration limits in order to calculate concentrations, dilution ratios and concentration factors (in preliminary concentration processes) for obtaining specified signals; special cases of limited sample concentration or sample size are also discussed. Some notes on the use of noise level values and absolute limits are included (*931*).

3. PROCEDURES FOR DETERMINING CONCENTRATION LIMITS AND SENSITIVITIES

It is most practicable to determine first the concentration limits, and then to calculate the sensitivities from them. The following aspects should be pointed out.

3.1. Percentual qualitative concentration limits

A dilution series is prepared from a standard solution or sample of the analyte, the solutions being kept as simple as possible in order to avoid the influence of other components; the solutions should preferably be saline and neutral, if no hydrolysis phenomena intervene[12]. The solutions are measured in the instrument under established instrumental conditions. If the sensitivity at the optimal instrument performance is desired, efforts must, of course, be made to have the instrument working perfectly at its maximum sensitivity; in this sense, sensitivity is understood as the response/stimulus relationship which would contribute most to improving the slope of the working curve (important factors are the selection and peaking of the wavelength, the slit width, the gas pressures, the burner height, etc.).

The experimental readings are transformed into absorbances, and the absorbances are plotted versus concentrations (working curve). Two ways may be used.

(1) *On ordinary scales.* On the graph the value of the absorbance corre-

[12] To determine sensitivities or limits under interfering conditions, the solutions will naturally have to contain the interfering components (in fixed or variable concentrations).

sponding to any particular concentration is measured within the linear interval of the curve. The absorbance corresponding to 1 p.p.m. is then calculated (1 p.p.m. as unit of the concentration scale). This absorbance (which represents the slope m in absorbance values) is divided by 0.0044. The concentration chosen for reading should be the highest possible to avoid errors in reading from the graph. If 1 p.p.m. produces sufficiently high absorbance and still is within the straight zone, it is better to read the absorbance corresponding to 1 p.p.m., so that calculations are avoided.

Alternatively, the slope of the rectilinear part can be calculated and the corresponding formula applied (see Table 13–2). The percentual qualitative concentration limit is obtained through the ratio m/0.0044.

A particular case is that of dilution series showing curved working curves. The concentration limit may be calculated for the lower region (lower concentrations) assuming that a small portion is linear. It is a good practice to determine the slope at different concentration ranges and to apply the ratio m/0.0044, which gives the variation of the concentration limit at different concentration intervals.

Computer techniques have been applied by Ramírez-Muñoz *et al.* (*601*) to avoid all the manual calculation involved in these steps. The computer output gives slope values, percentual qualitative concentration limits and percentual qualitative sensitivities.

(2) *On double-logarithmic scales.* This procedure is applicable when the points corresponding to low concentrations are situated on a line which is straight or practically straight. Whether by interpolation (cases of high sensitivity) or by extrapolation (cases of low sensitivity), the concentration corresponding to the ordinate $A = 0.0044$ is determined from the graph. Extrapolation or interpolation may also be done by calculation.

Finally, inverse values of the concentration limits are calculated to obtain the percentual qualitative sensitivities. The inverted scale of the slide ruler may be used.

3.2. Fluctuational qualitative concentration limits

The necessary data may be obtained, of course, by manual measurement (without strip-chart recorder), but it is an unquestionable help to use a recorder. A signal is recorded by means of a solution of a sufficiently low, known concentration (or even better, several signals are recorded using several solutions of decreasing concentration); the recorded signal should be very close, under the same experimental conditions, to that for the blank solution, previously adjusted at zero percent absorption level. This operation should be repeated at least three times.

On the strip chart, the peak-to-peak fluctuation of the blank and the magnitude of the signals for the analyte solution are read and averaged. The data are processed as follows.

(a) *If only one solution has been used.* Assuming linear response at the low level of concentrations, a concentration is calculated which would produce a recorded signal equal to the fluctuations at zero level (i.e. to peak-to-peak noise). The value obtained is the fluctuational qualitative concentration limit.

Alternatively, the concentration giving a signal equal to a given multiple of the standard deviation at zero level can be calculated.

For this procedure one can operate with percentages of absorption or with the corresponding absorbances.

It is also possible to search graphically for the concentration which would produce a signal equal to peak-to-peak noise on a straight line traced between the experimental point of the examined concentration and the point zero–zero.

Again, computer techniques can be applied (*601*). The computer output gives the fluctuational qualitative concentration limit and the fluctuational qualitative sensitivity.

(b) *If several solutions have been used.* Different solutions are measured until the signal corresponding to one of them cannot be distinguished from the noise recorded using a blank solution. For consistency $\frac{2}{3}$ of the noise level can be chosen in order to calculate the fluctuational qualitative concentration limit. If a definite multiple of the fluctuations at zero level is chosen, the values for each solution are represented graphically and the concentration corresponding to the prefixed multiple is sought on the graph.

4. SENSITIVITIES OBTAINABLE BY ATOMIC-ABSORPTION

Sensitivity charts have been published by various authors. A general collection of comparative values, most of them the best values achieved, is shown in Table 13–4.

The constant development of new techniques and of improvements aimed at increasing sensitivity makes any collection of sensitivity values invalid even before it has been printed, and this is particularly true at the present time when many papers are being published on atomic-absorption methods for, e.g. "refractory" metals.

The data obtained by different authors for a particular element are strongly dependent on the conditions and equipment used, and so their value to other investigators is debatable. Even when the same models of apparatus are used, their adjustments must be identical and the working

TABLE 13–4

PERCENTUAL QUALITATIVE CONCENTRATION LIMITS

Element	*Wavelength (Å)*	*Percentual concentration limit (p.p.m.)*		*Authors*	*Refs.*
Aluminum	3093	0.19	N	Hell *et al.*	315
Antimony	2176	0.60		Ramírez-Muñoz[13]	
Arsenic	1937	0.93		Ramírez-Muñoz[14]	
Barium	5536	0.33	N	Ramírez-Muñoz and Roth[15]	
Beryllium	2349	0.024	N	Amos and Willis[16]	
Bismuth	2231	1		Slavin *et al.*	709
Boron	2497	28	N	Ramírez-Muñoz and Roth[15]	
Cadmium	2288	0.012		Hell *et al.*	313
Calcium	4227	0.0060		Ramírez-Muñoz[14]	
Cerium	5200	46	N	Ramírez-Muñoz and Roth[15]	
Cesium	8521	0.40		Hell *et al.*	313
Chromium	3579	0.015		Ramírez-Muñoz[14]	
Cobalt	2407	0.080		Hell *et al.*	313
Copper	3248	0.0060		Ramírez-Muñoz[14]	
Dysprosium	4212	1.5	N	Amos and Willis[16]	
Erbium	4008	1.4	N	Amos and Willis[16]	
Europium	4594	0.17	N	Ramírez-Muñoz and Roth[15]	
Gadolinium	3684	38	N	Amos and Willis[16]	
Gallium	2874	0.23		Ramírez-Muñoz[14]	
Germanium	2652	0.42	N	Ramírez-Muñoz and Roth[15]	
Gold	2428	0.032		Ramírez-Muñoz[14]	
Hafnium	3073	14	N	Amos and Willis[16]	
Holmium	4104	2	N	Anderson[17]	
Indium	3040	0.13		Ramírez-Muñoz[14]	
Iridium	2850	34		Mulford[18]	
Iron	2483	0.0083		Ramírez-Muñoz[14]	
Lanthanum	3928	14	N	Hell *et al.*	315
Lead	2833	0.13		Hell *et al.*	313
Lithium	6708	0.012		Brace *et al.*	110
Lutetium	3360	12	N	Amos and Willis[16]	
Magnesium	2852	0.00045		Hell *et al.*	313
Manganese	2795	0.0033		Ramírez-Muñoz[14]	
Mercury	2537	1.25		Hell *et al.*	313
Molybdenum	3133	0.084	N	Hell *et al.*	315
Neodymium	4925	35	N	Anderson[17] (also Amos and Willis[16])	
Nickel	2320	0.0085		Ramírez-Muñoz[14]	
Niobium	3349	5.6	N	Ramírez-Muñoz and Roth[15]	
Osmium	2909	1	N	[20]	
Palladium	2476	0.027		Ramírez-Muñoz[14]	
Platinum	2659	0.26		Ramírez-Muñoz[14]	
Potassium	7665	0.0075		Ramírez-Muñoz[14]	
Praseodymium	4951	72	N	Amos and Willis[16]	
Rhenium	3461	1.4	N	Ramírez-Muñoz and Roth[15]	
Rhodium	3435	0.028		Ramírez-Muñoz[14]	
Rubidium	7800	0.082		Brace *et al.*	110
Ruthenium	3499	0.25		Allan	15

TABLE 13–4 (continued)

Element	*Wavelength (Å)*	*Percentual concentration limit (p.p.m.)*		*Authors*	*Refs.*
Samarium	4297	21	N	Amos and Willis[16]	
Scandium	3912	0.20	N	Ramírez-Muñoz and Roth[15]	
Selenium	1961	0.20		Ramírez-Muñoz[14]	
Silicon	2516	0.29	N	Hell *et al.*	315
Silver	3281	0.021		Hell *et al.*	313
Sodium	5890	0.0016		Ramírez-Muñoz *et al.*[19]	
Strontium	4607	0.019		Hell *et al.*	313
Tantalum	2715	5.4	N	Ramírez-Muñoz and Roth[15]	
Tellurium	2143	0.079		Ramírez-Muñoz[14]	
Terbium	4327	20	N	Anderson[17]	
Thallium	3776	0.13		Ramírez-Muñoz[14]	
Thorium	3245	850	N	Ramírez-Muñoz and Roth[15]	
Thulium	4094	3	N	Anderson[17]	
Tin	2863	0.70		Claus *et al.*	150
Titanium	3643	0.33	N	Ramírez-Muñoz and Roth[15]	
Tungsten	2551	1.7	N	Ramírez-Muñoz and Roth[15]	
Uranium	4244	112	N	Hell *et al.*	315
Vanadium	3184	0.36	N	Hell *et al.*	315
Ytterbium	3988	0.25	N	Amos and Willis[16]	
Yttrium	4102	4	N	Anderson[17]	
Zinc	2139	0.0012		Ramírez-Muñoz[14]	
Zirconium	3601	6.2	N	Ramírez-Muñoz and Roth[15]	

N = Nitrous oxide–acetylene flame.
[13] Data to be published.
[14] According to data published in the article by J. RAMÍREZ-MUÑOZ, Sensitivities in atomic-absorption spectrophotometry. II, *Flame Notes. Beckman*, 1 (2) (1966) 38.
[15] According to data published in the article by J. RAMÍREZ-MUÑOZ AND M. E. ROTH, Sensitivities in atomic-absorption spectrophotometry. IV, *Flame Notes. Beckman*, 2 (1) (1967) 18.
[16] According to data published in ref. (*20*).
[17] According to data communicated by J. W. ANDERSON, The application of atomic-absorption spectrophotometry to rare-earth analysis. Paper presented to the 5th National Meeting of the Society for Applied Spectroscopy. Chicago, Ill., June 13–17, 1966.
[18] According to data published by C. E. MULFORD, Iridium absorption, *Atomic Absorption Newsletter*, 5 (3) (1966) 63.
[19] According to data published in the article by J. RAMÍREZ-MUÑOZ, M. E. ROTH AND M. ÖSTRING, Sensitivities in atomic-absorption spectrophotometry. III, *Flame Notes. Beckman*, 1 (4) (1966) 104.
[20] Osmium has very recently been studied. At 2909 Å it gives a percentual concentration limit of 1 p.p.m., using a nitrous oxide–acetylene flame. Consult *Chem. Eng. News*, 45 (44) (1967) 42.

TABLE 13–5

FLUCTUATIONAL QUALITATIVE CONCENTRATION LIMITS*

Element	*Wave-length (Å)*	*Fluctuational concentration limit*		*Special conditions*	*Authors*	*Refs.*
Aluminum	3093	0.19	N	1 ×, 1 sec	Ramírez-Muñoz and Roth[15]	
Antimony	2176	0.15		1 ×, 10 sec	Ramírez-Muñoz[13]	
Arsenic	1937	0.41		2 ×, 10 sec	Ramírez-Muñoz[14]	
Barium	5536	0.065	N	1 ×, 10 sec	Ramírez-Muñoz and Roth[15]	
Beryllium	2349	0.003	N		Manning	453
Bismuth	2231	0.2			Slavin *et al.*	709
Boron	2497	3.0	N	1 ×, 1 sec	Ramírez-Muñoz and Roth[15]	
Cadmium	2288	0.01			Slavin *et al.*	709
Calcium	4227	0.0010		10 ×, 10 sec	Ramírez-Muñoz[14]	
Cerium	5200	11	N	5 ×, 10 sec	Ramírez-Muñoz and Roth[15]	
Cesium	8521	0.05			Slavin *et al.*	709
Chromium	3579	0.00030		5 ×, 10 sec	Ramírez-Muñoz[14]	
Cobalt	2407	0.070		1 ×, 0.4 sec	Hell *et al.*	313
Copper	3248	0.00030		5 ×, 10 sec	Ramírez-Muñoz[14]	
Dysprosium	4046	0.1	N		Anderson[17]	
Erbium	4008	0.1	N		Anderson[17]	
Europium	4594	0.026	N	1 ×, 10 sec	Ramírez-Muñoz and Roth[15]	
Gadolinium	3684	15	N		Anderson[17]	
Gallium	2874	0.012		5 ×, 10 sec	Ramírez-Muñoz[14]	
Germanium	2652	0.11	N	2 ×, 10 sec	Ramírez-Muñoz and Roth[15]	
Gold	2428	0.0035		5 ×, 10 sec	Ramírez-Muñoz[14]	
Hafnium						
Holmium	4054	0.3	N		Manning	453
Indium	3040	0.0090		5 ×, 10 sec	Ramírez-Muñoz[14]	
Iridium	2850	4			Mulford[18]	
Iron	2483	0.0011		5 ×, 10 sec	Ramírez-Muñoz[14]	
Lanthanum	3928	10.4	N	10 ×, 5 sec	Hell *et al.*	315
Lead	2833	0.080		1 ×, 0.4 sec	Hell *et al.*	313
Lithium	6708	0.0010			Ramírez-Muñoz[13]	
Lutetium	3082	50	N		Anderson[17]	
Magnesium	2852	0.000025		2 ×, 10 sec	Ramírez-Muñoz[14]	
Manganese	2795	0.00015		5 ×, 10 sec	Ramírez-Muñoz[14]	
Mercury	2537	0.13		1 ×, 0.4 sec	Hell *et al.*	313
Molybdenum	3133	0.050	N	1 ×, 0.4 sec	Hell *et al.*	315
Neodymium	4925	1	N		Anderson[17]	
Nickel	2320	0.0050		1 ×, 10 sec	Ramírez-Muñoz[14]	
Niobium	3349	1.6	N	5 ×, 10 sec	Ramírez-Muñoz and Roth[15]	
Osmium						
Palladium	2476	0.014		5 ×, 10 sec	Ramírez-Muñoz[14]	
Platinum	2659	0.032		2 ×, 10 sec	Ramírez-Muñoz[14]	
Potassium	7665	0.00070		1 ×, 10 sec	Ramírez-Muñoz[14]	
Praseodymium	4951	15	N		Manning	453
Rhenium	3461	0.19	N	10 ×, 10 sec	Ramírez-Muñoz and Roth[15]	
Rhodium	3435	0.13		2 ×, 10 sec	Ramírez-Muñoz[14]	
Rubidium	7800	0.0080		1 ×, 0.4 sec	Brace *et al.*	110
Ruthenium						
Samarium	5175	1	N		Anderson[17]	
Scandium	3912	0.023	N	5 ×, 10 sec	Ramírez-Muñoz and Roth[15]	

TABLE 13–5 (continued)

Element	*Wave-length (Å)*	*Fluctuational concentration limit*		*Special conditions*	*Authors*	*Refs.*
Selenium	1961	0.20		5 ×, 10 sec	Ramírez-Muñoz[14]	
Silicon	2516	0.10	N	1 ×, 0.4 sec	Hell *et al.*	315
Silver	3281	0.0030		1 ×, 0.4 sec	Hell *et al.*	313
Sodium	5890	0.00032		1 ×, 10 sec	Ramírez-Muñoz *et al.*[19]	
Strontium	4607	0.0020		1 ×, 0.4 sec	Brace *et al.*	110
Tantalum	2715	2.6	N	5 ×, 10 sec	Ramírez-Muñoz and Roth[15]	
Tellurium	2143	0.015		5 ×, 10 sec	Ramírez-Muñoz[14]	
Terbium	4327	3	N		Manning	453
Thallium	3776	0.013		5 ×, 10 sec	Ramírez-Muñoz[14]	
Thorium	3245	180	N	10 ×, 10 sec	Ramírez-Muñoz and Roth[15]	
Thulium	4094	5	N		Anderson[17]	
Tin	2863	0.70		1 ×, 0.4 sec	Claus *et al.*	150
Titanium	3643	0.012	N	10 ×, 10 sec	Ramírez-Muñoz and Roth[15]	
Tungsten	2551	0.38	N	1 ×, 10 sec	Ramírez-Muñoz and Roth[15]	
Uranium	4244	15	N	10 ×, 5 sec	Hell *et al.*	315
Vanadium	3184	0.050	N	1 ×, 0.4 sec	Hell *et al.*	315
Ytterbium	3988	0.01	N		Anderson[17]	
Yttrium	4077	0.5	N		Manning (also Anderson[17])	453
Zinc	2139	0.00035		2 ×, 10 sec	Ramírez-Muñoz[14]	
Zirconium	3601	1.6		5 ×, 10 sec	Ramírez-Muñoz and Roth[15]	

N = Nitrous oxide–acetylene flame.
* See footnotes by Table 13–4.

conditions must be identical, if strictly comparable data are to be achieved. However, Table 13–4 can serve as a basis for comparison between the sensitivities obtainable by atomic-absorption and other instrumental methods, e.g. the traditional emission flame photometry. In making such comparisons, the following factors must be kept in mind.

(a) The quality of the two limits must be the same, i.e. percentual limits must be compared with other percentual limits, fluctuational limits with fluctuational limits, etc. In emission flame photometry, fluctuational qualitative concentration limits are generally published.

(b) Attention must be paid *to distinguish whether the criteria for establishing the limits are the same*; e.g. signal equal to the peak-to-peak noise or another criterion, *the same damping*, etc.

Extreme positions of the instrumental controls (too small a slit, too much gain) may cause excessive noise from the electronic components, so that the corresponding fluctuational qualitative concentration limit calculated as a function of the recorded noise may be modified. On the other hand, extreme damping and recording the signals over a considerable period of time, may help to obtain apparent high sensitivities and very low fluctuational qualitative concentration limits. At present, there is no standardized criterion for the presentation of comparable fluctuational values; this has led some workers to seek more or less complicated formulae to enable them to calculate concentration limits (*280, 853*).

Table 13–5 presents some fluctuational values, most of which were obtained by Ramírez-Muñoz *et al.* (*602*); the data were obtained without damping unless otherwise indicated.

A very important detail is that the concentration limits mentioned in the literature are almost always determined under *ideal conditions* with a complete absence of other components in the solutions; thus, no other component can interfere and so contribute to losses of sensitivity, such as may occur in solutions prepared from actual samples. Even with the same experimental conditions and the same equipment, it may be difficult to reproduce values for a particular element if the sample solution is not a simple saline solution.

5. SUPERIOR VALUES OF SENSITIVITY IN ATOMIC-ABSORPTION

It is not surprising that in most cases higher sensitivity values are found in atomic-absorption than in emission flame photometry; the measurements in the former method involve the majority of the atoms supplied by the sprayed sample, whereas in emission, as is well known, only a small fraction of the atoms is effectively active.

Many modifications have been devised to increase sensitivity for many elements. It is curious to note that the concentration limits found for diverse elements tend towards a certain uniformity, if not in numbers, at least in order of magnitude (between p.p.m. and p.p.b.). This uniformity is not observed in the data obtained for concentration limits in emission flame photometry.

A graphical representation of the different levels of sensitivity is shown in Fig. 13–12.

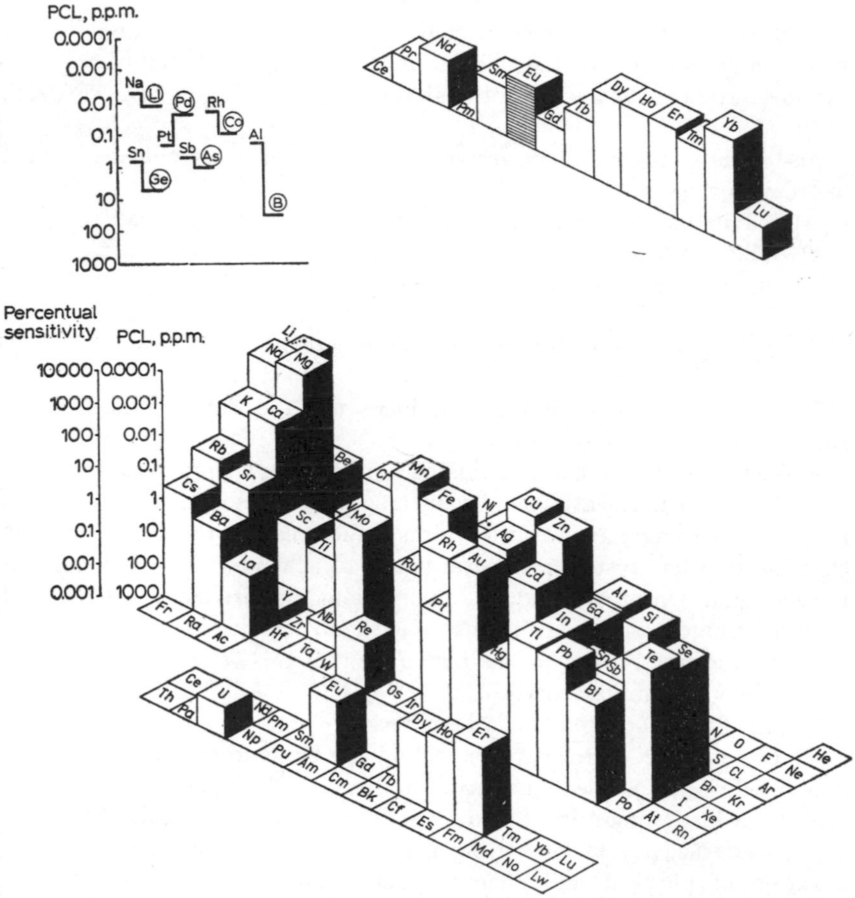

Fig. 13–12. Graphical representation of different levels of percentual sensitivity achieved for different elements. At the top (left), the positions of several elements hidden by others are shown at the same scale. At the top (right), the strip for the rare earths gives the recent values of Anderson (see Table 13–4). Europium is represented with the same height as in the main representation.

6. FACTORS WHICH INFLUENCE SENSITIVITY IN ATOMIC-ABSORPTION

Qualitative and quantitative sensitivity depend on the following factors:

(a) slope of calibration graphs and working curves (relates to relative percentual qualitative sensitivity),

(b) noise at blank level (relates to relative fluctuational qualitative sensitivity),

(c) feed rate,

(d) necessary reading time,

(e) precision desired.

Factors (c) and (d) are connected with the required volume V. The precision desired permits the calculation of factors p' and then of p.

Some authors have discussed the above-mentioned factors (*602, 709, 756, 757*).

According to these factors, instrumental performance should be studied in order to achieve:

(1) maximum slope of the working curve,

(2) minimum noise, and

(3) minimum reading time at a given feed rate.

6.1. Methods of increasing the slope

There are various possibilities for increasing the slope of the working curves.

(a) The lamp current can be adjusted to maximum energy output without exceeding the current at which broadening or self absorption occurs. Thus it is possible to use narrower slit widths, which reduces the effects of flame emission in a d.c. system and permits one to achieve better selection and use less gain. On other hand, the fluctuational sensitivity is also favored from the moment when, with the use of less gain, less noise may be achieved. Maximum energy output means high I_0. From this stems the interest in using lamps of high intensity.

(b) The flame background can be reduced.

(c) The efficiency of the sprayer section can be improved. In this respect it is beneficial to use heated spray chambers which impede large losses of analyte. A larger quantity of analyte goes to the flame per unit of time.

(d) The efficiency of generating atomic vapor can be increased (optimization of physical and chemical flame conditions—fuel-rich flames, reducing flames or cooler flames in some cases, i.e., in zinc determinations—and use of convenient additions such as solvents, buffer elements, releasers, protectors; modification of the nature and composition of the flame to decrease flame background).

(e) The optimum zone in the flame can be selected. It is possible that in the course of the measurement of a dilution series one may have to look for the optimum selection zone for each interval of concentrations so as to avoid distortions in the working curve, which can occur if the selection zone is kept fixed.

(f) The optical system can be designed to produce the narrowest beam consistent with the geometry of the flame.

(g) The optical path of the beam across the absorption medium can be increased by multiple passes, multiple burners, long-path adapters, long burner-slots.

(h) The peaking and isolation of the source line can be improved properly.

6.2. *Methods of minimizing noise*

Factors relating to the minimizing of noise include:

(a) choosing a low noise detection system, which permits work with greater signal-to-noise ratio;

(b) choosing a stable amplifier;

(c) choosing the best recorder conditions (gain settings and damping);

(d) stabilizing the operation of the source power supply;

(e) choosing the proper time to allow the instrument to reach equilibrium (electronics, gas regulators, chamber, burner);

(f) optimizing the source current to provide maximum stability;

(g) optimizing, for smaller fluctuations, the sprayer and burner operation;

(h) providing a stable and constant gas supply.

Most of these factors help to increase precision, and also to increase fluctuational sensitivity.

6.3. *Methods of decreasing reading time*

Some methods are:

(a) diminishing the inertia of the burner-sprayer section;

(b) decreasing the time constant of the photometric system;

(c) decreasing the time constant of the recording system;

(d) choosing a proper recorder chart speed, as the signal trace recorded with minimum response time of an average signal should be long enough for visual integration;

(e) improving the stability of the signal (noise level and drift) which influences the minimum length of trace acceptable for a reasonable visual integration.

It is pertinent here to add a few further comments on scale expansion and damping (cf. Chapter 10, Section 3.4). If the ordinate scale is expanded (in order to achieve better readability on the scale or on the strip-chart), noise level and drift are amplified as well as the signal, and it may be necessary to increase reading times in order to obtain some visual criterion for integration. Generally, if the time constant is increased to increase stability or reduce noise, then the required time to obtain a useful integrated reading is prolonged accordingly. A proper compromise of gain, damping, scale expansion, and noise level should be found to minimize the required sample volume and thus increase absolute sensitivity.

6.4. Factors which decrease sensitivity

Besides the effects mentioned in the preceding sections, the following factors should be considered.

(a) Intense emission produced by the flame (line and background), even when its effects are diminished by chopping or increasing I_0. In the instruments which do not use a chopper, it is best to adjust the 100% absorption by spraying a solution containing the analyte in a concentration equal or similar to the concentration to be measured by absorption. If the emission effects are about 1–3% only, it is possible to compensate the emission effects by simply adjusting the 100% absorption with a solution containing the analyte at the highest concentration level of the whole series of solutions. The highest standard can be use for this purpose. If the effects are greater than 3%, it is advisable to adjust each time with each solution to be measured. The emission effects are tested with the highest standard of the standard dilution series.

(b) A large number of reflecting or transmitting surfaces.

(c) Too high a current for the hollow-cathode lamp.

(d) Insufficient optical selection.

(e) Excessive noise in the source.

(f) Turbulence in the optical path.

(g) Excessive gain in the recorder.

Some of these factors affect percentual values, and others fluctuational values. Any instrumental variation (change of any parameter) must be carefully studied. For example, if attempts are made to decrease the broadening by diminishing the lamp current, the emitted line signal may be reduced too much; this may decrease excessively the signal-to-background ratio which would also reduce the sensitivity. Variations in the optical system may also be critical. For example, by centering and focusing the image of the hollow cathode in the flame itself, better results can be achieved for calcium. The height of the image focused in the flame—with respect to the top of the burner—is particularly critical, and great reductions of sensitivity may be found if the height is not properly adjusted.

7. EXPERIMENTAL REDUCTION OF SENSITIVITY

There are many possible procedures for achieving a reduction of sensitivity, e.g., the selection of less absorbent lines or the decrease of the beam path-length through the burner (by rotating the burner). It is also possible to combine a careful selection of some of the factors mentioned in the preceding section.

A rotation of the slot burner (see Chapter 8, Section 4.1) decreases the sensitivity, since the path is shortened, but it also gives rise to anomalous collateral effects. When the flame of the fish-tail type is inclined with respect to the optical axis, the beam crosses the flame at an angle and must then cross a greater surface (on both sides) of the lateral layers of the flame which are more in contact with the external medium; the beam, thus meets conditions different from normal. These differences, which are greater at small angles, are attenuated at greater angles.

The interest in decreasing the sensitivity in some cases may be easily explained. When an instrument is functioning under optimum conditions to achieve the maximum sensitivity, the optimum interval of analytical determinations is displaced towards the lower part of the concentration scale. High concentrations are then located in the curvature zone of the working curve. A decrease in sensitivity is needed in order to achieve a response which is, at least, almost linear in the high zone of the concentration scale. Any decrease of sensitivity displaces the operating zone upward.

The instruments equipped with multiple burner devices and with multi-pass devices offer a progressive form of decreasing the sensitivity and of taking advantage of more extensive working intervals. At the present time atomic-absorption flame photometry is being used for many analytical cases in which the maximum available sensitivity is not necessary.

Recently, Margoshes (*473*) has presented a study of the criteria used to select wavelengths for atomic-absorption work, in order to predict which are the most useful lines when the concentration of an element is too high to permit measurement with the most sensitive lines, and also to predict which lines will provide the best sensitivity.

Where it is permissible to reduce sensitivity, it is best to use methods which not only have this effect but also reduce the potential causes of variability in the results. Excessive noise is a major source of error, so that it is advisable to enlarge the slit width, provided that sufficient resolution is not lost in so doing, and work may be done with less gain. If noise is not a highly perturbing factor—even at high sensitivity—, reduction of the number of light passes, or in the number of burners (or both), or rotation of the burner can be used.

If there are different conditions for reduction of sensitivity, a linear response is always obtained, and at the same time what may be called an *instrumental expansion of linearity along the concentration scale* (see Fig. 13–13). If an analytical problem is to be solved by measuring concentrations in the region of the right of the concentration scale, there are two sets of experimental conditions which are of different sensitivity, as shown in Fig. 13–13. But when low concentrations towards the left of the scale have to be measured, then it is imperative to select the set of conditions which give the maximum sensitivity.

Operating at high sensitivity may facilitate the preparatory phase or even the operating conditions for some elements. For example, if a preliminary concentration by precipitation or extraction is necessary in instrumental conditions of low sensitivity, it may prove possible to carry out direct determinations at high sensitivity without preliminary concen-

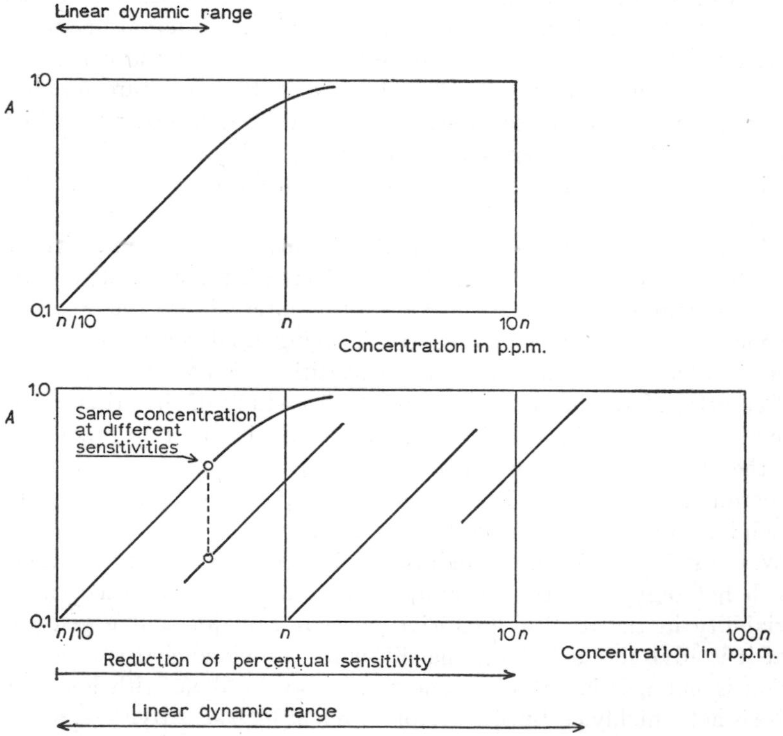

Fig. 13–13,a. Instrumental expansion of linearity along the concentration scale by reduction of percentual sensitivity.

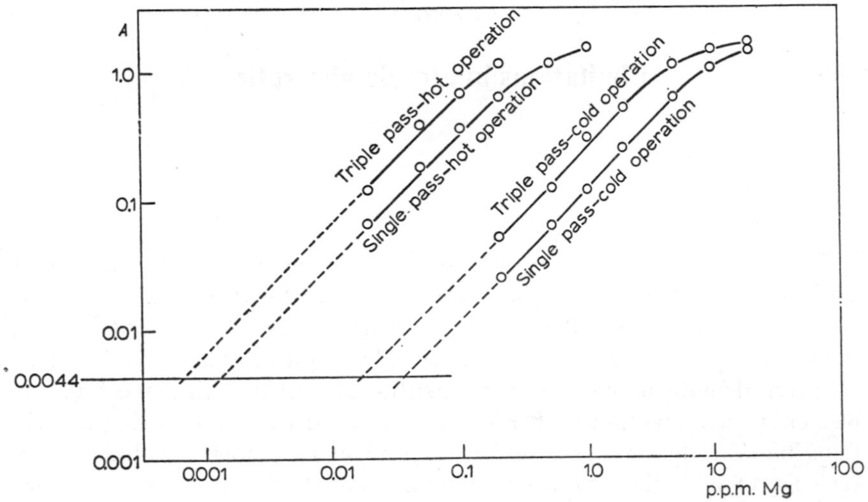

Fig. 13–13,b. Working curves for magnesium under different instrumental sensitivity conditions. See situation of the percentual concentration limits at the level $A = 0.0044$. (These curves were obtained with a Beckman atomic-absorption spectrophotometer, No. 97900, and a laminar flow burner).

tration. If it is possible to work at high sensitivity in cases in which physical interferences are observed (effects of high viscosity, the presence of organic matter, etc.), more dilute solutions may be prepared so that such interfering effects are decreased.

8. SPECIAL CASE OF HEAVY ELEMENTS

Since some heavy elements offer less sensitivity than is common for other elements, Lambie (*415*) was interested in knowing if this circumstance is a general phenomenon. Walsh (*804*) considers that for elements with very complicated spectra, the oscillator strength of the most intense line is lower than that of elements with simpler spectra. This is why lower sensitivities have been found.

Chapter 14

Limitations in atomic absorption

The elements that can be determined and the sensitivity that can be achieved have been discussed in Chapters 12 and 13 as two of the dimensions that define the range of the atomic-absorption method. In later Chapters, information will be given about its specific applications. In the previous chapters definite limitations were mentioned, either with respect to the elements themselves, or with respect to the sensitivity. This chapter will describe other limitations which greatly affect two other essential characteristics of analytical methods: *accuracy* and *precision*. *Interferences* are also mentioned and these may cause limitations of sensitivity. In fact, if sensitivity values are determined under ideal conditions in the absence of other components in the solutions sprayed, then when other components accompany the analyte, apparent or effective increases of sensitivity may be produced by enhancement phenomena, and decreases may be produced by depression phenomena.

A comprehensive study of the main limitations found in atomic-absorption work and also of the chemical means available for overcoming these limitations has been presented (*589*).

1. ACCURACY

Accuracy is determined by the proximity of the experimental values found to the values which are *designated as theoretical*. In experimental methods it is customary to compare the values found by the method with *added* concentrations (reference values) or to compare the found values for certified samples (standard analytical samples). The accuracy of the method is then expressed as a function of the experimental *errors* found, i.e. the differences between the experimental value and the value considered theoretical.

Since the atomic-absorption method is based on comparative procedures, i.e. working curve or comparison standards, the quality of the standards must have a considerable influence on the accuracy.

The accuracy may be limited by the action of other components which accompany the analyte in the sample and which may cause experimental

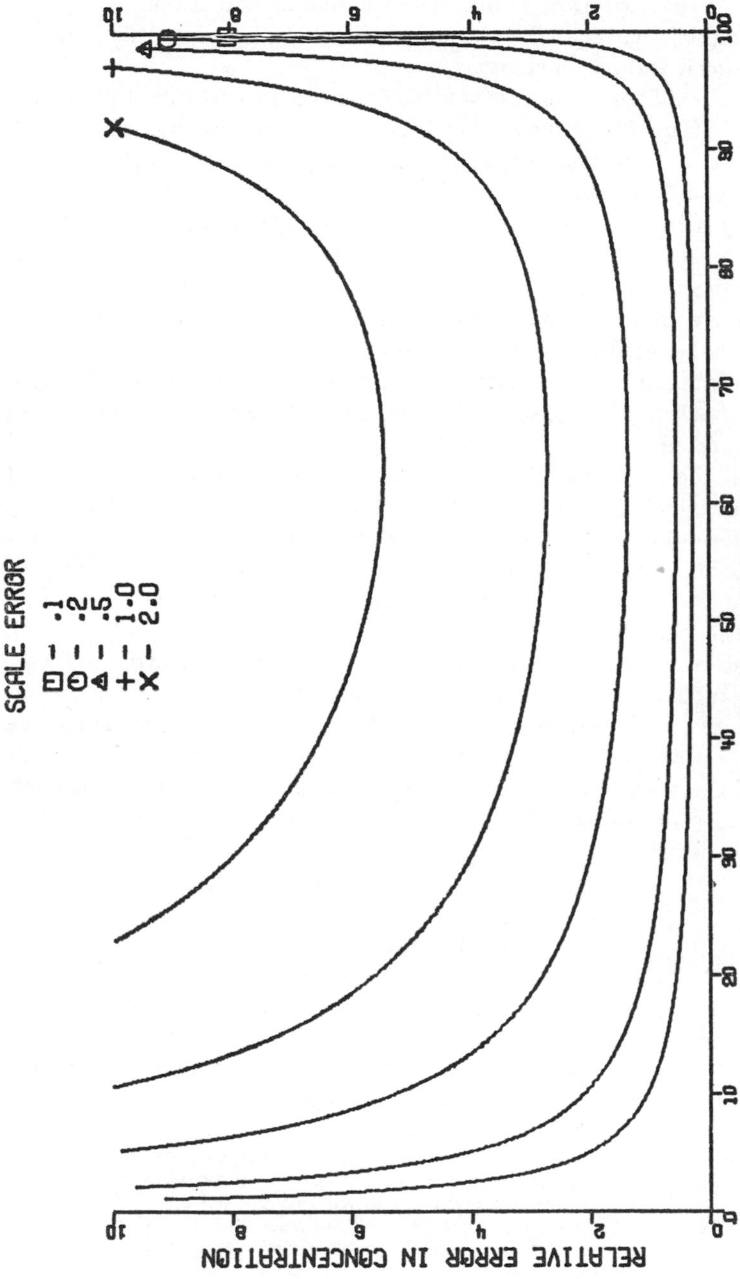

Fig. 14–1. Variations of the relative error in concentration with % absorption values at different scale errors. Direct reproduction of the graph automatically drawn from computer data (courtesy Beckman Instruments, Inc. and *Microchem. J.*)

deviations of the analytical results. If such components are absent, or do not interfere, the accuracy will be conditioned only by losses, contaminations, and operational and personal errors.

In general, a high accuracy can be achieved in analyses by atomic-absorption. If no interferences need be considered because of the low concentration of accompanying components, then comparison standards—simpler to reproduce than in other instrumental methods—may be prepared carefully with highly pure chemical compounds (*pro analisi* products). If the samples can be handled in aqueous solutions, the simultaneous preparation of aqueous solutions of standards is extremely simple.

If there are interference effects, procedures to attenuate these interferences can be used. In extreme cases in which interferences may be difficult to eliminate or attenuate, standard addition methods can be used to achieve final data of greater accuracy. The interfering components can also be separated.

Although the concepts of accuracy and precision are very different, it is also well known that accuracy is, to a certain extent, conditioned by the precision[1]. Precision receives special attention in atomic-absorption methods because it is the best index for expressing the repeatability of the method and its influence on the accuracy of the experimental values.

The relationship between accuracy and sensitivity in atomic-absorption, on the basis of the considerations used for other absorptiometric methods, has been studied and the best reading conditions for best accuracy established (*598, 935*). According to the distribution of errors along the % absorption scale (Fig. 14–1), readings should be made in the middle portion of the scale for better accuracy. For sample solutions with low concentrations of the analyte, this condition can only be achieved with instruments of high sensitivity.

2. PRECISION

In the literature one frequently finds data on precision and precision comparative tables. The table published by Walsh (*800*) may be cited, in which the deviations found in some determinations by atomic-absorption have been added; also of great interest is the comparative study presented

[1] For quantitative analytical data found by any method, two extreme cases may be encountered: (a) a good accuracy (between the average and the supposed theoretical value) with a poor precision (great deviations in each of the determinations). (b) A bad accuracy, but a good precision. Ideally, both accuracy and precision should be good. Case (a) might seem admissible since the error of the average is small, but this figure is the average of many values in which the deviations are "fortunately" compensated. Case (b) is not admissible if isolated determinations are to be handled.

by Gilbert (*275*). The data published by Walsh reflect the repeatability of determinations for different levels of concentration.

The precision is usually expressed in terms of standard deviation or as a function of the standard deviation: (a) related to the average—coefficient of variation in percentage—, or (b) related to full-scale value (concentration scale)—percentage of full scale—. In the second case an arbitrary upper end of the concentration scale is fixed. Different forms of expression are chosen by different authors so that care is needed in comparing data. For studies of repeatability along the concentration scale, it is more profitable to refer to them as coefficients of variation with respect to full-scale value (percentage of full scale).

To obtain a good repeatability in atomic-absorption, it is clearly necessary to control strictly all the experimental parameters subject to variability: solvents, emitter, flame, height of the selection zone in the flame, feed rate, slit width, and many others already mentioned in other chapters, as well as all the factors related to the nature of the sample itself (particularly with reference to other metallic components accompanying the analyte and predominant anions). Carroll and Neville (*143*) has discussed parameters such as light sources, burners, spectral resolution systems, etc., and has stressed that hollow-cathode lamp current, interaction of the sample with burner gas mixture and practical resolution of the monochromator should be studied before to analysis to insure sensitivity and *precision*. Neville and Carroll (*526*) mention that lead sensitivity and *precision* depends on the anions present, the resonance line chosen and the instrumental parameters involved; the best results were obtained with the line Pb 2170 Å.

In general terms, it may be said that the precision depends principally on the stability of the two systems which have the most direct influence on the absorption process: the emission and absorption systems. The precision is closely associated with the noise level. When very small luminous intensities are detected by photomultipliers, the shot noise of the detector limits the precision.

Good precision will be attained if the instrument presents good repeatability in the following aspects:

(a) good repeatability in measuring a single solution several times, under practically invariable operating conditions;

(b) stability of readings or recorded signal for a single solution under a long-term feeding;

(c) repeatability of results from one working session to another, if settings of the instrument are identical, but resetting is done each time.

It is interesting to observe not only the repeatability of a particular reading, but also the repeatability of the working curve (*shape*—linearity—and *position*—slope and intercept—). Svehla *et al.* (*754*) calculate the precision as the standard deviation of the concentration measurement (in percentage) as a function of the standard deviations observed for the absorbance measurements, for the intercept, and for the working curve slope, including in their equation the values of the absorbance, intercept and slope (cf. ref. (*393*)). These precision studies are very useful in the establishment of optimum working conditions. Erdey and Svehla (*216*) have reviewed the optimum conditions for determination of zinc, silver, copper and gold (cf. ref. (*217, 393*)).

Apart from the sample itself and the instrumental equipment, the preparation and dilution of the sample may contribute to a large loss of precision in the final results, where errors arising from the *preparative process* and the *instrumental process* are accumulated.

The repeatability of the atomic-absorption methods in comparison with other instrumental methods may be considered good, especially when samples are compared with good standards. *Occasional variations*, e.g. variations of the flame, affect only the measurement being made at that instant; fluctuations of this type seem to have a greater effect at short wavelengths. One of the reasons contributing to the wide acceptance of hollow-cathode lamps is that they are more stable than vapor lamps.

Malmstadt and Chambers (*451*) mention coefficients of variation of 0.1% (precision null point). Coefficients of variation are generally between 0.5% and 1% for most analyses with good established operating conditions. In adverse experimental conditions, the coefficient of variation may be considerably greater. Ordinarily, it is difficult to achieve a repeatability better than 0.5%, since the fluctuations of the emission system contribute a considerable fraction of that figure.

It is natural that the concentration should be a primary factor in repeatability. The coefficient of variation will be greater for low concentrations and in the concentration regions in which curvature appears. Appropriate dilution of the prepared solution may, in extreme cases, make it possible to achieve the interval of best repeatability.

Finally, of course, where chemical preparation of the sample is required, the fewer the number of separative steps involved, the better will be the total coefficients of variation obtained.

3. DISTURBANCES AND INTERFERENCES

Following the criteria used previously by the author (see ref. (*125*), pp. 174–175), the name *disturbance* is given to any anomalous phenomenon which causes experimental errors. *Interferences* are those particular anomalous phenomena which are produced by other components in the solutions containing the analyte and which affect the conduct of the analyte in the absorption process, as well as phenomena produced by the flame itself[2]. Thus interferences are a particular kind of disturbance. Various authors have presented different classifications of interferences; two of these are cited below.

(a) *Classification published by Allan* (*16*). Allan uses the criteria of Walsh, dividing the interferences into the following groups.

(i) *Radiation interferences* which may be eliminated with the use of modulation. However, in d.c. systems disturbances coming from the flame remain, especially those produced at wavelengths above 3200 Å.

(ii) *Physical interferences* which include gain or loss of excitation through collision with other atoms or molecules; this type of interference is not of great significance in the absorption process.

(iii) *Chemical interferences* in which the atomic concentration is changed because of some chemical reaction. These affect the emission process as much as the absorption process.

(b) *Classification published by Gilbert* (*274*). Gilbert groups the interferences in the following categories.

(i) *Spectroscopic interferences* or interferences of the instrumental type.

(ii) *Chemical interferences*, considered as element-specific interferences, characteristic of each analyte, provoked by actions produced in the vapor phase or in the condensed phase.

(iii) *Physical interferences* or interferences considered as non-specific, and which are general to the different analytes to be determined by atomic absorption.

Koirtyohann and Pickett (*409*) have recently reviewed the different causes of interferences which they divide into: (a) flame emission, considered in both d.c. and a.c. systems, (b) background and/or unabsorbed light in the source, (c) absorption by the flame and solvent, and (d) spectral absorption by the sample matrix or interelement chemical suppressants or enhancers. They emphazise molecular absorption, such as that found in some of the experiments, which cannot be due to simple scattering. This was proved by passing 0.4% powdered alumina in suspension.

The subsequent sections of this chapter, the principal causes which limit the application of atomic-absorption methods are discussed. The various limiting factors are classified according to the *three active components of the analytical process*: *instrument*, *operation*, and *sample*. Their nature will cause, according to the case, anomalous modification of the accuracy, precision and sensitivity.

---

[2] For preliminary information, see the paper on interferences in emission (*392*). See also references (*254, 410, 859, 902*).

4. LIMITING FACTORS DEPENDING ON THE INSTRUMENTAL SYSTEM

The limiting factors which originate in the different parts of the instrumental system are summarized below. Some of the factors which intervene in emission work (see ref. (*125*), p. 175 ff.) also affect atomic-absorption processes. Limitations in atomic-absorption work with respect to instrumental and sample factors have been reviewed (*588*).

4.1. Factors in the emission system

The following may be mentioned.

(a) Lack of stability in the power supply.

(b) Worn-out lamps. If they are of the multicathode type, the cathode may be contaminated. If they are of the single-cathode type, they may have suffered clean-up necessitating regeneration. The exit window may have lost its transparency owing to deposits.

(c) Inadequate lamps of small light output, or with a narrow window or a great distance between the cathode and the exit window. Thus the effective aperture of the lamp is decreased.

(d) Production of continuum.

4.2. Factors in the absorption system

The following factors are important where flame methods are used.

(a) Gases which are unsuitable since the flames produced are too hot or too cold for the element being determined.

(b) Burner with a path that is too short. If the slit is also too small, the optical path across the flame is too limited.

(c) Burner with a path which is too long. The process is exposed to excessive absorption by the flame itself.

(d) Critical characteristics of the burner. Turbulence phenomena—not expected in laminar burners—may be produced if gas flows different from those dictated by the design of the burner for normal operation are used.

(e) Inadequate characteristics of the sprayer, especially if it produces a spray very rich in large drops, intermittent spray, or small yield.

(f) Deficient gas regulator, especially if it shows excessive random variations (too noisy).

(g) Lack of stability in the heating of the spray chamber: slow progressive cooling, by excessive spraying of samples, standards, blanks, and washing solutions.

(h) Emissions coming from the flame (line and continuum emissions). Although modulation is used to eliminate these emissions, part of them are detected at the detector, due to a noise component concordant with the modulation frequency.

(i) Excessive loss of light in the mirror surfaces (transmitting and reflecting surfaces), especially in multipass systems, double-beam systems and instruments equipped with beam combiners.

(j) Pumping effect of the air compressor.

4.3. Factors in the selection system

This section should especially include the lack of sufficient resolution. Although the selection system does not require as much resolution as is necessary in emission, it still has the following functions: (a) to try to eliminate as far as possible the continuum proceeding from the emission system, which is *modulated* and therefore is not separated by the photometric system; (b) to resolve and separate adjacent lines also coming from the emission system. Lack of resolution immediately contributes to losses of sensitivity. Faulty efficiency of the gratings decreases the sensitivity for some wavelengths.

4.4. Factors in the photometric system

Such factors are as follows.

(a) Lack of stability of the electrical equipment.

(b) Inadequate tuning with the emission system or with the chopper.

(c) Excessive noise effects in the meter or in the recorder.

(d) Inadequate time constant in the meter or in the recorder.

(e) Detector showing excessive shot noise.

(f) Insufficient amplification.

5. LIMITING FACTORS ASSOCIATED WITH OPERATION

This section lists the operational factors which may be controlled to a certain degree by the operator.

5.1. Operational factors related to the emission system

Among this group the following are the most important.

(a) Excessive or insufficient current applied to the lamp.

(b) Inadequate alignment of the lamp in the instrument, off-center with respect to the optical axis.

(c) Auxiliary lenses out of focus.

(d) Inadequate vacuum in the open lamps.

5.2. Operational factors related to the absorption system

The following may be mentioned.

(a) Defective choice of the selection zone.

(b) Lack of alignment of the burner in the optical axis.

(c) Auxiliary lenses out of focus.

(d) Mirrors and semi-mirrors out of focus.

(e) Lack of cleanliness of the auxiliary optical instrumental parts.

(f) Inadequate gas pressures and/or flows.

(g) Lack of maintenance of established gas pressures and/or flows.

(h) Too little vigilance of vent suction, lateral currents of air or convection currents.

(i) Excessive or insufficient feed rates.

(j) Inadequate height of suction in tubing feeding[3].

(k) Excessively short or long feed time. Short times do not allow proper equilibrium to be reached in separate burner and sprayer devices. Long times favor the formation of deposits, especially with very rich saline solutions.

(l) Contaminations due to contributions of the burner or to accidental contaminations in the suction or spraying sections. The use of corrosive solutions should be avoided as much as possible.

(m) Saline deposits in the burner, in the spraying chamber or in the nozzle.

(n) Partial clogging in the suction capillary.

(o) Carbon deposits on the top of the burner.

5.3. Operational factors related to the selection system

The following factors are relevant.

(a) Incorrect position of the selector knob (defective peaking). The correspondence between the positions read on the monochromator and the wavelength selected should be previously verified, and if necessary, a correction table or curve should be established.

(b) Incorrect resolution due to defective settings.

(c) Slit which is too closed.

---

[3] The author has been able to prove the influence on experimental values obtained by occasional variations of suction height in tubing feeding, during repeatability tests. The suction of solutions with narrow plastic tubes has become general, but the possible variations introduced by excessive variations in suction height must be kept in mind.

5.4. Operational factors related to the recording system

The following points are important.
(a) Readings affected by parallax error.
(b) Inadequate adjustment of the gain.
(c) Inadequate damping.
(d) Defective zeroing.

6. LIMITING FACTORS DEPENDING ON THE SAMPLE

This section will include many factors which are normally labelled as chemical interferences, the most important in the field of atomic-absorption. A review of the articles published since the inception of atomic-absorption methods shows three very different periods: the first in which emphasis was constantly given to the absence of interfering effects, as a defense of the atomic-absorption methods compared to emission[4]; a second period in which interference phenomena were pointed out, discussed and published; and a third in which attention was turned towards the most suitable procedures for the suppression or reduction of interferences.

Many examples illustrate the absence of the so-called *inter-element interferences*; several of them are quite spectacular. The lack of disturbances in the determination of magnesium in the presence of appreciable quantities of sodium has already been mentioned. One of the most serious cases of interference presented in emission is that of the strontium bands which extend up to 6700 Å above the emission of lithium at 6708 Å; in atomic-absorption the determination of lithium may be carried out in the presence

[4] The absence of interferences and the independence of the temperature were two characteristics most praised in atomic-absorption methods. Then it was noted that the independence of temperature is relative. Although it does not have immediate influence in the atomic-absorption process itself—difference from emission—, it has been proved that temperature can control both the liberation of atoms and the interfering effects. Even in early studies, it was observed that although interfering effects were not as evident in atomic-absorption as in emission, they deserved attention, and especially those phenomena which influence emission and atomic-absorption determination in a similar manner (variations of sprayer efficiency with physically different solutions, different vaporization rates in the flame owing to different sample composition, change of flame characteristics by the presence of certain solution components, emission of radiations from the flame from elements different from the analyte, etc.). The so-called radiation and excitation interferences were not as marked as in emission; this was true at the start and continues to be so.

The fact is that the initial studies were made of possible interferences from other *metallic* elements which, except for a few cases, do not exercise great influence. The, explains why in early research more importance was given to the nature of the flame, fineness of the spray, rise-time of the particles in the flame, height of the selection zone, etc., than to the action of other components of the samples.

of considerable quantities of strontium (*864*). One may also recall the example cited by Allan (*9*) in which large quantities (500–3000 p.p.m.) of calcium, potassium, magnesium, sodium and phosphorus do not interfere in the determination of iron and manganese at the 10 p.p.m. level. Slavin (*676*) also mentions the absence of interference for those two elements, as well as others. In emission work, in order to obtain reliable measurements in determinations of manganese and iron, it is sometimes necessary to make a careful correction of background; this is not necessary in atomic-absorption work. The fact pointed out by Robinson that potassium does not interfere in the determinations of sodium is well known (*616*); anomalies are present in the determination of potassium, but to a lesser degree than in its determination by emission flame photometry.

Some of the most notable cases of absence of interferences are due to the absence of limiting factors in the sample itself and to the disappearance of limiting factors in the instrumental process. This is particularly the case with *spectral interferences* which are clearly classifiable within the *instrumental interferences*. Many of these are reduced—and even avoided—by the combined high selection which is used in atomic-absorption (source and monochromator); such is the case in the separation of very near radiations, although difficulties are still encountered in isotopic analysis.

Other examples are due to the lesser significance in atomic-absorption of interferences that may be classified as *chemical interferences* (see later in this chapter).

In this section separate treatment is given to factors of a physical nature which depend on the sample and are known as *physical interferences* and to other of chemical character which are the origin of the so-called *chemical interferences*. No difficulty should be experienced in distinguishing the physical interferences *depending on the sample* from other types of disturbances which are caused by physical factors, such as spectral interferences or instrumental interferences. The physical and chemical interferences included in this section are dependent upon the chemical composition of the solutions to be analysed. It is well known that some of the physical characteristics of the solutions are caused by the presence of certain components in them.

6.1. Physical interferences

These interferences are of a general character, i.e. they may affect different analytes in equal or similar fashion. In this group are classified all interferences caused by factors which modify the behaviour of the solution as a liquid undergoing the spraying process (formation of spray and aerosol) and its evaporation in the flame.

Important effects are exerted by diverse dissolved components—as true solutions or colloidal solutions[5]—or by non-aqueous solvents which are present or added, that is, by all the constituents that modify the efficiency of the transfer of the solution into the flame. In the same category are all those constituents of the solutions which modify the characteristics of the flame, by changing either its temperature, uniformity, composition or transparency.

Of course, if the non-aqueous solvents are voluntarily added to the samples, they cannot be considered as *occasional* factors which modify the final response of the analytes. A distinct case is that of samples which already contain variable quantities of these solvents, e.g. in the analysis of alcoholic beverages, or when solutions contain residual amounts of organic solvents after operations of separation and/or preliminary concentration. The papers of Zeeman and Butler should be consulted (*867*, *868*).

When solutions containing matrix components in high concentrations are being studied, many diverse phenomena can be produced that only can be observed by some final anomalous results, such as decrease or apparent increase of sensitivity. Losses of sensitivity can be due to changes in the feed rate; apparent increases of sensitivity may be considered sometimes as losses of energy, because a high saline content in the solution may cause a secondary effect: scattering of light, which is a non-selective phenomenon. This apparent absorption is observed even in lines which are not resonance lines, and that usually do not show absorption when analyte solutions of low salinity are sprayed. If an excessive salinity cannot be avoided in test solutions and standards, a subtractive correction can be tried; this is done by studying the apparent absorptions measured in lines which are not normally absorbed and which are at a wavelength near the analytical line.

The same effects observed in highly saline solutions (changes in feed rate, lowering of the sprayer efficiency) can happen when high concentrations of acids are present. The interferences of halogenated acids have been studied by Finkelstein and Jansen (*241*). Perturbations produced by excess of acids in the solution can be due not only to the spraying process, but also to displacement of the *ionization equilibrium*, with an increase in the electrical conductivity of the flame. This point has been discussed by Poluéktov (*561*). Prudnikov (*573*) has examined the influences of hydrochloric, nitric, sulfuric and phosphoric acids on determinations of sodium,

[5] For example, the organic matter present in biological samples, the excessive salinity resulting from the neutralization of acids, residual amounts of mineral acids which remain after wet ashing or acid redissolution of dry residues (in the analysis of minerals and alloys, for example).

potassium, rubidium and cesium. All these acids decreased the signals, and Prudnikov considered that, while hydrochloric and phosphoric acids participated in chemical processes, the other acids merely caused a variation of the physical properties. The present author has observed decreases of sensitivity in the determinations of magnesium and calcium in the presence of high concentrations of acetic acid.

The variations of density which cause the appearance of physical interferences may be classified as non-specific where they primarily affect the efficiency of the sprayer—the drop size of the mist varies—and thus cause variations in the quantity of atomic vapor in the flame.

At this point it is wise to clarify a basic concept in the study of interferences. All the physical factors mentioned in this section—and others of a physical nature—limit the *accuracy*, *precision* and *sensitivity* of the method. *Variable* factors affect the repeatability and the accuracy. If they are *constant* from one sample to another, they may not affect the repeatability too much, but they undoubtedly affect the accuracy. If the effects are constant and the standards are compensated, the determinations apparently give acceptable results, since it is possible to find experimental values with reasonable precision. However, whether the factors are variable or constant, the sensitivity is affected whenever depressions or enhancements of the absorption are produced; even if the factors are compensated in the standards, the sensitivity is still modified. Those factors which reduce sensitivity are more disturbing, because they immediately reduce the expected dynamic range.

Similar comments are applicable to the chemical interferences discussed in the next section.

6.2. Chemical interferences

The interferences discussed in this section are characteristic for each analyte. Gilbert (*274*) divides the chemical interferences into two types: those produced in the vapor phase, *vapor-phase interferences*, and others which may be catalogued as *condensed-phase interferences*. It might seem that in some cases the interferences are not chemical since they are of a physical nature—ionization, excitation—but it must remembered that these phenomena are governed by the *chemical composition* of the samples, or are induced by the presence of other chemical components in the absorbing medium, particularly in the flame. Gilbert's use of the term *condensed-phase interference* in several of his reviews on atomic-absorption (*272, 274, 275*) deserves careful consideration. In the paragraphs which follow, the group to which the interference belongs will be indicated where necessary.

In atomic-absorption, as in all analytical methods, proper studies of interferences are almost obligatory. To present a full account of all the interference studies that have been made would be impossible in these pages. Accordingly, the various types of interference are classified, and some pertinent information and representative examples are given. Some types of interference have become well-known; for example, the mutual increases of absorption when alkali metals are present in the samples, the enhancement of the absorption of calcium when sodium and potassium are present, and the anionic interferences. Readers interested in particular cases will find complementary information by consulting the bibliographic sources cited in this section and in Chapter 19.

6.2.1. Dissociation chemical interferences

These interferences result from a particular conjunction involving the composition of the sample solution and the conditions of the flame. Anomalies encountered in elements which present suitable resonance lines are due to insufficient dissociation of molecules at ordinary flame temperatures to form the correct free-atom concentration (the cases of calcium and molybdenum are typical examples). This matter has been discussed in preceding chapters. These phenomena are typical vapor-phase interferences.

These interferences may be called *thermal interferences*.

6.2.2. Ionization chemical interferences

These could also be classified as vapor-phase interferences. Enhancements have been found in studies of cationic interferences among Groups I and II. In emission, similar effects are attributed to increases of excitation, but in absorption they must be explained as depressions in the ionization which produce an increase in the number of atoms in the ground state. In the particular case of potassium, for example, in the presence of sodium, the degree of ionization of the potassium depends on the flame temperature and on the presence of other easily ionized atoms.

The introduction of an easily ionized element into the flame causes the equilibrium to be shifted in favor of the formation of neutral atoms, which increases the absorption to be measured. This phenomenon has been encountered repeatedly in the determination of potassium in the presence of an excess of sodium, e.g., in the determination of potassium in samples of biological origin (*829*). If the composition is variable, the solutions are corrected by equalizing the composition of sample solutions and standards by addition of an excess of the interfering element.

Potassium does not have the same effect in the determination of sodium (*616*), but the actions of sodium and potassium on the determination of calcium may be attributed to a similar phenomenon. David found these effects in the determination of calcium in plants (*163*) and Willis in the determination of calcium in blood serum (*827*). Trent and Slavin (*779*) have demonstrated that the addition of lanthanum (1% lanthanum in the solutions) in calcium determinations in biological materials prevents any enhancement of calcium values by the ionization interference of sodium. Values shown for absorbances obtained with 10 p.p.m. of calcium in the presence of 0, 50, 500 and 1000 p.p.m. of sodium differ only within 1%. The ionization interferences of sodium and potassium in the presence of other alkali metals (rubidium and cesium) have been tested by Manning *et al.* (*462*). Since the phenomena observed show a plateau region, a convenient addition of the interfering alkali (1000 p.p.m., for instance) can equalize sample solutions and standards.

For a complete study of new approaches to the problem of ionization, dissociation and self-absorption, the thesis of Hollander should be consulted (*346*) (cf. ref. (*576*)).

6.2.3. Excitation chemical interferences

This type of interference, which is also of the vapor-phase type and is so significant in emission, does not have great significance in atomic-absorption, where it is the atoms in the ground state which are predominantly active in the absorption process.

An excessive flame temperature may provoke increases in excitation which directly influence the determinations by increasing the light emitted by the flame; this may be eliminated by modulation. In d.c. systems, the emission contribution of the analyte during measurement should be instrumentally compensated (*110*). Instruments help to compensate for this chemical interference in atomic-absorption where the effects are less severe than in emission work. The particular case of strongly emitting elevents is discussed on p. 297. Excitation phenomena in flames have been studied in the literature (*3, 266, 622*).

6.2.4. Inhibition chemical interferences

These are typical examples of condensed-phase interferences, and can be classified as *anionic* and *cationic interferences*, both of which cause partial inhibitions of the analyte.

The effects of chemical interferences are so similar in atomic-absorption and emission that the interference curves (graphical representation of interference phenomena) found by different authors in the two fields are of the same pattern; e.g., the interference of phosphates or aluminum on calcium. All the measures used in emission to avoid or decrease such interferences can be applied to absorption. In his article on spectral methods by direct reading, Scott (*659*) discusses principally the similarity of the effects of phosphorus and aluminum in emission and in absorption.

Among examples of cationic inhibition, Firman (*243*) found a peculiar phenomenon due to iron in a study of interferences on magnesium (for silicate rock analysis); the absorbance of magnesium (2 p.p.m. of magnesium) was depressed in the presence of only 5 p.p.m. of iron, though there was no practical effect from 1000 p.p.m. of iron with an air–propane flame. Firman assumed the formation of a series of iron–magnesium compounds of varying volatility. This phenomenon in low-temperature flames does not occur in air–acetylene flames, and may be suppressed by using an organic solvent such as isopropanol.

The case of aluminum as an interference is not completely clear. On the one hand, the interference can be regarded as cationic since aluminum is a metal; on the other hand, the tendency of aluminum to form aluminates causes anionic interference; aluminates can be formed especially with magnesium, calcium and strontium, in the flame. The problem of the interferences by aluminum on alkaline earth elements, including barium, has received special attention[6].

In the experiments of Menzies on the aluminum–magnesium system (*496*), a superposition of cationic and anionic effects—distorted curve—was achieved by using sulfates in place of chlorides in the addition of interfering elements.

The most typical cases of anionic interferences which have been studied are the effects of sulfates, silicates and phosphates on determinations of magnesium, calcium and strontium[7]. Marked depressions with inflexions at the proximity of equimolar points are observed in the interference curves. The type of chemical interference found in the determinations of magnesium, calcium, strontium and barium are probably common to all analytes which

---

[6] Consult the following contributions: M. Galassi, W. F. Ulrich and J. Ramírez-Muñoz, Calcium and barium determinations by atomic-absorption flame photometry in the presence of aluminum. Paper presented at the 8th Annual Meeting Rocky Mountain Spectroscopy Conference, Society for Applied Spectroscopy. Aug. 8–9, 1966, Denver, Colo. W. F. Ulrich and J. Ramírez-Muñoz, Determinations of calcium in high interference systems by atomic-absorption flame photometry. Paper not yet presented.

[7] Several examples of this type of interference have been given by Gilbert (*274, 275*).

As representative studies of chemical interference systems, the following publications may be consulted: Andrew and Nichols (*22*), Baker and Garton (*66*), David (*173*), Herrmann and Lang (*323, 326*), Hinson (*344*), and Slavin *et al.* (*708*). An example of an exhaustive interference study is the work done by Belcher *et al.* (*83*) on the absorption of silver.

Interference systems are discussed in many other works. Baird and Envali (*64*) discussed various anionic effects. Extensive studies on interferences in the determinations of potassium and calcium (*764*), zinc (*198*) (0.1–6 g Zn/l), copper and gold (*393*) have been published. Interferences on magnesium have been reviewed (*302*).

have a similar tendency to form salts which are very difficult to dissociate. Among these are the elements which can now be determined by means of hot and reducing flames.

The interference of chlorides, in excess, on calcium could also be interpreted as the formation of calcium–chlorine molecules which are only slightly dissociated. The relative freedom of atomic-absorption from inter-element interferences has led to attempts to solve problems which cannot be efficiently resolved by conventional emission. For example, highly saline systems in emission produce large interferences unless separations are made. Large amounts of sodium (sea water, brines) in solution or large amounts of iron (metallurgical problems), calcium and magnesium have been tested in order to define the tolerance limits of atomic-absorption methods. The present author has found that large amounts of sodium in the determinations of potassium, calcium, magnesium, iron, copper, manganese and zinc do not severely affect sensitivity, precision and accuracy; the interference ratios in some cases reach 500 and 1000. The same has been observed with large amounts of magnesium in the presence of small amounts of calcium. In the systems containing large amounts of sodium (as sodium chloride), at increasing concentrations of the interfering element, a drastic change occurs in the flame profiles (absorbance found for the analyte as a function of the height of the selection zone). The changes are still more noticeable if the sodium is introduced by adding other compounds (e.g. as nitrate or hydroxide). The changes of signal observed in these systems at a given selection zone height should not be considered as decreases or increases of the atom concentration in the flame, but as a redistribution of the atom population along the flame (*934*).

The presence of another cation of similar behaviour to the analyte may give effects of *hyper-interference*. This happens in cases of anionic interference. For instance, strong interference by phosphates on strontium is observed in the presence of calcium, and strong interference by phosphates on magnesium with the addition of EDTA if calcium is present. The first case might be explained as an occlusion phenomenon, and the second as a suppression of the protection effect (*275*). In the author's laboratories enhancement of interference has also been observed in the system Al–Ca, Ba.

The attenuation or suppression of chemical interference effects has received much attention, and various suitable procedures have been described (see p. 307). Chemical interferences can be drastically suppressed if a chemical separation of the analyte from the other components of the sample is feasible, or if all or a significant amount of the other components can be removed. Although the determination and calculation steps influence the accuracy and precision the preparation step, including any chemical separations, have even more effect on the final data, so that these preliminary steps must be done very carefully (*589*).

6.2.5. Strongly emitting elements

Some elements produce intense emission in the flame. They represent a case of spectral interference (emission interference) which might be called spectral self-interference, that is added to the losses of atoms by excitation.

In a.c. work this emission can be eliminated by modulation, but the discrimination by modulation is not perfect because of the flickering of the flame; the flicker has a component at the modulation frequency, which acts as a noise component. In d.c. systems the emission signal is backed-off by means of the 100% absorption control, as shown in Fig. 14–2; this allows the operator to use the complete absorption scale.

There are several ways of decreasing the emission effects:

(a) Running the lamp hotter—higher lamp current—as it makes the line brighter (but this reduces the lamp life and the sensitivity). Fortunately, in most cases, the emission of the source outshines the flame emission which is practically negligible, being at worst a very small fraction of the total light transmitted.

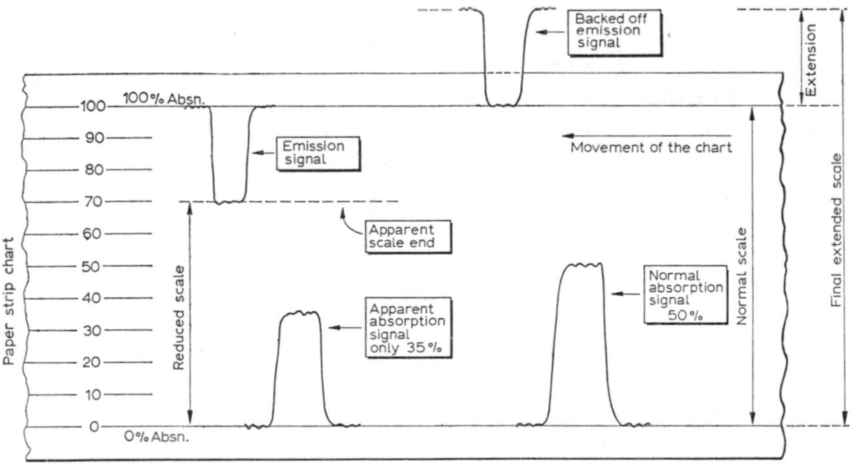

Fig. 14–2. Backing-off procedure in d.c. systems in the case of strongly emitting elements.

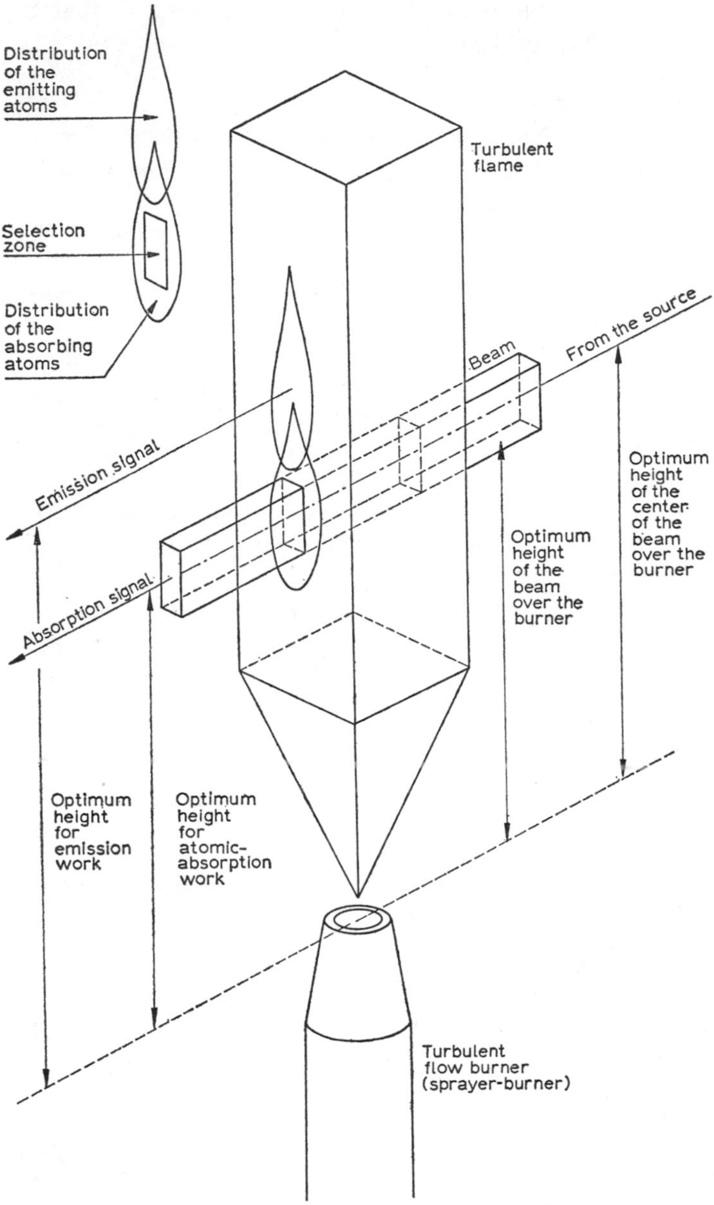

Fig. 14–3. Positions of maximum emission and atomic-absorption zones in a turbulent flame. The graph also shows the optimum heights commonly mentioned in the literature.

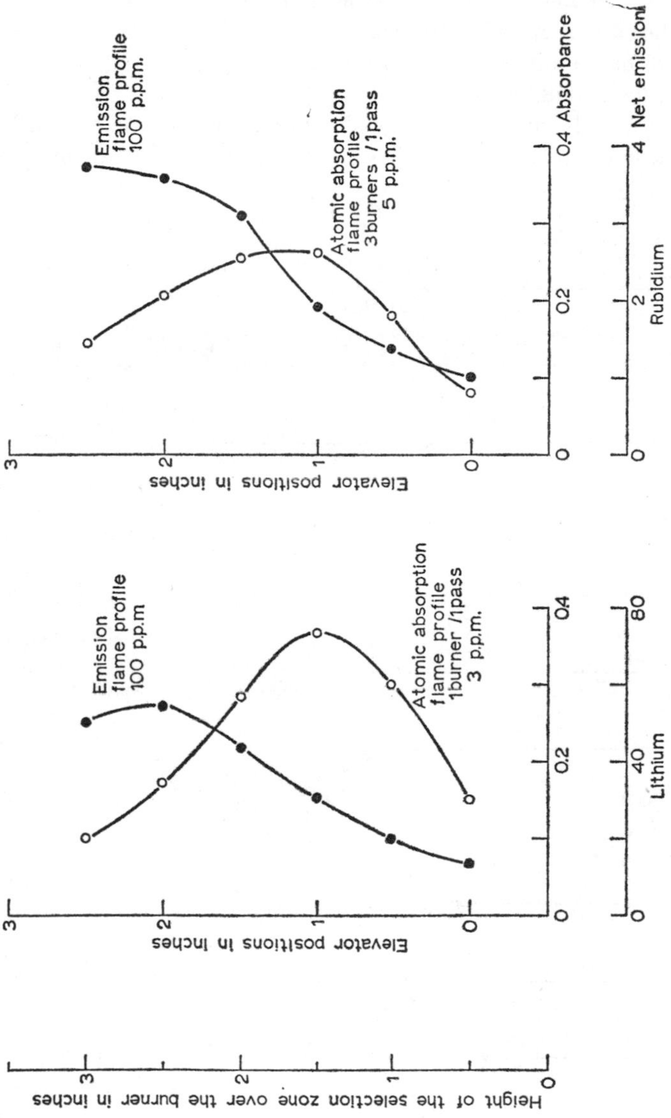

Fig. 14—4. Emission and atomic-absorption flame profiles for two strongly-emitting elements. (Data from ref. (*110*)).

(b) Screening the flame with a diaphragm, so that only the part of the flame through which the light from the lamp alone comes, can be seen.

(c) Choosing another line, if the concentration is high enough.

(d) Diluting the concentrated solutions.

(e) Using a cool flame (air–hydrogen, for instance).

(f) Making the flame smaller.

Poluéktov (*560*) points out that atomic-absorption measurements can be performed in the non-emitting gases above a flame, but this can only be

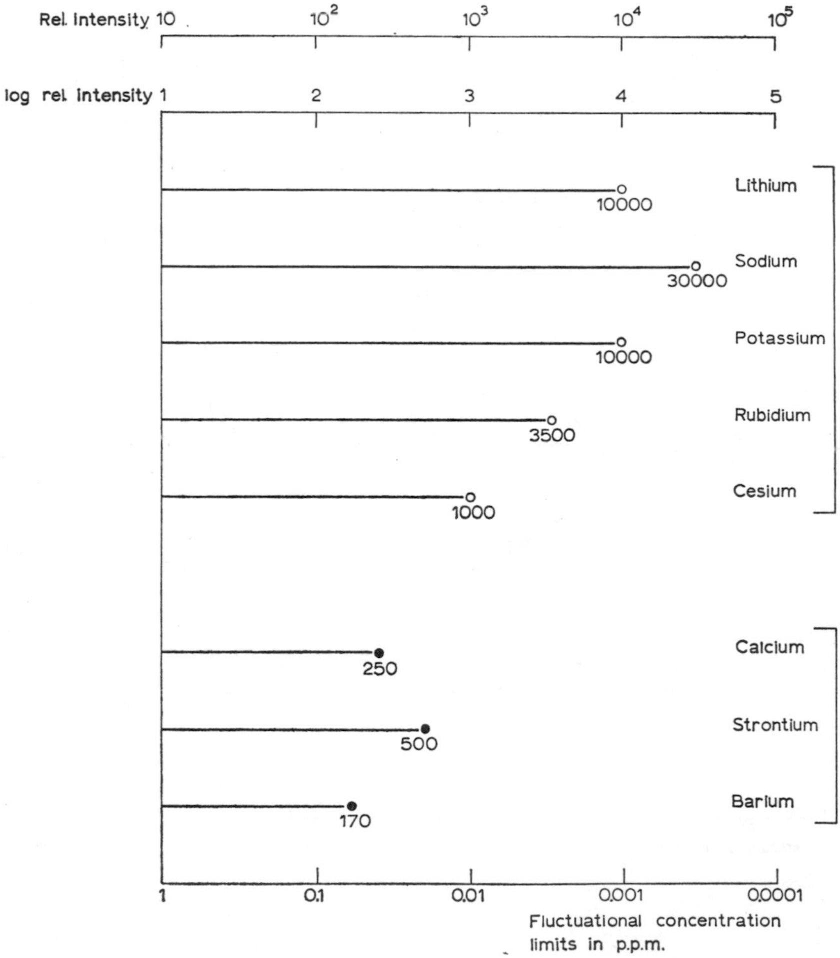

Fig. 14–5. Relative emission intensities for several strongly emitting elements.

done with certain elements which produce long-lived atoms.

The author has found, with turbulent flames, that there are in some cases markedly different selection zones for maximum emission and for maximum absorption at different heights over the top of the burner (see Fig. 14–3). Brace *et al.* (*110*) have found similar effects with, for example, lithium and rubidium. The emission and absorption profiles are valuable in reaching a decision on the selection zone height to be used; convenient scales should be used to represent the readings taken under identical flame conditions for emission and absorption (see Fig. 14–4).

If the emission is really troublesome, then the sensitivity of the emission process should be good and can be utilized. If there are not too many interferences, the emission flame photometric determination of such emitting elements should be satisfactory and the other elements present can be determined by atomic-absorption. In Fig. 14–5 the sensitivities of some of the strongly emitting elements are graphically compared.

A complete study of the behaviour of a group of emitting elements has been presented by Brace *et al.* (*110*) with a d.c. system instrument and turbulent flames (air–hydrogen). Turbulent flames give lower emission sensitivity, higher dynamic ranges and good sensitivity for atomic-absorption determinations.

7. GRAPHIC REPRESENTATION OF INTERFERENCE PHENOMENA

Many authors prefer to present their findings graphically rather than in tables, for graphs give a better idea of the variation involved. Interference phenomena can be represented in various ways.

In the vertical axis (ordinary or log scale)

(1) Percentage of absorption
(2) Absorbance
(3) Percentual sensitivity
(4) Percentual concentration limit
(5) Fluctuational sensitivity
(6) Fluctuational concentration limit
(7) Absolute sensitivity
(8) Absolute limit
(9) Slope value
(10) Experimental concentration (found values)
(11) Percentage of recovery
(12) Absolute error
(13) Relative error
(14) Correction factor, etc.

In the horizontal axis (ordinary or log scale)

(1) Concentration of the interfering element
(2) Interference ratio
(3) Ponderal interference ratio
(4) Any experimental variable or inherent factor producing interference (total saline concentration, density, viscosity, etc.).

Concentrations may be plotted in any units (g/ml, p.p.m., or others) or in pC values, in which case ordinary scales should be used.

Many combinations can be represented on a plane using two of the variables listed above. Flat diagrams including a third variable as a parameter are also used. Space diagrams may be prepared using two of the listed variables for the axes of the horizontal plane.

PART IV

EXPERIMENTAL METHODS

Chapter 15

Experimental process

The experimental process in atomic-absorption may be described briefly as follows. Once a sufficient stability has been achieved in the emission, absorption and recording systems, and the instrument has been optimized, the sample solution is aspirated and transferred to the instrument, and then measured; solutions of known concentration (standards) are also aspirated under the same conditions, and a comparison is then made of the absorptions.

For these purposes it is necessary to have adequate standards, the sample in solution form prepared for the measurement and the instrument prepared to be optimized just by the necessary settings.

1. KNOWN ANALYTICAL PROCESSES

When the determinations to be carried out are well-known in all their aspects (e.g. determination of calcium and magnesium in biological materials, determination of zinc in plant ashes), the analytical process is reduced to the following steps, which are common to most instrumental methods.

(a) *Preparation of a series of standards,* usually by simple dilution, from stock solutions, to cover the interval of concentatrions likely to be found in the sample solutions. The standards will need correction or compensation according to the nature of the samples.

(b) *Preparation of the sample solutions* by dissolving—if necessary—the original samples, and making preliminary dilutions, separations and additions.

(c) *Adjustment of the instrument for optimum operation conditions,* which in the case of atomic-absorption means *setting the wavelength selector, setting the lamp current, setting pressures and/or flows* (for the different gases in the case of the use of flame), *setting the slit, setting the electronic equipment* (expansion of scale, gain, etc.) and *adjustment of zero* (with the solvent—water or other—or with the blank solution) *and 100% absorption.*

Sufficient time must, of course, be allowed for warm-up of the power supplies and the electronics of the equipment. The warm-up time of the lamp must also be considered. If the complete unit has been unplugged overnight or for a longer period the time used to warm up the electronics can be used to warm up the lamp or lamps. If the unit is kept on all the time, *except for the lamps* (as is commonly advised to conserve the effective lamp life), the lamps will require a sufficient warm-up time. Heated chambers require a certain warm-up time too. Burners warm up quickly, but in the case of slot burners (with voluminous head) not cooled by water, it is best to wait for a short time to be sure that they have reached the appropriate temperature equilibrium before calibration and/or measurements are started.

All this implies that the optimum operating conditions have been established beforehand for each analyte and for each type of sample (with known accompanying components and for determined intervals of concentration). The analytical process is *repetitive* under known and invariable conditions. The instrument is placed in operation simply to *measure* the variations of the quantitative variable in each series of sample solutions as a function of the respective concentrations. During the process all the operational variables must be kept as constant as possible.

1.1. Switching lamps

One inconvenience in the use of atomic-absorption methods is the need for changing the lamp in switching from one element to another. Changes of lamp are necessary, except with *multiple hollow-cathode lamps* or *multi-element single hollow-cathode lamps* (see Chapter 7, Sections 2.3.2 and 2.3.3), but inconvenience can be reduced to minor proportions by proper planning.

The operator needs a warmed-up lamp, but the warming-up time required is the same as, or less than, that required to warm up the electronic equipment (ca. 30 minutes). The first lamp required can thus be warmed up at the same time as the electronics. The second and third lamps required for the same session may be warmed up during the same period, may be switched on for 30 minutes before use, while the first analyte is being determined. Subsequent lamps may be connected and switched on during work as soon as other lamps have been utilized. In some instruments several lamps may be connected at the same time using several channels[1].

[1] The operator should be careful to adjust to the correct lamp current needed during determination when the lamp is switched on for warming-up. If he uses, let us say, 10 mA, and later, before determination, adjusts it to 15 mA, some drift is observed. The same occurs if the lamp is warmed-up while connected to another power supply and is disconnected and connected rapidly to the power supply of the instrument.

A time-switch can be used if desired. Good planning will avoid waiting periods and will save lamp life.

In general, it is considered that the flame as an emission source is an universal source for all the excitable elements, and that it can be used under the same conditions for all determinable elements of a given sample. There are, however, some restrictions including: (a) the need for a different supporting gas, (b) the need for a different fuel (the burner may have to be changed), (c) clogging problems—because of the aspiration of suspensions, or viscous or highly saline samples—that necessitate a change of the burner to one with a large-bore capillary.

These are a few examples of how it is necessary to change the source in changing from one element to another or when the characteristics of the solutions are different.

In switching from one element to another in atomic-absorption work it is necessary to make several changes; the necessary settings may be ascertained by preliminary examination of the performance of the instrument.

(1) Change of lamp. The lamp should be connected previously to the corresponding channel and pre-warmed. The lamp should be previously aligned.

(2) Change of the wavelength control setting. Selection of the phototube and resistor, if necessary.

(3) Change of slit setting.

(4) Change of the height of the burner.

(5) Change of the gain adjustment.

(6) Change of gas control settings.

(7) Wavelength fine peaking.

(8) 100% absorption adjustment.

(9) Blank adjustment (reading operation begins at this point).

Operations (2), (3), (5), (6), (7), (8), and (9) are also carried out in emission flame photometry work. Actually, all these operations can be done in about 5–10 minutes, with a little practice. If all the corresponding checkings have been done beforehand, the operator may use a table of settings on the bench, so that in switching operations, the instrument can be prepared in minutes. Particular attention should be given to the resetting of the instrument of each control and especially to the peaking, and 100% absorption and blank adjustment.

2. UNKNOWN ANALYTICAL PROCESSES

For unknown processes, i.e., determinations of a new analyte, analysis of a new type of sample, use of a new interval of concentrations, and with any occasional or systematic variation of any analytical factor, the basic steps must be subjected to previous study to establish the proper working conditions.

(a) *Instrumental aspects*

(1) Choice of the source lamp with the appropriate cathode, and the most appropriate filler gas.

(2) Choice of the emission line.

(3) Verification of the wavelength setting.

(4) Determination of the optimum current applied to the lamp[2].

(5) Determination of the appropriate slit width[2].

(6) Choice of the appropriate gases.

(7) Choice of the most suitable pressures and/or flows[2].

(8) Choice of the most suitable conditions for the electrical components (photometric system).

(9) Verification of the behaviour of the instrumental system at the settings chosen, using a series of preliminary standards.

(b) *Aspects associated with the sample*

(1) Choice of the most suitable chemical treatment for the original sample.

(2) Necessary preparatory steps for carrying the concentration to the desired and *tested* (a, 9) interval of concentrations.

(3) Interference tests.

(4) Study of separations, compensations and necessary additions.

(5) Preparation of the series of definitive standards and blanks.

(6) Final verification of the behaviour of the instrument with the definitive series of standards.

(7) Experimental measurements.

3. OPTIMUM OPERATING CONDITIONS

The choice of optimum operating conditions has been discussed in several sections of this book. For all analytical methods, as a general rule, the optimum operating conditions should be used and the apparatus be optimized by varying all those factors necessary for the instrument to yield the best response. Atomic-absorption instruments depend on many variables (as is also the case for emission flame photometers). The optimization always requires a previous study of the effect of the change of conditions, which is often tedious and time-consuming.

---

[2] The settings providing the highest sensitivity and the better stability should be sought.

For these purposes, it is usual to vary *only one factor at a time*, while all the rest are kept constant. This procedure is good *as long as there are no interactions between two or more of the factors subject to variation*, and as long as a real relationship is not permitted to develop between the different variables subjected to observation. In fact, each of them is considered, experimentally, as if it were totally independent in order to obtain series of maximum responses.

Cellier and Stace (*144, 904*) discuss this procedure, a single factor at a time, along with the so-called *complete factorial procedure* and the selection of test points at random in order to present a statistical system completely elaborated for determining the optimum working conditions in atomic-absorption; this is based on sequential series of experiments beginning with one or more fractional factorials which may be continued experimentally where curvature in each or several variables is measured. These authors have followed this technique for the estimation of those settings—for several instrumental variables—at which maximum absorption is obtained. This method is more suitable than estimating single variables one at a time. The technique is known as *response surface* investigation. For further information consult G.E.P. Box, *Biometrics*, 10 (1954) 16.

Chapter 16

Standard solutions

The necessary calibration of atomic-absorption instruments—analytical calibration—is achieved by means of solutions of known concentration: *standard solutions*. Standards for analytical calibration are generally utilized to prepare a graphic representation of the variation of the analytical quantitative variable measured in the instrument as a function of the concentration. The *calibration standards* can also be used as *working standards*, i.e., for analytical measurement purposes.

Whenever the characteristics of the sample solutions permit, very simple working standards should be used—preferably, aqueous solutions of simple salts which contain the analyte. If the solutions prepared for analysis contain fixed or variable quantities of other components, the standards should be prepared so that their composition will be as close as possible to the samples with which they are to be compared[1].

1. SUBSTANCES FOR THE PREPARATION OF STANDARDS

Analytical reagent grade, spectrally pure substances or commercial products which are specially purified should be used. This applies to saline compounds (soluble or non-soluble), oxides, pure metals, acids, organic solvents, chelating agents, etc., which are used directly or indirectly in the preparation of standards or in the chemical preparation of samples (separative processes, additions, buffering). Where available reagents are insufficiently pure, prior purification must be done. For example, in the preliminary concentration of small quantities of lead before the instrumental determination, the reagents must be suitably purified by extraction.

Wherever possible, chemical substances with properties similar or equal to those recommended as primary standards for analytical work should be used. If not, at least analytical-reagent grade substances of known purity factor and composition should be used. Chemistry handbooks should

---

[1] All the considerations on standards for use in emission are applicable. See Chapter 12, p. 214 of ref. (*125*).

be consulted for temperature stability of the compounds to be used in order to avoid any losses, or changes of composition or in water of crystallization during drying (furnace, oven, or just desiccator). All substances should usually be dried, *if possible*, before weighing.

For ease of handling, it is much better to use water-soluble salts. If these are not available or do not have the necessary characteristics, pure metals should be used after degreasing with ether and drying before weighing. In some cases mechanical cleaning may be useful to avoid external layers.

Oxides and carbonates are also suitable and can be dissolved after weighing by using the necessary amount of acid (preferably hydrochloric acid or nitric acid). After acid treatment, the solution should be boiled to expel any developed gases. In some cases, it has been proved good practice to evaporate the solution to dryness on a steam bath and to take the residue up with water. (Careless drying on a hot plate may cause losses of solid particles). Evaporation to dryness and redissolution with water cannot be done when the salt undergoes hydrolysis.

In dissolution of metals, oxides or carbonates with acid, losses by effervescence and losses of liquid can be avoided with care; a watchglass should be placed on the beaker and rinsed at the end of the operation into the solution. Losses during evaporation processes can be avoided similarly. Transference steps involving solids or solutions are always liable to losses which can only be avoided by proper care.

The water used in all operations should be demineralized or distilled, or both demineralized and then distilled. The same quality of water should be used for both stock solutions and standard dilution series, and later for dilution of samples.

Demineralized water is satisfactory for most purposes, except sometimes for sodium in emission, or for calcium and magnesium in atomic-absorption methods. In these cases, double demineralized water (two columns in series) can give better results. For samples of biological origin, it is much better to use distilled water, storing it in sterile bottles. In other cases, clean and rinsed polyethylene containers will be adequate, as will the use of plastic transference tubes.

Glass and metal containers should be avoided as much as possible. For some special purposes, distilled water should be prepared with quartz or silver-plated metal stills. On special occasions, twice-distilled water may be needed.

2. STOCK SOLUTIONS AND STANDARDS

The exact composition of the series of standards and, finally, the accuracy of the determination depend on the accuracy with which the stock solutions are prepared. Concentrations of from 1% to 0.05% (i.e., 10,000–500 p.p.m.) are recommended. These solutions may be kept for a reasonable length of time: from several weeks to a few months. The concentrations recommended above are expressed with reference to the analyte in elementary state. Some commercial companies prepare and sell stock solutions specially prepared for flame photometric analysis (*882*).

Stock solutions must be carefully prepared, so that a dilution series (collection of standard solutions) can be conveniently obtained for use in developing the necessary calibration curves and working curves. The final quality of the analytical results will always depend on the quality of the primary stock solutions and on the care with which the dilution process is done.

2.1. Glassware

2.1.1. Pipettes and volumetric flasks

Pipettes and volumetric flasks should be completely cleaned by means of some non-contaminant cleaning solution; 6 *N* hydrochloric acid followed by three or four rinsings with demineralized water (or distilled water, according to the case) in small portions is generally satisfactory, though some workers prefer diluted nitric acid.

Very dirty glassware can be cleaned with potassium dichromate cleaning solution, but since this solution can produce contaminations of potassium and chromium, it is advisable to follow the first cleaning with a second cleaning with hydrochloric acid. Checking the neutral reaction of the water used for rinsings is good practice, but not entirely necessary. The hydrochloric acid can be approximately 6 *N*. Any cleaning solution should, of course, be cold in order to avoid any volume change in volumetric glassware.

Special care should be paid to the use of surface-coating agents; pipettes and volumetric flasks treated in this way should be recalibrated especially if they are of a small volume.

After cleaning, pipettes should be dried out by rinsing with alcohol and passing a current of clean air at room temperature. Never blow through a pipette with the mouth; avoid any dust after cleaning. Volumetric flasks can be used wet if they have to receive a pipetted aliquot of solution to be diluted afterwards with water.

2.1.2. Weighing bottles

Whatever size or shape, with stopper or without, weighing bottles should be used completely clean, dry and maintained at room temperature in a desiccator (silica gel or calcium chloride). Calcium chloride desiccators should be avoided in laboratories in which calcium determinations at low concentrations are performed. Weighing bottles should be carefully cleaned after use, dried, and returned to the desiccator.

2.2. Weighing procedure

General rules for analytical weighing are applicable. It is necessary to use a balance with a reasonable speed of weighing (automatic rider balance and vibrating spatula) and sufficient accuracy; any common source of contamination must be avoided. For general purposes, analytical balances with a precision of ± 0.1 mg are satisfactory for weighing amounts of products over one gram; semi-micro and micro-balances are seldom used.

2.3. Dilution process

General directions for analytical work should be followed in diluting stock solutions to prepare the necessary dilution series. Special care should be paid to the pipetting error, and the use of very small pipettes or too small flasks should be avoided.

Although a clean dry pipette can be introduced safely in any solution to remove an aliquot, it is good practice to take a fraction in a clean container—perfectly dry and/or rinsed with the solution being used—and to use this fraction for pipetting and discard it after use. One or two rinsing steps of the pipette with the solution to be measured is also good routine practice.

2.4. Storage of the solutions

Stock and standard solutions may be stored in polyethylene bottles with the necessary labels containing the preparation date. To avoid mistakes which lead to contamination the cap of every bottle should be identified. Stock solutions can be stored for some time (several months) if they are of 1000-p.p.m. or greater concentration. However, standard series (especially very dilute solutions) should be re-prepared quite frequently in order to avoid any changes in concentration. Very dilute solutions (1 p.p.m. or less) should always be freshly prepared; they are exposed to precipitations, partial evaporations or to adsorption on the walls of the containers. Preservative substances can be added if necessary.

2.5. Polyethylene bottles

These bottles should be perfectly clean, cleaned in the same condition as the glassware, and preferably dry. They can also be used wet if several rinsings are made with the solution. In any case, at least one rinsing is advisable even if the bottle is dry.

2.6. Additions

Any addition introduced into the stock solution should be maintained constant in the dilution series. This should be taken into account for the sample preparation stage. Simple aqueous standard solutions may be used when the analytes are determined after a high preliminary dilution from samples of high analyte content. If some of the original components are still present in the diluted samples in significant concentrations, then it is advisable to make some compensation in the standards. This helps to avoid differences, especially if some variation of efficiency in the sprayer has been noticed.

If it is required to analyze the original materials directly, without preliminary dilution, it is absolutely necessary to verify compensation in the standards with respect to the composition of the materials. A very simple way would be to prepare standards by merely adding increasing quantities of analyte to known quantities of the same type of material as is being analyzed. This can only be done if these materials are available *pure,* that is without any of the analyte which is being investigated (for instance, in the determination of contamination in used lubricating oil, unused oil can be used for the preparation of standards).

2.7. Calculations

Attention should be given to the formula weight stated on the label of the chemical bottles. It may have been calculated on the basis of an old atomic weight table, in which case it should be recalculated using the most recent published International Atomic Weights.

To avoid repeated calculations in the laboratory, it is advisable to prepare or to recalculate personally tables of conversion factors similar to those presented in the appendix of reference (*125*), covering all the analytes commonly used in each laboratory. For this step of calculation, short slide rules are unsatisfactory. A desk slide ruler (50 cm) may be used, or better, logarithm tables (five decimals or up) or a calculating machine.

The purity factor should be taken into account at this stage; a correction factor must be applied to the concentration read on the label, or the weight corrected before weighing.

Some solutions require standardization after preparation, e.g. solutions of rubidium or cesium, which can be easily standardized by determining accurately the analyte in an aliquot by conversion to sulfate and gravimetry. In other cases, more elaborate procedures may be advisable. For instance, Khalifa *et al.* (*393*) standardize copper solutions (prepared from copper nitrate) with disodium ethylenediaminetetraacetate (with murexide as indicator), and gold solutions (prepared from commercial $AuCl_3 \cdot HCl \cdot 3\ H_2O$) with standard iron (II) sulfate (by potentiometric end-point titration).

3. SERIES OF STANDARDS

Several types of standard series may be prepared.

3.1. Calibration and working standards

Dilution series are prepared to cover the desired interval of concentrations uniformly. Since in many cases in atomic-absorption the calibration graphs are linear, three or four standards are sufficient for calibration purposes, and afterward for measurement purposes.

If graphs with some curvature are obtained, non-uniform series may be used (*125*); an abundance of standards is used at the curvature zones, perfect tracing of the graphs thus being ensured.

3.2. Two close standards

For measurements by interpolation between two close standards (this is known as "sandwiching" or two-standard method), two-term series are sufficient; the concentrations of the standards should lie at values approximately 10% above and 10% below the suspected (or previously tested) concentration of the samples.

3.3. Single-analyte series and group series of standards

In carrying out analysis for a single analyte in a work session, it is usually more convenient to use a single-analyte series of standards. Group series of standards are appropriate in both the following cases.

(a) When several analytes are measured in a working session and it has been verified that there are no inter-element disturbances at all, if all analytes are maintained in the same solution at all concentrations tested.

(b) When several analytes are measured *simultaneously* with the instrument (instruments prepared for multi-element analysis).

4. CONCENTRATION RANGE

The series of standards should cover the proposed interval of concentrations. Their concentrations must be included within the dynamic range permitted for a certain type of analysis. The series of standards may extend between the two limiting points of the concentration scale.

The upper limit is defined by: (a) limitations of solubility, (b) mechanical limitations (deposit, clogging), (c) limitations by curvature, or (d) instrumental limitations so as not to achieve excessive absorption, e.g. beyond 80%.

The lower limit is determined by: (a) the relative fluctuational quantitative sensitivity, (b) a conventional limiting lower signal (instrumental limitation), or (c) the minimum concentration of the sample solutions which are to be measured in the instrument.

5. GRAPHICAL AIDS

For preparation of series of standards (also for preparation of comparison knowns and for preliminary dilution of sample solutions) calculation of the necessary aliquot volume, V, final volume, V', starting concentration, C, or final concentration, C', are carried out by means of the well-known equation

$$CV = C'V'$$

Repeated calculations are tiring and exposed to personal mistakes. A nomogram has been devised (*599*) in order to give the fourth variable directly, once the other three are known or chosen, and to verify, prior to laboratory work, any calculation made by slide rule or manually (see Fig. 16–1).

The nomogram has four scales: *For* C, single log scale, vertical; *for* V, multiple log scale, horizontal, according to the value chosen for V'; *for* C', single log scale, diagonal; and *for* V', single step log scale, vertical. Only major divisions of log scales are needed since no fractional volumes are common for pipettes from 1 to 50 ml and for flasks from 10 to 1000 ml.

Four cases of the use of this nomogram are considered.

(a) *Calculation of* V. This is one of the most frequent cases: $V = C'V'/C$. (1) Look for the value C on its scale; (2) follow a horizontal line until C' is reached at the diagonal C' (diagonals going from upper left to lower right); (3) drop a vertical from this point to the corresponding level of V'; (4) read V in the corresponding V scale, and check if the value V corresponds to available pipettes (if not, look for a bigger or smaller V').

(b) *Calculation of* C'. This is also quite frequent: $C' = CV/V'$. (1) Look for the level V'; (2) look for value V on the corresponding V scale at the level V'; (3) draw a vertical line up; (4) look for C on its scale and follow a horizontal line; (5) read the value C' according to the diagonal line (going from upper left to lower right) found at the intersection point.

(c) *Calculation of* V'. This is limited to the most frequent sizes of measuring glassware. It is useful to follow the order: (1) C; (2) C'; (3) V, if available when dropping the vertical, and then (4) read V' (level V').

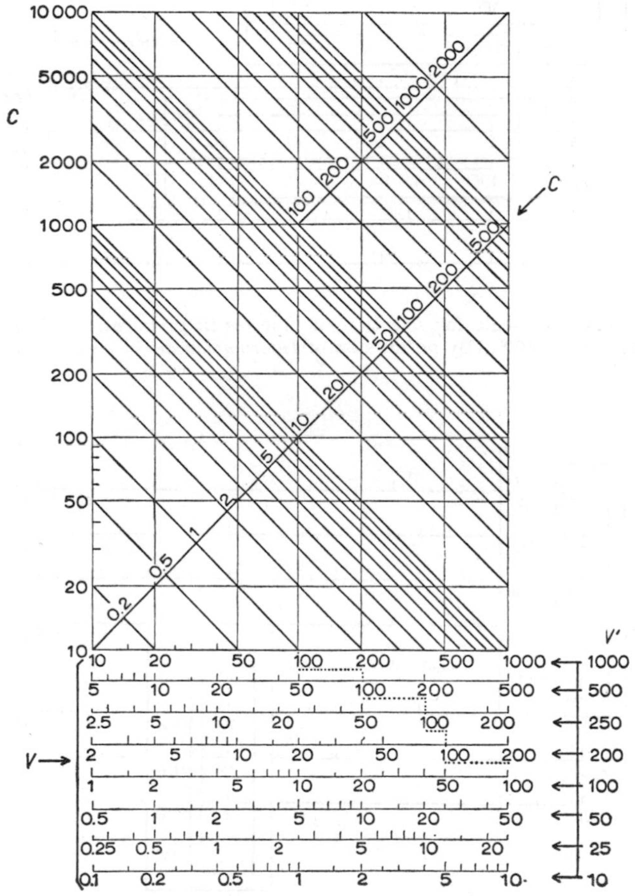

Fig. 16–1. Nomogram for volume–concentration calculations (*599*). See use in text. (By permission of *Información de Química Analítica*)

(d) *Calculation of C*. The order: (1) V'; (2) V; (3) C'; and (4) read C, is followed.

In the V group of scales there is a dead zone for volumes equal or bigger than 100 ml. Pipettes larger than 50 ml are unwieldy.

Confluence of the horizontal and diagonal lines at the right edge of the nomogram corresponds to *no dilution* (dilution ratio 1:1), and this edge acts as limiting edge.

By a couple of auxiliary scales (see Fig. 16–2) the operator can take

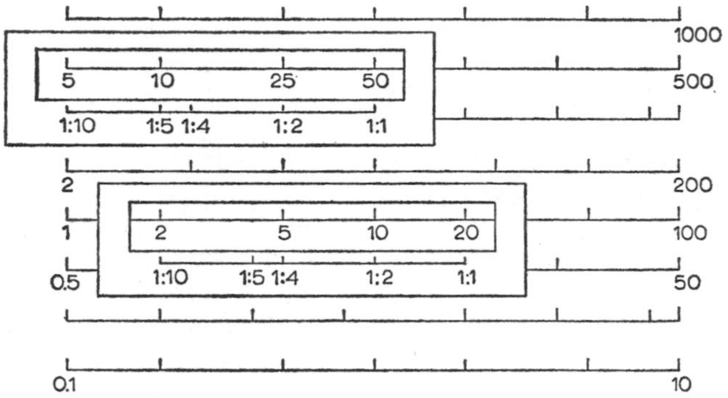

Fig. 16–2,a. Auxiliary scale for selection of pipettes in preparation of dilution series of standards (*599*). (By permission of *Información de Química Analítica*)

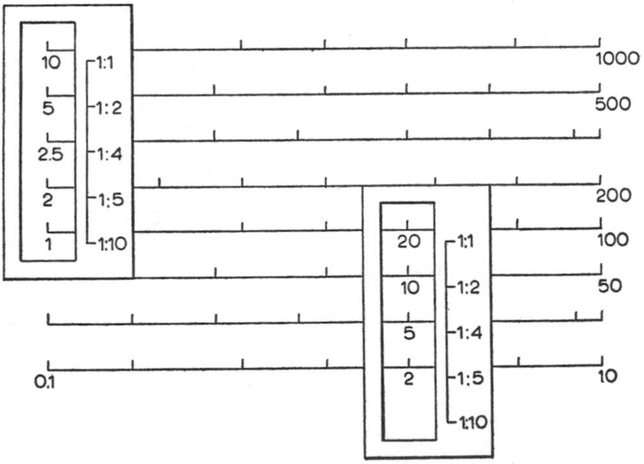

Fig. 16–2,b. Auxiliary scale for selection of pipettes in preparation of dilution series of standards (*599*). (By permission of *Información de Química Analítica*)

advantage of the lower group of scales (V scales) to determine immediately the values of aliquot volumes that he needs to prepare series of standards, following the sequence 1:1, 1:2, 1:4 (or 1:5), 1:10, and 1:20. Once the dilution volumes (V' and V for given C and C') are known, the auxiliary scales show the sequence of V aliquot volumes for the same V' final volume.

Chapter 17

Preparation of the sample

This heading includes many processes which are common to most types of instrumental analysis; they are the purely chemical preparative part of the analysis, aided by operations of a physical nature such as physical separations. The final result is a *solution prepared for analysis*, which either directly or after some further manipulations, becomes the *solution prepared for the measurement*; that is, a subsample with characteristics suitable for instrumental measurements.

The first group of operations is general and is comprised of the *dissolution of the solid sample*, *separations* and *auxiliary operations* (preliminary concentration or dilution). The other operations depend on the type of sample and the element which is to be determined.

Many of the processes mentioned here are similar to those currently used in emission flame photometry[1]. Some of the complementary operations used for correction of interferences may be used either for emission or for atomic-absorption flame photometry, especially those dealing with the correction of inhibition chemical interferences.

All the preparatory steps—chemical and physical—may affect the accuracy and precision by:

(a) impairing them, by losses or accidental contaminations, or both phenomena at the same time if there is no compensation effect;

(b) improving them, by removal of disturbing constituents, preliminary concentrations and suitable dilutions.

A series of preparatory processes which is well planned and carried out, allows one to take advantage of the relative percentual qualitative sensitivity of the component under determination.

The inclusion of *knowns* for purposes of checking the performance of these processes is recommended. Some knowns, devoid of analyte, may be likewise subjected to all preliminary operations. It is important to distinguish clearly between knowns and blanks:

(a) *Knowns* are solutions of samples of a *known concentration and composition* which are subjected to all the preliminary preparatory steps foreseen for the samples. The results obtained during instrumental measurement

---

[1] Chapter 13, p. 233 of ref. (*125*) may be consulted.

will indicate what is likely to happen with the samples. The known therefore contains analyte. The knowns should have a composition equal to or as similar as possible to the rest of the samples. They may or may not be synthetic.

(b) *Blanks* are prepared solutions, usually synthetic, *devoid of analyte*, whose composition should be similar or equal, as far as possible, to the samples prepared for measurement, with the exception, of course, of the analyte. In the case of very simple solutions, the blank may be distilled or demineralized water, i.e. when the pure solvent is aqueous. In other cases, the organic solvent or the background solution used in dilutions is used. In complicated cases all the components of the sample prepared for the measurement should be present—macro- and micro-components—as long as they are considered *active* in the measurement process.

(c) *Blank knowns*, finally, are samples *devoid of analyte* which are subjected to all the same processes as the ordinary knowns.

1. TREATMENT OF SOLID SAMPLES

For inorganic and organic samples, the same procedures may be applied as in emission (*125*). Ashing is a frequent step in the treatment of solid samples. Bersin (*96*) includes atomic-absorption in the cases which require low-temperature ashing of organic media for subsequent elemental analysis. Elements such as arsenic and selenium are lost at 500 °C, but can be conserved when organic materials are ashed by controlling the burning rate, temperature and percentage of oxygen present, and by being certain that the sample is surrounded by a stable-conducting gaseous plasma according to the surface area (not mass) of the sample.

2. SEPARATIONS

The methods already used in emission (*125*) are again applicable.

(a) *Physical separations*

By mechanical separation of phases: filtration[2], centrifugation.

By distribution equilibrium between two phases: selective disolution, selective adsorption, selective extraction.

(b) *Chemical separations*

Group precipitation

Selective precipitation

---

[2] See the use of Separan NP-10 as flocculating agent, added before filtration (p. 372).

Separations by adsorption and by extraction have received the most attention in atomic-absorption.

2.1. *Selective adsorption*

The phosphate ion lends itself easily to separation with anion-exchange resins; its disturbing effects on the determination of calcium and other alkaline earths can thus be eliminated. This procedure has been used in the analysis of vegetables (*176, 344*) and biological materials (*176*). David (*176*) and Hinson (*344*) agree that the acetate form of De-Acidite FF acts effectively in the preliminary separation of phosphate from strontium and barium. Small columns can be used for this purpose. The standards used to the same treatment prepare the working curves should undergo the same treatment.

2.2. *Selective extraction*

Selective extraction continues to be one of the simplest separation methods, which is still sufficiently quantitative. It has been widely applied in the preparatory steps in emission as well as atomic-absorption and its benefits are well-known (see, e.g. ref. (*583*)). Not only are separations achieved but in many cases the analyte can be concentrated into an organic phase of smaller volume.

In emission methods, the extraction procedures are generally made as highly selective as possible, because of the abundance of interference phenomena in the measurement step. However, in atomic-absorption, inter-element interferences are very few, so that less selective extractions are generally satisfactory. Extraction can be used for a group of analytes (of low concentration and easily determinable by atomic-absorption) which do not cause interferences among themselves, but which can only be determined in the absence of macrocomponents of the sample. The reagents used in the extraction procedures seldom interfere. For example, in their studies on chromium, Feldman and Purdy (*239*) extracted chromium (VI) in acidic solution with methyl isobutyl ketone; chromium (III) in 4 *M* sulfuric acid was first oxidized with a small excess of potassium permanganate, which did not interfere in the atomic-absorption measurement (in contrast to conventional colorimetric techniques).

Two types of extractions are recommended: specific extractions and groups selective extractions.

Group extractions, also known as bulk extractions, cause an increase of relative concentration. Two primary conditions are met: (a) preliminary concentration of the analyte or analytes, and (b) separation of the macrocomponents which are practically absent from the final solution.

Two other aspects must be considered. Extractions with organic solvents are more effective (more sensitive and more quantitative) if a suitable chelating agent is added, so that the organometallic complex of the analyte is extracted. And if the solution obtained with the organic solvent is fed directly to the flame, the process of evaporation and redissolution with an aqueous solvent (neutral, or slightly or highly acidic) can be avoided; in fact, some solvents used as extractants may enhance the absorption, so that their effects are beneficial.

The extraction process with organic solvents—including chelation—followed by direct aspiration of the extracts, is one way of solving problems which have proved difficult by other instrumental methods. For example, as an advantage over emission spectrographic analysis, Mansell cites the atomic-absorption measurement of less than 1-p.p.m. amounts of nickel, cobalt, copper and manganese in samples of 50% neutralized sodium hydroxide. This procedure may be used for bulk chemicals, not only for sodium hydroxide, but also potassium bromide and aluminum chloride, in the analysis of trace components. Mansell also discusses the determination of less than 1 p.p.m. of zinc and cadmium in potassium bromide, by extraction with methyl isobutyl ketone (*468*).

The extraction maxima of organometallic compounds depend, to a large extent, on the pH conditions, so that extractions of chelates can be made highly selective.

Many examples of the use of extraction process in atomic-absorption could be cited. Some of the most representative cases are mentioned below.

Extractions of copper with ethyl acetate (*11*), and of lead with methyl n-amyl ketone (*832*) have been used. Various authors have mentioned the use of ammonium pyrrolidinedithiocarbamate with subsequent extraction with methyl isobutyl ketone (hexone): Allan, in determinations of zinc in agricultural materials (*12*) and of copper (*11*), Berman for lead in blood and urine (*92*), Trent and Slavin for copper in rocks (*776*), Sprague and Slavin for copper and lead in potassium chloride (*723*) and for nickel in urine (*722*), Belcher *et al.* for determinations of silver (*83*), and Willis (*834*) for lead in urine[3]. The same extraction has been used in the determination of copper by Morgan (*508*). Dithizone has been used in many extractions. Gilbert (*275*) has published a compilation of useful extraction processes.

Delaughter (*192*) has given details on extraction of chromium with

---

[3] The analytical possibilities of ammonium pyrrolidinedithiocarbamate have been reviewed by Slavin (*687*). The reader should also consult H. MALISSA AND E. SCHÖFFMANN, *Mikrochim. Acta,* (1955) 187.

diphenylthiocarbazone, molybdenum with 4-methyl-1,2-dimercaptobenzene, and iron, nickel, copper and manganese with cupferron. Berman (*93*) mentioned extractions of copper with diethyldithiocarbamate and methyl isobutyl ketone. Mansell (*468*) described extractions of bismuth, cadmium, cobalt, copper, manganese, nickel, lead and zinc with ammonium pyrrolidinedithiocarbamate and cobalt, copper, nickel and manganese with diethyldithiocarbamate. The manganese chelate is unstable in methyl isobutyl ketone solution, and the determination should be performed immediately after extraction; manganese cannot be properly extracted below pH 6 whereas the other metals behave satisfactorily at pH 4–6.

Magnesium has been extracted by means of oxine and methyl isobutyl ketone (*752*).

A complete study on chelating extraction has been presented by Gomiscek and Malissa (*291*), who discuss the use of ammonium pyrrolidinedithiocarbamate, oxine, dithizone, cupferron, acetylacetone, and solvents such as chloroform, carbon tetrachloride, ethyl acetate, toluene and methyl isobutyl ketone. They used turbulent oxygen–acetylene flames and started mainly from acidic aqueous solutions.

A special case is that of Erink and Magee who determined palladium by extraction of palladium pyridine chloride in 50% ethanol and palladium pyridine thiocyanate in hexone (*218*).

3. PREVIOUS DILUTION

Absorption procedures permit determinations in low intervals of concentration because of the great sensitivity achieved for many elements. For many reasons, dilution will almost always be favorable in this type of determination, so long as the final concentrations do not approach the relative fluctuational concentration limits too closely. It should be remembered that the decrease of salinity allows better conditions for the sprayer section of the instrument. Although reasonable precision can be obtained by measuring small signals if the concentrations are not too close to the above-mentioned limits, in order to obtain acceptable accuracy it is best to use signals within the "optimum" region of the absorption scale; if the signals are under 30 or 25% absorption, scale expansion helps to achieve better readability. All these circumstances should be kept in mind in planning a dilution process.

In general, dilution can be very useful in converting the concentration of the sample solution to the best concentration range for measurement. Dilution is essential for very concentrated original solutions if the most sensitive lines are to be used. The use of less sensitive lines may permit determination without preliminary dilution, and of course, dilution errors are then avoided. If in a given problem, the choice lies between diluting and using a sensitive line, or not diluting and using less sensitive line, the decision may be made on the basis of the salinity of the solution. As a general rule, one should avoid very saline solutions which change the physical behaviour of the solutions and the efficiency of the sprayer.

If dilution is impossible because the analyte concentration is too low, and yet the solution is rich in other components, an addition method may be applicable to compensate for the effects of those components.

As an example of analytical systems which lend themselves to a choice of different lines, the determination of sodium, which can be done at 5890 Å and at 3303 Å, with the last line responding to high concentrations, may be cited. The proper successive use of two or more lines of greater to lesser sensitivity, would permit the broadening of the useful quantitative zone (dynamic range) for a given element.

4. PRELIMINARY CONCENTRATION

In the process of preliminary concentration[4] the chemical operations increase the danger of contamination and/or losses. Nevertheless, they constitute the most viable means of bringing low concentrations of analyte within the best concentration intervals for measurement. Preliminary concentration involves the transference of certain quantity of analyte (expressed in g) from an initial volume to a *smaller* final volume; the volume ratio is an index of the relative concentration performed: *concentration factor*.

5. SECONDARY PREPARATION OF SAMPLES

Grouped under this heading is a series of final operations which may be summarized in two different groups.

(a) *Variations of concentration.* These are generally final dilutions which can sometimes be made so that, once the sample solutions have been analyzed in a first approximation, they may be brought within the interval covered by the standards.

(b) *Additions.* This involves modification of the composition of the prepared sample solution by addition of new components which improve its behaviour during the instrumental measurement by enhancement of

[4] See p. 230 of ref. (*125*).

TABLE 17–1

ADDITIVES

1. *Additives whose effect is measured*
   1.1. *Internal standards*
   1.2. *Autostandards* (addition method and dilution method)

2. *Additives whose effect is not measured*
   2.1. *Enhancers*
      2.1.1. Physical enhancers (organic solvents, surfactants)
      2.1.2. Chemical enhancers
   2.2. *Counterinterferents*
      2.2.1. Releasers
      2.2.2. Protectors
   2.3. *Buffers*
      2.3.1. Deionizers
      2.3.2. Saturators (homo- and heterosaturators)

sensitivity, improvement of physical properties, or attenuation or removal of interference effects.

The classification of additives proposed by Gilbert (*279*) with regard to emission flame photometry is comprehensive. A summary is presented in Table 17–1.

5.1. Addition of non-aqueous solvents

Non-aqueous solvents are used in the preparatory phase of the samples in atomic-absorption for three purposes: (a) as separation agents, (b) as concentration agents (which is, of course, closely connected with (a)), and (c) as enhancement agents. Their use for purposes (a) and (b) have been discussed above; their use in enhancing sensitivity is discussed below.

Many authors have utilized organic solvents in atomic-absorption; Robinson (*615*) and Elwell and Gidley (*213*) were among the first. Elwell and Gidley discussed the use of water–isopropanol mixtures (3:2), with which they found favorable results in the determinations of iron, magnesium, zinc and lead. The use of organic solvents in other determinations later became more widespread (*11–13, 68, 229, 235, 262, 263, 439, 451, 615, 617, 623, 627, 658, 703, 734*). For example, the use of ethanol up to 90% has become quite general in the determinations of aluminum.

Robinson has used mixtures of solvents of widely different boiling point. This procedure can change the normal pattern of the flame; droplets introduced into the flame are disintegrated to much smaller droplets because of a sudden boiling of the lower-boiling solvent. This method thus increases sensitivity (*630*).

In a complete study of the atomic-absorption behaviour of chromium,

Feldman and Purdy (*239*) have studied the sensitivity that can be obtained when solvents like acetone, ethanol, ether and methyl isobutyl ketone are used. Ivanov and Kozyreva (*358*) have used propanol in the determination of copper. A detailed study of different solvents used in the determinations of lead has been done by Dagnall and West (*158*); they include isopropanol methyl ethyl ketone, acetone, acetic acid, dioxan, ethanol, methanol, ethylene glycol and glycerol. In their studies on palladium, Erinc and Magee (*218*) used methanol, ethanol, n-propanol, isopropanol, tert-butanol and acetone.

Organic solvents added to the samples usually increase the absorption measured. This is due largely to increased efficiency in the process of introducing the analyte into the flame (modification of the quantity of effective sample introduced into the flame per unit of time). This has been considered for its possible influence on the thermal balance. With reference to the notes of Magee (*446*) concerning the possible effect of decrease of atoms in the ground state by the use of organic solvents—those which increase the flame temperature—, Walsh (*804*) believes that even in this case the quantity of excited atoms is so small with respect to the ground-state atoms that the changes in temperature are unimportant unless they intervene in the degree of dissociation of the compounds which may be formed in the flame.

Some solvents used in separate sprayers may cause a reduction of the flame temperature. This effect may even be favorable in some cases if a greater concentration of atoms in the flame can be achieved by decreasing the expansion rate of the flame gases.

The influence of some solvents (methanol, ethanol) on sodium, potassium, rubidium and cesium determinations has been tested by Prudnikov (*573*), who found an increase of response with an air–acetylene flame. Glycerol decreased the absorption readings. Burrell (*124*) has reported double sensitivity with 50% isopropanol in an air–propane flame.

Some solvents may cause interfering effects in the flame itself. Since ethanol shows absorption bands in the region below 2300 Å, the direct determination of zinc in wines and alcoholic beverages is quite difficult (*867, 868*). Butler (*127*) points out that the use of organic solvents in some samples requires care because some inorganic acids react violently with them, producing explosive mixtures.

One frequently reads in the literature on flame photometry that the *addition* of organic solvents acts favorably on sensitivity or other aspects. Two cases may occur.

(a) If the addition of a certain volume of solvent to a given volume of solution so enhances the reading that it surpasses the effect of dilution, then the sensitivity actually becomes greater.

(b) If the enhancement is less, proportionally, than the decrease of concentration effected by dilution, the sensitivity apparently decreases.

If an organic extract is taken *directly* to the instrument after an extraction, the problem is different. Since the solvent carries a greater relative concentration of the analyte—due to the process of concentration—, greater signals are observed, i.e. the sensitivity is apparently enhanced. At the same time, the solvent can also increase the efficiency of the sprayer.

5.2. Various other additives

Most of the additions discussed in this section are intended to suppress (or at least minimize) the interference effects of components in the sample and in the prepared solution; the interferences involve definite chemical reactions, particularly inhibition effects.

Chemical interferences are best combatted by *modifying the composition of the solution*; this can be done in two ways:

(a) by *simplifying it*, i.e. by separating the analyte or by separating one or more of the interfering components, or

(b) by *complicating it*, through additions which improve the analytical instrumental behaviour.

Additions provide the only means when separations are impossible or are liable to serious losses. For example, the results for calcium are enhanced by the presence of sodium and potassium in the analysis of blood serum and vegetable matters. Potassium results are enhanced by sodium in the determinations of potassium in blood serum. The separation of alkali metals is very difficult. Calcium can be separated (for determinations of calcium), but there is a danger of losses, for example, with protein-bound calcium (if organic matter is eliminated beforehand by precipitation), or during a chemical precipitation of calcium.

Sometimes additions are preferred even to quantitative chemical separations, if the latter are excessively complicated and time-consuming. Additions can be made either to the standards or to the sample solutions, or to both. The discussion on the preparation of standards (Chapter 16, Section 2.6) should be recalled.

The additives recommended are quite varied: compensations with respect to some of the interfering components, large excesses, competing cations, competing anions, chelating agents. In accordance with this classification, some of these additives may be measured in the atomic-absorption process along with the analyte in the sample solution, e.g. in addition and dilution methods. The effects of other additives in the sample solution on the absorption *are not measured directly*, but *are observed indirectly* when the absorption due to the analyte is measured, e.g. in the case of enhancers—physical or chemical—counterinterferents and buffers.

For greater systematization the different cases are discussed separately in the following sections.

5.2.1. Homogeneous additions

These are additions of components which already exist in the samples or sample solutions (original samples or prepared sample solutions). With these additions, only the concentration of the components is changed up to more convenient ranges.

5.2.1.1. Moderate addition. This involves small additions up to concentrations which are equal or similar to those generally found in the samples for analysis. Within this category the following cases are observed.

Equalization. Additions are made until the concentrations in standards and sample solutions are perfectly equal. They may be additions of a single component or of a *group* of several components[5]. In practice the process of equalization should be extended only to those components which are truly *significant,* which produce or may produce interference. The additions may be made:

(a) *only to the standards,* so that the standards contain the same concentrations of interfering components as the sample solutions prepared;

(b) *only to some of the sample solutions,* i.e. those which contain less of the interfering element than the standards and most of the sample solutions; or

(c) *to both standards and sample solutions,* so that the contents of the standards and some sample solutions are raised to a level corresponding to the level ordinarily found in the type of sample being analyzed.

Compensation. Additions are made principally to the standards when the samples have moderately variable contents of the interfering species which make a perfect equalization difficult. The standards are compensated by adding to them quantities of the significant interferences until an average concentration is attained within the variation interval presented by the sample solutions.

This compensation does not reach the extreme of buffering (see p. 306), since it is intended to equalize the interferences as much as possible when their variation is not excessive.

These moderate additions merely follow the general rule in spectral analysis of trying, as far as possible, to make the standards simulate the

[5] This distinction between *single additions* and *group additions* is applicable not only to equalization methods but also to all other types of addition. Since this qualification has been made, this sub-division will not be repeated in other sections.

composition of the sample solutions. For this reason, they have been called *simulations*. These additions compensate not only the variability of chemical composition to reduce the effects of chemical interferences, but also the effects of physical interferences.

Addition method (see also p. 328). This is a moderate and homogeneous addition, but the analyte itself is added. Since it is also a means of compensating chemical interferences, it is included in this general classification, though it does not entirely correspond to the other additions mentioned. The addition method has become quite general in analytical applications of atomic-absorption, especially in the analysis of biological materials, plants and alloys.

Dilution method. The author has recently proposed the use of the *dilution method* as a derivative of the addition method (*590*). In this method a moderate homogeneous addition—the analyte at a lower relative concentration—is added to the existing amount of analyte. The mixing of the two measured volumes of solution produces a relative dilution. As in the addition method, it is assumed that the total amount of analyte found after dilution will undergo the same effects as the fraction of analyte originally present in the solution, due to the existence of interfering components. There are cases in which the effects are slightly distorted because of the decrease in the ratio of the concentration of interferent to the concentration of analyte.

5.2.1.2. Massive addition. This is also known as *buffering*, and is a *homogeneous addition* or *homogeneous buffering* for which a component already present in the sample solution is added. This is another general practice in spectral analysis; the addition of an *excess* of interfering component lessens the variation between one sample and other. Naturally, identical massive additions must be added to the standards.

This procedure can be accepted in atomic-absorption since there is far less danger of spectral interferences than in emission methods. But care must be taken to ensure that excessive salinity does not produce secondary disturbances, especially of a physical nature.

Massive additions may give good results when appreciable quantities of analyte are to be determined. However, the additions affect the sensitivity and so may make the determination of very small concentrations difficult.

5.2.2. Heterogeneous additions

These are additions of components which do not normally exist in the original samples or in the prepared sample solutions. The additions in this case are used as reference (internal standard) and for diminishing—through chemical actions—inhibition interferences.

5.2.2.1. Moderate addition.

Internal standard. A internal standard is an element which is added to serve as a reference element[6]. The use of internal standards offers good possibilities when multichannel instruments are used. An element already present in the solution may be used as internal standard, if it is liable to the same effects as the analyte and reflects them in the experimental measurements, and if its concentration is known exactly and unequivocally, by means of atomic-absorption or any other method. In most cases the internal standard is *added* in moderate amount to the solutions. An element not present in the solutions provides the opportunity of using the internal standard at *constant* concentration.

Releasing agents. These are moderate heterogeneous additions which liberate the analytes from the effects of inhibition caused by the interfering components. They are also called simply *releasers* or *competing ions*. Sometimes it is recommended that an excess of releasing agent be added; this may permit the inclusion of its use as an example of massive heterogeneous additions.

The addition of releasing agents has long been known; it has been used since the beginning of the application of flame methods in spectrography to diminish interfering effects[7]. The difficulty caused by this technique in emission flame photometry is that it complicates the spectrum. Since the additions do not have such marked effects in atomic-absorption, the releasers have been much more widely used. As a general rule, a reagent of a character and chemical behaviour similar to the analyte must be added to the solution.

Typical cases of the use of releasing agents in atomic-absorption are tabulated on p. 308

The use of lanthanum (lanthanum chloride) to overcome interferences in the determination of calcium in flame methods has been carefully studied by Williams (*822*). It has become general practice to use lanthanum in the determination of calcium[8]. It is customary to use concentrations varying from 1 to 0.1% in the final solution prepared for the instrumental determination. If the calcium concentration and the concentration of the interfering component are low, less than 1000 p.p.m. of lanthanum can be used. Additions of 1% lanthanum could almost be considered as massive additions. The present author has found it convenient to use blank solutions

---

[6] The reader should consult the section dealing with internal standards in Chapter 14, p. 236 of ref. (*125*).

[7] See the publication of R. L. MITCHELL AND I. M. ROBERTSON, The effect of aluminum on the flame spectra of the alkaline earths, *J. Soc. Chem. Ind.*, 55 (1936) 269 T. This publication illustrates the use of strontium to avoid the interference of aluminum in the determination of calcium by the Lundegårdh technique.

[8] Billings and Adams (*101*) and Trent and Slavin (*776, 777*) have discussed the application of lanthanum in atomic-absorption methods.

Analyte	*Interfering component*	*Releasing agent*	*Authors*	*References*
Calcium and magnesium	Several	Strontium	David[9]	(*166*)
Calcium and magnesium	Several	Lanthanum	David[9]	(*166*)
Magnesium	Calcium	Strontium	David	(*162*)
Molybdenum	Calcium and iron	Aluminum and phosphates	David[10]	(*168*)
Calcium	Phosphates	Magnesium and sulfuric acid	David	(*163*)
Magnesium	Aluminum	Strontium	Elwell and Gidley	(*213*)
Magnesium	Aluminum	Calcium, or calcium and sulfuric acid	Leithe and Hoffer	(*429, 430*)
Magnesium	Aluminum	Calcium or strontium	Menzies	(*495, 496*)
Calcium	Phosphates	Strontium	Newburn	(*527*)
Rhodium	Sodium, noble metals	Copper	Strassheim and Wessels *et al.*	(*733*)
Calcium	Several	Lanthanum	Williams	(*822*)
Calcium	Phosphates	Lanthanum	Willis	(*831*)
Calcium and magnesium	Phosphates	Strontium	Willis	(*827, 828*)
Calcium	Phosphates	Lanthanum	Yofé *et al.*[11]	(*858*)

containing the same quantity of lanthanum as the standards and sample solutions for routine calcium determinations.

The releasing action may be seen very clearly in graphic representations of aluminum interference by the appearance of horizontal parallel curves in the plots of readings *vs.* ratio La:Al beginning with La:Al ratios approximately equal to 10, for different concentrations of calcium. For lower La:Al ratios, ascending curves are produced, indicating the slow liberation of the calcium atoms.

A very special case, which may be called an *auto-releasing action*, is the phenomenon found by Andrew and Nichols (*22*) in the determination of magnesium in nickel alloys and nickel; the nickel itself found in the samples

[9] David (*166*) has compared the behaviour of strontium and lanthanum in the determinations of calcium and magnesium; strontium was found to be more efficient against interferences by aluminum, phosphates, silicates and sulfates.

[10] David (*168*) has also tested the effect of excesses of aluminum chloride in the determination of molybdenum.

[11] Yofé *et al.* (*858*) have studied the behaviour of lanthanum along with the chemical interference of phosphates on strontium and barium; lanthanum is said to displaces calcium, strontium and barium from the phosphates before they enter the hot region of the flame.

as a macroelement is capable of suppressing the effects of the interferences of aluminum and silicon.

Chelating agents. Chelating agents are also moderate heterogeneous additions. These agents, like releasing agents, diminish the inhibiting action of chemical interferences, but their action is different; chelating agents not only liberate the analyte from interferences but also protect it.

The mechanism of protection by chelation is very simple since the agent is limited to protecting the atoms of the analyte from any other component which might form stable compounds in the flame.

EDTA has been widely used as chelating agent because of its facility in forming chelates with calcium and magnesium, two of the elements most exposed to the formation of non-volatile compounds in the flame. Reference may be made to the research of Herrmann and Lang (*323*) who used EDTA to avoid interferences by phosphates on calcium, of Newburn (*527*) who also used EDTA in his determinations of calcium, and of Willis (*824, 827, 828, 831*) who has made extensive use of EDTA. Wallace (*796*) has used oxine in the determination of magnesium; he found that oxine is as good or better than strontium in the attenuation of interferences on magnesium. The addition of oxine has been recommended by Rubeška and Moldan (*641*) to avoid the interference by aluminum on magnesium. The reagent is used in 10% solution, and is added before diluting the prepared sample down to the appropriate magnesium concentration for instrumental determination.

The study made by Voinovitch *et al.* (*791*) may have notable repercusions in the field of atomic-absorption flame photometry. Since oxine hinders, to a large extent, the interference of aluminum in the determination of alkaline earths (especially calcium and strontium), the behaviour of 8-acetoxyquinoline, 2,4-dimethylquinoline, isoquinoline, quinoline, phenol and acetylacetone was studied. All of them acted in a similar way. The following agents showed low activity: pyridine, ethylenediamine, triethanolamine, benzyl alcohol and monoethylamine. Ethyl acetate, methanol, ethanol and acetone were almost inert.

Several protectors act similarly to the typical chelating agents. Among them is glycerol, which was used by Trent and Slavin (*778*). In an important contribution by Rains *et al.* (*577, 578*), to the study of phosphate interferences on calcium in emission flame photometry, the releasing behaviour of ethylene glycol, glycerol, mannitol, dextrose and lactose was reported; the best results were obtained with glycerol. This contribution opens new areas in the application of the atomic-absorption methods, since these investigators tried the procedure in pickling solutions, soil extracts, plant tissues, fish tissues, animal bones and other types of samples.

Other chemicals which show good potentialities for use as protectors in atomic-absorption are salicylic acid, oxalic acid and oxalates.

Detergent addition. Mooney (*507*) has used N-lauryl-β-aminopropionic acid (General Mills' Deriphat 170 C) in the proportion of 3 mg per 100 ml. This aditive prevents any clogging when highly saline solutions (lithium- and sodium-rich solutions) are used with a sprayer-burner of medium-bore capillary. This detergent was chosen because it was anphoteric and contained no metallic elements.

5.2.2.2. Massive addition. These include releasing or chelating agents which are added in large quantities, and also the large additions of a heterogeneous character which do not belong to the above classifications, e.g. radiation buffers, although their use is very limited in atomic-absorption.

Chapter 18

Experimental measurements and calibration

1. EXPERIMENTAL MEASUREMENTS

Operation with atomic-absorption instruments requires minimum movement of the operator around the bench, if the settings are stable and the controls, gauges and readout device are well distributed around the operator. It is only necessary to feed samples into the instrument and record readings, as is customary in other flame units.

In order to achieve experimental measurements representative of the concentration of the samples, it is necessary that all the variables be maintained constant, or if not constant, at least with minimum variations within very narrow variation intervals. Some variables are *predeterminable* (according to the element to be determined: nature of the gases, pressure or flow of support gas—this depends on the characteristics of the sprayer—, wavelength, etc.), while others must be studied before the experimental measurements to attain their optimum values (pressure or flow of the fuel gas, selection zone by variation of the height of the burner, angle of rotation of the burner, slit width, lamp current, gain, etc.), as has been indicated in preceding chapters. It can be helpful, and can also provide a very clear means of presenting experimental data, to prepare a series of *effect–variable* curves, e.g. absorption variation (in percentage of absorption), absorbance variation or sensitivity variation as a function of the gas pressures (pressure settings), slit widths, burner heights, etc.

Once the control settings and the positions of the auxiliary mechanical parts have been decided, standards, blanks and sample solutions can be measured.

Commercial instruments are usually accompanied by special recommendations from the manufacturer for the proper preliminary setting of the equipment. These settings should be taken as a starting point in looking for the definitive settings appropriate for each type of determination. It is a good practice to prepare a permanent step-by-step chart of operating directions, if one has not been provided by the manufacturer; its use prevents any mistakes in the preparation of the instrument at the beginning of a working period and in the switching off steps.

1.1. Order of the measurements

Two aspects should be mentioned.

(a) *A series of standards is used,* distributed along a certain interval of concentrations. The following directions are applicable for measurements with a series of standards to prepare and use a working curve. Each sample solution should be measured at least twice—the average value being used—and, if possible, in different series of sample solutions readings. Good results should be obtained by measuring in this order: blank (if the instrument is zeroed with the solvent), series of standards, series of sample solutions, blank, standards, sample solutions, blank, and standards. Each standard solution of the series and the blank are represented by three measurements, and the average of each set of readings is used in the construction of the working curve. Some operators take the measurements by inverting the concentration order when standards and/or sample solutions are measured (e.g., S_1, S_2, S_3, etc., and afterwards reading ....S_3, S_2, and S_1, if conc. S_1<Conc. S_2<conc. S_3, etc.). It is best not to invert the order, but to begin with those solutions containing the smallest concentrations of analyte, so that contaminations and memory errors from one sample to another can be avoided. Then, the standards should be measured beginning with the lower standard. In certain cases (samples and standards are excessively saline, or contain much organic matter) it is advisable to carry out repeated intermediate washings (with water or with the nonaqueous solvent used), and, if necessary, intermediate blank readings and zeroings. As a general rule, an intermediate washing by aspirating water or pure solvent should always follow the reading of the most concentrated sample solution and the most concentrated standard, and should precede zeroing, reading the blank, or reading another solution of low concentration. The intermediate washing may be replaced by one or several flushings with the solution which is about to be measured. After the flushing operation, the solution is sprayed and measured when the equilibrium is reached after a few seconds. If flushings are done, washings are still imperative before blanks and zeroing operations. In heated spray-chambers, a short period should be allowed to permit the chamber to re-attain the equilibrium distorted by the cooling action of the spraying operation. In some models of cold chambers, it is better to spray continuously.

(b) *A single standard is used.* The sample solutions should have a concentration sufficiently low to be included between the blank and the standard used. A single standard is used on the assumption that a linear response is obtained in the interval covered. More concentrated standards may be utilized if the linear response over a sufficient interval has been checked beforehand. One or several sample solutions may be measured with only one standard if all variables are kept sufficiently constant and if the measurement of the standard is repeated frequently. The best procedure is as follows: blank, sample solution, standard, blank, sample solution, standard, etc. Since there may be certain variations in very short periods of time, because it is not possible to measure three solutions simultaneously, the accuracy of the measurements—average values—may be increased by making the three readings and repeating them in the shortest possible time. Any appreciable variation of the reference solutions, one or the other, or both at the same time, introduces errors because of changes in the slope and/or the intersect.

Determinations made by reading a sample solution between two standards of concentration slightly higher and lower than the sample solution (or solutions) form a particular case of the single standard technique. This is a method which has been widely used in emission flame photometry and is known as the *two-standard method* or *sandwiching method*. It is of great value in analytical systems when the working plots are curved. The portion of the curve between both standards can be considered as linear (if the standards are close enough) for calculation purposes. In this method the solutions should be read *successively* and *rapidly*, for the reasons indicated above.

2. CALIBRATION

The process of calibration, in the restricted sense of *analytical calibration*, leads to the preparation of a *calibration curve*, which is, as is well known, a graphic representation of the variation of the experimental measurements (measurements of the quantitative variable of the analytical system) as a function of the concentration of analyte in solution. Measurements are made by using solutions of known concentration: standards.

The origin of the calibration curve—zero concentration—is determined by zeroing the instrument with the solvent or the blank solution, and rechecking it by measuring the solvent or the blank solution. For a result of 0% absorption at zero concentration, the curve begins at the point zero–zero.

In practice, the intensity I_0 is not measured in the absence of analyte. What is measured is the intensity of the beam emerging from the absorption cell in the absence of absorbing atoms: (a) by aspirating water or pure solvent, (b) by aspirating blank solution, or (c) by measuring the intensity of the emerging beam when no solution is aspirated. This last procedure is unusual, as in many cases some effect is noticed when water, solvent or blank solution is aspirated. Then, the instrument should be zeroed by aspirating the most convenient of these solutions (water and pure solvent are considered here as "solutions" of infinite dilution: zero concentration). Once the instrument has been zeroed, it is in a condition for reading 0% absorption (absorbance 0.0000) in the absence of analyte, although there may be absorbing entities in the absorption cell. The zeroing control actually backs this absorption off[1].

The practical end of the calibration curve will be determined by the most concentrated standard used, although this limit may not be reached if a strong curvature is observed at the end of the curve.

Calibration curves prepared for immediate analytical purposes, are called *working curves*. Working curves *should be repeated in each working session and for each set of sample solutions* even if all the operating conditions have been maintained invariable. This practice consumes some time but helps in obtaining higher accuracy.

2.1. *Types of calibration and working curves in atomic-absorption*

Several types of curve may be used in atomic-absorption.

2.1.1. *Absorbance–concentration curves*

These are perhaps the most suitable, since they maintain the linear relationship $A = mC$ along a considerable interval[2] or they show clearly

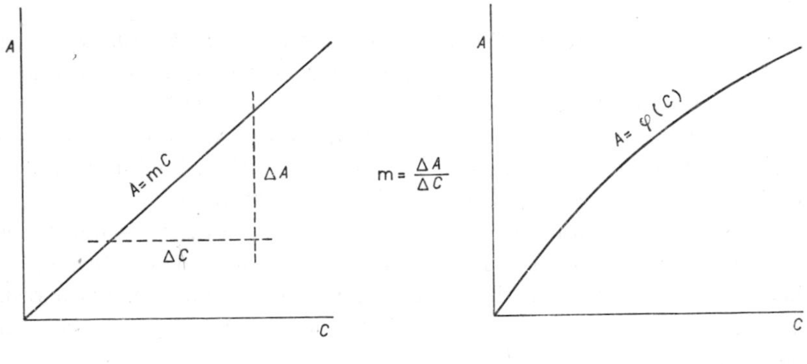

Fig. 18–1. Absorbance–concentration curves (working curves). Linear ($A = mC$) and curved ($A = \varphi(C)$).

[1] Another effect which is compensated by the zeroing control is the scattering of radiation by small particles present in the flame. The degree of scattering due to the small particles is proportional to $1/\lambda^4$. The reader is referred to the paper of Billings (*897, 942*).

[2] This relationship is derived from the basic linear equation of the atomic-absorption process: $A = abc$.

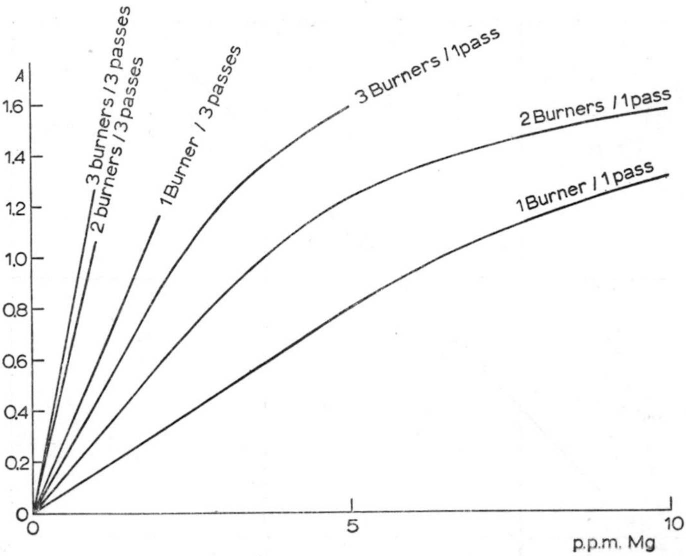

Fig. 18–2. Working curves for magnesium obtained with a Beckman DU-2 spectrophotometer with atomic-absorption accessory and turbulent flow burner.

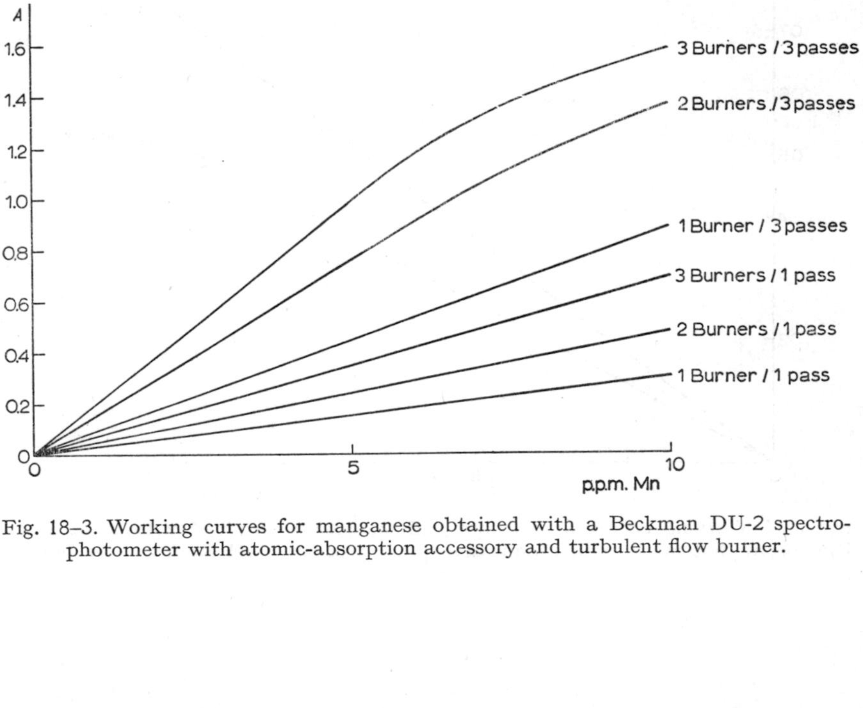

Fig. 18–3. Working curves for manganese obtained with a Beckman DU-2 spectrophotometer with atomic-absorption accessory and turbulent flow burner.

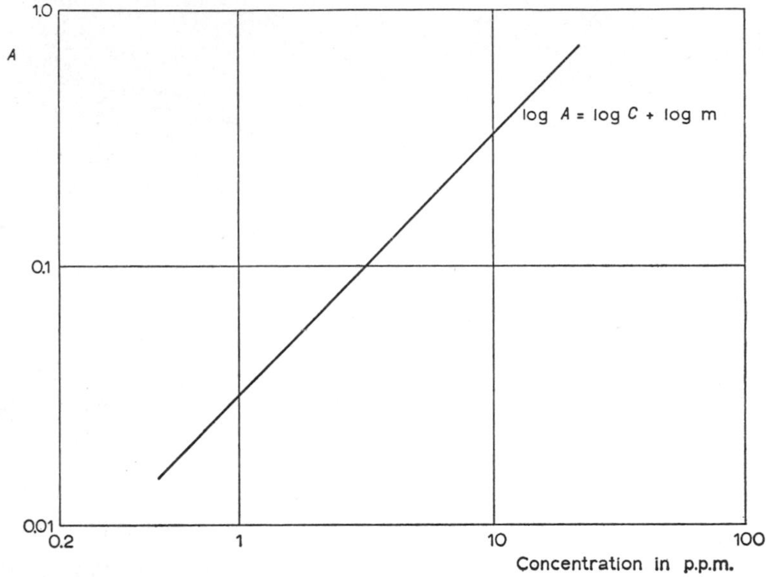

Fig. 18–4. Log–log representation of absorbance–concentration curves.

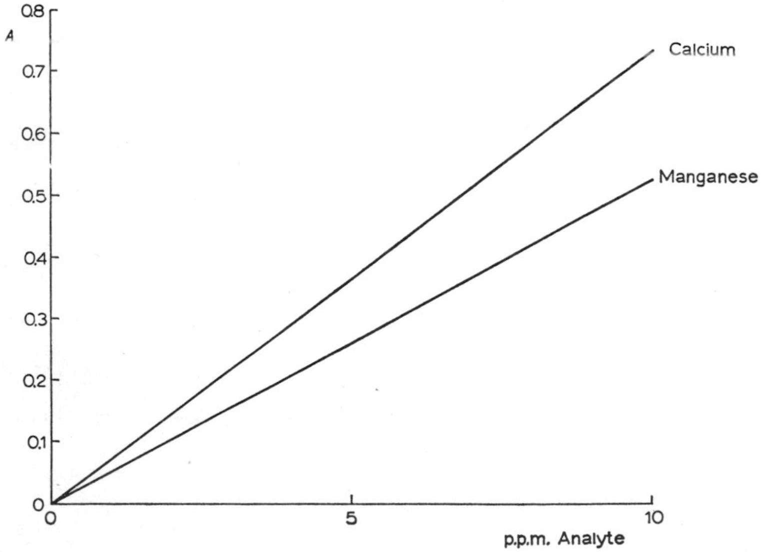

Fig. 18–5. Working curves for calcium and manganese obtained with a Beckman DB spectrophotometer with atomic-absorption accessory and laminar flow burner.

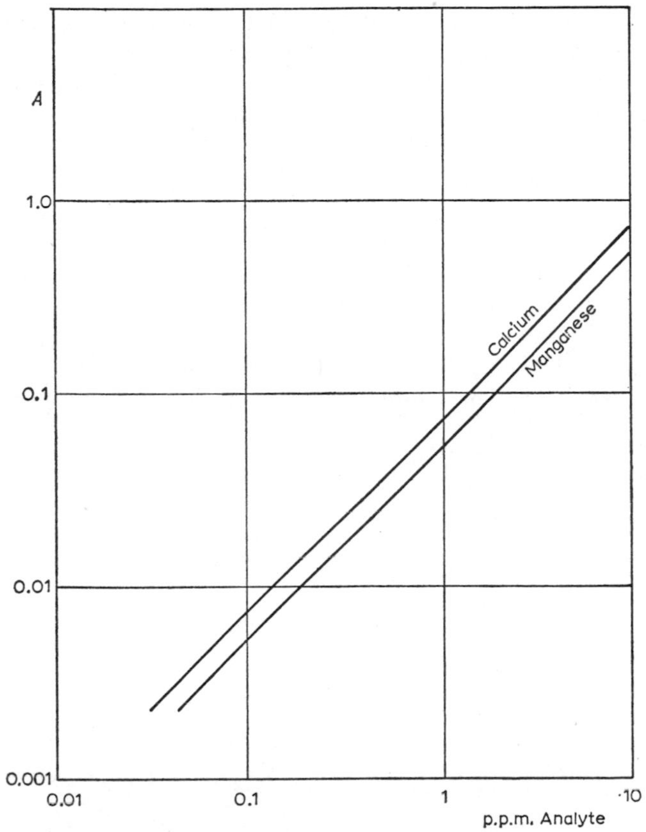

Fig. 18–6. The curves of Fig. 18–5 in log–log scales.

at which values of absorbance or concentration curvature appears.

The most appropriate interval for measurements extends from absorbances of 0.12 or 0.15 up to about 0.70 (if linearity is conserved at this absorbance value[3]). Measurements can be done, of course, outside these limits, but the accuracy will then be poorer.

Generally, sensitivity calculations are based on readings corresponding to low absorbance values. Measurements involved in addition and dilution methods (see p. 328) should sometimes be done at absorbance values below 0.12.

A curve prepared for an analyte is distinguished by the number of decades (or logarithmic units) it covers. Frequently the decades are referred to the concentration scale. They can also be referred to the absorbance

[3] These values correspond to readings of about 25–30 to 80% absorption.

scale. In Fig. 18–1, two cases of absorbance–concentration curves are shown and in Figs. 18–2 and 18–3 two practical cases. The absorbance–concentration curves can also be represented in log–log scales (see Fig. 18–4). The curves shown in Fig. 18–5 on ordinary scales are also represented in Fig. 18–6 on log–log scales.

It is advisable to use the full scale as far as possible, i.e., by adjusting the 0% absorption and the 100% absorption accurately with the corresponding controls of the instrument. If one wishes to know the relative absorption produced when the solvent or the blank solution is sprayed, it is usually possible to adjust the 0% absorption with the flame itself, and then to measure with a restricted scale, e.g., of 90 divisions (see Fig. 18–7). Values read or recorded under these conditions should be converted into percentage absorption before being converted into absorbance values.

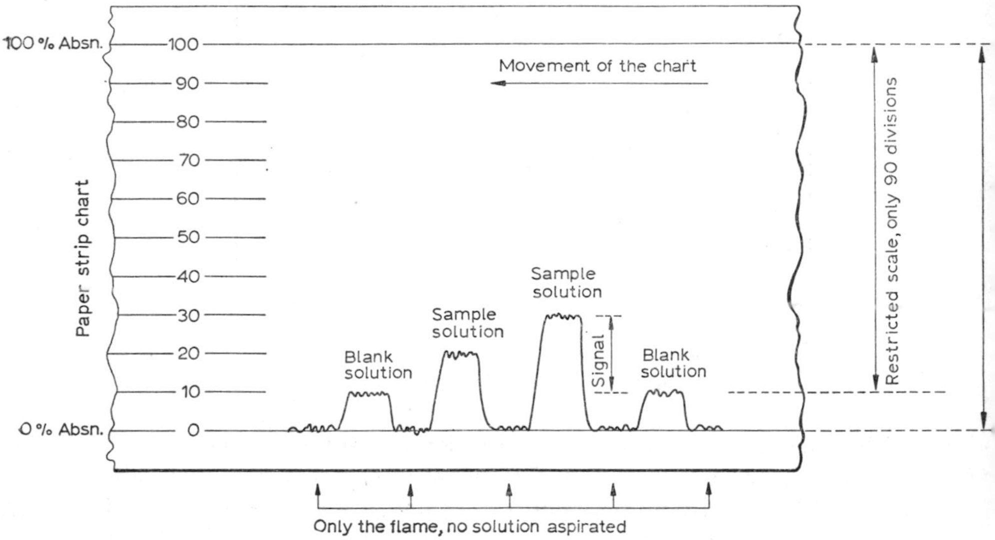

Fig. 18–7,a. Use of restricted scale in recording the signals for blank solutions with the flame signal adjusted at 0% absorption.

Fig. 18–7,b. Typical recordings when the blank solution (in these cases, water) is adjusted at 0% absorption: (I), magnesium, 0.02 p.p.m. Obtained with a Beckman DB spectrophotometer with atomic-absorption accessory and laminar flow burner. Single pass. (II), calcium, 0.5 p.p.m. Obtained with a Beckman atomic-absorption spectrophotometer, No. 97900, and laminar flow burner. Triple pass. (By courtesy of Beckman Instruments, Inc.).

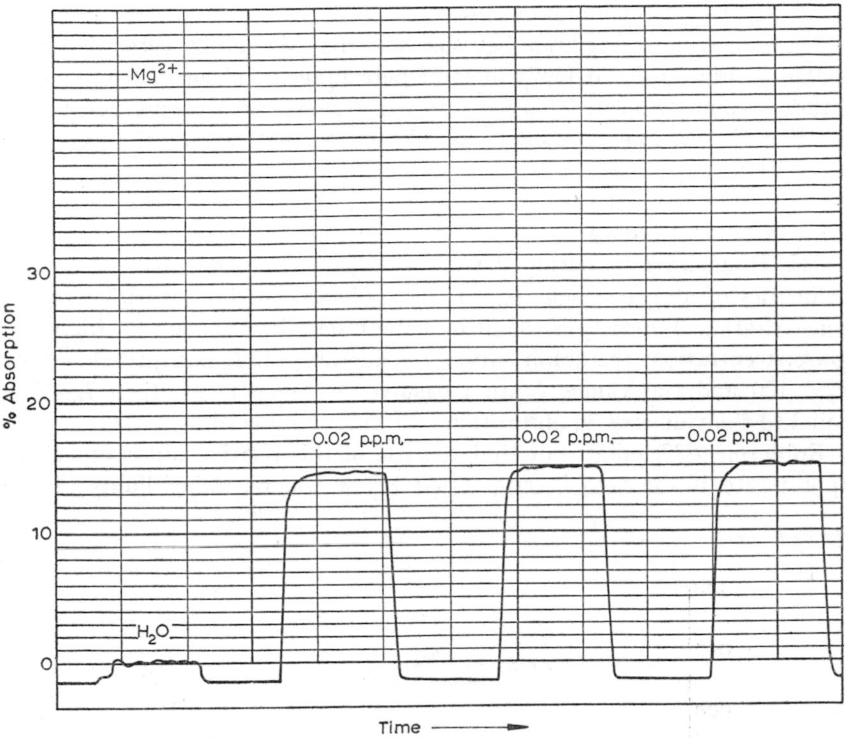

Mg2+
H2O
0.02 p.p.m.
0.02 p.p.m.
0.02 p.p.m.
30
20
10
0
% Absorption
Time

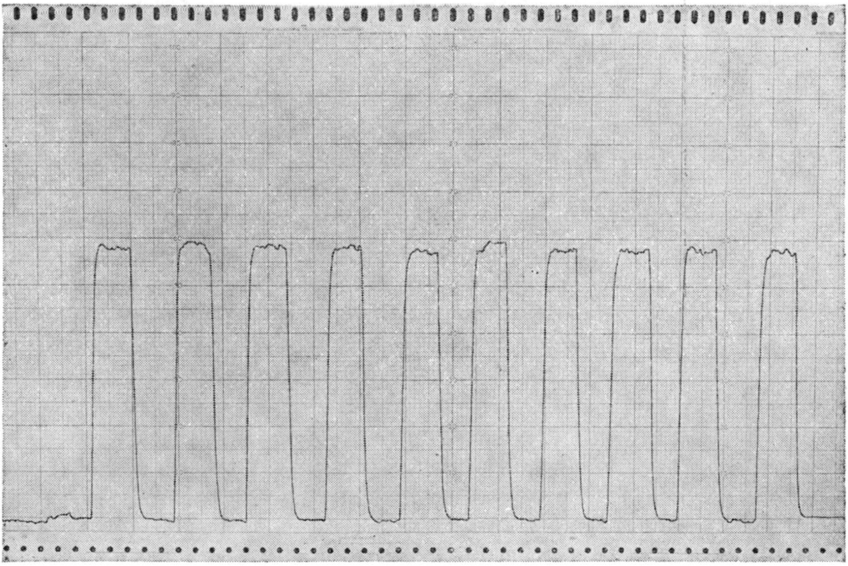

2.1.2. Absorption–concentration curves

The established correlation between absorbance and absorption is represented in Fig. 18–8. At low values of percentage of absorption the correlation is almost linear. This permits calibration and working curves *absorption (in %)–concentration* to be plotted for low values of percentage absorption (Fig. 18–9).

2.1.3. Ringbom relationship

The Ringbom relationship $\log C = k\ (I_0—I)$ may be used to express quantities of absorbed light $(I_0—I)$ as a function of the logarithm of the concentration. Linearity is found in some intervals, although for high and low concentrations the graph curves considerably. If I_0 is adjusted so that $I_0 = 100$ and the values I are measured as percentages, then $I_0—I$ is equal to the values of % absorption conventionally used.

Robinson (*623*) points out that the use of this relationship is especially appropriate if the zero is suppressed below the recording limits of the

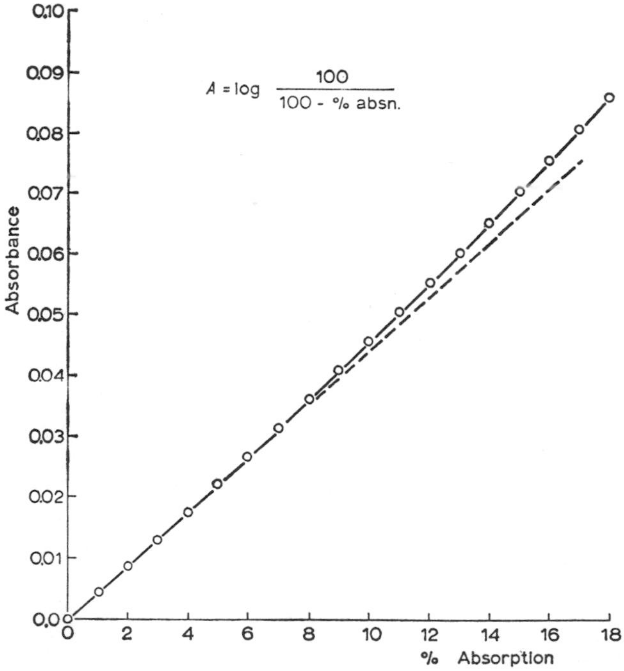

Fig. 18–8,a. Correlation between absorbance and % absorption (range 0–18% absorption).

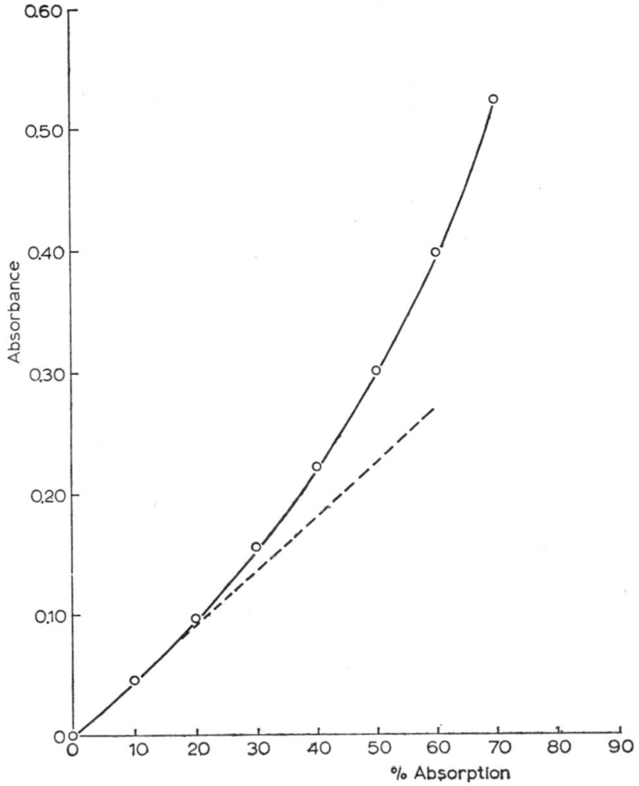

Fig. 18–8,b. Correlation between absorbance and % absorption (range 0–70% absorption).

instrument, and that if the position of the zero is reproducible, analytical results can be calculated without making absolute measurements of I_0 and I.

The present author has used this relationship to demonstrate the advantage of being able to work at different instrumental sensitivities for the determination of an analyte in different concentration ranges (see Fig. 18–10) (*602*). It is also useful to have readily available a graph, such as that represented in Fig. 18–11, that shows the Ringbom curves for several cases in which linearity is obtained in absorbance–concentration curves. Thus, by observing the signals recorded on the strip chart the operator can deduce if the readings will follow a linear relationship when later converted to absorbances and plotted versus concentration.

2.2. Shape of the curves

A careful examination of the shape of the analytical calibration curve should be made for each set of experimental conditions. It is difficult to foretell how calibration curves will come out under certain conditions; on many occasions, curvature can be produced.

2.2.1. Curvature of the calibration curves

The curvature of the calibration curves depends on a series of factors

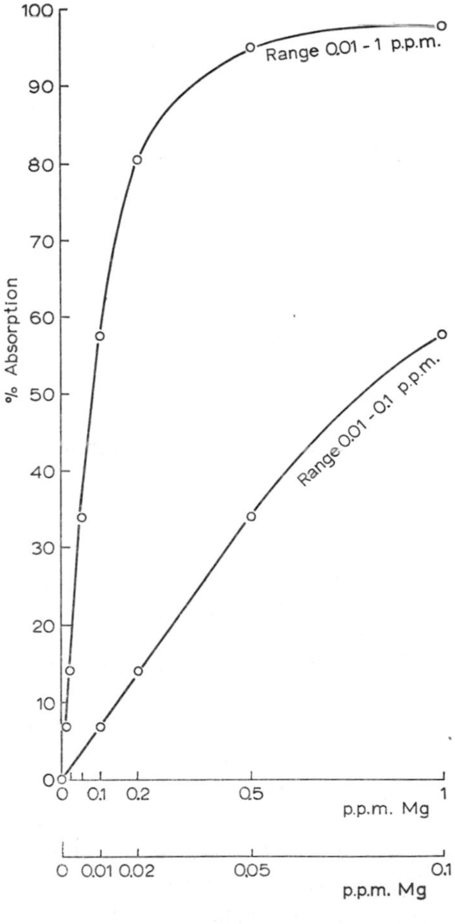

Fig. 18–9. Percent absorption–concentration curves for magnesium. Values obtained with a Beckman DB spectrophotometer with atomic-absorption accessory and laminar flow burner.

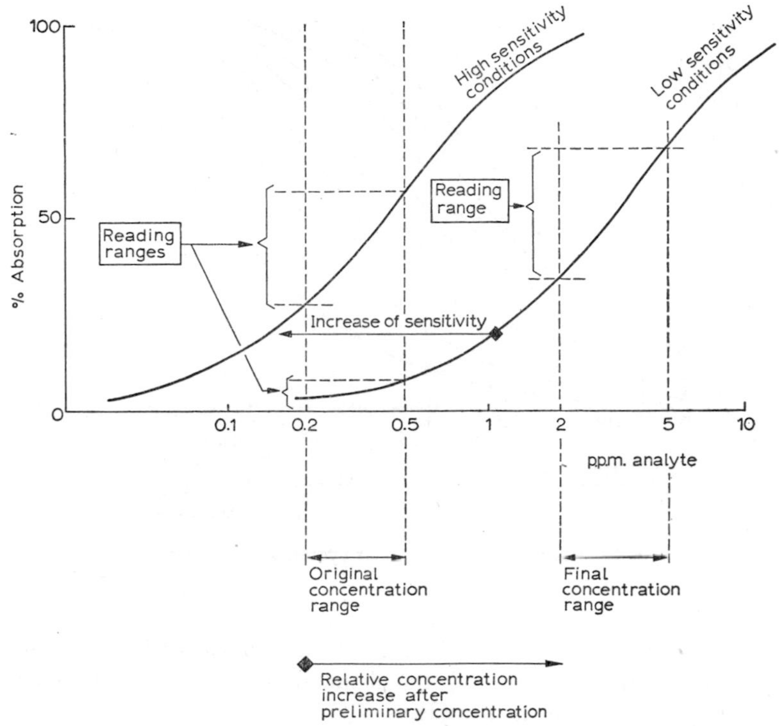

Fig. 18–10. Curves % absorption–concentration (concentration in log scale) for two sensitivity conditions. After preliminary concentration it is possible to make the readings at low instrumental sensitivity in a convenient reading range. If high sensitivity is used, preliminary concentration is not necessary.

among which figure: other components accompanying the analyte in the solutions (i.e., if the standards used in calibration are made exactly equal in composition to the sample solutions or at least compensated), any non-aqueous solvents used, the optical system, the nature of the flame, the characteristics of the emitter and the current intensity used.

A good linear response is obtained:

(a) if the concentration of the atomic vapor is kept uniform throughout the volume of flame traversed by the beam; and

(b) if the measurement is made at the peak wavelength, or so close to it that the absorptivity may be considered *constant* along the range of wavelength selected for measurement and unaffected by the factors causing line broadening.

It is interesting to attempt to determine experimentally for each type

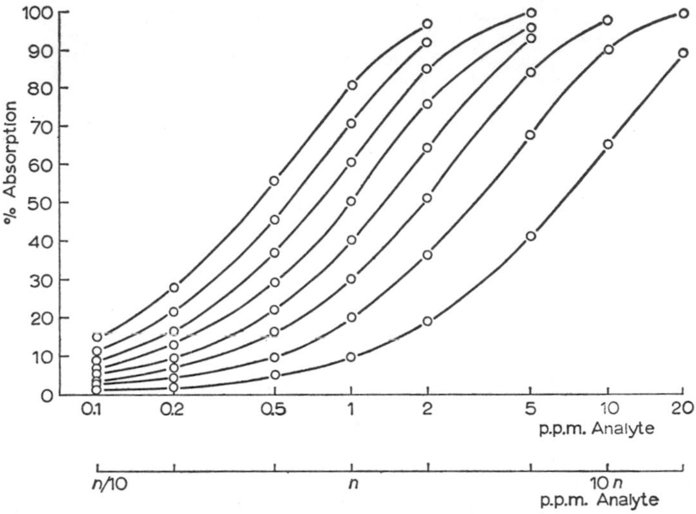

Fig. 18–11. Ringbom curves for ideal linear systems at different sensitivities.

of analysis—for each element—whether a lack of linearity found is due to (a) the instrumental system, (b) the flame in the region of wavelength used, or (c) the nature of the sample.

The problem of curvature of the calibration and working curves is receiving more and more attention. The use of linear curves has been discussed by Sprague *et al.* (*717*). Rubeška and Svoboda (*643*) have concluded that curvature of analytical curves in atomic-absorption spectroscopy may be due to several factors, particularly, resonance broadening and resonance shift of the absorption line; the ratio of the line widths as well as their hyperfine structure were found also to play a part. A very complete study of the different calibration curves for cobalt, using several lines, has been presented by Harrison (*307*). The attainment of linear working curves has been studied by Brace *et al.* (*110*) in the case of high-emitting elements.

Shimazu and Hashimoto (*669*), who have studied the relation between the shape of curves and spectral line profiles, have concluded that when the peak absorption method is used, the curves are always straight if emission from the flame is negligible; that in both peak and total absorption methods, the curves deviate from straight lines if the emission of the flame is not negligible; that, again in both cases, when the self-absorption in the source increases, there is a decrease of sensitivity; and finally, that the peak absorption method is more sensitive in any case than the total absorption method. A schematic representation of the different cases studied by these authors is shown in Fig. 18–12.

The curves generally show curvature when the concentrations are quite distant from the fluctuational qualitative concentration limit, e.g., at concentrations 100 or 300 times above (2–2.5 logarithmic units). However, the working curves can still be used for analytical purposes beyond those limits, even if they present some curvature.

Better linearity can usually be found by optimizing the support gas:fuel gas ratios and the selection zone in the flame.

The background emission (from the source or the flame) received by the photodetector may also cause curvature (see below). More linear curves have been found in photographic methods, because it is then easier to

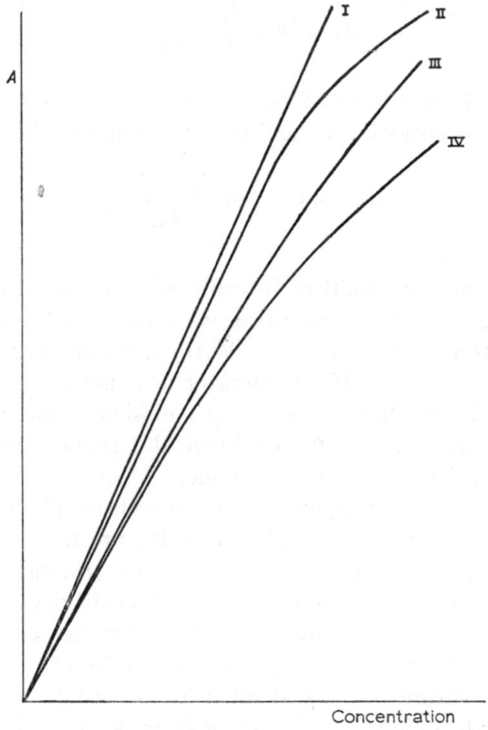

Fig. 18–12. Different shapes of working curves: (I), peak absorption (no flame emission); (II), peak absorption (with flame emission); (III), total absorption (no flame emission); (IV), total absorption (with flame emission). For a complete discussion, consult ref. (*669*).

control the effects of background. Source emission can cause losses of linearity if the lamp is run too hot.

The different curvatures found for the same analyte by different authors working under different experimental conditions are associated with the differences of slope. For some elements these differences are often due simply to the use of different gases; gases giving flames of lower temperature tend to give curves of smaller slope, i.e. less sensitivity.

The use of modulation helps to suppress curvature in some cases (principally if curvature is due to emission coming from the flame). The effect of residual emission has been studied by Elwell and Gidley (*213*) and by Menzies (*496*). (The effect of pressure broadening on curvature has also been mentioned by these authors and by Russell *et al.* (*647*)). Residual emissions may cause apparent absorbance values, A_a, as a function of the residual emission I_R

$$A_a = \log \frac{I_0 + I_R}{I + I_R}$$

For sufficiently large values of I_R, which may become more significant than I for large concentrations, the following limit would be considered

$$\lim_{I \to 0} A_a = \log \frac{I_0 + I_R}{I_R}$$

This extreme condition could be interpreted as a curvature of the curve towards the abscissa axis—concentration axis—and asymptotic for the *limit* value situated on the ordinate. With high-emitting elements these phenomena are very marked if the operator does not back off the emission detected. With lithium, due to its strong emission, a maximum has been observed at high concentration and then the curve bends toward the concentration axis if no backing-off is made.

In general, excessive curvature can be prevented if high light output at the source and a narrow spectral bandwidth are used. When measurements are made at a spectral bandwidth which is not sufficiently narrow, there is a loss of linearity (as well as a loss of sensitivity) because the absorption at the peak is masked by the light transmitted at adjacent wavelengths, where the absorptivity is definitely much lower.

The type of curvature may be defined at low ranges of concentration through computer techniques by following expressions such as

$$y = A_0 + A_1x + A_2x^2 + A_1x^3 + \dots$$

If the instrument is adjusted to 0% absorption for zero concentration, then $A_0 = 0$. In curves of perfect linear response all the coefficients are nullified except A_1 (i.e., what has been called slope m in preceding chapters). In this expression the variable y is the absorbance and the variable x is the concentration (*601*).

2.3. Concentration range

In Chapter 16, Section 4, some of the limitations of the concentration range of the determinations were pointed out. The extent of the concentration range should always be verified for a particular set of operating conditions in spite of the fact that in many publications details on concentration range are given[4]. A simple way of representing concentration ranges is shown in Fig. 18–13, where a logarithmic scale is used for concentrations.

By common usage, the abscissa scale of the calibration and working curves corresponds to the concentration scale. It is logical to do this in the calibration step because the absorbances are calculated as a function

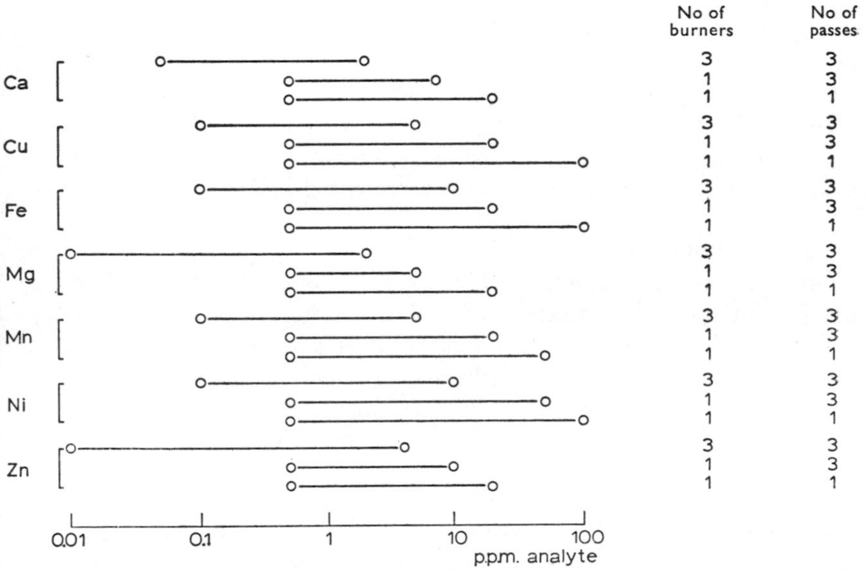

Fig. 18–13. Representation of concentration ranges on a log scale. Data from ref. (*313*).

[4] Walsh (*800*) has published a summary of different applications of atomic-absorption flame photometry in which he indicates, for each analyte and line utilized, the intervals which have been used in the concentration scale (cf. refs. (*313, 314*)).

of the concentration of the standards. In the determination step, the plotting might be reversed on the basis that concentrations are found from the absorbances calculated from the readings, but for uniformity it is advisable to conserve the horizontal scale for concentrations in all cases.

In order not to exaggerate the curves too much, it is best to use a scale unit agreeing with the limits of the range gf the series of standards. If possible, equal units should be used in both axes (e.g., 1 unit of absorbance for 1 p.p.m.); at least, definite ratios between units should be used (1 unit of absorbance for 10, 100, ... p.p.m.; 0.1 unit for absobance for 10, 100, ... p.p.m.).

An abbreviated expression has been recently proposed to express simultaneously the dynamic range of concentrations (actually dynamic range ratio), percentual qualitative concentration limit and noise level (by using the ratio between the percentual qualitative concentration limit and the fluctuational qualitative concentration limit) (*111*).

2.4. Special cases in working curves

This section deals with special cases of working curves derived from the use of a restricted number of standard solutions.

2.4.1. Use of one standard

This is the case in which the operator uses only the zeroing solution (water, solvent, blank solution) and one reference standard (see Section 1.1 in this chapter). The working curve is represented in Fig. 18–14.

2.4.2. Use of two standards

Two close standards are used. If the curve is linear the results from the sample solutions can be interpolated as shown in Fig. 18–15. This procedure is very useful for non-linear systems. If it is assumed that the interval comprised between close standards is linear, and if it is known that the sample solutions are intermediate in concentration between the standards, the concentrations can be found as shown in Fig. 18–16 (*938*).

2.4.3. Addition method

The addition method is a simple means of obtaining experimental concentration values corresponding to the unknown concentrations of the sample solutions. It may be considered as a special case of restricted number of standards because a restricted number of solutions are prepared and measured, but no series of standard solutions is required. Instead of series of standards, known amounts of analyte are added to aliquots of the sample solution, and these solutions are measured in the instrument.

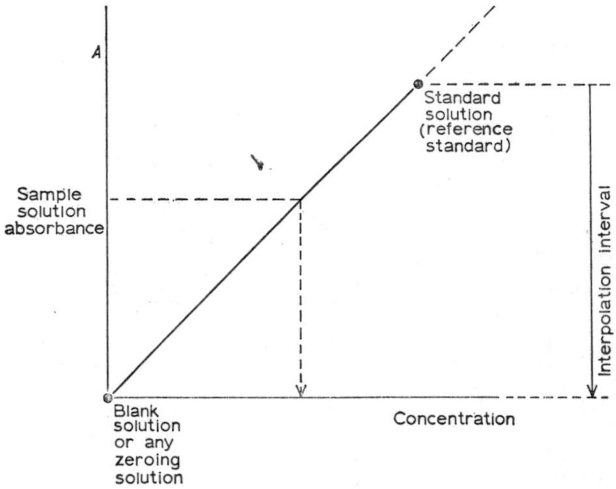

Fig. 18–14. Single-standard method.

The addition method, which has given excellent results in emission flame photometry, has become popular in atomic-absorption, particularly because linear response is readily obtained in most cases, and this is a prerequisite for accurate results.

The addition method has been given many different names. Vallee and

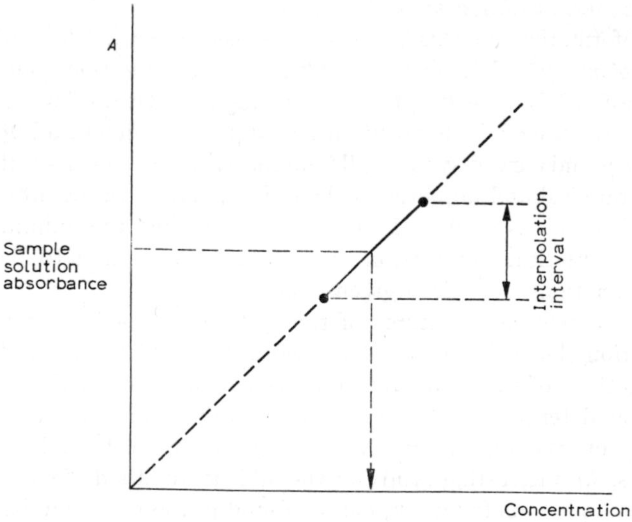

Fig. 18–15. Two-standard method (linear systems).

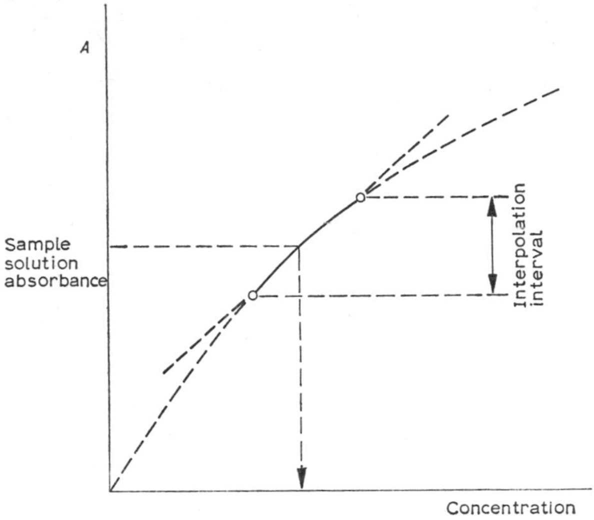

Fig. 18–16. Two-standard method (curved systems).

Thiers (*787*) mention the terms *standard addition, mixture method, addition-standard method, incremental addition* and *method of additions*, and they use the term *self-standardization* themselves. Gilbert (*279*) adds *admixture method* and *method of increments* and uses *autostandardization*. The present author prefers the term *addition method*.

Preliminary information on this method has been given in the earlier book *Flame Photometry* (*125*). The capabilities of the addition method have been discussed (*585*) according to the following aspects: (a) deviations to be expected in the use of single-addition techniques at different addition ratios, and in linear and curved systems, (b) comparison with multi-addition techniques (by graphical and numerical calculation), and (c) representative data and experimental examples. Directions for finding the minimum deviations in the practical application of the addition method to flame analytical determinations have been given (*585*).

Among the best-known applications of the addition method in atomic-absorption, mention should be made of the work of David (*165, 173, 174*) on the determinations of molybdenum and strontium, of Strasheim *et al.* (*734, 738*) on the determinations of several impurities in gold, and of Willis (*828, 834*) on the determination of magnesium, lead, and other metallic elements. An interesting study of the addition method, developed especially for flame photometry work, can be found in the paper published by Beukelman and Lord (*97*).

The reasons for which the addition method has been accepted and adopted in flame photometry are mainly as follows. (a) The addition method offers a very effective means of compensating for the variations caused by physical and chemical interferences which appear from one sample solution to another; (b) it can be used with any linear analytical system; (c) most cases can be resolved by graphical calculation or by very simple numerical calculation; (d) there is no need to prepare special series of specific standards, and to read them along the sample solutions in each working session; and (e) the final preparation of the sample solutions is very simple.

The method consists of adding a known amount of analyte (or several increasing amounts) to an aliquot (or several aliquots) of the sample solution; then, all the prepared solutions (with and without additions) are measured in the instrument, and finally the concentration of the unknown sample solution can be calculated.

Some criteria must be met for application of the method: (a) linear response; (b) equal effect of interfering components on the analyte in the sample solution itself and on the final concentration of analyte after known amounts have been added; and (c) convenient ratio between the concentration of the analyte in the sample solution and the added concentration.

In atomic-absorption, the addition method can be used more extensively than in the emission method, for the following reasons. The working curves obtained with many analytes are perfectly linear at low concentration ranges (or at higher ranges, but at low instrumental sensitivity). Moreover, most of the interferences in atomic-absorption are of physical and chemical nature. And, finally, in normal operation the instruments are zeroed before measurement; this preliminary operation avoids subsequent corrections for the reading obtained for solutions without analyte, as is done frequently in emission flame photometry.

In many applications of atomic-absorption flame photometry the addition method allows determinations without preliminary separations of the macrocomponents of the samples. For example, Goto *et al.* (*292*) have shown that magnesium can be determined in cast iron samples by the addition method without any preliminary chemical separation.

If the linear relationship is assumed (see Figs. 18–17 and 18–18), then

$$\frac{A_T}{A_S} = \frac{C_S + C_A}{C_S}$$

and

$$C_S = C_A \frac{A_S}{A_T - A_S}$$

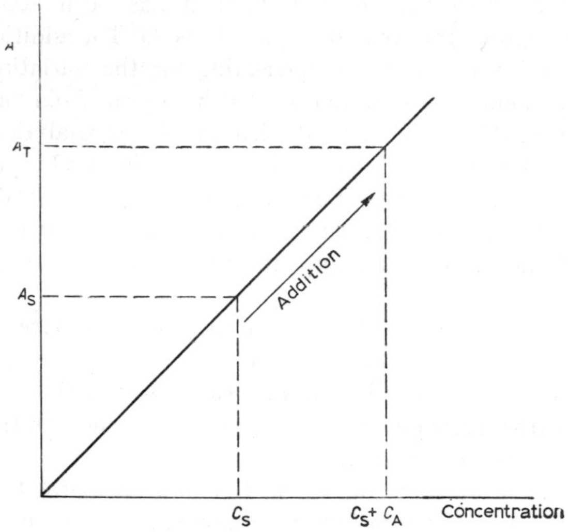

Fig. 18–17. Addition method.

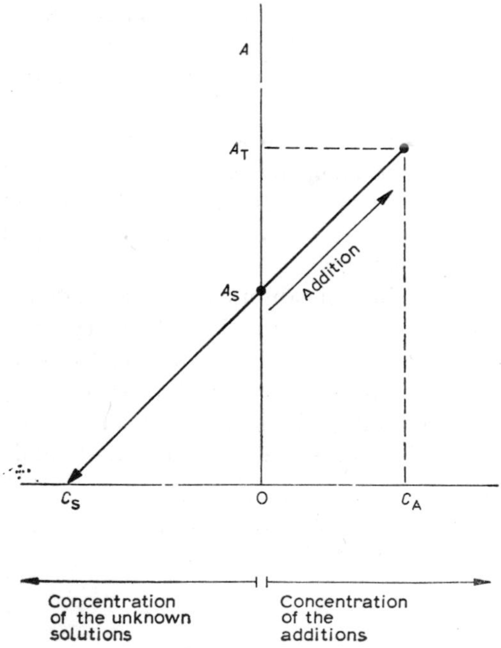

Fig. 18–18. Addition method (graphical extrapolation).

where A_T = absorbance of the mixture solution (sample solution plus addition),

A_S = absorbance of the sample solution,

C_A = concentration of the addition,

C_S = concentration of the sample solution (unknown concentration).

To avoid corrections of volumes, the necessary aliquots of sample solution and the aliquots plus the addition should be diluted to a suitable *constant* volume. Then, C_S and C_A represent concentration *before dilution*.

Any departure from the linear response causes errors which are the more marked, the greater the curvature in the interval used. If linearity is uncertain it should be first tested by making several increasing additions, and plotting the experimental points. This test need be done only once, if the operating conditions are kept constant and if the samples analyzed are of the same kind.

From this simple testing procedure, a graphical method of calculation can be derived: the absorbances calculated from readings are plotted against the concentrations of two, three or more additions. The straight line traced is prolonged until it intersects the abscissa; the point of intersection gives the concentration of the sample solution directly (see Fig.

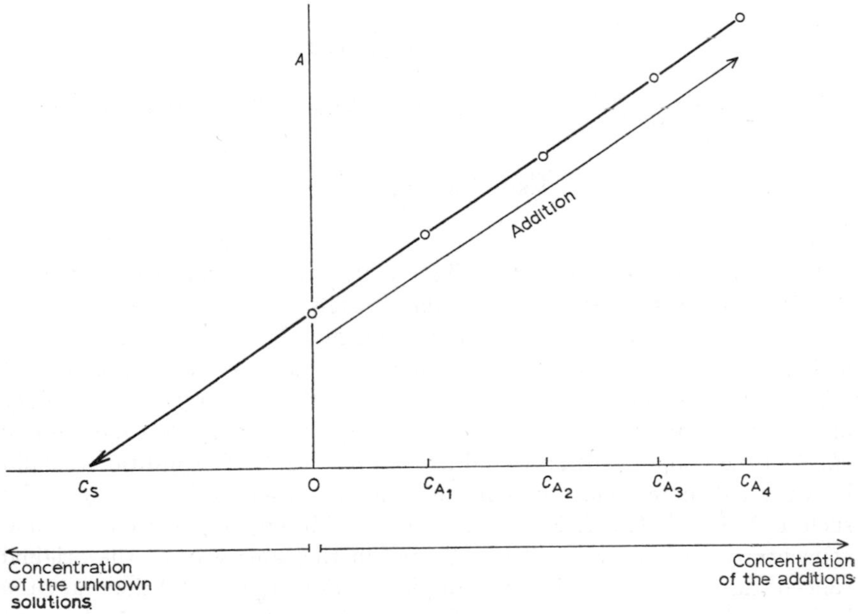

Fig. 18–19. Addition method (multi-addition technique by graphical extrapolation).

18–19). It is possible to use only one addition, but several additions help in tracing better curves, so that better accuracy is obtained.

If the aliquot of the sample solution is mixed with an aliquot of solution of known analyte concentration, and no dilution is made, and if the sample solution is measured without any prior dilution, the following equations should be used:

$$C_{\mathrm{T}} = \frac{C_{\mathrm{S}} V_{\mathrm{S}} + C_{\mathrm{A}} V_{\mathrm{A}}}{V_{\mathrm{T}}}$$

where C_{S} and C_{A} represent the values previously mentioned, and

C_{T} = concentration of the solution resulting from the mixture of both aliquots,

V_{T} = total volume with the total concentration C_{T},

V_{S} = volume of the aliquot of the sample solution,

V_{A} = volume of the aliquot of the known analyte solution.

Then (see Fig. 18–20),

$$\frac{A_{\mathrm{T}}}{A_{\mathrm{S}}} = \frac{(C_{\mathrm{S}} V_{\mathrm{S}} + C_{\mathrm{A}} V_{\mathrm{A}})/V_{\mathrm{T}}}{C_{\mathrm{S}}}$$

and finally,

$$C_{\mathrm{S}} = C_{\mathrm{A}} \frac{A_{\mathrm{S}}}{A_{\mathrm{T}}\, V_{\mathrm{T}}/V_{\mathrm{A}} - A_{\mathrm{S}}\, V_{\mathrm{S}}/V_{\mathrm{A}}}$$

If $V_{\mathrm{T}} = 2\, V_{\mathrm{S}} = 2\, V_{\mathrm{A}}$ (i.e., $V_{\mathrm{S}} = V_{\mathrm{A}}$, equal volume aliquots), then

$$C_{\mathrm{S}} = C_{\mathrm{A}} \frac{A_{\mathrm{S}}}{2\, A_{\mathrm{T}} - A_{\mathrm{S}}}$$

This last case is represented in Fig. 18–21. This particular case is recommended in order to shorten the calculation step.

Special care is recommended in the magnitude of the concentrations added. They should be neither very small (because the measurable effects might not be significant and might coincide with the margin of variability of the atomic-absorption method) nor excessive (because the measurable effect of the sample solution would not be significant). The additions should be within definite concentrations in order to attain ratios $C_{\mathrm{S}}/(C_{\mathrm{S}} + C_{\mathrm{A}})$ such as $\frac{1}{2}$, $\frac{1}{3}$ or $\frac{1}{4}$ *(97)*. It is assumed in the addition method that the final concentration of analyte will be affected in the same way as the original concentration of analyte in the sample solution. If the additions are too large, the interference ratios found in the final solution are too different from those in the sample solution before the addition.

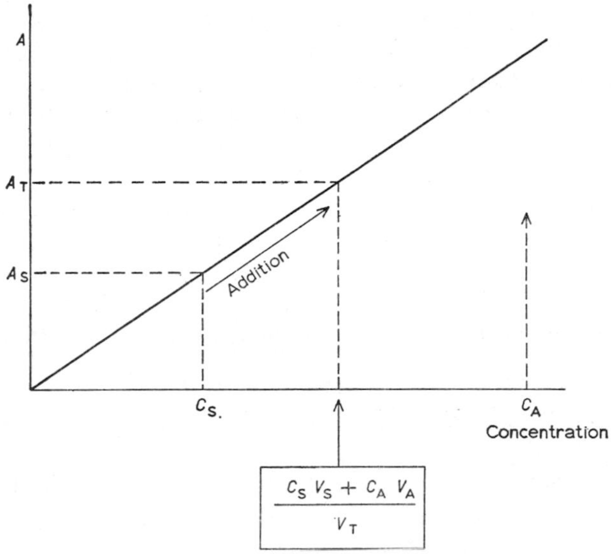

Fig. 18–20. Addition method with variation of volume.

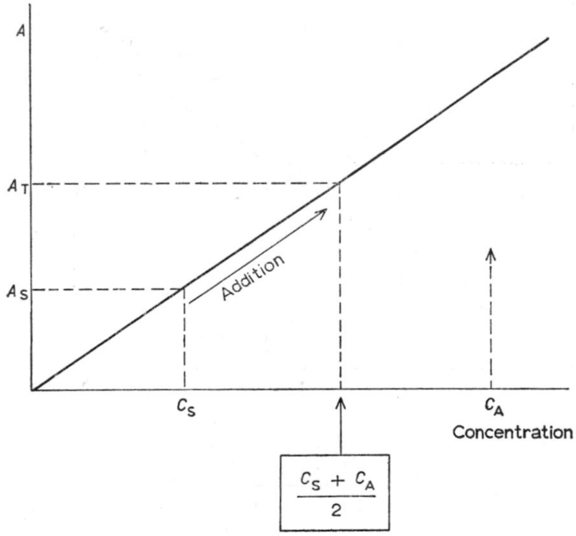

Fig. 18–21. Addition method by mixing equal volumes.

In severe cases of interference, the graphs obtained in the addition method show much less sensitivity than graphs obtained with standards of the same concentration but without interferences. But whenever a linear relationship is maintained, the method is applicable.

2.4.4. Dilution method

The dilution method is actually derived from the addition method (see Chapter 17, Section 5.2.1.1) (*590*). If linear response is achieved, to a volume V_S of sample solution of concentration C_S, a volume V_A of concentration C_A is added. If A_T and A_A the absorbances obtained for the mixture solution and the solution of concentration C_A, then,

$$\frac{A_T}{A_A} = \frac{(C_S V_S + C_A V_A)/V_T}{C_A}$$

This expression comes from the relationship shown in Fig. 18–22. It should be noted that the absorbance corresponding to C_S is not shown in the graph. This value may be too high, or may be situated in curved parts of the working curve. The unknown concentration of the sample solution is given by

$$C_S = C_A \frac{A_T \, V_T/V_S - A_A \, V_A/V_S}{A_A}$$

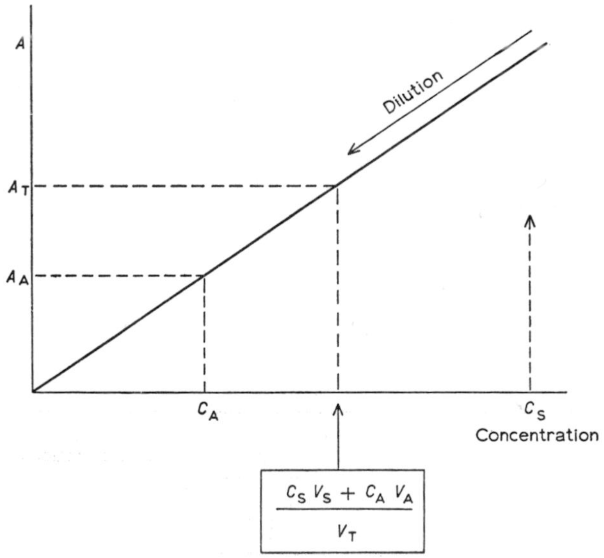

Fig. 18–22. Dilution method.

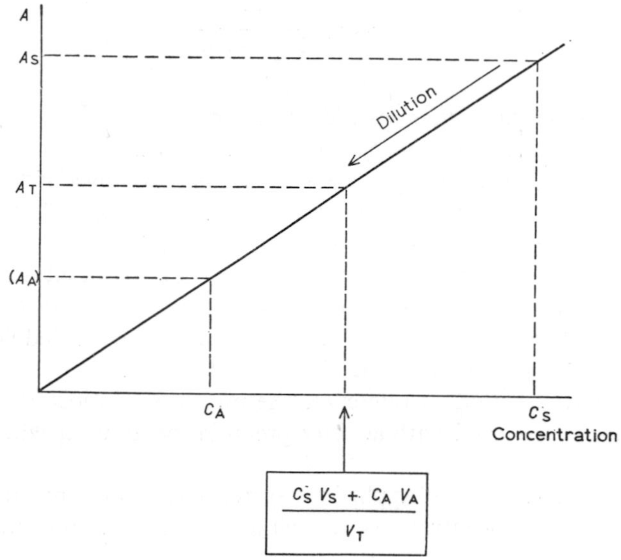

Fig. 18–23. Dilution method.

The solution of known concentration used in this method should be of lower concentration than that of the sample solution.

In a second case, if the concentration of the sample solution C_S can be measured (absorbance A_S) and the concentration of the solution of known concentration, C_A, is very small, the expressions used in the addition method can be used:

$$\frac{A_T}{A_S} = \frac{(C_S V_S + C_A V_A)/V_T}{C_S}$$

and

$$C_S = C_A \frac{A_S}{A_T\, V_T/V_A - A_S\, V_S/V_A}$$

This case has been represented in the Fig. 18–23. In both cases when $V_T = 2\, V_S = 2\, V_A$ (i.e., $V_S = V_A$):

$$C_S = C_A \frac{2\, A_T - A_A}{A_A}$$

and

$$C_S = C_A \frac{A_S}{2\,A_T - A_S}$$

The dilution method offers several advantages.

(a) It is possible to use a wide range of dilution ratios.

(b) The method may be applied to a very small volumes of solution.

(c) If a solvent other than water is used, there is a saving in solvents when many sample solutions have to be measured.

(d) Only two measurements with pipettes are required without any further filling of volumetric flasks up to the mark (less volumetric error).

(e) The mixture of the measured volumes may be carried out in any kind of container provided that it is completely dried.

(f) The solutions used as reference, the mixture solution, the unknown and the blank, are used without any preliminary dilution with water or solvent.

(g) The method may be applied to systems that present curvature at the high range of concentrations, as well as to the measurement of highly absorbing solutions.

(h) It is possible to introduce buffers and to equalize by dilution the contents of macrocomponents.

Some examples of the application of the method to determinations of sodium and potassium in samples of biological origin (serum samples) have been given (*590*). Other elements can be determined in the same way by atomic-absorption.

3. CALCULATIONS

The auxiliary calculations which are required in atomic-absorption are relatively simple. Apart from those necessary during the preparation of stock solutions and standards (dilution series), the calculations may be grouped as indicated below.

3.1. Calculations of the variations of concentrations

At times the measurement is done with the original sample solution, but generally an aliquot is used, the concentration of which varies according to the preliminary concentration or dilution. In every case it is most important to keep in mind any variation of concentration since the measurements refer to *relative values* (concentrations) and not to absolute values (total contents).

If dilutions have been made during the preparation, they will be represented by a *dilution factor*. When the concentrations of the original samples are calculated, the experimental values must be multiplied by the inverse of that factor. Analogously preliminary concentrations introduce a *concentration factor*, the inverse of which is again used for the final calculation.

If the concentrations are to be expressed in different units, the corresponding *conversion factors* are used[5].

3.2. *Calculations on the expression of the concentration of the analyte*

If the standards have been prepared with their concentrations expressed in p.p.m., for example, in terms of the metallic element, and if one wishes to express the results in p.p.m. also, but in terms of the oxide or another compound, the corresponding *analytical quantitative factors* must be applied[6].

3.3. *Post-photometric calculations*

The experimental measurements (percentage of absorption) should be transformed into absorbance values. If the instrumental scale is graduated in percentage of transmission or transmittance (% T), the following equation may be applied:

$$A = \log (100/\% T)$$

which is equivalent to

$$A = \log (1/T)$$

These relationships are derived from the well-known expression

$$A = \log (I_0/I)$$

If the reading scale is graduated directly in percentage of absorption, the absorbance values are calculated by means of the equation

$$A = \log [100/(100-\% \text{ absorption})]$$

Any of these calculations may be made easily with the help of a desk

[5] The tables published in ref. (*125*), pp. 278 and 427, may be used.
[6] Some of these factors are given on p. 426 of ref. (*125*).

slide rule. In order to handle a sufficient number of significant figures, logarithm tables may be used. In practice, the calculation of absorbance values may be done by numerical calculation, by conversion graphs or with a conversion table.

Since the absorbance values are obtained in the same way as optical densities and extinctions, they are sometimes expressed as such in some publications. Leithe (*428*), for example, uses extinctions: $E = \log (I_{H_2O}/I_{sample})$. For non-aqueous solutions this should be written: $E = \log (I_{solvent}/I_{sample})$.

In the preceding equations the 100% T and the value I_0 correspond to the reading obtained by aspirating water, solvent or blank solution, i.e., the solutions used to adjust the zero percent absorption in the instrument.

3.4. Calculation of errors

The calculation of errors may be done in atomic-absorption by following the well-known norms applicable to other analytical problems, which have been published in many textbooks.

The representation of errors as deviations, relative errors or other expressions as a function of the variables which cause interference is often used in atomic-absorption. When the causes of interference to be represented are components of the sample, the errors can be represented as a function of the concentrations of these components or as a function of the *interference ratios*: concentration of the interfering component/concentration of the analyte[7].

For purposes of presentation in the study of interference systems, it is preferable to calculate the interference ratios from *added concentrations* used in the preparation of synthetic solutions of known concentration.

3.5. Routine calculations

The enormous amount of experimental data collected in routine analytical laboratories involves a great consumption of time in calculations. The application of computer techniques can be very helpful in such situations.

---

[7] Interference ratios are very useful if one of the two components—analyte or interfering species—does not vary. If the concentration of both varies between definite intervals, it becomes necessary to use families of curves or *ponderal interference ratios*. ponderal interference ratios have been extensively used in emission flame photometry; see, e.g. F. Burriel-Martí and J. Ramírez-Muñoz, *Inform. Quím. Anal. (Madrid)*, 11 (1957) 169 and F. Burriel-Martí, J. Ramírez-Muñoz and M. C. Asunción-Omarrementería, *Actas do Congresso. 15 Congresso Internacional de Química Pura e Aplicada (Química Analítica)*. Vol. II, Communication No. IV-9, Lisboa, Portugal, 1958.

Various computer programs for calculations in atomic-absorption (addition method, dilution method, sensitivity calculations, precision studies, etc.) have been described by Ramírez-Muñoz *et al.* (*601*).

3.6. *Special cases*

The calculation of sensitivities has been discussed in Chapter 13, and the necessary calculations in the addition and dilution methods have been summarized in this chapter.

Special calculations are required in some methods described in the literature, e.g., in the differential method used by Malmstandt and Chambers (*451*) in which the instrumental responses of the sample solution and the standard are equalized by volumetric addition of successive quantities of analyte to the standard. Lang and Herrmann (*424*) have suggested a calculation procedure referring to working curves of unit slope in log–log representation.

4. PRECAUTIONS

To conclude this chapter, some precautions which should be observed in the use of atomic-absorption instruments are outlined. Many of these precautions are relevant to work with all kinds of flame equipment, although some are specifically intended for atomic-absorption. The contents of this chapter are divided into *instrumental precautions*, *precautions with the sample* and *personal precautions*.

4.1. *Instrumental precautions*

The flame unit creates a large amount of heat. Extreme care should be taken to avoid damage to other parts.

All the necessary precautions should be taken for the handling of gases under pressure. If possible, the tanks should be kept outside the laboratory, with the gases being brought to the bench by low-pressure lines. The outside tanks should be equipped with appropriate regulators. Leaks in the gas tubes and in the connections should be avoided. They should be inspected with soap solution, and connections secured with plastic tape on the threads.

The formation of explosive mixtures should be avoided and attention should be given to whether or not the burner is suitable for use with certain gases. The use of gases other than those for which the burner has been designed creates the danger of violent strike-backs. The slits and orifices must be appropriately calibrated; their calibration depends on the type of gas mixture to be used. Divided or multiple slots tend to minimize the danger of strike-back.

The passage of the fuel gas to the burner should be opened last, and closed first when the flame is extinguished at the close of each working session. A water trap at the drain tube, especially if it is recommended, should always be filled with water before the burner is lit.

If possible, the fuel gas line should be equipped with a quick cut-off valve for closing the fuel supply in case of emergency. Some types of safety valves cut off the fuel when the pressure of the supporting gas is reduced.

Care should be taken that the gas supply tubing is not squeezed, twisted, broken, leaking or subject to pulse effect (with an extreme length of soft tubing), especially if the tubes are of soft rubber or very flexible tygon.

It is convenient to use safety switches with heated chambers to prevent excessive heat, should the cooling water accidentally stop running through the cooling coils.

Cigarette smoke and other kinds of smoke should not reach the burner. Likewise, lateral drafts and excessive suction of the vents should be avoided.

If the sample is fed in through plastic tubing, efforts should be made to avoid twisting or squeezing in any part of the tube.

The sprayer and the burner should be thoroughly cleaned if there is any danger of formation of saline deposits after the use of very concentrated solutions. If the flame changes shape, the orifices or the slot should be cleaned very carefully *without producing scratches or changes of shape.* The spray and condensing chambers (if the equipment includes them) should be washed thoroughly with distilled or demineralized water, by means of a strong jet, after highly concentrated solutions—saline solutions—have been sprayed. Then abundant water should be sprayed along the chambers and burner. If the burner is detachable all the loose parts should be carefully adjusted. This applies especially to retainers and anchors.

The feed rate and the suction time (feed time) should be carefully observed so that the amount of sample sprayed and the time factor will not be detrimental in the determinations.

Care must be taken not to change the feed to the connections of the lamp (except when recommended for lamp regeneration); the correct color code in the terminals (cathode, black; anode, red) must be used if key plugs are not available.

The lamps should be disconnected after the operating period to prolong the life of the hollow-cathode lamp as much as possible. If the hollow-cathode lamps or vapor discharge lamps are kept in operation for a long time, they become quite hot. Any obstacle which might obstruct the natural dissipation of heat from the lamps should be removed.

Extreme care must be exercised in keeping the mirrors clean, especially if they are not coated, and even if they are prepared with hard aluminum deposits. Great caution must be taken in moving the movable optical parts so as to avoid later defects of alignment or focusing.

At the end of a working session, a check must be made to see if the main gas valves are tight closed and if the lines are empty.

For the installation of equipment in the laboratory, the usual recommendations for emission flame laboratories should be followed[8].

4.2. Precautions with respect to the samples

The dangers of contamination should be avoided as far as possible. The sample solutions used in atomic-absorption flame photometry are usually very dilute and exposed to various kinds of contamination. Special attention should be given to contamination coming from the fingers of the operator, dust, ashes, smoke or other samples and standards. Special care should be taken with contamination from glass containers; it is better to use polyethylene flasks and polyethylene or teflon cups.

Solutions which are excessively acidic may burners made from metals and alloys which are easily corroded. If the analyte is the same as one of the components of the burner material, anomalous absorptions may be encountered even in the absence of the analyte (e.g., with brass burners in the analysis of samples for copper and zinc determinations).

Loss of sample solution by evaporation must, of course, be avoided.

Efforts must be made to keep agents which may provoke anomalous absorption from reaching the flame. For example, excesses of organic solvent may produce lack of transparency at short wavelengths, thus limiting the intensity of radiations which would otherwise reach the detector. Solutions producing clouds of solid particles that are not vaporized in the flame, also decrease the transparency of the flame; here there is no absorption process in the formal sense, but the absorption readings are modified, causing high results.

4.3. Precautions of a personal nature

In atomic-absorption work, attention should be given to possible burns from the flame or from lamps which have been in operation for some time,

---

[8] Consult p. 419 of ref. (*125*).

especially in lamp alignment operations and when lamps are changed. They should be allowed to cool sufficiently or held by their supports, or protective gloves should be worn.

Many instruments have high voltage sections. The lines should be perfectly protected and, if necessary, earthed. If some part of the circuit must be touched, the apparatus should be disconnected, unless it is essential to have the instrument in operation[9].

If the chopper is not covered, and the instrument does not have safety switches, the hands should not be near the chopper while it is rotating.

The operator should take care not to receive ultraviolet radiations from the flame. An ultraviolet-opaque sheet helps in models which are not provided with a protective chimney. The sheet or chimney also protects the operator from contact with the flame.

Appropriate vents and ventilating hoods should be used to avoid breathing noxious fumes and vapors, as well as liberated acids coming from very acidic sample solutions[10].

Safety glasses are advisable, not only to avoid particles striking the eyes, but also to eliminate ultraviolet radiations coming from the burner in prolonged sessions, especially if there is no chimney or protecting sheets. In some cases, the use of a protective mask is advisable. For handling poisonous or corrosive liquids, the use of fine plastic gloves or surgical gloves is suggested; protective hand creams are also useful.

---

[9] One hand should be kept in the pocket while the other hand manipulates the electrical circuit; this precaution prevents serious shocks.

[10] It is sufficient to review the lists of maximum permissible concentrations of contaminants. A very complete list has been published as a Supplement to the journal *Salud Ocupacional, Lima, Perú,* 8 (1) (1963). This list mentions some contaminants which may be present in any chemical laboratory with the maximum permissible limits:

Gas or vapor contaminants	*p.p.m. in volume*	*mg/m³*
Acetic acid	10	25
Carbon monoxide	100	110
Hydrochloric acid	5	7
Hydrofluoric acid	3	2
Nitric acid	10	25
Sulfuric acid		1

Metallic contaminants	*mg/m³*
Antimony	0.5
Arsenic	0.5
Barium	0.5
Cadmium	0.1
Chromium (as CrO_3)	0.1
Iron	15
Lead	0.2
Magnesium	15
Manganese	5
Mercury	0.1
Selenium	0.1
Tellurium	0.1
Uranium	0.05
Zinc	5

Other elements which should be avoided in the laboratory air are beryllium, calcium and silicon.

PART V

APPLICATIONS

Chapter 19

Applications

In this last chapter, the different applications of atomic-absorption methods published to date are reviewed, with special attention to atomic-absorption flame photometric procedures. The applications have been grouped according to the types of samples analyzed.

Many general publications give information on various elements, tables of sensitivity, comparative studies and other topics of interest. Among these general studies, attention is called to the following refs. (*15, 69, 84, 164, 170, 194, 198, 213, 258, 274, 275, 384, 428, 466, 496, 563, 615, 621, 623, 625, 636, 647, 667, 679, 797, 800, 801, 814, 910, 920, 922, 925*). A complete summary has been given of applications and potentialities of the method, with a discussion on costs involved, in comparison with other analytical methods appropriate for trace metal determination (*584*). The publications mentioned in Chapter 4 should also be consulted. In the present Chapter, when specific applications are discussed, other general studies relevant to those analytical problems are cited.

Since the quality of the results obtained in atomic-absorption depends largely on the methods used for the sample preparation, it is not surprising that most authors give special attention to the preparatory process. Truschke (*780*), in particular, has studied this problem. Many of the publications cited in this Chapter contain detailed procedures for sample preparation; obviously, not all of these can be included here, but some information is given. Collections of procedures have been prepared for work with specific instruments (*45, 551*).

Methods of determining mercury by means of the absorption of light crossing a chamber containing mercury vapor are not discussed in this Chapter[1].

---

[1] However, for first orientation on early and modern methods for mercury, see ref. (*238, 360, 471, 484, 538, 649, 811, 834, 854, 855, 879*). The different methods of micro-determination of mercury (urine, tissues, blood, fecal materials and air) have been reviewed by Vignoli *et al.* (*790*), who give details of different procedures of mineralization, separation, determination, sensitivity, and discuss advantages and disadvantages.

1. ANALYSIS OF WATERS

From the standpoint of sample preparation, the analysis of water is one of the simplest in flame methods. This field of analysis by atomic-absorption promises to be even more abundant in publications than the analysis of water by emission flame photometry.

A complete review of the potentialities of atomic-absorption methods for water analysis, and of the problems involved in certain determinations has been presented by Ulrich (*783*). The applications of the method to the analysis of water and deposits from water have been reviewed by Platte and Marcy (*558*), who compared the results obtained by atomic-absorption with those obtained by colorimetric methods[2]. Various other papers (*308, 557, 559, 917*) should also be consulted.

Allan (*7, 8*) mentions the possibility of analysis of lysimeter waters in his research on magnesium. Butler and Brink (*130*) studied the determinations of calcium, magnesium, sodium, potassium, copper and iron. Fabricand *et al.* (*223*) have devoted attention to the determination of microcomponents in sea water, among which are iron, manganese, nickel, zinc and copper.

As is the case in almost all applications of absorption methods, most attention has been given to those elements which are not easily determined by emission[3].

In the analysis of waters, atomic-absorption methods have the following advantages.

(a) The samples arrive at the laboratory as solutions; this decreases the period of preparation of samples and increases the number of samples which can be analyzed per day.

(b) Frequently, the elements which may be determined by emission (sodium, potassium, calcium, magnesium, lithium, strontium) can also be determined with atomic-absorption instruments; other elements (iron, copper, zinc, manganese, lead, nickel, vanadium, cobalt) can then be added.

(c) Interference effects are not as serious for some of these elements as in emission methods.

---

[2] Iron, copper and zinc (in cooling water, river and well water, condensate, plating waste and boiler water treated with EDTA); manganese, calcium and magnesium (in cooling water, well water, boiler feed and tap water); copper and iron (in boiler feed and saturated steam); and iron, copper, magnesium, calcium, zinc and nickel—compared with gravimetric and volumetric procedures (in water-formed deposits: boiler scale, corrosion products and boiler sludge).

[3] See Chapter 20, p. 312, of ref. (*125*).

1.1. Preparation of samples

(a) *Dilution,* if the original samples are excessively concentrated in some of the components. The samples may be diluted to the limit imposed by the recommended dynamic concentration range of the particular method. Butler and Brink (*130*) found that river and borehole natural waters needed no dilution because of their low concentrations, whereas sewage and industrial effluents required preliminary dilution in accordance with their contents.

(b) *Concentration by evaporation,* e.g. in the determination of minor elements.

(c) *Additions,* such as releasing agents, to prevent the action of some of the components. For example, Butler and Brink (*130*) use strontium chloride to achieve 1500 p.p.m. of strontium in the prepared samples; strontium has produced good results in obviating interference effects whereas barium chloride limits the effects, but does not eliminate them completely. Butler and Brink recommend the addition of 2 ml of formaldehyde for each 5 l of water to overcome biological activity which might produce changes of pH and, therefore, precipitation of calcium and magnesium during storage of samples.

(d) *Filtration,* to eliminate coarse particles which might cause clogging of the sprayer capillary. During the filtration process it is wise to avoid contaminations if wide filters with slow filtration rates are used.

(e) *Preliminary concentration,* applicable to minor elements which are present below the lower limits admissible for quantitative work. This is often necessary in the determinations of lead, nickel, cobalt and other microcomponents. Preliminary concentration methods can be applied to the analysis of waters in the same way as in the analysis of brines for copper and lead, by extraction with ammonium pyrrolidinedithiocarbamate and methyl isobutyl ketone (*723*).

Preliminary concentration methods offer good potentialities for the determination of some microconstituents in sea water.

Cobalt and nickel are present in natural waters at a level of ca. 1 p.p.b. Burrell (*123*) advises that these elements be coprecipitated twice with iron(III) hydroxide from samples of 10 l; the iron should then be separated and an extraction with ammonium pyrrolidinedithiocarbamate carried out.

Low concentrations of copper, lead, zinc, cadmium, nickel and iron can be determined in waste waters by means of an ion-exchange concentration on Chelex-100 from the water buffered with ammonium acetate solution at pH 5.2 ± 0.2 (*99*). The trace elements are eluted with 4.0 M nitric acid and then diluted in the ratio 1:2. Nitric acid of the same concentration was used as a blank; nitric acid greater than 6.0 *M* damaged the burner parts.

1.2. Determinable elements

Besides the elements already mentioned, copper and lead have been studied by Sprague and Slavin (*723*) and rubidium by Slavin *et al.* (*712*). These authors also studied the different emitters suitable for rubidium determinations and the most convenient flame conditions.

Robinson *et al.* (*634*) have recently studied the termination of vanadium in drinking water; high natural vanadium contents in drinking water are connected with a low incidence of coronary problems (perhaps because of a reduction in the cholesterol level). These workers used oxygen–acetylene flames (fuel-rich) and extracted the vanadium as cupferrate. The absorbance for 1000 p.p.m. of vanadium increased in the following sequence: acetone, methanol, ethanol, propanol-2, and methyl isobutyl ketone. The last solvent was therefore used and 22% of oleic acid was added to improve the sensitivity.

For sodium determinations, Fishman (*244*) has used the line Na 3302 Å for concentrations greater than 8 p.p.m.

1.3. Interference effects

In addition to the effects of cationic components, interferences may be expected from sulfates, phosphates and aluminum. The addition of releasing agents improves the conditions of analysis.

Butler and Brink (*130*) consider it necessary to add 1500 p.p.m. of strontium as releasing agent to prevent interferences by magnesium, sodium, phosphates and aluminum in determinations of calcium, and interferences by magnesium and calcium in determinations of sodium, although this is not necessary in determinations of copper and iron.

Many workers who use the atomic-absorption method for water analysis find trouble with the interference of excesses of sodium in determinations of calcium and magnesium. The present author has shown, however, that the determinations of these analytes are feasible even in the most unfavourable conditions found in natural samples.

An addition of 200 p.p.m. of sodium has been used by Fishman (*244*) to prevent potassium enhancement by sodium. Interferences of aluminum, silicon and phosphorus with analytes such as calcium, strontium and magnesium can be prevented by the addition of lanthanum in acidified solution; the acid content helps to prevent the interferences noticed in calcium determinations if the pH is higher than 7.

1.4. Standards

These may simply be aqueous standards but they should contain quantities of any releasing agents similar to those added to the samples. The same applies to acids, buffers or any other type of addition.

2. ANALYSIS OF AGRICULTURAL MATERIALS

General and specific studies have been published in this area. Special attention has been given to the determinations of magnesium and zinc, which are both of great agricultural importance, and with which difficulties have been encountered in emission flame photometry (*159, 167, 170–172, 274, 506, 612, 676, 701, 833*). Slavin (*676*) points out that two of the first investigators to apply atomic-absorption methods were Allan and David, both agricultural chemists. The valuable and constant contributions of both authors have provided a great impetus in further applications of the method.

This section is divided into several subsections to deal with the most interesting types of agricultural samples.

2.1. Fertilizers

The macrocomponents in fertilizers have been determined by emission flame photometry for many years[4], but the analysis of fertilizers has been extended by atomic-absorption flame photometry to the determination of microcomponents such as cobalt, molybdenum, nickel, strontium and zinc.

2.1.1. Preparation of samples

Fertilizers require special preparation (especially for elements determinable by atomic-absorption methods) by means of acid dissolution—with 3 *N* hydrochloric acid—, evaporation to dryness, extraction of the residue with more dilute hydrochloric acid, and then any necessary further dilution; alternatively, acid treatment with both nitric and hydrochloric acids may be used.

In case of difficulties on the part of other constituents, a preliminary separation may be recommended, as well as a preliminary concentration along with some of the separation steps.

McBride (*482, 483*) prefers to treat the samples with reagent-grade

---

[4] See Chapter 21, p. 326 of ref. (*125*).

hydrochloric acid, boiling and evaporating almost to dryness; the residue is redissolved with 0.5 *N* hydrochloric acid and the solution filtered before dilution in a volumetric flask (1 g of sample diluted finally to 100 ml containing 0.1 *N* hydrochloric acid). This procedure has been used for the determination of copper, iron, magnesium, manganese and zinc as minor nutrients in fertilizers. The solutions prepared are afterwards diluted with 0.1 *N* hydrochloric acid as required to bring the elements to the necessary concentration ranges for determination.

2.1.2. *Determinable elements*

Atomic-absorption methods have been studied mainly for analytes which cannot easily be determined by emission because of their low concentrations and/or interference effects. Thus, the determinations of cobalt (*14*), copper (*11, 482, 483*), iron (*482, 483*), magnesium (*482, 483*), manganese (*482, 483*), molybdenum (*165, 168*), nickel (*14*), strontium (*173*), and zinc (*12, 261, 482, 483*) have been reported.

The review on fertilizers published by Gehrke and Ussary in 1965 (*260*) includes, in the potassium section, the atomic-absorption studies carried out by Takeuchi and Suzuki (*761*). In referring to secondary elements and micronutrients, Gehrke and Ussary mention the work done by Fuwa *et al.* on the determination of zinc (*250*) (see also ref. (*924*)).

2.1.3. *Interference effects*

The effects produced by acids employed in the dissolution step must be kept in mind. They can be compensated by equalization in the standards. Allan (*12*) has proved that different acids do not produce anomalous absorptions in the determination of zinc. When equipment with brass burners is used, possible contamination by attack of brass parts in contact with the spray must be considered; this should be checked by preliminary inspection of the behaviour of the standards at the prefixed acid concentration.

2.1.4. *Standards*

Standards should be corrected by equalization with respect to the contents of the residual acids in the samples. Thus, for example, McBride (*482, 483*) prepares his standards containing 0.1 *N* hydrochloric acid in the same way as for the preparation of samples (see Section 2.1.1 of this chapter).

2.1.5. *Other possibilities in the analysis of fertilizers*

The possibility of determining copper in copperized superphosphates has been discussed (*11*); good results were obtained in the analysis of fertilizers composed of superphosphates, limonites and saline additions, among which was copper sulfate.

Since the atomic-absorption determinations of iron and manganese are very practicable, and since it is necessary to study these elements in some types of fertilizers which are used in cases of iron and manganese deficiencies, routine determinations have been recommended; the work of Allan (*9*) should be consulted.

2.2. *Plant materials*

Atomic-absorption methods are also very useful in the analysis of plant materials; not only macroelements for which emission flame photometry is satisfactory (e.g. sodium and potassium), but also more difficult elements such as calcium and magnesium, can easily be determined. Thus, analysis for various microelements of great interest in vegetable physiology and edaphology becomes readily available.

Mitchell (*504*) has briefly compared the determination of zinc by atomic-absorption with the use of excitation spectral techniques, and has discussed application to the analysis of agricultural materials.

As a special case, Herrmann and Neu (*331*) have described the determinations of magnesium and zinc in chloroplasts. The chloroplasts are isolated by the dry method of Behrens *et al.*[5]; the materials are ashed and 1 g of ash, after hydrochloric acid treatment, is diluted to 100 ml. Further dilutions (1:5 for zinc, and 1:100 for magnesium) give the final solutions for the instrumental determination. Contents of 1.82–5.12% magnesium and 0.14–0.37% zinc were found in the ashes (content 6–16%). This explains the differences of dilution required, apart from the requirements of the sensitivity for the individual analytes.

2.2.1. *Preparation of samples*

So long as standards are properly prepared, atomic-absorption methods are sufficiently versatile to allow the determination of constituents of vegetable matter after quite different methods of sample preparation; extraction (aqueous, acid or saline extracts), acid treatment or digestion, or calcination followed by aqueous or acid extraction of the dry residue can all be used.

If several constituents of different chemical nature and behaviour are to be determined after a single preliminary treatment, and if there is any fear that simple extraction may not dissolve some of the constituents,

[5] M. Behrens, W. Neu, R. Thalacker and H. J. Thimm, *Experientia*, 20 (1964) 607.

then acid treatment should be used. The acid treatment may consist of digestion with nitric and perchloric acids, or with sulphuric and perchloric acids with additions of nitric acid (*161, 163*). Digestion with nitric acid and perchloric acid is adequate for the determination of zinc. For other elements it may be better to digest with sulphuric acid, the residual nitric acid added being eliminated by heating during the digestion process. Acid treatments are recommended if microconstituents, such as zinc and copper, are to be determined, particularly when extractions with non-aqueous solvents and chelating agents are involved (*12, 13*).

Stupar (*742*) recommends dissolving 1 g of air-dried sample with 5 ml of a mixture of nitric, perchloric and sulfuric acids (10:1:4), evaporating the solution to dryness, dissolving the residue in acetone–water (1:1) and diluting the solution to 10 ml after any necessary filtration. He compensates the standard solutions with calcium, magnesium, potassium, sodium, ammonium dihydrogen phosphate and ammonium sulfate for rubidium determinations.

If samples treated with sulfuric acid are not brought to dryness, some acid usually remains in the final solutions.

Dry ashing has been recommended for the determination of strontium (*170*), and has been used by Trent and Slavin (*778*) for the determination of strontium in hay. Trent and Slavin added lanthanum as releasing agent. The residues of the calcination, after they have been evaporated in the presence of hydrochloric acid and the residues extracted with 0.1 *N* hydrochloric acid, form solutions which may be treated with an anion exchanger; strontium can be determined in the final solutions by the addition method (*170*). Buchanan and Muraoka (*116*) have used dry ashing for the determinations of zinc and manganese in tree leaves; afterwards the ashes are dissolved in a 1:1 mixture of hydrochloric acid and nitric acid. The present author has determined zinc in plant samples, after a similar ashing and acid treatment of the ash. The results agreed with the values obtained by means of conventional spectrophotometric methods (*933*).

For determination of selenium in wheat, Rann and Hambly (*606*) have used a Parr calorimeter bomb, burning the ground wheat in oxygen at a pressure of 30 atm. The bomb is washed out with water and the solution is filtered, evaporated and finally diluted, before the actual determination. Actually, there is no real dilution in the method recommended by these authors, because 10 g of wheat produce 10 ml of final prepared solution.

The use of exchange resins offers great potentialities in the determination of calcium, in order to avoid anion interferences.

For extractions of copper with ammonium pyrrolidinedithiocarbamate (*11*), it has been found that acids, other than nitric acid, do not interfere even in high concentrations. This is not the case for extractions with EDTA or its salts, where interferences arise from acidity as well as any iron present (iron interferes with the extraction and separation processes).

It is most appropriate to add any necessary releasing agents, e.g. lanthanum (III) to prevent interference in calcium determinations, during the preparation of the solution[6].

2.2.2. Determinable elements

It is possible to add other elements to the list of those that can be determined in vegetable materials by emission flame photometry (*125*). Calcium has been very widely studied, despite the chemical interferences which affect its determination[7]. Other elements which are readily determined are cobalt (*10*), copper (*11, 161, 162, 908*), iron (*8, 9, 161, 162, 170, 171*), magnesium[8] (*7, 161, 162, 170, 171, 345, 371, 407, 429, 855, 856*), manganese (*8, 9, 170, 171, 908*), nickel (*10*), potassium (*170, 171*), rubidium (*170, 171, 742*), selenium (*606*), sodium (*170, 171*) and zinc[9] (*8, 12, 161, 162, 170, 171, 261, 908*). Strontium can also be determined (*165, 170, 171, 173*). Zinc and manganese have been determined by Buchanan and Muraoka (*116*).

2.2.3. Interference effects

Only very small or no interference effects are caused in the determinations of magnesium, zinc, copper and iron, by the more common components in vegetable materials (sodium, potassium, calcium, magnesium, phosphorus, sulfur and aluminum) (*161*). Magnesium may be affected by some interferences which can be remedied through the action of releasing agents. Calcium determinations can be affected by the presence of sodium and potassium in large and variable concentrations. Calcium is also affected by some of the elements and anions consistently present in solutions prepared from vegetable materials, and releasing agents, particularly lanthanum, are very useful for correcting the chemical interferences on calcium. The use of ion-exchange resins is also valuable (*344*); magnesium and calcium have been determined in the double-beam spectrophotometer of Hinson and Kitching (*345*) after removal of interfering anions by means of resin columns (*344*). Magnesium has been determined by Jones and Thomas (*371*), who studied the interferences produced by other elements and the use of strontium chloride as releaser.

Trent and Slavin (*778*) use lanthanum addition to avoid interference

---

[6] For more details on preliminary treatments of vegetable materials, consult Chapter 21, Section 2, of ref. (*125*).

[7] See, particularly, refs. (*162, 163, 344, 345*). The references for calcium mentioned on p. 360 should also be consulted.

[8] See also refs. (*130, 166, 437*).

[9] See also Chapter 17, Section 2.1.2.

effects in the determination of strontium; the interferences of phosphates, silicon, aluminum and acids (used in the dissolution of the ashes) are thus diminished (see also p. 366).

Residual concentrations of acids may interfere in determinations of zinc (*12*); this may be mitigated by equalizing the composition of standards and sample solutions. The same criterion is applicable to other analytes. Acids modify the physical properties of the solutions, and thus alter the efficiency of the sprayer. For the same reason, high salt concentrations (from some extractants) also affect the measurements.

Stupar (*742*), in studying the determination of rubidium in plants, has investigated the interferences produced by cesium, hydrochloric acid, phosphoric acid and perchloric acid at concentrations of rubidium in the range 5–70 p.p.m.

2.2.4. Standards

Low concentrations of some elements in prepared solutions at high dilution can be determined by comparison with aqueous standards. The present author has obtained very similar results for the determination of zinc in plant material ashes, by the addition method and by comparison with aqueous zinc standards.

If the sample solutions contain appreciable residual quantities of acids, the standards should contain the same acids in equal or very similar concentration. This applies principally to standards used for samples which have undergone digestion in the presence of sulfuric acid (*170*). The standards for the determination of calcium in presence of chemical interferences should be compensated with lanthanum at the same concentration as that used in the sample solutions. They may also be compensated with sodium and with potassium (*163, 170*).

For determinations of zinc after digestion in the presence of perchloric acid, the standards should also contain this acid if the digested solutions are not evaporated to dryness before dilution.

2.3. Soils

As with other materials of interest in agricultural chemistry, the analysis of soils has been extended and simplified by atomic-absorption flame photometry. Some of the components which can be determined by emission flame photometry (calcium, sodium, potassium, magnesium) are also included within the framework of elements determinable by atomic-absorption.

2.3.1. Preparation of samples

Most frequently, interest is centered on the assimilable fraction of the components of the soils; the preliminary preparation of the corresponding extracts should be studied carefully in order to obtain suitable solutions for flame analysis, for these extracts will be the original solutions in which the analytes must be determined in the atomic-absorption flame photometer. In some cases the total content of a component in agricultural soils may be of interest; in this case the analysis should be oriented toward a preliminary digestion of the samples—acid digestion—which allows the component to pass into solution, e.g. in determinations of total contents of copper and zinc[10]. Fusion procedures should be avoided as far as possible.

When the assimilable fraction is to be analyzed, a suitable extractant must be carefully chosen. The most common extractants in the analysis of soils are well known[11]. In recent years the list has grown with the addition of extractions with hydrochloric acid (*130*), 0.1 *N* hydrochloric acid and 2.5% acetic acid (*11*), ammonium chloride (*130*) and 1% solutions of the disodium salt of EDTA (*11, 12*).

Extraction ratios such as 1:10 and 1:20 are appropriate. Whenever possible, efforts should be made to choose an extractant whose acid and/or saline content may be sufficiently decreased by preliminary dilution, according to the sensitivity of the instrument for the analytes involved.

During or after the extraction process, chelating agents (e.g., EDTA and its salts) may be used. Releasing agents may be added to the extracts, e.g. addition of lanthanum to solutions for determination of calcium, and addition of strontium for determinations of calcium and magnesium (*166*).

The extracts may be suitably diluted (before the determinations, especially if the extracted components attain relatively high concentrations. Dilutions may be made (a) with distilled water, (b) with extractant solution (keeping the same background solution), or (c) with a solution which contains releasing agent (until the dilution suitable for the analyte and the prefixed concentration for the releasing agent in the final prepared solution is attained).

Extraction with 1% solution of the disodium salt of EDTA is suitable

---

[10] For the determination of rubidium in soils, Stupar (*742*) suggests boiling 20 g of air-dried sample with 10% hydrochloric acid, filtering and evaporating to dryness. After separation of the silica, rubidium is leached out with 5 ml of concentrated nitric acid, and the solution is diluted to 50 ml. The determination of rubidium in soils is similar to that for plant materials (see p. 358).

[11] Different types of extractant solutions are listed in Section 3, Chapter 21, of ref. (*125*). Atomic-absorption procedures are applicable to the aqueous, acid and saline extracts and to acid–saline extracts currently analyzed by emission flame photometry. If possible, an excessive salinity should be avoided in the extracts which have to be examined.

for the determination of zinc (*12*). For determination of low contents of copper, it may be better to extract copper in presence of ethyl acetate with a solution of ammonium pyrrolidinedithiocarbamate (*11*).

In some cases, extracts rich in iron or ammonium (ammonium salt extracts such as ammonium chloride) may necessitate a preliminary elimination of these components; precipitation of iron with ammonium hydroxide increases the content of ammonium salts in the solutions, which is also undesirable. Excessive concentrations of ammonium salts should be removed as far as possible before the final step. It has been effectively proved that there is little difference between extracts treated for the elimination of the cited components (at moderate concentrations) and untreated extracts (*130*).

In the case of acid digestion of the soils for total determination of some component (zinc, for example), this stage should be utilized for the elimination of silica. The residues after the elimination of silica may be extracted with a solution of perchloric acid.

Interfering anions in the analysis of soils for strontium can be removed by treatment with anion-exchange resins. The strontium is determined in the solutions obtained, either directly—working curve—or by the addition method.

2.3.2. Determinable elements

The principal elements which have been determined are: calcium (*130, 162, 166, 822*), copper (*11*), iron (*8*), magnesium (*7, 130, 162, 166, 429, 437*), manganese (*8*), potassium (*161, 166*), rubidium (*742*), sodium (*162, 166*), strontium (*165*) and zinc (*8, 12, 261*). The determination of selenium has been discussed (*606*).

2.3.3. Interference effects

Interference effects may be caused by the soil components which pass to the solution prepared by extraction or by digestion, and by new components added during the preparative process. In either case, if they are not eliminated previously, their effects may be compensated by equalizing the composition of the comparison standards.

Anion exchange, and addition of releasing or chelating agents serve to prevent many interferences.

2.3.4. Standards

The advisability of equalizing the composition of the standards with that of the sample solutions should be re-emphasized. If the extractants used are always the same, a series of standards can be easily prepared by using the same extractant solution as a background solution. In determinations after acid digestion, the standards should contain quantities equivalent to the residual acid contents of the sample solutions. If the elements are determined by extraction with organic reagents (chelating reagent and solvent), it is good practise to carry out parallel extractions with synthetic standards covering the prefixed concentration range.

3. ANALYSIS OF BIOLOGICAL MATERIALS

Atomic-absorption methods have extensive applications in biological analysis which are as important as the applications in agricultural analysis. There are two main aspects to be considered.

(a) The determination by atomic-absorption flame photometry of elements which have previously been determined by emission with special attention to those which produced greater analytical difficulties in emission work (calcium and magnesium). This has been the case in the determinations of calcium, sodium, potassium and magnesium in blood materials, calcium and magnesium in urine, calcium in saliva, calcium and magnesium in milk, calcium and magnesium in tissues, magnesium in feces, and calcium, magnesium, potassium and sodium in bones.

(b) The determination of very low concentrations of other elements, which cannot easily be determined by emission. The most typical is zinc (urine, tissues), to which may be added a long list of other components (see below). Most of them are sought for in urine, the main natural means of elimination of ionic components from the organism. These components can give significant information for the diagnosis of pathological conditions in toxicological examinations.

The high sensitivity of many determinations, along with the practical absence of interference effects, has made possible the extensive application of flame methods to biological analysis. Very often, the preparation of the sample is simpler than that required for other types of instrumental analysis. Sensitivity, simple preparation, speed and acceptable accuracy have provided the basic reasons for the wide acceptance of atomic-absorption methods. Another point in favor of the methods is the small quantity of original sample required (an essential in analytical examinations in human biology).

This section is divided into several subsections, each of which is devoted to a different type of sample of biological origin. In each subsection the necessary references are included. The following references contain information of general relevance for this type of sample: (*34, 94, 148, 182, 183, 259, 274, 275, 412, 454, 680, 707, 833, 835, 940*). The publications by Berman (*894, 895*) are worth consulting. The microdeterminations of copper reported by Rousselet and Girard (*640*) and of nickel described by Sunderman (*749*). can be applied to a variety of biological samples Determinations of calcium, magnesium and iron have also been described (*871*).

For a preliminary orientation on biological analysis by flame methods, consult Chapter 22 of ref. (*125*).

General reviews of biological analysis have mentioned various atomic-absorption methods. Mason (*475*) in his report on bioanalytical chemistry mentions the work of Boling (*104, 105*). In his review on recent applications of spectroscopy in clinical chemistry, Zak (*866*) mentions atomic-absorption spectroscopy as representative of recent methods which are useful for rapid, accurate quantitative analysis. Kingsley (*395*), also discussing clinical analysis, mentions the determinations of copper (*93*) and zinc (*250, 347*). Willis (*837*) divided the biological applications into three main classes: (a) determination of the principal constituents of body fluids; (b) determination of trace amounts of heavy metals in body fluids; and (c) determination of metals—major or minor constituents—in tissues. Various procedures has been collated by Zettner and Berman in a small volume (*872*); most of these procedures require relatively high concentrations of analytes in solution. Mavrodineanu and Hughes (*480*) have reported the possibility of determining sodium, potassium, calcium and magnesium in biological samples by combining emission and atomic-absorption flame photometry.

3.1. Blood

This subsection includes all biological samples coming from blood, although for analytical purposes there are only two types: blood serum and blood plasma. Some studies have also been made on the analysis of whole blood. The analytical methods proposed for serum and plasma can of course, be extended to the analysis of whole blood and most similar biological liquids. For some elements (e.g., heavy metallic elements), it is recommended that analyse be done for blood and urine samples in parallel.

3.1.1. Preparation of samples

The preparation of samples for atomic-absorption flame photometry may be simpler than for emission methods (*125, 767*).

For the determinations of sodium and magnesium, for example, with instruments of sufficient sensitivity, it is necessary only to dilute the original samples with watei in the required dilution ratio to bring the components within the most appropriate concentration range; compensation of the comparison standards is not usually needed. For determination of potassium in blood simple preliminary dilution again suffices, but the standards should be compensated with sodium. Preliminary treatment with trichloroacetic acid may be needed in analyse for calcium; the mixture is then centrifuged and the supernatant liquid is used, care being taken to avoid losses of calcium as protein-bound calcium. To avoid interference effects in determinations of calcium, a releasing agent may be needed (e.g., lanthanum). The preliminary dilutions can be made with a solution of disodium salt of EDTA (*827*).

Berman (*93*) states that organic matter should be removed or extraction procedures should be applied in some cases when lead, copper, mercury, magnesium, calcium, and manganese are determined in blood, urine and tissue.

At present, there is a tendency to use the smallest possible quantities of biological samples. With special techniques, very small amounts of sample suffice. For example, Lang and Herrmann (*420*) have described results in the analysis of micro-quantities of solution with the help of an oscillograph. Ammonium pyrrolidinedithiocarbamate with methyl isobutyl ketone have been used by Berman (*92*) for the extraction of lead from small amounts of whole blood. Sprague and Slavin (*724*) have analysed blood serum for iron, copper and zinc at 1:1 dilutions (0.4 ml of serum plus 0.4 ml of distilled water), with a modified (wide slot) burner head. Direct determinations by the addition method, of iron and copper in blood serum and of iron in whole blood at normal human levels, have been done by R. W. Claus in the Beckman laboratories; the samples were diluted with distilled water in the ratio 1:2. This procedure is feasible for these analytes when small volumes of the original samples are used, and no clogging problems have been observed during rapid readings (paper strip recorder). These determinations have been reported by Hell *et al.* (*316*).

Helfer and Rodgerson (*310*) recommends the addition of protein to all standards when iron is determined in serum. These workers use scale expansion (2.5 $\times$ and 10 $\times$) and apply integration so that sample flow variations and high noise levels can be tolerated.

3.1.2. Determinable elements

The following elements can be determined by atomic-absorption flame photometry: cadmium (*454, 682, 710*), calcium (*28, 42, 183, 185, 542, 714, 825–827, 874, 875*), chromium (*454, 682, 710*), cobalt (*682*), copper (*91, 316, 724*)[12], iron (*37, 310, 316, 707, 724*), lead (*682, 707, 945*), magnesium (*7, 8, 28, 42, 149, 185, 323, 348, 353, 452, 714, 793, 824, 825, 828*)[13], manganese

---

[12] These methods may be extended to urine and tissues.

[13] Jones and Thomas (*371*) have also described the determination of magnesium in serum. See comments on p. 357.

(*454*), mercury (*361*)[14], molybdenum (*454*), potassium (*147, 183, 185, 322, 829*), sodium (*115, 147, 183, 185, 322, 829*), thallium (*682, 710*) and zinc (*347, 724, 830*)[15].

Berman (*93*)[16] describes the determination of copper, mercury, lead, magnesium, calcium and manganese. Prasad *et al.* (*568*) have given special attention to the determination of zinc in biological fluids in normal and cirrhotic subjects; zinc levels were studied in plasma, red blood cells and urine, the values found being comparable to those obtained previously by the dithizone method. The determinations of calcium and magnesium have also been reported by Sunderman and Carroll (*750*) who found good agreement with values obtained by EDTA titration. Trent and Slavin (*779*) have reported calcium and magnesium determinations in serum and urine on calibrated scales in concentration units.

3.1.3. *Interference effects*

Calcium is subject to interference from sodium and, to some extent, from potassium. The interference of sodium may be compensated by the addition of sodium to the comparison standards. This is necessary if the dilutions used for calcium determination are not too large (e.g., dilution ratio 1:10). A releasing agent may be added to compensate interferences from phosphates and other components. The interference effects on magnesium may be decreased by dilution with EDTA solution or by addition of strontium chloride as a releasing agent (*827, 828*).

Any interference by phosphates in determinations of calcium and strontium may be overcome by using an ion-exchange column, as recommended by David (*177*).

A complete study of interferences in determinations of calcium in serum has been described by Zettner and Seligson (*875*). They discuss the effects of single and mixed interfering species, protein interference, and tests on separation of calcium, separation of proteins, buffering methods, masking (with EDTA), and use of competitive cations (lanthanum as releaser). They also proved that water saturated with n-butanol (ca. 8% v/v) leads to enhancement of the calcium absorption signals, although butanol failed in the presence of lanthanum chloride to enhance the calcium signal beyond the extent achieved by the releaser alone. The presence of n-butanol produced foam in the spray chamber, but this effect was controlled by adding

---

[14] Consult also ref. (*431*).
[15] Consult also refs. (*42, 261*).
[16] Copper was determined in serum, urine and tissues (autopsy tissues such as liver, kidney, spleen, lung, heart and tumor) by means of diethyldithiocarbamate extractions with methyl isobutyl ketone.

octanol to the diluant (0.02% v/v). These authors recommended addition of 0.5% lanthanum chloride to the final solutions; the releasing agent prevented interferences from sulfates and phosphates at very high concentrations, higher than those ever encountered in diseases.

The addition of lanthanum to avoid interferences in determination of calcium from phosphorus and silicon (analysis of serum, bone, urine and feces) has also been used by Waring *et al.* (*807*).

The effects encountered in determinations of potassium can be mitigated by dilution of the samples with a solution of EDTA or by compensation of the standards with sodium (*829*).

In their determinations of magnesium in plasma, Hurst and McSwiney (*353*) found interference effects from sodium and potassium, while urea produced no apparent effects. Enhancements of up to 4% by sodium in determinations of magnesium were reported.

3.1.4. Standards

The standards may be straightforward aqueous solutions or may be compensated with respect to diluants, releasing agents, masking agents or interfering components.

3.2. Saliva

As described by Newburn (*527*), saliva samples may be prepared for determination of calcium in any of the following ways:

(a) simple dilution with distilled water;

(b) dilution with water and a solution EDTA (disodium salt);

(c) dilution with water, strontium (or lanthanum) chloride solution and trichloroacetic acid.

Treatment with trichloroacetic acid (up to 4%) should be followed by centrifugation and separation of the supernatant liquid, which is then used for the determination. Strontium (up to 2500 p.p.m.) and lanthanum (up to 10,000 p.p.m.) are used as releasing agents.

To avoid interference by sodium, the standards should be compensated with sodium.

Saliva samples centrifuged to avoid dangers of clogging during determinations show a notable loss of calcium, so that centrifugation of the original samples should be avoided. Saliva may be taken as total saliva or may be selected as parotid or submaxillary secretions. The segregation of saliva may be stimulated with dental paraffin) or with citric acid (see also ref. (*141*)).

3.3. *Milk*

The methods for determination of magnesium in biological liquids may be employed with samples of milk (*7, 8*). The usual procedures for the determinations of calcium may also be utilized.

Strontium has been determined in powdered milk (*173*). Trent and Slavin (*778*) determined strontium in powdered milk after a preliminary ashing; a final 1% concentration of lanthanum was added to the solution of the ashes to counteract interference effects[17].

Milk is ashed for copper determination, as described by Morgan (*508*), and the acid solution of the ash is extracted with ammonium pyrrolidine-dithiocarbamate and methyl isopentyl ketone.

3.4. *Urine*

A large number of elements have been determined in urine by atomic-absorption methods. Only very simple preparation is required for urine samples; in may cases, preliminary centrifugation and dilution may be sufficient for determination of the major components. More elaborate procedures are required for microconstituents.

3.4.1. *Preparation of samples*

If the samples of urine are to be analyzed immediately, they need not be preserved; if they are to be kept for some time, the addition of acid preservants is necessary (acetic acid or hydrochloric acid). It is best to centrifuge the samples to eliminate solid particles, such as cells, mucosities and deposits of uric acid.

Two main general methods are used in urine analysis.

(a) *Without extraction with organic solvents*. Use is made of simple dilution procedures, incineration or chemical separation.

(1) Simple dilution with water until the samples are brought to the most suitable concentration interval coincident with the interval covered by the standards[18].

(2) Dilution, with addition of the most suitable releasing agent (e.g., in determinations of calcium).

---

[17] These authors, who also determined strontium in hay, bone and shellfish ashes, studied chemical interferences on strontium, principally those due to mineral acids, phosphates, aluminum and silicon, for which they recommended lanthanum as releasing agent. They also tested the effects of lithium, rubidium, cesium, sodium, potassium and barium on the absorptions measured as representative signals of the concentrations of strontium in solution.

[18] This has been done in the determination of magnesium (*831*). Those cases in which dilution is not required may also classified in this section.

(3) Dry ashing, then carefully dissolution of the ashes with hydrochloric acid. A releasing agent may be added to the resulting solution, if necessary (e.g., in determinations of calcium).

(4) Separation by precipitation (e.g., calcium with oxalate).

(b) *With extraction with organic solvents.* The extractions in the presence of ammonium pyrrolidinedithiocarbamate recommended by Willis (*834*) are good examples of this type of preparative process, especially for lead, mercury, bismuth and nickel. Although zinc lends itself readily to extraction processes, in some cases it can be determined directly, without extraction, because of its great sensitivity in atomic-absorption. The same may be said of other heavy metals (e.g. cadmium) although at very low concentrations, better results are achieved by extraction (*834*).

The extraction process may be applied directly to urine samples or to solutions obtained from urine ashes. For copper and iron in urine, Hussein *et al.* (*354, 355*) concentrate the metals 20-fold by extraction of copper–pyrrolidinedithiocarbamate and iron cupferronate with 2-heptanone. The urine samples are first acidified with concentrated distilled hydrochloric acid and boiled, in order to prevent emulsification during extraction.

The extraction technique is very useful in conjunction with the addition method; extractions of the blank solution, sample solution and sample solution with addition (a single addition or several at spaced intervals) are done in parallel. The addition method is recommended in the case of lead and nickel. The addition method has been used by Ferrigan (*240*) to determine zinc in urine[19].

Before extraction is carried out, the solutions should be subjected to a rigorous adjustment of pH. Berman (*92*) has determined lead in urine, following extraction with ammonium pyrrolidinedithiocarbamate and methyl isobutyl ketone, in the same way as for determinations of lead in whole blood (see p. 364). For the determination of nickel in urine at toxicological levels, Sprague and Slavin (*722*) recommend extraction using ammonium pyrrolidineditiocarbamate and methyl isobutyl ketone; they studied different pH conditions.

3.4.2. Determinable elements

The principal elements that have been determined in urine are: bismuth (*834*), cadmium (*31, 682, 710, 830, 834*), calcium (*28, 542, 831*), chromium (*682, 710*), cobalt (*682, 710*), copper (*91, 354, 355, 707*), iron (*354, 355, 873*), lead (*682, 707, 710, 832, 834*), magnesium (*183, 185, 348, 730, 831*), mercury

---

[19] Ferrigan mentions the need to determine zinc, manganese, cadmium, chromium and copper in rat kidney slices, in order to know the effects of these metals in gluconeogenesis.

(*834*)[20], nickel (*25, 757, 834*), thallium (*682, 710*), and zinc (*44, 240, 258, 682, 834*).

Sodium and potassium can be included in the list although they are easily determined by emission flame photometry. Metals such as silver and gold can also be easily determined by atomic-absorption in urine. The contributions of Berman (*93*) (see p. 364) and of Prasad *et al.* (*568*) (see p. 364) should also be consulted.

3.4.3. *Interference effects*

The most marked effects are found in determinations of calcium. The use of releasing agents (especially lanthanum) diminishes the effects of phosphates (*831*).

Zettner and Mansbach (*873*), in their determinations of iron[21] in urine with a wide-slot burner and a moderately rich flame (air–acetylene), found no perturbing effect of other likely components in this type of sample, unless the salt concentration exceeds 1.5% (they consider that the depression produced is due to the presence of solids in the flame). The small enhancement found in natural samples of urine is considered to be due to the foaming action of the urine, which results in a better volatilization of the sample and thus an enhancement of the sprayer efficiency.

3.4.4. *Standards*

Standards must be prepared according to the different forms of sample preparation. As a general rule, for the purposes of matching the composition of the sample solutions, the standards must contain preservants, additions, residual acids, etc., in equal proportions. In extraction processes, it is best to extract the standards themselves under equivalent operating conditions.

3.5. *Feces*

Magnesium (*185*) and chromium (*823*) have been determined. With this type of sample, it is preferable to incinerate and to treat the resulting ash with acid. For the determination of chromium, Williams *et al.* (*823*) recommend treatment with phosphoric acid in the presence of manganese sulfate and potassium bromate. These authors suggest the use of calcium

---

[20] Mercury has been determined in urine by means of the absorptions produced by its vapor (non-flame methods).

[21] Zettner and Mansbach determined urine iron (as well as serum iron and iron-binding capacity) in patients with acute iron poisoning, before and after treatment (see also refs. (*872, 876*)).

(500 p.p.m.) as releasing agent to avoid interference by silicate. Besides calcium, the standards should contain similar quantities of residual reagents which remain in the solutions after the preparation process.

3.6. *Tissues*

In dealing with non-liquid organic samples, it is preferable to use dry ashing (which is appropriate for calcium and zinc) or digestion with nitric acid (which is advisable for magnesium determination). In the analysis of tissue samples for calcium and/or magnesium, the addition of lanthanum as releasing agent may be very convenient.

Griffith *et al.* (*295*) digest weighed amounts of tissue samples with nitric acid, and dilute the resulting solutions so that the magnesium lies in the range 0.2–1 p.p.m. Strontium is added as a releaser. This method is applied to liver and kidney tissues[22].

Calcium (*542*), copper (*91*), magnesium (*149, 542*) and zinc (*542, 737*) have been determined in tissues[23].

Powell (*567*) has reported determinations of manganese, copper and zinc in dried liver, starting with a sample of 400 mg, and determinations of copper, potassium and zinc in dried muscle, with 300 mg of sample. He studied digestion techniques, ashing temperatures and interference effects, and compared the values obtained with air–propane and air–acetylene flames. Magnesium determinations made by Cheek *et al.* (*149*) have contributed to the knowledge of the effect of fat intake on the mineral levels in heart and skeletal muscle of rats.

The standards should contain quantities of acids equivalent to those in the sample solutions after acid solution of ashes or to residues of digestion. They should also contain releasing agents identical to those which have been added to the solutions for analysis.

3.7. *Bones*

An excessive content of calcium and phosphates may cause difficulties, even in atomic-absorption flame photometry[24].

Calcium, magnesium, potassium and sodium have been determined in bones. Trent and Slavin (*778*) have determined strontium in bone ash[25].

---

[22] They have also determined magnesium in bone and in plasma. For blood plasma samples, only dilution was applied.

[23] See also refs. (*93, 237, 905, 919*).

[24] Consult pp. 368 and 369 of ref. (*125*).

[25] See note on p. 366, and ref. (*36*).

3.8. Cerebrospinal fluid

Decker *et al.* (*190*) have published data on the determinations of magnesium and calcium in diluted samples: 0.1 ml diluted to 5.0 ml for magnesium, 0.2 ml diluted to 4.0 ml for calcium. These authors compare their data with the normal values for human levels given by other authors.

3.9. Special studies

Magnesium has been examined by Heaton and Hodgkinson (*309*) in their study on external factors affecting diurnal variations in electrolyte excretion. Magnesium has also been determined in studies of the metabolism of magnesium in hypertension by Seller *et al.* (to be published).

Hemoglobin has been determined by measuring the iron contents in whole blood, starting from only 20 μl of original sample (*330*).

The atomic-absorption flame photometer has helped in mineral metabolism studies. Its applicability in this field has been reviewed by Parker (*543*) who recommends digestion of biological samples with nitric acid and dilution, unless the original concentration of the analyte must be maintained at about the same level—low concentrations of analyte—, in which case ashing methods are preferable. Sodium and potassium have been determined in fats (*929*).

3.10. Shellfish

Determinations of strontium in shellfish ashes have been reported by Trent and Slavin (*778*) (see also p. 368).

4. ANALYSIS OF MINERAL PRODUCTS AND RELATED MATERIALS

This section is divided into two subsections, one devoted to solid mineral products and the other to petroleum and petroleum products.

4.1. Solid mineral products (rocks, minerals and ores)

Although atomic-absorption has been widely used in this field for the determinations of magnesium and zinc, the method has also proved very useful for the determinations of heavy elements, among which lead and copper and the noble metals, silver and gold, are prominent. The latter analyses can replace, to great advantage, the complicated manipulations of the classical method; the results obtained are comparable to those from the most accurate techniques of evaluation of noble metals in mineral products[26].

The applications of the method to geochemical prospecting and mining have been reviewed by Slavin (*690*).

4.1.1. Preparation of samples

In general, the preparation of the samples is reduced to dissolving them in order to bring the analytes into solution and to dilute or concentrate the solutions to the most appropriate concentrations for the instrumental determination. In special cases, such as the determination of silver in concentrates rich in lead (*293, 608–610*), it is necessary to use very concentrated mineral acid solutions, not only during the process of dissolution of the sample, but also for the stabilization of the final solutions. The necessity of working with highly acid solutions for the determination of silver obliged Rawling *et al.* (*608–610*) to replace the capillaries of the EEL sprayers with capillaries of glass or platinum–iridium. The addition of diethylenetriamine not only maintains the analytes in solution, but also permits a definitely lower acidity (*293*).

For determination of calcium, cadmium, cobalt, iron, potassium, magnesium, sodium, nickel, rubidium and strontium in potassium felspar and biotite samples, Billings and Adams (*101*) dissolved the samples in hydrofluoric acid and nitric acid, adding enough lanthanum chloride to have 1% lanthanum as releasing agent in the final solutions. They used 0.25 g of original sample to prepare 50 ml of final solution.

Trent and Slavin (*776*) used two solubilization procedures for granitic and diabasic rocks in analysis of these samples for sodium, potassium, iron, manganese, magnesium and calcium determinations: (a) treatment with hydrofluoric acid and sulfuric acid, and (b) sodium carbonate fusion. For determination of magnesium and calcium they used lanthanum as releasing agent (1% in the final solution).

In the determination of gold, it has been found best to use preliminary extraction with methyl isobutyl ketone in the presence of an excess of hydrobromic acid, the bromoaurate anion being extracted.

A preliminary report on gold assay in ores and residues has been published by Olson (*535*). He tried several procedures: (a) direct analysis of acid solutions (poor results because of losses of gold and interferences by the high calcium concentration), (b) organic solvent extraction (too involved for plant use and limited by the efficiency of the extraction); (c) fusion

[26] See also refs. (*577, 921*).

(extra equipment is required, and the method compares badly with the fire assay), and (d) cyanide extraction (found to be the most satisfactory). The cyanide extraction has been used also by Simmons (*673*) for the determination of gold in carbonate rock. Preleminary ignition at low temperature (450–600 °C) helps to avoid retention of gold. Continuous shaking and heating of the solution during extraction are necessary for satisfactory results. Filtering was preferable to centrifugation; Simmons found that the addition of Separan NP-10 as flocculating agent (2–4 drops of a 0.5% solution) was helpful when added before filtration.

For determination of selenium in galena, Rann and Hambly (*606*) recommend a sodium peroxide fusion, the mixture being covered with anhydrous sodium carbonate. The soluble fraction can then be leached out with boiling water and the extract evaporated, filtered (here the precipitated lead dioxide is removed) and then diluted for the instrumental determination.

Farrar (*224*) has reported the determinations of copper and zinc in ores after bisulfate treatment followed by dissolution with hydrochloric acid and dilution. Copper, zinc and lead were determined in concentrates after treatment with bromine, elimination of the bromine with additions of nitric acid, addition of perchloric and hydrofluoric acids, and finally addition of tartaric acid and ammonium acetate. The final solutions obtained were diluted to suitable concentrations for the instrumental measurement. Farrar also reported copper determinations in drill core samples.

Even with elements for which high sensitivity is possible, in some cases it is not advisable to use high dilution ratios. Belt (*87*) has determined copper and zinc after dissolution of samples at a dilution ratio of only 1:50. Higher dilutions can be used when the instrumental sensitivity can be increased and/or the original concentration of the analyte in the samples allows.

4.1.2. Determinable elements

The following elements have been determined: antimony (*296*), cadmium (*101*), calcium (*100, 101, 736, 741, 776, 913*), cobalt (*101*), copper (*87, 224*), gold (*293 535, 673*), iron (*100, 101, 776, 913*), lead (*296, 741*), magnesium (*429, 776*), manganese (*776, 913*), nickel (*101*), potassium (*100, 101, 776*), rubidium (*100, 101*), selenium (*606*), silver (*270, 293, 608–610*), sodium (*100, 101, 196, 197, 642, 776*), strontium (*100, 101*), and zinc (*87, 224, 741*).

A study of the accuracy of atomic-absorption methods compared with X-ray fluorescence, emission flame photometry (potassium) and colorimetry (iron) has been made by Billings (*100*) using igneous minerals (rubidium, iron, strontium, potassium, sodium, calcium), igneous rocks (calcium, iron, potassium, rubidium), potassium felspars (potassium), biotites (iron), U.S.

Geological Survey standards—G-1 and W-1[27]—(rubidium, strontium), limestones (calcium), and acid solutions of modern salcium carbonate sediments (calcium, iron, strontium). He found that the atomic-absorption method produces satisfactory accuracy for geochemical analysis.

The determination of lead and animony, and of lead in antimony sulfide flotation concentrate has been reported by Groenewald (*296*), who determined lead in parallel by atomic-absorption methods and polarography.

Silver has been determined in ores and the results compared with colorimetric results by the rhodanine method by Gómez-Coedo and Jimenez-Seco (*290*).

4.1.3. Interference effects

Naturally, accompanying elements and, even more so, the strong acid concentrations may produce disturbances during the determinations. The effects can be minimized by equalization of the contents of added reagents and by compensation or separation of the other sample components.

Extraction with organic solvents serves to eliminate various disturbing components, and a preliminary concentration of the analyte is achieved. This has been verified for the determination of gold (*293*).

Lanthanum has been widely used as releasing agent in mineral analysis (see p. 371), but, although it has always been recommended as a suppressor of interference on calcium, Belt (*90*) considers that lanthanum does not completely release calcium; he found low calcium values in his rock analysis. Large amounts of sodium do not seriously affect potassium if the solutions are made 2 *N* with respect to hydrochloric acid.

4.1.4. Standards

Acid solutions are generally used (corrected for the acid concentration of the samples).

Trent and Slavin (*776*) recommend the addition of sodium to potassium standards for determination of potassium in rocks.

In the determination of sodium in limestone, Rubeška *et al.* (*642*) recommend the addition of calcium and chloride ion to the standards. The addition of chloride ion is advisable because the residues obtained in the evaporation processes during pretreatment of samples were dissolved in hydrochloric acid (3 ml of 1:4 hydrochloric acid, which was then diluted to 100 ml).

---

[27] A summary of new data on rock samples (granite G-1 and diabase W-1) has been published by Fleischer and Stevens (*246*).

4.2. Petroleum and petroleum products

Atomic-absorption methods present great possibilities for the analysis of petroleum, gasoline and lubricating oils[28]. The determination of metallic components in lubricating oils may be an index of malfunctions and also of abrasions of bearings and metallic pieces of engines and mechanisms subjected to movement[29].

Sprague and Slavin (*726*) describe a procedure for the determination of trace metals in used aircraft lubricating oils. Kahn (*380*) emphasizes the convenience of examining the lubricating oil of an engine as an indication

---

[28] Besides the references cited in this subsection, consult refs. (*32, 70, 833*).

[29] Bond (*106*) has reported many cases of metal determinations which are potential applications of atomic-absorption methods. He used emission spectrometric determinations to monitor aircraft engines and other aircraft mechanisms. It is necessary to take oil samples systematically at established regular intervals and at other times when the integrity of the system is in question. The samples must be truly representative. The time between sampling and reporting must be the least possible. From the cases reported by Bond:

Elements found at higher concentration than normal:	*Defects found in engines:*
Fe, Al	Oil pressure pump impellers were spalled and four intake valve faces were cupped.
Al, Fe, Cu	Impeller shaft splines were worn, as well as front and rear bearing journals.
Al	One cylinder had loose valve guides.
Al, Fe	A valve guide had dropped in one cylinder.
Al, Fe	One cylinder head was cracked.
Al	There was a broken valve spring in one cylinder.
Al, Fe, Cr, Cu	The rocker box cover was damaged because of a loose screw.
Fe	Reduction pinion gears were worn.
Al, Fe	There were three broken rings in a cylinder.
Fe	Several parts were excessively worn.
Fe, Pb	Several parts were excessively worn.

For complete details on cases studied and laboratory methods the report by Bond should be consulted.

of the wear of its parts (becoming a routine check of lube oil samples from planes after a given number of hours of flight; the engine oil should be analyzed after each flight for iron, copper, silver and magnesium, while nickel and chromium are also determined when anything appears suspicious). Kahn also mentions the possibility of examining Diesel fuels for contamination with gasolines (determination of lead).

The following metallic components have been determined by atomic-absorption in petroleum and petroleum products: barium (*718*), chromium (*126, 491, 718*), copper (*32, 68, 491, 684, 718*), iron (*32, 68, 126, 491, 684, 718*), lead (*126, 158, 620, 684, 718*), nickel (*32, 49, 68, 491, 684*), silver (*126, 491, 718*), sodium (*684, 718*) and vanadium (*140, 901*).

If samples are ashed and the ash is dissolved, aqueous standards may be used. If samples are diluted with organic solvents, then the standards should be prepared with the same type of solvent. In the well-known determinations of lead in gasoline, the standards may be prepared easily by dissolving tetraethyl lead in iso-octane (*620, 684*). This same solvent is used to dilute the samples, when necessary.

For petroleum, lubricating oil and related products, n-heptane may be used to advantage. The standards can be prepared with National Bureau of Standards metallo-organic compounds which are specially recommended for this type of sample. Most of them are metallic salts of cyclohexane-butyric acid (*68, 684, 718*).

Means and Ratcliff (*491*) use fresh lubricating oil and National Bureau of Standards metallo-organic compounds, diluting the original samples with xylene in the dilution ratio 1:5. These authors describe in detail how to prepare silver naphthenate standards for atomic-absorption.

Fresh oil, when used for the preparation of comparison standards, should be checked in the atomic-absorption flame photometer for freedom from analytes.

Traces of metals (chromium, copper, iron, lead and silver) have been determined in used lubricating oils in solutions of the oil in methyl isobutyl ketone. Metallo-organic compounds and the same solvent were used for the preparation of the standards (copper butylphthalate, chromium acetyl-acetonate and ferric aceylacetonate). For lead, a standard oil containing 1000 p.p.m. of lead as naphthenate was used, and for silver, silver nitrate dissolved in 1:1 nitric acid, diluted with ethanol and diluted again with methyl isobutyl ketone. Solutions containing more than 20% (w/v) of oil were found too viscous to be sprayed efficiently (*126*).

Dagnall and West (*158*) have given special attention to the determination of lead. They investigated the determination of lead in aqueous solutions (with a complete interference study), organic extracts [30], and gasoline. They obtained satisfactory results by preparing the standards with solutions of tetraethyl lead. Trent (*772*) has studied the behaviour of tetraethyl lead and tetramethyl lead in lead determinations by atomic-absorption. The second compound allows one to reach the absorption plateau much faster than the former. Both cyclohexane and iso-octane were used to prepare the standards, but iso-octane was preferred because it gave better results and was more readily available.

Since nickel tends to poison cracking catalysts, nickel determinations are of great interest in feedstocks to petroleum refinery catalytic crackers. A few comments on the applicability of the method to this problem have been published (*49*); for more details on the determination of nickel in catalytic cracking feedstocks, the paper by Trent and Slavin (*775*) should be consulted.

5. ANALYSIS OF METALLURGICAL PRODUCTS

This is another type of analysis in which atomic-absorption methods have rapidly achieved widespread application. Specific papers and general reviews have been numerous[31]. The 1965 review on Ferrous Metallurgy by Beeghly and Pasztor (*77*) cites several atomic-absorption applications for the determination of chromium in stainless steel (*398*) and determination of cobalt at low concentration (*490*). In his review on Nonferrous Metallurgy (I. Light metals), Will (*821*) mentions the contributions to the analysis of aluminum alloys by Eisen (*207*), Wilson (*839, 840*) (determination of silver), and Wallace (*794, 796*) (determinations of magnesium and zinc).

McPherson (*488*) has summarized Australian work in the field of metallurgical analysis: determinations of magnesium in iron, lead in steel, cobalt in steel, and lead and bismuth in steel, as well as other applications in other analytical fields[32].

It is important to stress that the determination of magnesium by atomic-

---

[30] In their research program these authors include experiments on extractions of lead 8-hydroxyquinolinate in chloroform and methyl isobutyl ketone, and also lead diethyldithiocarbamate in ethyl acetate. Chloroform was quickly abandoned as a solvent owing to the noxious gases produced during combustion and also because the spraying chamber became clogged with deposits of solid 8-hydroxyquinoline produced by the rapid evaporation of the chloroform.

[31] Besides the references included in the different parts of this Section, the following should be consulted: (*67, 209–215, 242, 256, 268, 274, 481, 487, 489, 677, 719, 741, 753, 833*).

[32] Lead and cadmium in polyvinylchloride-base materials, and analysis of galvanized coatings, protective coatings, and water.

absorption has solved the analytical problem of the determination of this analyte in spheroidal and nodular graphite cast iron (*571*).

5.1. Preparation of samples

In many cases, it is not necessary to use prior separations; it is enough to dissolve the sample in the most suitable acid and to dilute this solution until the analyte concentration lies in the most appropriate interval of concentration. In the determination of magnesium in aluminum alloys, the aluminum present may protect the magnesium from interference effects by silicon (*430*). On other occasions, it is advisable to use total, or almost total, separation of accompanying components, especially the silicon, as indicated below.

The dissolution of the samples can often be done with hydrochloric acid, e.g., in the determinations of aluminum in steels and other alloys, of magnesium in aluminum alloys, of manganese in various alloys, of lead in steels and other alloys, and of zinc in different alloys. Acid mixtures have also been used: for example, hydrochloric acid followed by oxidation with nitric acid[33] (in determinations of magnesium in cast iron, molybdenum in steel, lead in steel); hydrochloric acid and phosphoric acid, followed by addition of nitric acid (determinations of iron in tungsten carbide); sulfuric acid and phosphoric acid (in determinations of nickel in iron, and chromium in irons and steels); and aqua regia (determination of various elements in pure gold).

For the determination of chromium, magnesium, and manganese in nickel alloys, Dyck (*204*) recommends boiling with 1:1 hydrochloric acid, since these alloys are difficult to dissolve in the cold. Because of the great sensitivity of the method for magnesium, the original solutions (500 mg diluted to 50 ml) should be diluted in the dilution ratio 1:5 before determination; the dilution ratio may be smaller if the instrumental system can be adjusted to very high instrumental sensitivity.

For the determinations of selenium and tellurium in copper, Sprague *et al.* (*716*) simply dissolve the samples in concentrated nitric acid, heating until complete dissolution is obtained and fuming to remove nitrogen oxide. Solutions from 1-g samples are finally diluted to 50 ml with distilled water. For determinations of copper, nickel, manganese, cobalt and magnesium in irons and steels, Sprague and Slavin (*720*) use acid dissolution, and aliquots of the prepared solution are taken for the individual determinations. The determinations of manganese, copper, chromium, nickel and

---

[33] Hydrogen peroxide can replace nitric acid in the dissolution of nonferrous alloys for the determination of aluminum.

magnesium in cast iron and steel have been reported by Beyer (*98*). Samples and National Bureau of Standard standards (exactly 0.5 g) were dissolved with 10 ml of 1:1 hydrochloric acid on a hot plate, oxidized with about ten drops of concentrated nitric acid, boiled, and diluted to 100 ml when cool. Copper-base alloys can be dissolved with nitric acid for determinations of lead, nickel and iron (*132*). Farrar (*224*) has determined copper in type metal. He recommends treatment with hydrobromic acid and bromine for dissolution of lead-base bearing and type metals. The standards should be corrected for the excess of reagents, and it is advisable to run a control sample simultaneously.

For the determination of magnesium in uranium, Humphrey (*351*) recommends dissolution of the sample with hydrochloric acid. If hydrogen peroxide is used, the solution should be boiled and evaporated to dryness, and the residue taken up again with acid. Some interference may be produced by the presence of acid in the solution; there was no excessive interference with determinations of iron, chromium, manganese, nickel, silicon and molybdenum under Humphrey's conditions.

Copper and silver determinations with and without the use of gold as comparison element (a gold line as monitor) have been reported (*132*). The samples of gold bullion for this type of analysis can be dissolved in aqua regia, the solutions being evaporated to near dryness and the residue being taken up in nitric acid.

Particular attention is required in the separation of silica, which is recommended in the determination of copper in copper alloys, in determinations of magnesium in nickel and nickel alloys (after dissolution with nitric acid, the insolubilization of the silica can be done by treatment with hydrochloric acid) (*22*), in the determination of lead in steels (*214*), and in the determination of zinc in different alloys (*270, 794*). For copper determinations, the silica may be eliminated by treatment with hydrofluoric acid instead of the well-known insolubilization process and filtration; this method of elimination is also suitable in the determination of zinc in zirconium alloys (*270*).

Depending on the content of silica in the sample, the choice lies between: (a) dissolution of the sample without any special treatment for silica, (b) dissolution, insolubilization of silica and filtration, (c) dissolution and treatment with hydrofluoric acid. Method (b) should be followed when considerable amounts of silica are present.

In the preparation of samples, any necessary releasing agent should be introduced. In the determination of magnesium, calcium corrects for the effect of aluminum (*430*) while strontium addition is useful in the determination of magnesium in cast iron (*79, 80*). In determinations of molybdenum in steels, aluminum helps to prevent interferences. Any organic solvent necessary to enhance the absorption process (e.g., in determinations of aluminum and in determination of diverse components in gold samples) should also be added. In the analysis of gold samples it is advisable to use aqua regia, but at 50% concentration to avoid the precipitation of silver, and to add ethanol to the final solutions (*658, 734*).

Extractions with organic solvents are extremely important in the analysis of metallurgical samples (see, e.g., ref. (*583*)).

Takeuchi and Suzuki (*761*) use sodium diethyldithiocarbamate to extract nickel in the determination of nickel in iron and steel[34]. Atsuya (*59*) discusses direct determinations of 0.05–1% of iron in aluminum metal and aluminum alloys; extractions with methyl isobutyl ketone are advised for determinations between 0.0005 and 0.1%. Atsuya prefers to dissolve with perchloric acid or nitric acid rather than with sulfuric or hydrochloric acids (under his conditions, only nickel interferes in the presence of sulfuric acid).

For silver and gold assay, Tindall (*770*) recommends acid dissolution and filtration for silver and extraction with methyl isobutyl ketone for gold. Magnesium in aluminum alloys and aluminum can be determined after extraction with oxine and methyl isobutyl ketone (*752*).

5.2. *Determinable elements*

In metallurgical samples the following elements have been determined: aluminum (*529*), bismuth (*488*), cadmium (*39, 207*), calcium (*207, 292*), chromium (*98, 398*), cobalt (*207, 490, 721*), copper (*98, 132, 224, 333, 492, 494, 496, 658, 734, 795*), gold (*336, 764, 770*), iron (*59, 78, 132, 157, 530, 658, 734*), lead (*132, 207, 212, 214, 268, 333, 494, 496, 658, 741, 906*), magnesium (*21, 22, 79, 80, 98, 207, 212, 268, 292, 351, 430, 468, 488, 530, 728, 751, 752, 760, 796*), manganese (*98, 333, 494, 496*), molybdenum (*165, 168, 511*), nickel (*98, 132, 396, 494, 496, 530, 761*), palladium (*336, 734, 738*), platinum (*336, 738*), rhodium (*336, 738*), rubidium (*530*), selenium (*716*), silver (*132, 207, 336, 658, 734, 770, 839, 840*), sodium (*207, 212, 268*), tellurium (*716*), vanadium (*140, 901*) and zinc (*207, 212, 222, 267, 268, 270, 271, 333, 437, 492, 494, 496, 658, 794*).

In a general review, Nonnenmacher and Schleser (*530*) mention the determination of rubidium in potassium and magnesium; iron, nickel and

---

[34] These authors recommend different methods according to the nickel concentration. For relatively high nickel contents, they use acid dissolution, evaporation and final dilution. For lower contents of nickel (less than 0.1%) they extract the nickel with diethyldithiocarbamate and methyl isobutyl ketone. For very low concentration of nickel (less than 0.02%) they advise first extracting the iron in 8 *N* hydrochloric acid with methyl isobutyl ketone.

magnesium in indium; and traces of lead, cadmium, magnesium, as well as percentages of iron, nickel and manganese in stainless steel. Wilson (*839*) reports the determination of silver in aluminum alloys, and Ezell (*222*) the determination of zinc also in aluminum materials. Magnesium determination in aluminum alloys and magnesium alloys has been reported by Mansell *et al.* (*470*). Eisen (*207*) mentions the determination of lead, magnesium, zinc, cadmium, cobalt, calcium, silver and sodium in copper and aluminum alloys; his results agreed well with gravimetric methods. Determinations of magnesium and calcium in cast iron and slags have been reported by Goto *et al.* (*292*). Iron in tantalum and niobium has been determined by Coyle *et al.* (*156*). Stansfield describes the determination of traces in steels (*729*)[35].

5.3. Interference effects

Interference effects are much fewer than might be expected in the analysis of solutions containing small concentration of analytes in the presence of large concentrations of accompanying components, i.e., the principal elements of each alloy.

The following list gives a general picture of analytical systems in which the analyte can be determined in some of the commonest types of metallurgical samples.

Analyte	*Types of sample*
Aluminum	Aluminum alloys, steels
Cadmium	Aluminum alloys, copper alloys
Calcium	Aluminum alloys, copper alloys
Chromium	Iron, steels, nickel alloys
Cobalt	Steels, alloyed metals, nickel
Copper	Copper alloys, lead-base alloys, ferrous alloys
Gold	Various alloys
Iron	Tungsten carbide, tantalum, niobium
Lead	Steels, various alloys
Magnesium	Aluminum alloys, magnesium alloys, aluminum, cast iron, ferrous alloys, nickel, nickel alloys, uranium
Manganese	Nickel alloys, ferrous alloys, various alloys
Molybdenum	Steels
Nickel	Iron, steels, copper-base alloys
Selenium	Copper
Silver	Aluminum alloys, copper alloys
Sodium	Aluminum alloys, copper alloys
Tellurium	Copper
Vanadium	Steels
Zinc	Aluminum alloys, copper alloys, zirconium alloys, various alloys

[35] Consult also ref. (*356*).

In very typical cases, such as the determination of magnesium, strong interference effects can be expected, but most of these can be corrected by the addition of releasing agents; similar procedures are suitable in the determination of molybdenum in steels. Other cases have needed a careful preliminary study of the interference systems involved.

Goto *et al.* (*292*) have found that addition of 1500 p.p.m. of strontium prevents interferences by aluminum, silicon and other components in determinations of magnesium and calcium in slags and cast iron. According to various published data on the determinations of platinum, palladium, rhodium, gold and silver by atomic-absorption methods (*436*), these metals offer good potentialities for being determined in complex systems. However, since interferences wer efound in the determination of platinum and rhodium in the presence of other noble and base metals, Strasheim and Wessels (*738*) have studied in detail the determinations of platinum, palladium, rhodium and gold in complex analytical systems; they recommend calibration techniques—working curves—for platinum, palladium and gold, and an addition method for rhodium.

The presence of acids also causes interferences, as is the case with hydrochloric acid in the determination of zinc (*271*). Silicon interferes in many cases; the necessity of eliminating it if its concentration is moderate or excessive has been discussed on p. 378. If the sample is very rich in aluminum, this component prevents interference by silicon in magnesium determination (*430*). Sprague and Slavin (*720*) have paid special attention to the interferences caused by silicon, molybdenum and tungsten in the determination of manganese in ferrous samples.

Takeuchi *et al.* (*763*) have found interferences by molybdenum, phosphates and sulfates in nickel determination in iron and steel.

Wilson (*839, 840*) has done a complete review of the interferences on silver absorption (determination of silver in aluminum alloys). He paid attention to the effects of nitric acid and aluminum, and also tested the instrumental responses in the presence of the elements most frequently found in this type of alloy (zinc, magnesium, copper, manganese, iron, nickel, chromium, titanium). Other complete studies on interferences are those presented by Kinson and Belcher (*397*) in their publication on copper and iron determinations in steel (interferences on copper) and by Belcher and Kinson (*82*) in their work on manganese determinations in iron and steel (interferences on manganese).

5.4. Standards

An adequate correction with respect to acids is necessary, particularly when the acids used for the dissolution steps are not completely eliminated.

Special attention must be given to the problems in the use of aqua regia (analysis of gold samples) (*734*), hydrochloric acid and phosphoric acid (analysis of tungsten carbide) (*78*), and sulfuric acid and phosphoric acid (determinations of nickel in iron and of chromium in iron and steels) (*396*, *398*). In the determination of iron in tungsten carbide, the standards should be prepared by attacking weighed amounts of tungsten under the same conditions as the samples, or by dissolving known quantities of sodium tungstate, adding iron and preparing a suitable dilution series with respect to iron.

For the preparation of standards for the determination of magnesium, chromium and manganese in nickel alloys, Dyck (*204*) recommends beginning with pure nickel carbonyl powder, in which the contents of these three analytes are very low so that no residual corrections are really needed. The solutions obtained by attack with hydrochloric acid, are mixed with the necessary quantities of analyte to prepare the standards with nickel as background component.

Releasing agents and solvents should, of course, be added in quantities similar to those used in the sample solutions.

6. ANALYSIS OF FOODS AND BEVERAGES

Samples of this type have received some attention in the field of atomic-absorption. Slavin (*691*) has reviewed recent advances in analysis by atomic-absorption in the food industry. Determinations of lead (*867*, *868*) in wines, of magnesium (*185*), as a part of a program of analysis of biological materials, and of strontium (*173*) in powdered milk[36] have been described.

The determinations of calcium, magnesium and zinc (*542*) in the feeding stuffs should be mentioned, as well as the determination of lead (*735*) in fish flour (see also ref. (*923*)).

Copper has been determined by Willis (*836*) by means of nitric acid extracts and the addition method. Willis considers solvent extraction techniques for small concentrations of copper to be very promising for this type of sample.

Dilution ratios of 1:10 have been used by Frey in order to determine copper, iron, calcium, sodium, and potassium in beer (*248*).

---

[36] For the analysis of milk ash (powdered milk) see p. 366.

7. ANALYSIS OF INDUSTRIAL PRODUCTS

In this section, various industrial applications are mentioned.

7.1. Cement

References may be found in the literature to determinations of calcium (*715*), magnesium (*429, 715*) and also iron, sodium, potassium and aluminum (*715*). Some applications (calcium, iron, potassium, sodium and magnesium determinations) have been reviewed by Kahn (*381*). The work of Capacho and Manning (*900*) should also be mentioned. Determinations of sodium, potassium, magnesium, manganese and calcium have been discussed by Takeuchi and Suzuki (*761*), who found that calcium may affect the determinations of sodium and potassium; manganese was determined in cement without serious effects from the other elements normally present. The interferences on magnesium were suppressed by the calcium concentration present in the samples; this represents a case of *auto-counterinterference.* Strontium was added as releasing agent for the determination of calcium, thus suppressing the interfering effects of aluminum, silicon and phosphorus. The cement samples were decomposed with 4 *M* hydrochloric acid, the solutions being evaporated to dryness and the residue dissolved in 4 *M* hydrochloric acid. After filtration and dilution to 100 ml (0.5 g of cement corresponds to 100 ml of prepared sample *stock* solution), aliquots of the solution were used for the determination of each element.

7.2. Industrial solutions

Iron and chromium have been determined in plating solutions and cobalt and manganese in caustic solutions (*40*). Copper and zinc have been determined in Bayer process liquor (*88*). Analyses for copper and zinc impurities in Watts-type nickel solutions for electroplating have been described (*820*). Shafto (*664*) has published results for the determinations of copper, iron, lead and zinc in nickel plating solutions, for which the addition method was used.

Gold has been determined in waste solutions in gold mining (*133*) by means of an internal standard method with palladium; the chemical treatment was fully automated. The internal standard method compensated for fluctuations coming from the lamp, the flame and the sprayer. Gold cyanide was converted to chloride which was extracted with methyl isobutyl ketone along with the palladium dimethylglyoxime complex added for standardization purposes. The determination of gold in cyanide solutions has been discussed by other workers (*739, 941*).

The analysis of brines deserves mention. Mansell and Emmel (*469*) have determined metallic components in brines by extraction with oxine. Determinations of chromium and molybdenum in strong sodium chloride solutions have been reported by Delaughter (*192*), who extracted chromium with diphenylthiocarbazone and methyl isobutyl ketone, and molybdenum with 4-methyl-1,2-dimercaptobenzene (dithiol) and the same solvent. Special features of this method are large volume of brine extracted (800 g) and the recovery of the analytes in a small volume of organic solvent (10 ml). This preliminary concentration allows the determination of these analytes in the p.p.b. range in the original sample. Delaughter also mentions the determinations of iron, nickel, copper and manganese with methyl isobutyl ketone as extractant and cupferron as chelating agent. Suzuki *et al.* (*752*) have also discussed this type of analysis (see below).

7.3. Chemical products

Copper and lead have been determined in potassium chloride after extraction with ammonium pyrrolidinedithiocarbamate and methyl isobutyl ketone (*723*). Suzuki *et al.* (*752*) mention the possibility of determining magnesium in purified brine, sodium carbonate and sodium bicarbonate after preliminary extraction of magnesium with oxine and methyl isobutyl ketone. Ivanov and Kozyreva (*358*) have reported the determination of copper in nickel nitrate, cobalt chloride, cobalt nitrate, calcium nitrate, cadmium nitrate, magnesium chloride and manganese chloride; 5% solutions of these salts and additions of propanol were used. Magnesium has been determined in strontium nitrate by Ivanov and Kozyreva (*359*), with a continuous aource.

Agazzi (*2*) has described the determination of tin in hydrogen peroxide solutions by diluting the samples to 45% hydrogen peroxide or even lower concentrations. The solutions prepared in this way can be injected into a turbulent oxygen–hydrogen flame. The absorption measured for the line Sn 2863 Å was compared with the absorption produced by the standards (working curve) prepared with sodium stannate in hydrogen peroxide solutions; variations in the hydrogen peroxide concentration had no effect. The determination of tin is of interest because sodium stannate is often used as a stabilizer, but its concentration should be kept within narrow limits. It is assumed that the flame can decompose the tin polymers, which are difficult to handle by other methods. Agazzi used a long-path quartz tube, and obtained a percentual concentration limit of 0.025 p.p.m. of tin.

Other determinations described in the literature are: sodium determination in calcium phosphate and tungstic oxide (*40*); potassium determination in soda ash and in sodium iodide (*437*); determinations of alkaline earth metals in alkaline earth carbonates (*810*) cadmium determinations in uranium compounds (*743*); and potassium determinations in sodium salts (*759*).

7.4. Plastics and related products

Musha *et al.* (*518*) have reported the possibility of determining (by the addition method or by working curves) zinc, lead and calcium in polyvinyl chloride in concentrations of 0.3 to 6 p.p.m. of zinc, 20 to 100 p.p.m. of lead, and 5 to 25 p.p.m. of calcium (the standards containing similar amounts of polyvinyl chloride). The analysis of paints and plastics has been described (*411, 489*). Dissolution of the sample in an appropriate solvent and direct aspiration of the solution is the general rule for the analysis of this type of sample, but wet ashing can also be applied, the residue being dissolved and used as if it were an original inorganic sample. Determinations of small amounts of metals in the plastics industry are of interest as metals frequently come from the catalysts used in polymerization processes. The determination of manganese in synthetic fibers has been reported by Slavin (*696*). The addition method is used after ashing, cooling and diluting with nitric acid (1:3 nitric acid); 2 g of fiber corresponds to 10 ml of final prepared solution. Slavin also reports the possibility of using the experimental values for metal concentration in order to determine the *blend ratio* when two synthetic fibers have been blended.

7.5. Fungicides

The analysis of fungicides has been described by Gudzinowicz and Luciano (*297–299*) for organo-metallic fungicides and related compounds. The effects of chloride and nitrate anions on sensitivity were studied. In order to establish calibration curves for iron, zinc and manganese, high-purity iron sponge, zinc metal and also zinc, manganese and iron cyclohexanebutyrates (National Bureau of Standards) were used.

7.6. Silicate samples and refractories

Trent and Slavin (*777*) have used the following procedures for preparation of samples before atomic-absorption measurements. Limestones and silica brick were heated in a muffle furnace, then treated with sulfuric and hydrofluoric acids; the solutions were evaporated and the residues taken up with hydrochloric acid. Liming materials were treated with the same acids and the solution diluted with dilute hydrochloric acid. Refractory materials were treated with sulfuric and hydrofluoric acids, and the residue was fused with sodium carbonate before final dissolution in dilute hydrochloric acid. Calcium, magnesium, iron, strontium and copper were determined in silicate samples. For calcium and strontium determinations, it was necessary to add 1% lanthanum as a releasing agent. For copper determination, the conventional extraction with ammonium pyrrolidinedithiocarbamate and methyl isobutyl ketone was used.

7.7. *Glass and ceramics*

Glass and ceramic frit can be analyzed by atomic-absorption (*369, 370*) for elements such as alkali metals, alkaline earths, nickel, copper, cobalt, zinc and magnesium. Determinations of arsenic in glass have been reported by Slavin *et al.* (*706*) who used the line As 1937 Å[37]; the glass should be dissolved in perchloric and hydrofluoric acids, boric acid being added to aid in the elimination of fluoride, and potassium permanganate to oxidize the arsenic and thus prevent any losses by volatilization. Zinc and iron can be determined in glass and refractories (*544*) after dissolving 0.1 g of sample with concentrated perchloric acid and 48% hydrofluoric acid, repeated perchloric acid treatment. Other applications have been mentioned (*1, 137*).

7.8. *Miscellaneous applications*

Graphites. Cesium impregnated in graphites has been investigated by atomic-absorption methods by Gullikson *et al.* (*300*), who found that the working curves were concave to the absorbance axis. Potassium was used to suppress ionization.

Phosphors. Determinations of sodium in fluorescent phosphors have been described (*554*).

Coal ash. Determinations of strontium have been metnioned (*81*).

Other applications. After a description of the method and the instrumental system used, Rawling and Amos (*607*) have discussed a series of miscellaneous applications done in two industrial corporations. They mention analysis of *lead sulfide concentrates, zinc sulfide concentrates*, many *ores, minerals and mill intermediate products, bearing alloys, foundry products*, and *water samples*, for metals such as silver, zinc, copper, bismuth, cadmium, calcium, cobalt, iron, manganese, magnesium, lead, etc. They also discuss

---

[37] Determination of arsenic in gold, methane arsonic acid and in plant and soil extracts was also discussed.

cadmium plant solutions, for lead, zinc and cadmium; *slags* and *sinter samples*, for lead, zinc, cadmium, copper, silver, arsenic, iron, calcium, magnesium, aluminum; and, finally, minor elements in *metal samples used as standards for direct reading spectrographs* (lead bullion, zinc metal and cadmium metal).

8. ISOTOPIC ANALYSIS

Atomic-absorption presents an excellent opportunity for isotopic analysis[38]. Special attention has been given to systems containing lithium and uranium. L'vov *et al.* (*445*) have studied the problem of the determination of isotopic composition in materials other than metals.

Isotopic investigations on lithium (*459, 860, 861, 864*) have been carried out with different instrumental systems, using an open flame of isotopic lithium as a source (*459*). The fine structure of the lithium isotopes permits the measurement of the absorption for one isotope without severe interference from another. It is thus possible to obtain curves which relate the absorption of lithium-7 to the isotopic relationship for a given total constant content of lithium.

Overlapping of resonance lines is an important limiting factor in atomic-absorption isotopic analysis. The analysis will be feasible in those cases in which the differences in the emission wavelengths of the different isotopes ($\Delta\lambda$) are bigger than the band widths of the corresponding emission lines. This happens for light elements as well as for heavy elements.

For the determination of lithium isotopes by atomic-absorption, Goleb and Yokoyama (*288, 289*) have used a water-cooled hollow-cathode discharge tube as absorption cell, instead of a flame. They found a certain number of advantages in this: (a) only microgram quantities are needed in the electrode; (b) several readings may be obtained and the sample can even be kept for later reference; (c) spreading of toxic materials is avoided; and (d) the cost of the samples is very low because of the small quantities used.

Uranium isotopes have been studied (*283*) with the use of two lamps (emission tube and absorption tube), one of which acts as absorbing medium (absorption cell).

The research done to date with these systems shows excellent possibilities for future research in isotopic analysis.

---

[38] Besides the references mentioned below, the reader should consult refs. (*274, 284, 285, 460, 538, 771, 862, 865, 877, 878, 911*).

9. SPECIAL STUDIES

Some applications are listed in this section in which atomic-absorption have been used as a complementary experimental technique in some special studies.

Microbiology. Determination of calcium in microcultures has been described (*165*).

Criminology. In a review of some curious applications, Kahn (*380*) discusses the determination of antimony in paraffin casts of hands of bodies and suspects. This type of examination has also been studied by menas of activation analysis[39]. Kahn (*380*) mentions the potentialities of atomic-absorption for investigations in hit-and-run accidents; portions of the paint may be treated with perchloric acid and examined for lead, chromium, zinc and iron.

Toxicology. Determination of elements at toxicological level are usually done with less difficulty than the determination of the same elements at normal levels (*688, 689*).

Air pollution. Atomic-absorption is an extremely suitable method for the determination of metal contaminants in the air because of its sensitivity, precision and simplicity. The emission spectrograph can also be used, but more skilful operators are needed. For air control purposes, the air can be sampled for 24 hours through a filter, and the filter and collected deposit can then be analyzed. Elements such as iron, lead, magnesium and manganese are collected usually at a level of ca. 1 p.p.m. There are two main problems: (a) metallic contaminants in the filter itself, and (b) metallic contaminants collected at very low concentrations, under the quantitative concentration limits (cobalt comes in this category). Some studies have been made in this field (*221*).

Animal metabolism. Zinc eliminated by animal organisms has been determined by atomic-absorption methods (*161*).

Geological problems. Burrell (*122*) has reported the determination of iron, cobalt, and nickel in recent marine sediments; the dry sediments were treated with chloroform and the lipids separated with petroleum ether. The chloroform fractions were mixed with methanol before measurement. Aqueous solutions mixed with 3:2 methanol–chloroform mixtures were used as standards.

Atomic energy. Normand (*531*) has reviewed some applications of atomic-absorption in atomic energy fields, and compares the method with emission

---

[39] For further information read the article by A. TRAVESÍ-JIMÉNEZ, Applications of activation analysis in criminal research, *Energía Nucl. (Madrid)*, 9 (35) (1965) 217 (in Spanish).

flame photometry, colorimetry and activation analysis. He mentions the determinations of lithium, potassium and magnesium in Antarctic ice cores; lithium, potassium, magnesium, zinc and aluminum in alloys; magnesium and molybdenum in uranium metal; and cesium in fission products.

Oscillator strength measurements. Atomic-absorption procedures allow the measurement of oscillator strengths if the system is calibrated for a reference element, i.e., an element whose oscillator strength is previously known. This can be advantageous in studying the excitation capabilities of different elements. Details of a method of measuring absolute oscillator strength have been given by King (*394*).

Chemical systems. Kahn (*380*) has mentioned the possibility of determining chlorine in xylene by adding sodium diphenyl in order to convert the sodium to sodium chloride, and of determining silver (indirect method) after precipitation of silver chloride. Atomic-absorption methods have been used by Roth (*638, 939*) for the determination of antimony trisulfide: potassium chlorate ratios for rejection criteria for igniter beads. Hicks (*332*) has made a complete study of some ligands effects in atomic-absorption flame photometry for coordination complexes of organic phosphite triesters and copper(I) halides. The signal variations found could be related to the number and kind of neutral ligands coordinated to a metal atom. Solutions of the complexes in nonpolar solvents were aspirated into fuel-rich and lean pre-mixed air–acetylene flames. For a given *ligand*:*CuX* ratio, the signal decreased in the order $CuCl > CuBr > CuI$. Fleisher (*245*) has studied the reaction $NaCl + HBO_2 \rightarrow NaBO_2 + HCl$. The concentration of unreacted sodium was found by atomic-absorption. Various gaseous systems have been studied (*103, 193, 485, 486*) and also systems involving the BO_2 radicals (*646*).

Analysis of ruby. Consult ref. (*947*).

Metallic carbonyls. The determination of iron and nickel carbonyls in town gas has been described by Denholm *et al.* (*193*).

In this rapid review of modern applications of atomic-absorption methods, an attempt has been made to draw attention to the diversity of elements which can be determined in different types of sample, and to give some idea of the preparative and operative problems which may be present. But the most important purpose has been to indicate how many possibilities and applications of atomic-absorption still remain to be investigated.

Appendix

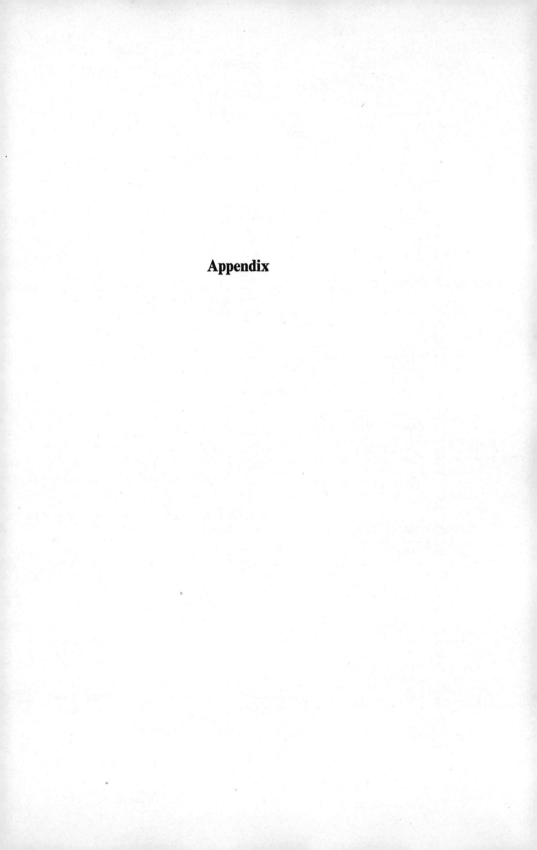

TABLE 1

CONVERSION TABLE TO TRANSFORM % ABSN. AND % *T* TO ABSORBANCE VALUES

	1.0	0.9	0.8	0.7	0.6	0.5	0.4	0.3	0.2	0.1	% *T*
% *Absn.*	0.0	0.1	0.2	0.3	0.4	0.5	0.6	0.7	0.8	0.9	
0.	0.0000	0.0004	0.0009	0.0013	0.0017	0.0022	0.0026	0.0031	0.0035	0.0039	99.
1.	0.0044	0.0048	0.0052	0.0057	0.0061	0.0066	0.0070	0.0074	0.0079	0.0083	98.
2.	0.0088	0.0092	0.0097	0.0101	0.0106	0.0110	0.0114	0.0119	0.0123	0.0128	97.
3.	0.0132	0.0137	0.0141	0.0146	0.0150	0.0155	0.0159	0.0164	0.0168	0.0173	96.
4.	0.0177	0.0182	0.0186	0.0191	0.0195	0.0200	0.0205	0.0209	0.0214	0.0218	95.
5.	0.0223	0.0227	0.0232	0.0236	0.0241	0.0246	0.0250	0.0255	0.0259	0.0264	94.
6.	0.0269	0.0273	0.0278	0.0283	0.0287	0.0292	0.0297	0.0301	0.0306	0.0311	93.
7.	0.0315	0.0320	0.0325	0.0329	0.0334	0.0339	0.0343	0.0348	0.0353	0.0357	92.
8.	0.0362	0.0367	0.0372	0.0376	0.0381	0.0386	0.0391	0.0395	0.0400	0.0405	91.
9.	0.0410	0.0414	0.0419	0.0424	0.0429	0.0434	0.0438	0.0443	0.0448	0.0453	90.
10.	0.0458	0.0462	0.0467	0.0472	0.0477	0.0482	0.0487	0.0491	0.0496	0.0501	89.
11.	0.0506	0.0511	0.0516	0.0521	0.0526	0.0531	0.0535	0.0540	0.0545	0.0550	88.
12.	0.0555	0.0560	0.0565	0.0570	0.0575	0.0580	0.0585	0.0590	0.0595	0.0600	87.
13.	0.0605	0.0610	0.0615	0.0620	0.0625	0.0630	0.0635	0.0640	0.0645	0.0650	86.
14.	0.0655	0.0660	0.0665	0.0670	0.0675	0.0680	0.0685	0.0691	0.0696	0.0701	85.
15.	0.0706	0.0711	0.0716	0.0721	0.0726	0.0731	0.0737	0.0742	0.0747	0.0752	84.
16.	0.0757	0.0762	0.0768	0.0773	0.0778	0.0783	0.0788	0.0794	0.0799	0.0804	83.
17.	0.0809	0.0814	0.0820	0.0825	0.0830	0.0835	0.0841	0.0846	0.0851	0.0857	82.
18.	0.0862	0.0867	0.0872	0.0878	0.0883	0.0888	0.0894	0.0899	0.0904	0.0910	81.
19.	0.0915	0.0921	0.0926	0.0931	0.0937	0.0942	0.0947	0.0953	0.0958	0.0964	80.
20.	0.0969	0.0975	0.0980	0.0985	0.0991	0.0996	0.1002	0.1007	0.1013	0.1018	79.
21.	0.1024	0.1029	0.1035	0.1040	0.1046	0.1051	0.1057	0.1062	0.1068	0.1073	78.
22.	0.1079	0.1085	0.1090	0.1096	0.1101	0.1107	0.1113	0.1118	0.1124	0.1129	77.
23.	0.1135	0.1141	0.1146	0.1152	0.1158	0.1163	0.1169	0.1175	0.1180	0.1186	76.
24.	0.1192	0.1198	0.1203	0.1209	0.1215	0.1221	0.1226	0.1232	0.1238	0.1244	75.
25.	0.1249	0.1255	0.1261	0.1267	0.1273	0.1278	0.1284	0.1290	0.1296	0.1302	74.
26.	0.1308	0.1314	0.1319	0.1325	0.1331	0.1337	0.1343	0.1349	0.1355	0.1361	73.
27.	0.1367	0.1373	0.1379	0.1385	0.1391	0.1397	0.1403	0.1409	0.1415	0.1421	72.
28.	0.1427	0.1433	0.1439	0.1445	0.1451	0.1457	0.1463	0.1469	0.1475	0.1481	71.
29.	0.1487	0.1494	0.1500	0.1506	0.1512	0.1518	0.1524	0.1530	0.1537	0.1543	70.
30.	0.1549	0.1555	0.1561	0.1568	0.1574	0.1530	0.1586	0.1593	0.1599	0.1605	69.
31.	0.1612	0.1618	0.1624	0.1630	0.1637	0.1643	0.1649	0.1656	0.1662	0.1669	68.
32.	0.1675	0.1681	0.1688	0.1694	0.1701	0.1707	0.1713	0.1720	0.1726	0.1733	67.
33.	0.1739	0.1746	0.1752	0.1759	0.1765	0.1772	0.1778	0.1785	0.1791	0.1798	66.
34.	0.1805	0.1811	0.1818	0.1824	0.1831	0.1838	0.1844	0.1851	0.1858	0.1864	65.
35.	0.1871	0.1878	0.1884	0.1891	0.1898	0.1904	0.1911	0.1918	0.1925	0.1931	64.
36.	0.1938	0.1945	0.1952	0.1959	0.1965	0.1972	0.1979	0.1986	0.1993	0.2000	63.
37.	0.2007	0.2013	0.2020	0.2027	0.2034	0.2041	0.2048	0.2055	0.2062	0.2069	62.
38.	0.2076	0.2083	0.2090	0.2097	0.2104	0.2111	0.2118	0.2125	0.2132	0.2140	61.
39.	0.2147	0.2154	0.2161	0.2168	0.2175	0.2182	0.2190	0.2197	0.2204	0.2211	60.
40.	0.2219	0.2226	0.2233	0.2240	0.2248	0.2255	0.2262	0.2269	0.2277	0.2284	59.

TABLE 1 (continued)

	1.0	0.9	0.8	0.7	0.6	0.5	0.4	0.3	0.2	0.1	% *T*
% *Absn.*	0.0	0.1	0.2	0.3	0.4	0.5	0.6	0.7	0.8	0.9	
41.	0.2291	0.2299	0.2306	0.2314	0.2321	0.2328	0.2336	0.2343	0.2351	0.2358	58.
42.	0.2366	0.2373	0.2381	0.2388	0.2396	0.2403	0.2411	0.2418	0.2426	0.2434	57.
43.	0.2441	0.2449	0.2457	0.2464	0.2472	0.2480	0.2487	0.2495	0.2503	0.2510	56.
44.	0.2518	0.2526	0.2534	0.2541	0.2549	0.2557	0.2565	0.2573	0.2581	0.2588	55.
45.	0.2596	0.2604	0.2612	0.2620	0.2628	0.2636	0.2644	0.2652	0.2660	0.2668	54.
46.	0.2676	0.2684	0.2692	0.2700	0.2708	0.2716	0.2725	0.2733	0.2741	0.2749	53.
47.	0.2757	0.2765	0.2774	0.2782	0.2790	0.2798	0.2807	0.2815	0.2823	0.2832	52.
48.	0.2840	0.2848	0.2857	0.2865	0.2874	0.2882	0.2890	0.2899	0.2907	0.2916	51.
49.	0.2924	0.2933	0.2941	0.2950	0.2958	0.2967	0.2976	0.2984	0.2993	0.3002	50.
50.	0.3010	0.3019	0.3028	0.3036	0.3045	0.3054	0.3063	0.3072	0.3080	0.3089	49.
51.	0.3098	0.3107	0.3116	0.3125	0.3134	0.3143	0.3152	0.3161	0.3170	0.3179	48.
52.	0.3188	0.3197	0.3206	0.3215	0.3224	0.3233	0.3242	0.3251	0.3261	0.3270	47.
53.	0.3279	0.3288	0.3298	0.3307	0.3316	0.3325	0.3335	0.3344	0.3354	0.3363	46.
54.	0.3372	0.3382	0.3391	0.3401	0.3410	0.3420	0.3429	0.3439	0.3449	0.3458	45.
55.	0.3468	0.3478	0.3487	0.3497	0.3507	0.3516	0.3526	0.3536	0.3546	0.3556	44.
56.	0.3565	0.3575	0.3585	0.3595	0.3605	0.3615	0.3625	0.3635	0.3645	0.3655	43.
57.	0.3665	0.3675	0.3686	0.3696	0.3706	0.3716	0.3726	0.3737	0.3747	0.3757	42.
58.	0.3768	0.3778	0.3788	0.3799	0.3809	0.3820	0.3830	0.3840	0.3851	0.3862	41.
59.	0.3872	0.3883	0.3893	0.3904	0.3915	0.3925	0.3936	0.3947	0.3958	0.3969	40.
60.	0.3979	0.3990	0.4001	0.4012	0.4023	0.4034	0.4045	0.4056	0.4067	0.4078	39.
61.	0.4089	0.4101	0.4112	0.4123	0.4134	0.4145	0.4157	0.4168	0.4179	0.4191	38.
62.	0.4202	0.4214	0.4225	0.4237	0.4248	0.4269	0.4271	0.4283	0.4295	0.4306	37.
63.	0.4318	0.4330	0.4342	0.4353	0.4365	0.4377	0.4389	0.4401	0.4413	0.4425	36.
64.	0.4437	0.4449	0.4461	0.4473	0.4485	0.4498	0.4510	0.4522	0.4535	0.4547	35.
65.	0.4559	0.4572	0.4584	0.4597	0.4609	0.4622	0.4634	0.4647	0.4660	0.4672	34.
66.	0.4685	0.4698	0.4711	0.4724	0.4737	0.4750	0.4763	0.4776	0.4789	0.4802	33.
67.	0.4815	0.4828	0.4841	0.4855	0.4868	0.4881	0.4895	0.4908	0.4921	0.4935	32.
68.	0.4948	0.4962	0.4976	0.4989	0.5003	0.5017	0.5031	0.5045	0.5058	0.5072	31.
69.	0.5086	0.5100	0.5114	0.5129	0.5143	0.5157	0.5171	0.5186	0.5200	0.5214	30.
70.	0.5229	0.5243	0.5258	0.5272	0.5287	0.5302	0.5317	0.5331	0.5346	0.5361	29.
71.	0.5376	0.5391	0.5406	0.5421	0.5436	0.5452	0.5467	0.5482	0.5498	0.5513	28.
72.	0.5528	0.5544	0.5560	0.5575	0.5591	0.5607	0.5622	0.5638	0.5654	0.5670	27.
73.	0.5686	0.5702	0.5719	0.5735	0.5751	0.5768	0.5784	0.5800	0.5817	0.5834	26.
74.	0.5850	0.5867	0.5884	0.5901	0.5918	0.5935	0.5952	0.5969	0.5986	0.6003	25.
75.	0.6021	0.6038	0.6055	0.6073	0.6091	0.6108	0.6126	0.6144	0.6162	0.6180	24.
76.	0.6198	0.6216	0.6234	0.6253	0.6271	0.6289	0.6308	0.6326	0.6345	0.6364	23.
77.	0.6383	0.6402	0.6421	0.6440	0.6459	0.6478	0.6498	0.6517	0.6536	0.6556	22.
78.	0.6576	0.6596	0.6615	0.6635	0.6655	0.6676	0.6696	0.6716	0.6737	0.6757	21.
79.	0.6778	0.6799	0.6819	0.6840	0.6861	0.6882	0.6904	0.6925	0.6946	0.6968	20.
80.	0.6990	0.7011	0.7033	0.7055	0.7077	0.7100	0.7122	0.7144	0.7167	0.7190	19.

TABLE 1 (continued)

% Absn.	1.0 / 0.0	0.9 / 0.1	0.8 / 0.2	0.7 / 0.3	0.6 / 0.4	0.5 / 0.5	0.4 / 0.6	0.3 / 0.7	0.2 / 0.8	0.1 / 0.9	% T
81.	0.7212	0.7235	0.7258	0.7282	0.7305	0.7328	0.7352	0.7375	0.7399	0.7423	18.
82.	0.7447	0.7471	0.7496	0.7520	0.7545	0.7570	0.7595	0.7620	0.7645	0.7670	17.
83.	0.7696	0.7721	0.7747	0.7773	0.7799	0.7825	0.7852	0.7878	0.7905	0.7932	16.
84.	0.7959	0.7986	0.8013	0.8041	0.8069	0.8097	0.8125	0.8153	0.8182	0.8210	15.
85.	0.8239	0.8268	0.8297	0.8327	0.8356	0.8386	0.8416	0.8447	0.8477	0.8508	14.
86.	0.8539	0.8570	0.8601	0.8633	0.8665	0.8697	0.8729	0.8761	0.8794	0.8827	13.
87.	0.8861	0.8894	0.8928	0.8962	0.8996	0.9031	0.9066	0.9101	0.9136	0.9172	12.
88.	0.9208	0.9245	0.9281	0.9318	0.9355	0.9393	0.9431	0.9469	0.9508	0.9547	11.
89.	0.9586	0.9626	0.9666	0.9706	0.9747	0.9788	0.9830	0.9872	0.9914	0.9957	10.
90.	1.0000	1.0044	1.0088	1.0132	1.0177	1.0223	1.0269	1.0315	1.0362	1.0409	9.
91.	1.0458	1.0506	1.0555	1.0605	1.0655	1.0706	1.0757	1.0809	1.0862	1.0915	8.
92.	1.0969	1.1024	1.1079	1.1135	1.1192	1.1249	1.1308	1.1367	1.1427	1.1487	7.
93.	1.1549	1.1611	1.1675	1.1739	1.1805	1.1871	1.1938	1.2007	1.2076	1.2147	6.
94.	1.2218	1.2292	1.2366	1.2441	1.2518	1.2596	1.2676	1.2757	1.2840	1.2924	5.
95.	1.3010	1.3098	1.3188	1.3279	1.3372	1.3464	1.3566	1.3665	1.3763	1.3872	4.
96.	1.3979	1.4089	1.4202	1.4318	1.4437	1.4559	1.4685	1.4815	1.4948	1.5086	3.
97.	1.5229	1.5376	1.5528	1.5686	1.5850	1.6021	1.6198	1.6383	1.6576	1.6778	2.
98.	1.6990	1.7212	1.7447	1.7696	1.7959	1.8231	1.8539	1.8661	1.9208	1.9586	1.
99.	2.0000										0.
100.											

TABLE 2

HOLLOW-CATHODE LAMPS FOR ATOMIC-ABSORPTION SPECTROSCOPY

Data collected in this table come from refs. (*74*) and (*818*) (by courtesy of Beckman Instruments, Inc. and Westinghouse Electric Corporation, Electronic Tube Division).

SINGLE ELEMENT TYPES

Cathode material	*Window*[1]	*Gas fill*[2]	*Maximum current (mA)*[3]	*Size*[4]	*Line emission wavelengths (in mμ)*
Aluminum	Q	Ar	20	B, A	309.2, 396.2
	P	Ne	20	A	
	Q	Ne	20	B, A	
Antimony	Q	Ar	25	B, A	217.6, 231.1
	Q	Ne	25	B, A	
Arsenic	Q	Ne	20	B, A	193.7, 197.2
Barium	P	Ne	30	A	553.6
Bismuth	Q	Ar	12	B, A	223.1, 306.8
	Q	Ne	12	B, A	
Boron	Q	Ar	25	B, A	249.7
Cadmium	Q	Ar	12	B, A	228.8, 326.1
	Q	Ne	12	B, A	
Calcium	P	Ne	20	A	422.7
Cerium	Q	Ne	20	B, A	569.9
Cesium	P	Ar	30	A	852.1, 455.6
	P	Ne	30	A	
Chromium	P	Ar	30	A	357.9, 425.4
	Q	Ar	30	B, A	
	Q	Ne	30	B, A	
Cobalt	P	Ar	35	A	240.7, 345.4, 352.7
	Q	Ar	35	B, A	
	Q	Ne	35	B, A	
Copper	P	Ne	40	A	324.7, 327.4
	Q	Ar	40	B, A	
	Q	Ne	40	B, A	
Dysprosium	Q	Ne	25	B, A	404.6, 418.7, 421.2
Erbium	Q	Ne	25	B, A	400.8
Europium	Q	Ne	20	B, A	459.4, 462.7
Gadolinium	P	Ne	20	A	368.4, 371.3
	Q	Ne	20	B, A	

Footnotes on p. 398

TABLE 2 (continued)

Cathode material	*Window*[1]	*Gas fill*[2]	*Maximum current (mA)*[3]	*Size*[4]	*Line emission wavelengths (in mμ)*
Gallium	Q	Ne	15	B, A	287.4, 417.2
Gold	Q	Ar	15	B, A	242.8, 267.6
	Q	Ne	15	B, A	
Holmium	Q	Ne	20	B, A	405.4, 598.3, 416.3, 410.4
Indium	Q	Ar	12	B, A	304.0
	Q	Ne	12	B	
Iron	P	Ar	40	A	248.3, 372.0
	P	Ne	40	A	
	Q	Ar	40	B, A	
	Q	Ne	40	B, A	
High purity iron	Q	Ne	35	B, A	248.3, 372.0
Lanthanum	Q	Ar	20	B, A	401.5, 357.4, 392.8, 418.7, 579.1
	Q	Ne	20	B	
Lead	Q	Ar	15	B, A	217.0, 283.3, 261.4
	Q	Ne	15	B, A	
Lithium-nat.	P	Ar	30	A	670.8, 323.3
	Q	Ar	30	B	
	P	Ne	30	A	
Lithium-6	P	Ne	30	A	670.8
	P	Ar	30	A	
Lithium-7	P	Ne	30	A	670.8
	P	Ar	30	A	
Lutetium	Q	Ne	20	B, A	308.1, 331.0
Magnesium	Q	Ar	20	B, A	285.2, 202.5, 265.9
	Q	Ne	20	B, A	
Manganese	Q	Ar	35	B, A	279.5, 280.1
	P	Ar	35	A	
	Q	Ne	35	B, A	
Mercury	Q	Ar	15	B, A	253.7
Molybdenum	Q	Ar	35	B, A	313.3, 317.0
	Q	Ne	35	B, A	
Neodymium	Q	Ne	20	B, A	492.5
Nickel	P	Ar	40	A	232.0, 341.5
	Q	Ar	40	B, A	
	Q	Ne	40	B, A	

Footnotes on p. 398

TABLE 2 (continued)

Cathode material	*Window*[1]	*Gas fill*[2]	*Maximum current (mA)*[3]	*Size*[4]	*Line emission wavelengths (in mμ)*
Niobium	Q	Ne	30	B, A	405.9, 408.0
Palladium	Q Q	Ar Ne	30 30	B, A B, A	244.8, 340.4, 247.6
Platinum	Q	Ar	30	B, A	265.9
Potassium	P	Ne	25	A	766.5, 404.4
Praseodymium	Q	Ne	20	B, A	495.1, 513.3
Rhenium	Q	Ne	30	B, A	346.0, 346.5
Rhodium	Q Q	Ar Ne	30 30	B, A B	343.5, 369.2
Rubidium	P Q	Ne Ne	30 30	A B	780.0
Samarium	Q	Ne	30	B, A	395.1, 476.0, 429.7
Selenium	Q Q	Ar Ne	15 15	B, A B, A	196.0, 204.0
Silicon	Q Q	Ar Ne	20 20	B, A B, A	251.6
Silver	Q	Ar	20	B, A	328.1, 338.3
Sodium	P P	Ar Ne	25 25	A A	589.0, 330.2
Strontium	P	Ne	30	A	460.7
Tantalum	Q Q	Ar Ne	30 30	B, A B, A	331.1, 481.3
Tellurium	Q Q	Ar Ne	15 15	B, A B, A	214.3, 238.6
Terbium	Q	Ne	30	B, A	431.9, 433.8, 432.7
Thorium	Q	Ne	30	B, A	576.1
Thulium	Q	Ne	35	B, A	409.4, 410.5
Tin	Q Q	Ar Ne	15 15	B, A B, A	286.3
Titanium	Q	Ne	25	B, A	364.3, 399.8

Footnotes on p. 398

TABLE 2 (continued)

Cathode material	*Window*[1]	*Gas fill*[2]	*Maximum current (mA)*[3]	*Size*[4]	*Line emission wavelengths (in mμ)*
Tungsten	Q	Ne	35	B, A	400.9, 429.4
	Q	Ar	35	B, A	
Uranium	Q	Ne	30	B, A	424.4, 592.0
Vanadium	Q	Ar	35	B, A	318.4, 385.5
	Q	Ne	35	B, A	
Ytterbium	Q	Ar	20	B, A	398.8
Yttrium	P	Ne	20	A	407.7, 410.2
	Q	Ne	20	B, A	
Zinc	Q	Ar	18	B, A	213.9, 307.6
	Q	Ne	18	B, A	
Zirconium	Q	Ar	30	B, A	352.0, 360.1
	Q	Ne	30	B	

MULTIPLE ELEMENT TYPES

Cathode material	*Window*[1]	*Gas fill*[2]	*Maximum current (mA)*[3]	*Size*[4]
As–Ni	Q	Ne	20	B
Au–Ni	Q	Ne	15	B
Ba–Ca–Sr	P	Ne	25	A
Ba–Ca–Sr–Mg	Q	Ne	25	B
Ca–Mg–Al	Q	Ar	20	B, A
Ca–Mg–Al	Q	Ne	20	B, A
Ca–Mg–Al–Li	Q	Ar	18	B, A
Cr–Fe–Mn–Ni	Q	Ne	30	B
Cu–Ga	Q	Ne	20	B
Cu–Mn	Q	Ne	35	B
Cu–Pb–Zn–Ag	Q	Ne	15	B
Cu–Zn–Fe–Mn	Q	Ne	15	B
Cu–Zn–Mo	Q	Ne	15	B
Cu–Zn–Pb–Sn	Q	Ne	12	B
Fe–Cu–Mn	Q	Ne	35	B
In–P	Q	Ne	20	B
Na–K–Li	Q	Ar	30	B
Se–Ni	Q	Ne	15	B

[1] P = Pyrex (>70% transmission at 305 mμ); Q = Quartz (>75% transmission at 220 mμ).
[2] Ar = Argon gas fill; Ne = Neon gas fill.
[3] The current rating shown is the maximum permissible figure and does not represent typical operation. For optimum performance and life, a tube should be operated at the lowest current consistent with the desired output characteristics.
[4] A = 1½ inch diameter window; B = 1 inch diameter window.

TABLE 3

DILUTION SERIES FOR STANDARDS

Volume desired (ml)	*Concentration desired (p.p.m.)*	*Pipette (ml)*	*Conc. of soln. to be diluted (p.p.m.)*
500	100	50	1000
500	50	25	1000
500	20	10	1000
1000	10	10	1000
500	5	25	100
500	3	15	100
500	2	10	100
1000	1	10	100
500	0.5	25	10
500	0.2	10	10
1000	0.1	10	10
500	0.05	25	1
500	0.02	10	1
500	0.01	5	1

TABLE 4*

CONCENTRATION CONVERSION FACTORS

To convert	*into*									
	p.p.m. mg/l γ*/ml*	*g/l mg/ml*	*g/ml*	%	*mg/ 100 ml*	*meq./l*	*meq./ 100 ml*	*mg atom/ 100 ml*	C_N	C_M
p.p.m. mg/l γ/ml	1	10^{-3}	10^{-6}	10^{-4}	10^{-1}	$\frac{1}{W_{meq.}}$	$\frac{10^{-1}}{W_{meq.}}$	$\frac{10^{-1}}{W_a}$	$\frac{10^{-3}}{W_{eq.}}$	$\frac{10^{-3}}{W_m}$
g/l mg/ml	10^3	1	10^{-3}	10^{-1}	10^2	$\frac{10^3}{W_{meq.}}$	$\frac{10^2}{W_{meq.}}$	$\frac{10^2}{W_a}$	$\frac{1}{W_{eq.}}$	$\frac{1}{W_m}$
g/ml	10^6	10^3	1	10^2	10^5	$\frac{10^6}{W_{meq.}}$	$\frac{10^5}{W_{meq.}}$	$\frac{10^5}{W_a}$	$\frac{10^3}{W_{eq.}}$	$\frac{10^3}{W_m}$
%	10^4	10	10^{-2}	1	10^2	$\frac{10^4}{W_{meq.}}$	$\frac{10^3}{W_{meq.}}$	$\frac{10^3}{W_a}$	$\frac{10}{W_{eq.}}$	$\frac{10}{W_m}$
mg/ 100 ml	10	10^{-2}	10^{-5}	10^{-3}	1	$\frac{10}{W_{meq.}}$	$\frac{1}{W_{meq.}}$	$\frac{1}{W_a}$	$\frac{10^{-2}}{W_{eq.}}$	$\frac{10^{-2}}{W_m}$
meq./l	$W_{meq.}$	$\frac{W_{meq.}}{10^3}$	$\frac{W_{meq.}}{10^6}$	$\frac{W_{meq.}}{10^4}$	$\frac{W_{meq.}}{10}$	1	10^{-1}	$\frac{10^{-1}}{n}$	10^{-3}	$\frac{10^{-3}}{n}$
meq./ 100 ml	$10\ W_{meq.}$	$\frac{W_{meq.}}{10^2}$	$\frac{W_{meq.}}{10^5}$	$\frac{W_{meq.}}{10^3}$	$W_{meq.}$	10	1	$\frac{1}{n}$	10^{-2}	$\frac{10^{-2}}{n}$
mg atom/ 100 ml	$10\ W_a$	$\frac{W_a}{10^2}$	$\frac{W_a}{10^5}$	$\frac{W_a}{10^3}$	W_a	$10\ n$	n	1	$10^{-2}\ n$	10^{-2}
C_N	$10^3\ W_{eq.}$	$W_{eq.}$	$\frac{W_{eq.}}{10^3}$	$\frac{W_{eq.}}{10}$	$10^2\ W_{eq.}$	10^3	10^2	$\frac{10^2}{n}$	1	$\frac{1}{n}$
C_M	$10^3\ W_m$	W_m	$\frac{W_m}{10^3}$	$\frac{W_m}{10}$	$10^2\ W_m$	$10^3\ n$	$10^2\ n$	10^2	n	1

* *Key to symbols*:

$W_{meq.}$: Milliequivalent weight (in mg).
$W_{eq.}$: Equivalent weight (in g).
W_a : Atomic weight (in g).
W_m : Molecular weight or ionic weight (in g).
n : Number of equivalents.
C_N : Concentration expressed as normality.
C_M : Concentration expressed as molarity.

TABLE 5

RECOMMENDED OPERATING CONDITIONS FOR DETERMINATIONS BY ATOMIC-ABSORPTION FLAME PHOTOMETRY

Element	*Analytical lines for maximum percentual sensitivity (Å)*	*Other lines (Å)*	*Most recommended flames*[1]	*Type of flame*	*Other flames*	*Lamp*[2]	*Selection zone*[3]	*Slit width*[4]
Aluminum	3093	2367 2373 2375 3082 3944 3961	NOAF	Rich	OAF	HCL	S	
Antimony	2176	2068 2312	AAF	Rich		HCL	S	
Arsenic	1937	1972 (1890)	AHF	Lean	AAF	HCL	L	
Barium	5536		AAF	Rich	NOAF	HCL	S	
Beryllium	2349		NOAF	Lean		HCL	S–H	
Bismuth	2231	2062 2228 3068	AAF	Lean	NOAF	HCL	S	
Boron	2497		NOAF	Rich		HCL	S	
Cadmium	2288	3261	AAF	Lean		HCL	L	
Calcium	4227	2239	AAF	Rich	NOAF	HCL	S	
Cerium	5200		NOAF	Lean		HCL	L	
Cesium	8521	4556	AAF	Lean	ACGF APF	VDL	L	
Chromium	3579	4254	AAF	Rich	NOAF	HCL	L–S	

[1] AAF, air–acetylene flame; ACGF, air–coal gas flame; AHF, air–hydrogen flame; APF, air–propane flame; NOAF, nitrous oxide–acetylene flame; OAF, oxygen–acetylene flame.

[2] HCL, hollow-cathode lamp; VDL, vapor discharge lamp.

[3] L, low selection zone, very close to the inner colored zone, at less than about 5 mm from the top of the burner; S, standard selection zone, at 5 to 8 mm over the top of the burner; H, high selection zone, at more than 8 mm over the top of the burner.

[4] N, narrow slit; VN, very narrow slit.

TABLE 5 (continued)

Element	*Analytical lines for maximum percentual sensitivity (Å)*	*Other lines (Å)*	*Most recommended flames*	*Type of flame*	*Other flames*	*Lamp*	*Selection zone*	*Slit width*
Cobalt	2407	2411 2425 2521 3454 3527	AAF	Lean		HCL	S	N
Copper	3248	2226 2244 2442 2492 3274	AAF	Lean		HCL	S	
Dysprosium	4046 4212	4187 4195	NOAF	Lean		HCL	S	
Erbium	4008	3332 3863 3893 3944 3974 4088 4151 4607	NOAF	Lean		HCL	S	
Europium	4594	4627 4662	NOAF	Lean		HCL	S	
Gadolinium	3684 4097	3714 3718 3783 4057 4058 4191	NOAF	Lean		HCL	S	
Gallium	2874	2944 4033 4172	AAF	Lean		HCL	S	
Germanium	2652	2593 2691 2709 2755	NOAF	Rich		HCL	L–S	
Gold	2428	2676 6278	AAF	Lean		HCL	S	
Hafnium	2866 3073	2898 2965	NOAF	Lean		HCL	S	

TABLE 5 (continued)

Element	*Analytical lines for maximum percentual sensitivity (Å)*	*Other lines (Å)*	*Most recommended flames*	*Type of flame*	*Other flames*	*Lamp*	*Selection zone*	*Slit width*
Holmium	4054 4104	4041 4127 4163 4254 5983	NOAF	Lean		HCL	S	
Indium	3040	2560 2754 3256 4102 4105 4511	AAF	Lean		HCL	S	
Iridium	2850	2089 2373 2640 2665 2925	AAF	Lean		HCL	S	
Iron	2483	2488 2523 2527 2719 2721 2967 3021 3441 3720 3860	AAF	Lean	NOAF	HCL	L–S	N
Lanthanum	3928	3574 5501	NOAF	Rich		HCL	S	
Lead	2833	2170 2614 4058	AAF	Lean		HCL	S	
Lithium	6708	3233	AAF	Lean	ACGF APF	HCL VDL	S	
Lutetium	3082 3360	2989 3118 3279 3282 3312 3377 3397 3568 4519	NOAF	Lean		HCL	S	

TABLE 5 (continued)

Element	*Analytical lines for maximum percentual sensitivity (Å)*	*Other lines (Å)*	*Most recommended flames*	*Type of flame*	*Other flames*	*Lamp*	*Selection zone*	*Slit width*
Magnesium	2852	2025 2796	AAF	Lean	NOAF	HCL	L–S	
Manganese	2795	2798 2801 4031	AAF	Lean	NOAF	HCL	S	N
Mercury	2537	(1849)	AAF	Lean		HCL VDL	S	
Molybdenum	3133	3112 3158 3170 3194 3209 3798 3864 3903	NOAF	Lean	AAF	HCL	S	
Neodymium	4634 4684 4925	4719 4897	NOAF	Rich		HCL	S–H	
Nickel	2320	2311 2346 3003 3051 3415 3462 3525	AAF	Lean		HCL	S	VN
Niobium	3349	4059 4080 4101 4124	NOAF	Lean		HCL	S–H	
Osmium	2909	3018	NOAF	Lean		HCL		
Palladium	2476	2448 2763	AAF	Lean		HCL	S	N
Platinum	2659	2175	AAF	Lean		HCL	S	
Potassium	7665	4044	AAF	Lean	ACGF APF	VDL	S	
Praseodimium	4951	5046 5133	NOAF	Lean		HCL	S	

TABLE 5 (continued)

Element	*Analytical lines for maximum percentual sensitivity (Å)*	*Other lines (Å)*	*Most recommended flames*	*Type of flame*	*Other flames*	*Lamp*	*Selection zone*	*Slit width*
Rhenium	3461	3452 3465	NOAF	Rich		HCL	S	
Rhodium	3435	3397 3435 3503 3507 3658 3692 3701	AAF	Lean		HCL	H	
Rubidium	7800	4202	AAF	Lean	ACGF APF	VDL	S	
Ruthenium	3499	3728	AAF	Lean		HCL	S	
Samarium	4297 5175	4728 4760 4884 5201 5283	NOAF	Lean		HCL	S	
Scandium	3912	3270 3274 3908 4020 4024	NOAF	Lean		HCL	S	
Selenium	1961	2040	AHF	Lean	AAF	HCL	S	
Silicon	2516	2208 2211 2217 2507 2514 2519 2524 2529	NOAF	Rich		HCL	S	
Silver	3281	3383	AAF	Lean		HCL	S	
Sodium	5890	3302	AAF	Lean	ACGF APF	VDL	S	
Strontium	4607	4078	AAF	Rich	NOAF	HCL	S	
Tantalum	2715	2559 2609 2776	NOAF	Rich		HCL	H	

TABLE 5 (continued)

Element	*Analytical lines for maximum percentual sensitivity (Å)*	*Other lines (Å)*	*Most recommended flames*	*Type of flame*	*Other flames*	*Lamp*	*Selection zone*	*Slit width*
Tellurium	2143		AAF	Lean		HCL	S	
Terbium	4327	3901 4062 4105 4319 4338	NOAF	Lean		HCL	S	
Thallium	3776	2380 2768	AAF	Lean		VDL HCL	S	
Thorium	3245		NOAF	Rich		HCL	L	
Thulium	4094	3718 3744 3883 3887 4106 4188 4204 4360	NOAF	Lean		HCL	S	
Tin	2863	2246 2355 2430 2840 3009 3034	AHF	Lean	AAF NOAF	HCL	L	
Titanium	3643	3200 3342 3355 3636 3654 3753 3999	NOAF	Lean		HCL	S–H	
Tungsten	2551	2681 2724 2944 2947 4009	NOAF	Rich		HCL	H	
Uranium	4244	3489 3515 3944 4154 5027	NOAF	Rich		HCL	S	

TABLE 5 (continued)

Element	*Analytical lines for maximum percentual sensitivity (Å)*	*Other lines (Å)*	*Most recommended flames*	*Type of flame*	*Other flames*	*Lamp*	*Selection zone*	*Slit width*
Vanadium	3184	3066 3704 3841 3856 4379	NOAF	Rich	OAF	HCL	S	
Ytterbium	3988	2465 2672 3464	NOAF	Lean		HCL	S	
Yttrium	4077 4102	4128 4143	NOAF	Lean		HCL	S	
Zinc	2139	3076	AAF	Lean		HCL	S	
Zirconium	3601		NOAF	Rich		HCL	S–H	

Percentual and fluctuational concentration limits. Consult data shown in the text in Tables 13–4 and 13–5.

Lines. For top percentual sensitivity the lines shown in the first column should be used. Other lines listed in the second column give the opportunity of working at lower percentual sensitivity, thus extending the dynamic concentration range. Another extension toward higher concentrations (lower sensitivity) can be achieved in some instruments by operating at cold operation (cold spraying chamber). If the instrument used has the capability of using more than one light pass, the utilization of several passes extend the dynamic concentration range toward the lower concentrations (higher sensitivity). When more than one wavelength is given, they are listed by increasing wavelength expressed in Ångstroms.

Type of flame. According to the element, lean flame or fuel-rich flame conditions are advised. The optimum conditions can vary from one type of burner to another.

Lamp current. For vapor discharge lamps the current should be as small as possible. For hollow-cathode lamps, optimization of this parameter should start at a current equal to $\frac{1}{2}$ or $\frac{2}{3}$ of the limiting current shown on the lamp.

Selection zone. The height of the selection zone (burner elevation) should be optimized for each element in each particular instrument. In the selection zone column a suggested starting level is given to begin the optimization. The height of the selection zone depends very much on the type of flame and on the type of burner. For turbulent flame burners a much higher elevation of the selection zone over the tip of the burner is applicable.

Slit width. The slit width, in general, should be as small as possible. In some cases it is advised narrow, or very narrow slit when this operating factor is imperative. As a general rule, for NOAF work the slit should be maintained sufficiently narrow.

Concentration range and optimum measuring range. This can be calculated *a priori* for each element as soon as the percentual and fluctuational concentration limits are known under a given set of operating conditions (PCL and FCL, respectively). The concentration range can be considered between concentrations expressed by $7 \times$ FCL and $135 \times$ PCL. The optimum measuring range can be considered between concentrations calculated by the expressions $30 \times$ PCL and $135 \times$ PCL, for linear systems.

Special case of the nitrous oxide–acetylene flame. At the gas flows generally used, this flame is actually a fuel-rich flame. It is usual, however, to use "*lean* flame" for the flame showing a red cone about $\frac{3}{4}''$ high and a plume not excessively luminous, mostly bluish. It is considered as a *rich* flame when it is really luminous, which occurs when the acetylene flow is increased.

Osmium conditions. For osmium determinations the line 2909 Å has been recommended as the most sensitive line (see p. 245). The line 3018 Å can also be used. Osmium requires the use of a nitrous oxide–acetylene flame. Data reported have been obtained with the use of an osmium hollow-cathode lamp. Consult the article *Atomic absorption used to detect osmium*, published in *Chem. Eng. News*, 45 (44) (1967) 42.

Bibliography

In this bibliographic list the author has included various papers which have been presented at different meetings; many of these have not yet been published, while others have appeared later in journals with the same or similar titles and contents. There are sometimes basic differences between a presented paper and the final publication, which is often only a summarized version for publication. For this reason, information has been included as separate references when possible. Only in a few cases has it been included in footnotes. This allows the reader, when contacting the authors personally, to ask them for preprints or manuscripts prepared at the time of presentation and to compare them with the printed articles or, if necessary, to complete these with the original manuscript.

For the same reason, the author has listed as separate papers those that have been presented with the same title but at different meetings; there are often basic differences between them, as the speaker may present the same general subject but use different slides, different tables, and different fundamental contents.

1 Adams, P. B. and W. O. Passmore, Critical factors in the atomic-absorption determination of the alkaline earth elements in glass. Paper presented to the 150th American Chemical Society Meeting, Atlantic City, N. J., September 12–17, 1965.

2 Agazzi, E. J., Determination of tin in hydrogen peroxide solutions by atomic-absorption spectrometry, *Anal. Chem.*, 37 (3) (1965) 364.

3 Alkemade, C. T. J., Excitation and related phenomena in flames. *Proc. Colloq. Spetros. Intern. 10th (Univ., Maryland, June, 1962)*, (1963) 143.

4 Alkemade, C. T. J., Recent developments in flame photometry, *Cronache di Chimica*, 40 (1964) 3 (in Italian).

5 Alkemade, C. T. J. and J. M. W. Milatz, A double bean method of spectral selection with flames, *Appl. Sci. Res. Sect. B*, 4 (1955) 289.

6 Alkemade, C. T. J. and J. M. W. Milatz, A double bean method of spectral selection with flames, *J. Opt. Soc. Am.*, 45 (1955) 583.

7 Allan, J. E., Atomic-absorption spectrophotometry with special references to the determination of magnesium, *Analyst*, 83 (1958) 466.

8 Allan, J. E., Application of analytical absorption spectroscopy to agricultural analyses. Paper presented to the 2nd Australian Spectroscopy Conference, Melbourne, Australia, June 1–3, 1959. Abstract in *Spectrochim. Acta*, 15 (9) (1959) 784. See also N. S. Ham (*303*).

9 Allan, J. E., Determination of iron and manganese by atomic-absorption, *Spectrochim. Acta*, 15 (10) (1959) 800.

10 Allan, J. E., Determination of nickel and cobalt by atomic-absorption, *Nature*, 187 (4743) (1960) 1110.

11 Allan, J. E., The determination of copper by atomic-absorption spectrophotometry, *Spectrochim. Acta*, 17 (4) (1961) 459.

12 Allan, J. E., Determination of zinc in agricultural materials by atomic-absorption spectrophotometry, *Analyst*, 86 (1025) (1961) 530.

13 ALLAN, J. E., The use of organic solvents in atomic-absorption spectrophotometry, *Spectrochim. Acta*, 17 (4) (1961) 467.
14 ALLAN, J. E., Paper presented to the 3rd Australian Spectroscopy Conference, Sydney, Australia, August 1961, *Nature*, 192 (4806) (1961) 929. See also R. A. Durie (*203*).
15 ALLAN, J. E., Atomic-absorption spectrophotometry absorption lines and detection limits in the air–acetylene flame, *Spectrochim. Acta*, 18 (2) (1962) 259.
16 ALLAN, J. E., Review of recent work in atomic-absorption spectroscopy, *Spectrochim. Acta*, 18 (5) (1962) 605.
17 ALLAN, J. E., Absorption flame photometry below 2000 Å. Paper presented to the 4th Australian Spectroscopy Conference, Canberra, Australia, August 20, 1963.
18 AMOS, M. D. AND P. E. THOMAS, Stability and sensitivity in analysis by atomic-absorption spectroscopy. Paper presented to the 4th Australian Spectroscopy Conference, Canberra, Australia, August 20, 1963. According to C. K. COOGAN *et al.* (*153*).
19 AMOS, M. D. AND P. E. THOMAS, The determination of aluminum in aqueous solution by atomic-absorption spectroscopy, *Anal. Chim. Acta*, 32 (2) (1965) 139.
20 AMOS, M. D. AND J. B. WILLIS, Use of high-temperature premixed flames in atomic-absorption spectroscopy, *Spectrochim. Acta*, 22 (7) (1966) 1325.
21 ANDREW, T. R., The application of atomic-absorption to the rapid determination of magnesium in electronic nickel and nickel alloys, *Stahl Eisen*, 82 (14) (1964) 995.
22 ANDREW, T. R. AND P. N. R. NICHOLS, The application of atomic-absorption to the rapid determination of magnesium in electronic nickel and nickel alloys, *Analyst*, 87 (1030) (1962) 25.
23 Anonymous, Atomic-absorption spectroscopy, *Hilger J.*, 5 (1) (1958) 12.
24 Anonymous, New analytical comer: absorption spectroscopy, *Chem. Eng. News*, (1960) 108.
25 Anonymous, High sensitivity atomic-absorption spectroscopy, *Jarrell-Ash Newsletter*, (11) (1961) 1.
26 Anonymous, Atomic-absorption gear modified, *Res. Develop. Ind.*, (9) (1962) 59.
27 Anonymous, Bibliography and general applications, *Atomic Absorption Newsletter*, (1) (1962) 1.
28 Anonymous, Calcium and magnesium in human blood serum by atomic-absorption spectrophotometry, *Atomic Absorption Newsletter*, (3) (1962) 1.
29 Anonymous, Model 214 Atomic-Absorption Spectrometer provides facilities for routine and research application. The Perkin-Elmer Corp., Norwalk, Conn., *Bulletin MPL 5615*, (1962).
30 Anonymous, A review of the reviews, *Atomic Absorption Newsletter*, (6) (1962) 1.
31 Anonymous, Instruments grow more useful, *Chem. Eng. News*, (1962) 70 (see pp. 76 and 77).
32 Anonymous, Technology newsletter, *Chem. Weekblad*, 90 (1962) 64.
33 Anonymous, Atomic-absorption spectrophotometer, *Rev. Sci. Instr.*, 34 (1963) 458.
34 Anonymous, Some biological applications of atomic-absorption spectrophotometry, *Atomic Absorption Newsletter*, (11) (1963) 1.
35 Anonymous, A bibliography to application of atomic-absorption spectrophotometry, *Atomic Absorption Newsletter*, (16) (1963) 1.
36 Anonymous, Calcium, magnesium, sodium, and potassium in bone ash, *Atomic Absorption Newsletter*, (11) (1963) 9.
37 Anonymous, Iron in protein solutions, *Atomic Absorption Newsletter*, (11) (1963) 6.
38 Anonymous, Instruments for clinical chemistry laboratories. II. The uncommon becomes common, *Chem. Eng. News*, 41 (50) (1963) 112.
39 Anonymous, Metal determination in alloys, *Atomic Absorption Newsletter*, (14) (1963) 11.
40 Anonymous, Metals in plating and other solutions, *Atomic Absorption Newsletter*, (14) (1963) 12.
41 Anonymous, New atomic-absorption spectrophotometer analyzes for metals with speed, sensitivity, *Instrument News*, 14 (2) (1963) 1.

42 Anonymous, Recovery of calcium, magnesium, and zinc in biological materials, *Atomic Absorption Newsletter,* (11) (1963) 7.
43 Anonymous, Hollow-cathode lamps and atomic-absorption spectroscopy, *El Ingeniero Westinghouse,* 20 (2) (1963) 60 (in Spanish).
44 Anonymous, Zinc in urine, *Atomic Absorption Newsletter,* (11) (1963) 5.
45 Anonymous, A cookbook for atomic-absorption spectrophotometry, *Atomic Absorption Newsletter,* (21) (1964) 6.
46 Anonymous, Cesium and rubidium on the model 214 atomic-absorption spectrophotometer, *Atomic Absorption Newsletter,* (20) (1964) 10.
47 Anonymous, Louisiana State University Annual Analytical Methods Symposium. Instrumental analysis and new reagents head topics covered by speakers, *Anal. Chem.,* 36 (4) (1964) 50A; 55A.
48 Anonymous, Recent developments in analytical instrumentation, *Anal. Chem.,* 36 (10) (1964) 25A; 33A.
49 Anonymous, Atomic-absorption analysis monitors metals in oils, *Chem. Eng.,* (1965) 8.
50 Anonymous, Atomic-absorption spectrophotometer, *Hilger J.,* 9 (3) (1965) 54.
51 Anonymous, Aluminum, vanadium, titanium determined with nitrous oxide burner head, *Instrument News,* 16 (2) (1965) 7.
52 Anonymous, New digital concentration readout accessory improves speed and precision of atomic-absorption analyses, *Instrument News,* 16 (1) (1965) 12.
53 Anonymous, New model 290 atomic-absorption spectrophotometer gives direct concentration readout, *Instrument News,* 16 (1) (1965) 16.
54 Anonymous, New multi-element hollow-cathode lamps speed analyses, save cost, *Instrument News,* 16 (1) (1965) 12.
55 Anonymous, New products. Equipment, apparatus, instruments, *Anal. Chem.,* 37 (3) (1965) 127A.
56 Anonymous, Wider usefulness for atomic-absorption in chemical analysis. *C.S.I.R.O. Indust. Res. News,* (52) (1965) 1.
57 Atomic-Absorption Spectroscopy Discussion Panel (Chairman, W. T. ELWELL), *Analyst,* 88 (1963) 744.
58 Atomic Absorption and Electronics Corp., Atomic-absorption spectrophotometer. Model 100. Bulletin (1964) 2 pp.
59 ATSUYA, I., Determination of traces of iron in aluminium metal and aluminium alloys by atomic-absorption spectroscopy, *Bunseki Kagaku,* 14 (7) (1965) 592 (in Japanese).
60 Aztec Instruments, Inc.[1], Hollow-cathode and Osram lamps. Brochure (1963) 6 pp.
61 Aztec Instruments, Inc., Techtron AA-3 atomic-absorption spectrophotometer. Brochure (1964) 6 pp.
62 Aztec Instruments, Inc., Kniseley burner. Bulletin (1965) 1 p.
63 Aztec Instruments, Inc., Laminar-flow burners. Bulletin (1965) 2 pp.
64 BAIRD, G. C. AND B. ENVALI, Paper presented to the 4th Australian Spectroscopy Conference, Canberra, Australia, August 20, 1963. According to C. K. COOGAN *et al.* (*153*).
65 BAKER, C. A., The flame as a source of atoms. Paper presented to the Society of Analytical Chemistry, *Analyst,* 85 (1012) (1960) 461.
66 BAKER, C. A. AND F. W. J. GARTON, A study of interferences in emission and absorption flame photometry, *U.K. At. Energy Authority, AERE-R-3490,* (1961) 21 pp.
67 BARABAS, S., Rapid multi-element sequential analysis of complex metallurgical materials by atomic-absorption spectroscopy. Paper presented to the Pittsburgh Conference on Analytical Chemistry and Applied Spectroscopy, Pittsburgh, Pa., March 1965.
68 BARRAS, R. C., Application of atomic-absorption to the petroleum industry. *Jarrell-Ash Newsletter,* (13) (1962) 1.
69 BARRAS, R. C., J. F. BOYLE AND H. W. SMITH, Rapid determination of trace

[1] Aztec Instruments, Inc. 2, Silverbrook Road, Westport, Conn. 06882, U.S.A.

metals by atomic-absorption. Paper presented at the Pittsburgh Conference on Analytical Chemistry and Applied Spectroscopy, Pittsburgh, Pa., March 4–8, 1963.
70 BARRAS, R. C. AND J. D. HELWIG, Rapid metal analysis for plant control. Am. Petroleum Inst., May, 1963, *Atomic Absorption Newsletter*, (16) (1963) 3.
71 Beckman Instruments, Inc., The Beckman atomic-absorption accessory for ultraviolet spectrophotometers. Advance Product Information, Bulletin 7064 (1964) 6 pp.
72 Beckman Instruments, Inc., Atomic-absorption accessory. Beckman Instructions No. 1373 (1965) 63 pp.
73 Beckman Instruments, Inc., Detectability of the elements by emission and absorption flame photometry. Bulletin No. 7071 and 7071A (1965) 1 p. Revised edition: Detectability of elements by atomic-absorption and emission flame photometry. Bulletin No. 7071B (1964) 1 p.
74 Beckman Instruments, Inc., Hollow-cathode lamps for atomic-absorption spectroscopy. Bulletin No. 7080 (1965) 4 pp.
75 Beckman Instruments, Inc., Laminar flow burner assemblies for atomic-absorption accessory. Beckman Instructions No. 1463 (1965) 7 pp.
76 Beckman Instruments, Inc., Turbulent flow burner assembly for atomic-absorption accessory. Beckman Instructions No. 1402 (1965) 7 pp.
77 BEEGHLY, H. F. AND L. C. PASZTOR, Ferrous metallurgy, *Anal. Chem.*, 37 (5) (1965) 87R.
78 BELCHER, C. B., The determination of iron in tungsten carbide by atomic-absorption spectrophotometry, *Anal. Chim. Acta*, 29 (1963) 340.
79 BELCHER, C. B., The determination of magnesium in iron by atomic-absorption spectrophotometry. *Proc. Roy. Austr. Chem. Inst.*, 30 (3) (1963) 111.
80 BELCHER, C. B. AND H. M. BRAY, Determination of magnesium in iron by atomic-absorption spectrophotometry, *Anal. Chim. Acta*, 26 (1962) 322.
81 BELCHER, C. B. AND K. A. BROOKS, The determination of strontium in coal ash by atomic-absorption spectrophotometry, *Anal. Chim. Acta*, 29 (1963) 202.
82 BELCHER, C. B. AND K. KINSON, The determination of manganese in iron and steel by atomic-absorption spectrophotometry, *Anal. Chim. Acta*, 30 (5) (1964) 483.
83 BELCHER, R., R. M. DAGNALL AND T. S. WEST, An examination of the atomic-absorption spectroscopy of silver, *Talanta*, 11 (1964) 1257.
84 BELL, G. F., Some applications of atomic-absorption spectrometry at Alcoa Research Laboratory, *Instrument News*, 15 (1) (1963) 12.
85 BELL, G. F., Mechanical mount for the burner for the Perkin-Elmer 214 atomic-absorption spectrophotometer, *Atomic Absorption Newsletter*, (21) (1964) 4.
86 BELL, W. E., A. L. BLOOM AND J. LYNCH, Alkali metal vapor spectral lamps, *Rev. Sci. Instr.*, 32 (1961) 688.
87 BELT, C. B. (JR.), Atomic-absorption spectrophotometry and the analysis of silicate rocks for copper and zinc, *Econ. Geol.*, 59 (1964) 240.
88 BELT, C. B. (JR.), The determination of copper and zinc in Bayer process liquor, *Atomic Absorption Newsletter*, (19) (1964) 7.
89 BELT, C. B. (JR.), Notes on the interpretation of atomic-absorption peaks obtained with a premix burner, *Atomic Absorption Newsletter*, 4 (9) (1965) 345.
90 BELT, C. B. (JR.), Partial analysis of rocks by atomic-absorption. Paper presented at the 4th Annual Meeting of the Society for Applied Spectroscopy, Denver, Colo., August 31, 1965.
91 BERMAN, E., An application of atomic-absorption spectrometry in clinical chemistry: determination of copper in biological materials. Paper presented to the 5th International Congress on Clinical Chemistry, Detroit, Mich., August 19–23, 1963. Abstract in *Clin. Chem.*, 9 (4) (1963) 459.
92 BERMAN, E., The determination of lead in blood and urine by atomic-absorption spectrophotometry, *Atomic Absorption Newsletter*, 3 (9) (1964) 111.
93 BERMAN, E., Application of atomic-absorption spectrometry to the determination of copper in serum, urine, and tissue, *Atomic Absorption Newsletter*, 4 (6) (1965) 296.
94 BERMAN, E., Applications of atomic-absorption spectrophotometry to trace metal

analysis of biological materials. Paper presented to the 1965 Anachem Conference, Detroit, Mich., October 19–21, 1965.
95 BERMEJO-MARTÍNEZ, F., Instrumental methods of analysis: II. Atomic-absorption spectrophotometry, *Quím. Ind. (Bilbao)*, 10 (2) (1963) 39 (in Spanish).
96 BERSIN, R., LTA-600. Low temperature dry asher. Technical application guide. Tracerlab/West brochure (1965) 6 pp.; see also: Tracerlab/West (2030) Wright Ave., Richmond, Calif., LTA-600. Low temperature asher for precision elemental analysis. Brochure (1965) 5 pp.
97 BEUKELMAN, T. E. AND S. S. LORD (JR.), The standard addition technique in flame spectrometry, *Appl. Spectr.*, 14 (1) (1960) 12.
98 BEYER, M., The determination of manganese, copper, chromium, nickel, and magnesium in cast iron and steel, *Atomic Absorption Newsletter*, 4 (3) (1965) 212.
99 BIECHLER, D. G., Determination of trace copper, lead, zinc, cadmium, nickel, and iron in industrial waste waters by atomic-absorption spectrometry after ion exchange concentration on Dowex A-1, *Anal. Chem.*, 37 (8) (1965) 1054.
100 BILLINGS, G. K., The analysis of geological materials by atomic-absorption spectrometry: II. Accuracy tests, *Atomic Absorption Newsletter*, 4 (7) (1965) 312.
101 BILLINGS, G. K. AND J. A. S. ADAMS, The analysis of geological materials by atomic-absorption spectrometry, *Atomic Absorption Newsletter*, (23) (1964) 1.
102 BIRKS, F. T., The application of the hollow-cathode source to spectrographic analysis, *Spectrochim. Acta*, 6 (1954) 169.
103 BOCHKOVA, O. P. AND E. YA. SHREIDER, Special analysis of gas mixtures. Gostekhteorizdat, Moscow, U.S.S.R. 1955, p. 151 (in Russian).
104 BOLING, E. A., Data collection in atomic-absorption spectrophotometry. Paper presented to the Eastern Analytical Symposium, New York, N. Y., November 11–13, 1964.
105 BOLING, E. A., An integrating analog computer for atomic-absorption spectrometry, *Anal. Chem.*, 37 (4) (1965) 482.
106 BOND, B. B., Effectiveness of the spectrometric oil analysis methods for monitoring aircraft mechanisms. Laboratory Report No. 0A20-64. Materials Engineering Division. Overhaul and Repair Department. Naval Air Station, Pensacola, Fla. Processed by Clearinghouse for Federal Scientific and Technical Information of the U.S. Dept. of Commerce (unclassified) AD 609 746, Code 834, June 26, 1964, 15 pp.
107 BOWMAN, J. A., J. V. SULLIVAN AND A. WALSH, Isolation of atomic resonance lines by selective modulation, *Spectrochim. Acta*, 22 (2) (1966) 205.
108 BOX, G. F. AND A. WALSH, Work of these authors mentioned in the article "Si-Ro-Spec" published in *C.S.I.R.O. Indust. Res. News*, (17) (1959).
109 BOX, G. F. AND A. WALSH, A simple atomic-absorption spectrophotometer, *Spectrochim. Acta*, 16 (3) (1960) 255.
110 BRACE, R. O., R. W. CLAUS AND J. RAMÍREZ-MUÑOZ, Atomic-absorption determination of strongly emitting elements. Paper presented at the 4th National Meeting, Society for Applied Spectroscopy, Denver, Colo., August 30–September 3, 1965.
111 BRACE, R. O. AND J. RAMÍREZ-MUÑOZ, A comprehensive abbreviated expression for dynamic ranges in atomic-absorption flame photometry (not yet submitted for publication).
112 BRECH, F., Atomic-absorption. Problem areas, solutions, and direction of future growth. Discussion presented to the Symposium "Unresolved problems in spectrochemical analysis" (Organized and sponsored by the A.S.T.M. Committee E-2 on Emission Spectroscopy). 4th National Meeting of the Society for Applied Spectroscopy, Denver, Colo., September 3, 1965.
113 BRECH, F., Atomic-absorption spectroscopy—Current status and its future potentials. Paper presented to the 4th Annual Pacific Conference on Spectroscopy. Instrumentation and Chemistry, Pasadena, Calif., September 22–24, 1965.
114 BRECH, F. AND J. A. NORRIS, Multi-channel atomic-absorption. Paper presented to the Pittsburgh Conference on Analytical Chemistry and Applied Spectroscopy, Pittsburgh, Pa., March 1965.
115 BROWNELL, P., The estimation of sodium by atomic-absorption. Paper presented

to the Second Australian Spectroscopy Conference, Melbourne, Australia, June 1–3, 1959. Abstract in *Spectrochim. Acta*, 15 (9) (1959) 785.

116 BUCHANAN, J. R. AND T. T. MURAOKA, Determination of zinc and manganese in tree leaves by atomic-absorption spectroscopy, *Atomic Absorption Newsletter*, (24) (1964) 1.

117 BUCKERT, H. AND I. RAFFAELE, Description of a device for atomic-absorption. *Met. Ital.*, 53 (5) (1961) 263 (in Italian).

118 BUDD, A., The elements of emission and absorption flame photometry. Lecture presented at the Milwaukee Section of the Society for Applied Spectroscopy, Milwaukee, Wis., December 15, 1965.

119 BURGER, J. C. AND W. GILLIES, Performance characteristics of hollow-cathode gas discharge devices for atomic-absorption spectroscopy. Paper presented to the Pittsburgh Conference on Analytical Chemistry and Applied Spectroscopy, Pittsburgh, Pa., March 1962.

120 BURGER, J. C., W. GILLIES AND G. K. YAMASAKI, Hollow-cathode tubes for atomic-absorption spectroscopy. Paper presented to the 10th Detroit Anachem Conference, Detroit, Mich., October 22, 1962.

121 BURGER, J. C., W. GILLIES AND G. K. YAMASAKI, Performance characteristics of hollow-cathode discharge devices for atomic-absorption spectroscopy. Westinghouse Electric Corp. Product Engineering Memo, ETD-6403 (1964) 8 pp.

122 BURRELL, D. C., An atomic-absorption method for the determination of cobalt, iron and nickel in the asphaltic fraction of recent sediments, *Atomic Absorption Newsletter*, 4 (8) (1965) 328.

123 BURRELL, D. C., The determination of nickel and cobalt in natural waters by atomic-absorption spectrophotometry: a preliminary study, *Atomic Absorption Newsletter*, 4 (7) (1965) 309.

124 BURRELL, D. C., The geochemistry and origin of amphibolites from Bamble, South Norway[2]. *Norsk Geol. Tidsskr.*, 45 (Part 1) (1965) 21.

125 BURRIEL-MARTÍ, F. AND J. RAMÍREZ-MUÑOZ, *Flame Photometry. A Manual of Methods and Applications*, Elsevier, Amsterdam, Netherlands, 1960, 3rd reprint.

126 BURROWS, J. A., J. C. HEERDT AND J. B. WILLIS, Determination of wear metals in used lubricating oils by atomic-absorption spectrometry, *Anal. Chem.*, 37 (4) (1965) 579.

127 BUTLER, L. R. P., Atomic-absorption spectroscopy, *S. African Ind. Chem.*, 15 (9) (1961) 162.

128 BUTLER, L. R. P., The manufacture of hollow-cathode lamps for atomic-absorption spectroscopy, *J. S. African Inst. Mining Met.*, 62 (12, Part II) (1962) 780.

129 BUTLER, L. R. P., A plastic burner for atomic-absorption analysis of highly corrosive solutions, *J. S. African Inst. Mining Met.*, 62 (12, Part II) (1962) 786.

130 BUTLER, L. R. P. AND D. BRINK, The determination of magnesium, calcium, potassium, sodium, copper, and iron in water samples by atomic-absorption spectroscopy. Paper presented at the Golden Jubilee Celebration of the S.A.C.I., Univ. of the Witwatersrand, July, 1962. *S. African Ind. Chem.*, 17 (1963) 152.

131 BUTLER, L. R. P. AND A. STRASHEIM, private communication. Also, L. R. P. BUTLER, Approach to multiple element atomic-absorption spectroscopy. Lecture presented atBeckman Instruments Inc., Fullerton, Calif., July 1967.

132 BUTLER, L. R. P. AND A. STRASHEIM, Multiple element atomic-absorption analysis, *Spectrochim. Acta*, 21 (7) (1965) 1207.

133 BUTLER, L. R. P., A. STRASHEIM, F. W. E. STRELOW, P. M. MATHEWS AND E. C. FEAST, The determination of gold in mine solutions by automatic or semiautomatic absorption spectroscopy. Paper presented to the XII. Colloquium Spectroscopicum Internationale, Exeter, England, July, 1965.

134 BYRNE, F. P., Advances in chemical instrumentation, *Industrial Res.*, (1965) 52.

135 BYSTROFF, R. I., Some experiments with oxy–acetylene burners for atomic-absorption spectroscopy. Paper presented at the 1965 Eastern Analytical Symposium, New York City, N. Y., November 17–19, 1965.

[2] I. The determination of zinc in amphibolites by atomic-absorption spectroscopy.

136 Campbell, T. L., ACHEMA, World's Largest Chemical Engineering Congress, Shows Scientific Instruments of 23 Nations, *Science*, 145 (1964) 1026.
137 Camuñas, A. and M. Domínguez, Analysis of optical glass by the atomic autoabsorption of the spectral lines. Proceedings of the 15th International Congress of Pure and Applied Chemistry, Lisbon, Portugal, *(Anal. Chem.)*, (1956) 139.
138 Capacho-Delgado, L. and D. C. Manning, Determination of tin by atomic-absorption, *Atomic Absorption Newsletter*, 4 (7) (1965) 317.
139 Capacho-Delgado, L. and D. C. Manning, Determination of tin by atomic-absorption spectroscopy, *Spectrochim. Acta*, 22 (1966) 1505.
140 Capacho-Delgado, L. and D. C. Manning, Determination of vanadium by atomic-absorption spectroscopy. Paper presented to the 4th Annual Pacific Conference on Spectroscopy, Instrumentation and Chemistry, Pasadena, Calif., September 22–24, 1965.
141 Care, A. D., Secretion of magnesium and calcium in parotid saliva of sheep, *Nature*, 199 (1963) 818.
142 Carnes, W. J., Studies on the reaction zone of an oxygen–acetylene flame. *Doctoral Thesis*, Univ. of Tennessee, Part C, 1961, p. 74.
143 Carroll, J. E. (Jr.), and G. J. Neville, Instrumental effects on the sensitivity of atomic-absorption spectrophotometry. Paper presented to the 12th Ottawa Symposium on Applied Spectroscopy, Ottawa, Canada, October 18–20, 1965.
144 Cellier, K. M. and H. C. T. Stace, The estimation of optimum operating conditions in atomic-absorption spectroscopy. Paper presented to the 4th Australian Spectroscopy Conference, Canberra, Australia, August 20, 1963.
145 Chakrabarti, C. L., Discussion to the paper of A. Walsh (*804*), in *Analytical Chemistry 1962*, Proc. Feigl Anniversary Symp., Birmingham, England, 1962; Elsevier, Amsterdam, 1963, p. 286.
146 Chakrabarti, C. L., G. R. Lyles and F. B. Dowling, The determination of aluminum by atomic-absorption spectroscopy, *Anal. Chim. Acta*, 29 (6) (1963) 489.
147 Chambers, W. E., Precision null-point atomic-absorption spectrochemical analysis. Univ. Microfilms (Ann Arbor, Mich.), L.C. Card No. Mic. 60-1623, 102 pp.; *Dissertation Abstr.*, 20 (1960) 4506.
148 Cheek, D., Preliminary experience with atomic-absorption spectrophotometry with respect to body composition and growth. Paper presented to the Symposium on Recent Developments in Research Methods and Instrumentation, National Institute of Health, Bethesda, Md., October 7, 1963.
149 Cheek, D. B., J. E. Graystone, J. B. Willis and A. B. Holt, Studies on the effects of triglycerides, glycero phosphate, phosphatidyl ethanolamine on skeletal and cardiac muscle composition, *Clin. Sci.*, 23 (1) (1962) 169.
150 Claus, R. W., R. O. Brace, J. Ramírez-Muñoz and N. Shifrin, Rich hydrogen–air flames in atomic-absorption flame photometry. Paper presented to the 4th Annual Pacific Conference on Spectroscopy, Instrumentation and Chemistry, Pasadena, Calif., September 22–24, 1965.
151 Clinton, O. E., A burner for atomic-absorption spectrophotometry, *Spectrochim. Acta*, 16 (9) (1960) 985.
152 Collins, G. C., The development of an atomic-absorption flame photometer for routine measurements. Paper presented to the Pittsburgh Conference on Analytical Chemistry and Applied Spectroscopy, Pittsburgh, Pa., February 21–25, 1966.
153 Coogan, C. F., J. D. Morrison, A. Walsh and J. K. Wilmshurst, Spectroscopy in Australia, *Nature*, 200 (4904) (1963) 319.
154 Cooke, W. D., J. H. Gibson and W. E. L. Grossman, Atomic-absorption spectroscopy with continuous sources, in *Analytical Chemistry 1962*, Proc. Feigl Anniversary Symp., Birmingham, England, 1962; Elsevier, Amsterdam, 1963, p. 288.
155 Cooke, W. D., Discussion to the paper of A. Walsh (*804*).
156 Cooke, W. D., Atomic-absorption spectroscopy. Paper presented to the Society of Applied Spectroscopy, Delaware Valley Section, Philadelphia, Pa., April 16, 1963.
157 Coyle, F. T., R. J. Goulden, W. C. Gannon and J. E. Foster, Determination of iron in tantalum and columbium by atomic-absorption spectrophotometry.

Paper presented to the Middle Atlantic Regional Meeting of the American Chemical Society, Philadelphia, Pa., February 3–4, 1966.

158 DAGNALL, R. M. AND T. S. WEST, Observations on the atomic-absorption spectroscopy of lead in aqueous solution, in organic extracts and in gasoline, *Talanta*, 11 (11) (1964) 1553.

159 DAVEY, B. G., Paper presented to the 3rd Australian Spectroscopy Conference, Sydney, Australia, August 1961, *Nature*, 192 (4806) (1961) 929. See R. A. DURIE (*203*).

160 DAVEY, B. G., Modification of a spectrophotometer for atomic-absorption spectrophotometry, *Spectrochim. Acta*, 19 (8) (1963) 1319.

161 DAVID, D. J., Determination of zinc and other elements in plants by atomic-absorption spectroscopy, *Analyst*, 83 (993) (1958) 655.

162 DAVID, D. J., The application of atomic-absorption spectrophotometry to plant and soil analysis. Paper presented to the 2nd Australian Spectroscopy Conference, Melbourne, Australia, June 1–3, 1959. Abstract in *Spectrochim. Acta*, 15 (9) (1959) 785. See also N. S. HAM (*303*).

163 DAVID, D. J., Determination of calcium in plant material by atomic-absorption spectrophotometry, *Analyst*, 84 (1002) (1959) 536.

164 DAVID, D. J., Application of atomic-absorption to chemical analysis. A review, *Analyst*, 85 (1016) (1960) 779.

165 DAVID, D. J., Atomic-absorption spectrophotometric determination of molybdenum and strontium, *Nature*, 187 (4743) (1960) 1109.

166 DAVID, D. J., The determination of exchangeable sodium, potassium, calcium and magnesium in soils by atomic-absorption spectrophotometry, *Analyst*, 85 (1012) (1960) 495.

167 DAVID, D. J., Paper presented to the 3rd Australian Spectroscopy Conference, Sydney, Australia, August 1961, *Nature*, 192 (4806) (1961) 929. See R. A. DURIE (*203*).

168 DAVID, D. J., Determination of molybdenum by atomic-absorption spectrophotometry, *Analyst*, 86 (1961) 730.

169 DAVID, D. J., Aspects of atomic-absorption analysis. Paper presented before the Atomic Absorption Spectroscopy Discussion Panel, Soc. Anal. Chem., London, England, December 12, 1962.

170 DAVID, D. J., Atomic-absorption spectrochemical analysis with special reference to plants, *Rev. Univ. Ind. Santander*, 4 (1962) 207 (in Spanish).

171 DAVID, D. J., Atomic-absorption spectrochemical analysis of plant materials with particular reference to manganese and iron, *Atomic Absorption Newsletter*, (9) (1962) 1.

172 DAVID, D. J., Emission and atomic-absorption spectrochemical methods. In K. PAECH, M. V. TRACEY AND H. F. LINSKENS (Eds.), *Moderne Methoden der Pflanzenanalyse*, Springer Verlag, Berlin, Vol. 5, 1962.

173 DAVID, D. J., Determination of strontium in biological materials and exchangeable strontium in soils by atomic-absorption spectrophotometry, *Analyst*, 87 (1036) (1962) 576.

174 DAVID, D. J., The elimination of interferences in atomic-absorption spectrochemical analysis. Paper presented to the Pittsburgh Conference on Analytical Chemistry and Applied Spectroscopy, Pittsburgh, Pa., March 1962.

175 DAVID, D. J., The use of the method of additions in atomic-absorption spectrochemical analysis. Paper presented to the X. Colloquium Spectroscopicum Internationale, College Park, Md., 1962.

176 DAVID, D. J., Recent developments in atomic-absorption analysis. Paper presented to the 4th Australian Spectroscopy Conference, Canberra, Australia, August 20, 1963.

177 DAVID, D. J., An ion-exchange column for use with atomic-absorption analysis, *Analyst*, 89 (1064) (1964) 747.

178 DAVID, D. J., Recent developments in atomic-absorption analysis, *Spectrochim. Acta*, 20 (7) (1964) 1185.

179 DAVIES, D. A., R. VENN AND J. B. WILLIS, An adjustable atomizer for atomic-absorption spectroscopy, *J. Sci. Instr.* 42 (11) (1965) 816.

180 DAWSON, J. B., The problems in design and construction of atomic-absorption apparatus. Paper presented to the Atomic Absorption Spectroscopy Discussion Panel (Chairman, W. T. ELWELL), *Analyst*, 88 (1963) 252.
181 DAWSON, J. B., A brief review of progress in the field of atomic-absorption spectroscopy. Paper presented to the Soc. Anal. Chem., University of Leicester, Great Britain, February 25, 1964; Abstract in: *Mikrochim. Acta*, (1964) 583.
182 DAWSON, J. B., The spectrochemical analysis of biological materials, *Postgraduate Medical J.*, 40 (1964) 143.
183 DAWSON, J. B. AND D. J. ELLIS, The application of atomic-absorption spectrophotometry to the estimation of elements in biological materials. IX Colloquium Spectroscopicum Internationale, Lyons, France, June 1961, *Publ. Group. Avan. Methodes Spectrog.*, 3 (1962) 318.
184 DAWSON, J. B. AND D. J. ELLIS, The simultaneous estimation of sodium, potassium, calcium, and magnesium by emission and absorption flame photometry using an automatic, multichannel, high speed scanning spectrometer. Paper presented to the XII Colloquium Spectroscopicum Internationale, Exeter, England, July 1965.
185 DAWSON, J. B. AND F. W. HEATON, The determination of magnesium in biological materials by atomic-absorption spectrophotometry, *Biochem. J.*, 80 (1) (1961) 99.
186 DEAN, J. A., *Flame Photometry*, McGraw-Hill, New York, 1960.
187 DEAN, J. A., Developments in flame emission and flame absorption photometry. Paper presented to the 15th Mid-America Symposium on Spectroscopy, Chicago, Ill., June 4, 1964.
188 DEAN, J. A., Developments in flame emission and flame absorption, *Develop. Appl. Spectry.*, 4 (1965) 443.
189 DEAN, J. A. AND W. J. CARNES, A study of the emission spectra of arsenic, antimony, and bismuth from the reaction zone of acetylene–oxygen flames, *Analyst*, 87 (1962) 743.
190 DECKER, C. F., A. ARAS AND L. E. DECKER, Determination of magnesium and calcium in cerebrospinal fluid by atomic-absorption spectroscopy, *Anal. Biochem.*, 8 (3) (1964) 344.
191 DEKALB, E. L., R. N. KNISELEY AND V. A. FASSEL, Purification of materials optical emission spectroscopy as an analytical tool. Paper presented at the Conference on Purification of Materials, May 6–8, 1965.
192 DELAUGHTER, B., The determination of sub-p.p.m. concentrations of chromium and molybdenum in brines, *Atomic Absorption Newsletter*, 4 (5) (1965) 273.
193 DENHOLM, A. B., P. A. A. BEALE AND R. PALMER, Determination of Fe and Ni carbonyls in town gas, *J. Appl. Chem.*, 13 (1963) 576.
194 DEVANEY, J. D., Analysis of various solutions by atomic-absorption spectroscopy. Paper presented to the 10th Detroit Anachem Conference, Detroit, Mich., October 22, 1962.
195 DEVANEY, J. AND F. BRECH, High sensitivity approaches to atomic-absorption. Paper presented to the Conference on Analytical Chemistry and Applied Spectroscopy, Pittsburgh, Pa., March 1962.
196 DOERFFEL, K., R. GEYER AND G. MUELLER, Determination of sodium in minerals by means of atomic-absorption spectral analysis, *Chem. Anal. (Warsaw)*, 7 (1) (1962) 229 (in Polish).
197 DOERFFEL, K., R. GEYER AND G. MUELLER, Determination of sodium by atomic-absorption analysis, *Z. Chem.*, 3 (6) (1963) 212.
198 DOERFFEL, K. AND U. NITZSCHE, Determination of zinc by atomic-absorption spectroscopy, *Wiss. Z. Tech. Hochsch. Chem. Leuna-Merseburg*, 7 (1) (1965) 9 (in German).
199 DOWLING, F. B., C. L. CHAKRABARTI AND G. R. LYLES, Atomic-absorption spectroscopy of aluminum, *Anal. Chim. Acta*, 28 (4) (1963) 392.
200 D'SILVA, A. P., R. N. KNISELEY AND V. A. FASSEL, The premixed, fuel-rich oxy–acetylene flame in flame emission spectrometry, *Anal. Chem.*, 36 (7) (1964) 1287.
201 D'SILVA, A. P., R. N. KNISELEY, V. A. FASSEL, R. H. CURRY AND R. B. MYERS,

Analytical applications of the flame spectra of the rare earth elements and scandium, *Anal. Chem.*, 36 (3) (1964) 532.
202 DUNKEN, H., G. PFORR AND W. MIKKELEIT, Application of plasma flames in combination with an ultrasonic atomiser as an emission source for solution spectral analysis, *Z. Chem.*, 4 (6) (1964) 237 (in German).
203 DURIE, R. A., 3rd Australian Spectroscopy Conference, *Nature*, 192 (4806) (1961) 927.
204 DYCK, R., The determination of chromium, magnesium, and manganese in nickel alloys by atomic-absorption spectrophotometry, *Atomic Absorption Newsletter*, 4 (1) (1965) 170.
205 EICHHOFF, H. J. AND R. VOIGT, Use of metallic hollow-cathode for spectrochemical analysis. IX Colloquium Spectroscopicum Internationale, Lyons, France, June 1961, *Publ. Group. Advan. Methodes Spectrog.*, 3 (1962) 309.
206 EICKHOFF, C. P. AND B. J. SYKES, An adjustable mount for use in atomic-absorption spectroscopy, *J. Sci. Instr.*, 41 (1964) 113.
207 EISEN, J., Atomic-absorption in nonferrous metal analysis, *Z. Erzbergbau Metallhuettenw.*, 16 (1963) 579 (in German).
208 ELENBAAS, W. AND J. RIEMENS, Light sources for line spectra, *Phillips Tech. Rev.*, 11 (1950) 299.
209 ELWELL, W. T., Application of atomic-absorption spectrophotometry to metallurgical analysis. Paper presented to the Society of Analytical Chemistry, *Analyst*, 86 (1961) 686.
210 ELWELL, W. T., Modern methods for the analysis of Cu alloys. Paper presented to the BNF Analytical Conference, Malvern, Australia, 1961.
211 ELWELL, W. T., Atomic-absorption spectrophotometry for accurate trace analysis. *Res. Devel. Ind.*, (6) (1962) 50.
212 ELWELL, W. T. AND J. A. F. GIDLEY, The application of atomic-absorption spectrophotometry to metallurgical analysis. Paper presented to the Society of Analytical Chemistry, *Analyst*, 85 (1960) 462.
213 ELWELL, W. T. AND J. A. F. GIDLEY, Atomic-Absorption Spectrophotometry. Pergamon Press, Oxford, 1961, and Macmillan, N. Y., 1962.
214 ELWELL, W. T. AND J. A. F. GIDLEY, Determination of lead in copper-base alloys and steel by atomic-absorption spectrophotometry, *Anal. Chim. Acta*, 24 (1) (1961) 71.
215 ELWELL, W. T. AND J. A. F. GIDLEY, Atomic-absorption in metallurgical analysis, in *Analytical Chemistry 1962*, Proc. Feigl Anniversary Symp., Birmingham, England, 1962; Elsevier, Amsterdam, 1963, p. 291.
216 ERDEY, L. AND G. SVEHLA, Determination of some heavy metals by atomic-absorption spectroscopy. Paper presented to the XX International Congress of Pure and Applied Chemistry, Moscow, U.S.S.R., July 9, 1965.
217 ERDEY, L., G. SVEHLA AND L. KOLTAI, The accuracy of zinc determination by atomic-absorption methods, *Talanta*, 10 (4/5) (1963) 531.
218 ERINC, G. AND R. J. MAGEE, The determination of palladium by atomic-absorption spectroscopy, *Anal. Chim. Acta*, 31 (3) (1964) 197.
219 Evans Electroselenium, Ltd., Atomic Absorption Spectrophotometer EEL 140. Brochure (1965) 7 p.
220 Evans Electroselenium, Ltd., EEL Atomic Absorption Spectrophotometer. Catalog No. I-140 (1965) 4 p.
221 EYE, M., Discussion at Symposium on the Air Polution Control in Los Angeles. American Chemical Society Western Regional Meeting, Los Angeles, Calif., November 18–20, 1965.
222 EZELL, J. B., (JR.), Determination of zinc in aluminous materials by atomic-absorption spectroscopy. Paper presented to the Pittsburgh Conference on Analytical Chemistry and Applied Spectroscopy, Pittsburgh, Pa., February 21–25, 1966.
223 FABRICAND, B. P., R. R. SAWYER, S. G. UNGAR AND S. ADLER, Trace metal concentrations in the ocean by atomic-absorption spectroscopy, *Geochim. Cosmochim. Acta*, 26 (10) (1962) 1023.

224 FARRAR, B., Determination of copper and zinc in ore samples and lead-base alloys, *Atomic Absorption Newsletter*, 4 (8) (1965) 325.
225 FASSEL, V. A., Recent advances in analytical emission spectroscopy, *Proc. Intern. Symp. Mol. Struct. Spectry., Tokyo, 1962.*
226 FASSEL, V. A., The spectroscopic properties of fuel-rich oxyacetylene flames. Paper presented to the 11th Annual Southeastern Seminar of Spectroscopy, Gainesville, Fla., January 23, 1963.
227 FASSEL, V. A., Recent developments in flame atomic-absorption and emission spectroscopy. Paper presented to the 2nd National Meeting, Society for Applied Spectroscopy, San Diego, Calif., October 17, 1963.
228 FASSEL, V. A., Some recent advances in flame emission and absorption spectroscopy. I. The premixed, fuel-rich, oxy–acetylene flame. II. Spectral continua as primary sources in atomic-absorption spectroscopy. Paper presented to the Phoenix Symposium on Flame Spectrometric Methods of Analysis. 151st American Chemical Society Meeting, Phoenix, Arizona, January 16–21, 1966.
229 FASSEL, V. A., R. H. CURRY AND R. N. KNISELEY, Flame spectra of the rare-earth elements, *Spectrochim. Acta*, 18 (1962) 1127.
230 FASSEL, V. A., R. H. CURRY, R. B. MYERS AND R. N. KNISELEY, Excitation of line spectra in fuel-rich oxy–acetylene flames. Paper presented to the X Colloquium Spectroscopicum Internationale, College Park, Md., June 1962.
231 FASSEL, V. A., R. N. KNISELEY AND V. G. MOSSOTTI, Progress in the atomic-absorption spectrometric determination of previously unrealized elements. Paper presented to the Symposium on Recent Developments in Research Methods and Instrumentation. Bethesda, Md., October 7, 1963.
232 FASSEL, V. A., R. N. KNISELEY, V. G. MOSSOTTI, T. C. COWLEY AND D. GOLIGHTLY, Spectroscopic observations on the interconal zone of premixed, fuel-rich oxy–acetylene flames. Paper presented to the XX International Congress of Pure and Applied Chemistry, Moscow, U.S.S.R., July 9, 1965.
233 FASSEL, V. A., R. N. KNISELEY, R. H. WENDT AND J. FIORINO, Recent developments in atomic-absorption spectroscopy. Paper presented to the Pittsburgh Conference on Analytical Chemistry and Applied Spectroscopy, Pittsburgh, Pa., February 21–25, 1966.
234 FASSEL, V. A. AND V. G. MOSSOTTI, Atomic-absorption spectra of vanadium, titanium, niobium, and the rare earths. Paper presented to the Pittsburgh Conference on Analytical Chemistry and Applied Spectroscopy, Pittsburgh, Pa., March 4–8, 1963.
235 FASSEL, V. A. AND V. G. MOSSOTTI, Atomic-absorption spectra of vanadium, titanium, niobium, scandium, yttrium, and rhenium, *Anal. Chem.*, 35 (2) (1963) 252.
236 FASSEL, V. A., V. G. MOSSOTTI, W. E. L. GROSSMAN AND R. N. KNISELEY, Evaluation of spectral continua as primary light sources in atomic-absorption spectroscopy. Paper presented to the Pittsburgh Conference on Analytical Chemistry and Applied Spectroscopy, Pittsburgh, Pa., March 1965.
237 FELDMAN, C., The place of atomic-absorption in tissue analysis. Paper presented to the 12th Annual Anachem Conference, Detroit, Mich., October 21–23, 1964.
238 FELDMAN, C. AND R. K. DHUMWAD, An atomic-absorption tube for use with an atomizer-burner: application to the determination of mercury. Paper presented to the 6th Conference on Analytical Chemistry in Nuclear Reactor Technology, Gatlinburg, Tenn., October 1962.
239 FELDMAN, F. J. AND W. C. PURDY, The atomic-absorption spectroscopy of chromium, *Anal. Chim. Acta*, 33 (3) (1965) 273.
240 FERRIGAN, M., Trace metal studies aid therapeutic methods, *Instrument News*, 16 (2) (1965) 10.
241 FINKELSTEIN, N. P. AND A. V. JANSEN, An investigation of the reported interference by halogen acids in the determination of zinc by atomic-absorption spectrophotometry, *S. African Ind. Chemist*, 15 (6) (1961) 106.
242 FINKELSTEIN, N. P. AND D. N. LOCK, A comparative assessment on the fire assay and various indirect methods for the determination of the fineness of high purity gold, *J. S. African Inst. Mining Met.*, 62 (12, Part II) (1962) 820.

243 FIRMAN, R. J., Interferences caused by iron and alkalies on the determination of magnesium by atomic-absorption spectroscopy, *Spectrochim. Acta*, 21 (1965) 341.
244 FISHMAN, M. J., Atomic-absorption methods for analysis of natural waters. Paper presented to the 4th National Meeting of the Society for Applied Spectroscopy, Denver, Colo., August 30–September 3, 1965.
245 FLEISCHER, D., Trace species in combustion gases. The formation of sodium metaborate (solid propellant tracing methods). Technical Report Contract AF49 (638)-1197, Thiokol Chemical Corporation, Reaction Motors Division, Air Force Office of Scientific Research, Office of Aerospace Research, November 1964. Clearinghouse for Federal Scientific and Technical Information (unclassified) AD 619492.
246 FLEISCHER, M. AND R. E. STEVENS, Summary of new data on rock samples G-1 and W-1, *Geochim. Cosmochim. Acta*, 26 (1962) 525.
247 FRANSWA, C. E. M., Atomic-absorption spectrophotometry, *Chem. Weekblad*, 58 (16) (1962) 177 and 189 (in Dutch).
248 FREY, S. W., The determination of copper, iron, calcium, sodium and potassium in beer by atomic-absorption spectroscopy, *Atomic Absorption Newsletter*, 3 (10) (1964) 127.
249 FRIEND, K. E. AND A. J. DIEFENDERFER, A new sample introduction system for atomic-absorption spectroscopy, determination of aluminum. Paper presented to the Middle Atlantic Regional Meeting of the American Chemical Society, Philadelphia, Pa., February 3–4, 1966.
250 FUWA, K., P. PULIDO, R. MCKAY AND B. L. VALLEE, Determination of zinc in biological materials by atomic-absorption spectrophotometry, *Anal. Chem.*, 36 (13) (1964) 2407.
251 FUWA, K. AND B. L. VALLEE, Improved instrumentation in atomic-absorption spectroscopy. Paper presented to the X Colloquium Spectroscopicum Internationale, College Park, Md., 1962.
252 FUWA, K. AND B. L. VALLEE, Physical basis of analytical atomic-absorption spectrometry. Pertinence of the Beer–Lambert law, *Anal. Chem.*, 35 (8) (1963) 942.
253 FUWA, K. AND B. L. VALLEE, Extended absorption path in atomic-absorption spectroscopy. Paper presented at the 1965 Eastern Analytical Symposium, New York City, N. Y., November 17–19, 1965.
254 GARTON, W. E. S., Atomic-absorption spectra and configuration interaction effects. *J. Quant. Spectry. Radiative Transfer*, 2 (4) (1962) 335.
255 GATEHOUSE, B. M., J. V. SULLIVAN AND A. WALSH, Paper presented to the 3rd Australian Spectroscopy Conference, Sydney, Australia, August 1961, *Nature*, 192 (4806) (1961) 929. See R. A. DURIE (*203*).
256 GATEHOUSE, B. M. AND A. WALSH, Analysis of metals and alloys using atomic-absorption spectroscopy. Paper presented to the 2nd Australian Spectroscopy Conference, Melbourne, Australia, June 1–3, 1959. Abstract in: *Spectrochim. Acta*, 15 (9) (1959) 786. See also N. S. HAM (*303*).
257 GATEHOUSE, B. M. AND A. WALSH, Analysis of metallic samples by atomic-absorption spectroscopy, *Spectrochim. Acta*, 16 (5) (1960) 602.
258 GATEHOUSE, B. M. AND J. B. WILLIS, Performance of a simple atomic-absorption spectrophotometer, *Spectrochim. Acta*, 17 (7) (1961) 710.
259 GAUMER, M., S. SPRAGUE AND W. SLAVIN, An automated procedure for the determination of trace metals by atomic-absorption spectroscopy. Paper presented to the Pittsburgh Conference on Analytical Chemistry and Applied Spectroscopy, Pittsburgh, Pa., February 21–25, 1966.
260 GEHRKE, C. W. AND J. P. USSARY, Fertilizers, *Anal. Chem.*, 37 (5) (1965) 67-R.
261 GERSTENFELDT, H., Determination of zinc in vegetable and animal substances, fertilizers, and soils by absorption flame photometry, *Landwirtsch. Forsch.*, 15 (1962) 64 (in German).
262 GIBSON, J. H. AND W. D. COOKE, Factors affecting excitation in flame spectroscopy. Paper presented to the Pittsburgh Conference on Analytical Chemistry and Applied Spectroscopy, Pittsburgh, Pa., March 1961.
263 GIBSON, J. H., W. E. GROSSMAN AND W. D. COOKE, Excitation processes in flame

spectroscopy. Paper presented to the 10th Detroit Anachem Conference, Detroit, Mich., October 1962.
264 GIBSON, J. H., W. E. GROSSMAN AND W. D. COOKE, The use of continuous sources instead of hollow-cathode tubes in atomic-absorption spectroscopy. Paper presented to the X Colloquium Spectroscopicum Internationale, College Park, Md., June 1962.
265 GIBSON, J. H., W. E. L. GROSSMAN AND W. D. COOKE, The use of continuous sources in atomic-absorption spectroscopy, in *Analytical Chemistry 1962*, Proc. Feigl Anniversary Symp., Birmingham, England, 1962; Elsevier, Amsterdam, 1963, p. 288.
266 GIBSON, J. H., W. GROSSMAN AND W. D. COOKE, Excitation processes in flame spectrometry, *Anal. Chem.*, 35 (1963) 266.
267 GIDLEY, J. A. F., Communication included in Anonymous, Atomic-Absorption Spectroscopy, *Hilger J.*, 5 (1958) 12.
268 GIDLEY, J. A. F., The application of atomic-absorption spectrophotometry to metallurgical analysis. IX Colloquium Spectroscopicum Internationale, Lyons, France, June 1961, *Publ. Group. Avan. Methodes Spectrog.*, 3 (1962) 263.
269 GIDLEY, J. A. F., Limitations in trace determinations by atomic-absorption spectrophotometry. In *Limitations of Detection in Spectrochemical Analysis*, Abingdon, Berkshire, 1964, p. 25.
270 GIDLEY, J. A. F. AND J. T. JONES, Determination of zinc in metallurgical materials by atomic-absorption spectrophotometry, *Analyst*, 85 (1009) (1960) 249.
271 GIDLEY, J. A. F. AND J. T. JONES, Determination of zinc in metallurgical materials by atomic-absorption spectrophotometry, *Analyst*, 86 (1021) (1961) 271.
272 GILBERT, P. T., Analytical flame photometry: new developments. Symposium on Spectroscopy, *Am. Soc. Testing Mater.*, *Spec. Tech. Publ.*, 269 (1960) 73.
273 GILBERT, P. T., New horizons in flame spectrophotometry, *Analyzer*, 2 (4) (1961) 3.
274 GILBERT, P. T., Absorption flame photometry, *Anal. Chem.*, 34 (5) (1962) 210R.
275 GILBERT, P. T., Atomic-absorption spectroscopy. A review of recent developments. Paper presented at the 6th Annual Conference on Analytical Chemistry in Nuclear Reactor Technology, Gatlinburg, Tenn., October 11, 1962, *U.S. Atomic Energy Comm. TID-7655*, (1962) 333.
276 GILBERT, P. T., Absorption flame photometry, *Anal. Chem.*, 34 (13) (1962) 1848.
277 GILBERT, P. T., Atomic-absorption spectroscopy. Lectures at Utah State University, March 1963; ACS, Idaho Falls, March 1963; ACS, Butte, Mont., March 1963; ACS, Grand Forks, N. D., March 1963; Soc. Appl. Spectroscopy, Denver, Colo., May 1963; Northern Calif. Soc. Spectroscopy, San Francisco, Calif., October 1963.
278 GILBERT, P. T., Chemiluminescent flame spectrophotometry. *Proc. Colloq. Spectros. Intern. 10th, Univ. Maryland, June, 1962*, (1963) 171.
279 GILBERT, P. T., Advances in emission flame photometry. Paper presented to the Analysis Instrumentation Symposium, Instrument Society of America, San Francisco, Calif., June 1–3, 1964.
280 GILBERT, P. T., Theory of detection sensitivity in atomic-emission flame spectrophotometry. Paper presented to the Pacific Southwest Regional Meeting (ACS), Costa Mesa, Calif., December 1964.
281 GILBERT, P. T. AND W. F. ULRICH, Notes on theory, technique and applications of flame spectroscopy. Lecture presented at the Beckman Instruments, Inc. Symposium on Atomic-Absorption Flame Photometry, Pico Rivera, Calif., May 11–12, 1965.
282 GINZBURG, V. L. AND G. I. SATARINA, Use of different light sources for atomic-absorption analysis, *Ind. Lab. USSR (English Trans.)*, 31 (2) (1965) 302; *Zavodsk. Lab.*, 31 (2) (1965) 249 (in Russian).
283 GOLEB, J. A., Uranium isotope investigations by atomic-absorption, *Anal. Chem.*, 35 (12) (1963) 1978.
284 GOLEB, J. A., The determination of uranium isotopes by atomic-absorption spectrometry. Paper presented to the 8th Conference on Analytical Chemistry in Nuclear Technology, Gatlinburg, Tenn., October 7, 1964.

285 GOLEB, J. A., The determination of uranium isotopes by atomic-absorption spectrophotometry. Paper presented to the 12th Detroit Anachem Conference, Detroit, Mich., October 21–23, 1964.
286 GOLEB, J. A., Preparation of hollow-cathode lamps as sample and light sources in atomic-absorption spectroscopy. Paper presented to the 1st Joint International Symposium on Analytical Instrumentation and Chemical and Petroleum Instrumentation (ISA), Montreal, Canada, May 1965.
287 GOLEB, J. A. AND J. K. BRODY, Atomic-absorption studies using a hollow-cathode tube as an absorption source. Paper presented to the X Colloquium Spectroscopicum Internationale, College Park, Md., 1962, *Anal. Chim. Acta,* 28 (5) (1963) 457.
288 GOLEB, J. A. AND Y. YOKOYAMA, Determination of lithium isotopes by atomic-absorption using a discharge tube as an absorption source. Paper presented to the XI Colloquium Spectroscopicum Internationale, Belgrade, Yugoslavia, October 1963.
289 GOLEB, J. A. AND Y. YOKOYAMA, The use of a discharge tube as an absorption source for the determination of lithium-6 and lithium-7 isotopes by atomic-absorption spectrophotometry, *Anal. Chim. Acta,* 30 (1964) 213.
290 GÓMEZ-COEDO, A. AND J. L. JIMÉNEZ-SECO, Atomic-absorption technique for silver in ores, *Rev. Met. (Madrid),* 12 (1965) 153 (in Spanish).
291 GOMISCEK, S. AND H. MALISSA, Atomic-absorption spectrophotometry using metal complexes in organic solvents. Paper presented to the XX International Congress of Pure and Applied Chemistry, Moscow, U.S.S.R., July 9, 1965.
292 GOTO, H., S. IKEDA AND I. ATUYA, A study of atomic-absorption spectrometry: Determination of magnesium and calcium in slag and cast iron, *Bunseki Kagaku,* 13 (1964) 111 (in Japanese).
293 GREAVES, M. C., Determination of gold and of silver in solution by atomic-absorption spectroscopy, *Nature,* 199 (4893) (1963) 552.
294 GREENFIELD, S., I. L. JONES AND C. T. BERRY, High-pressure plasmas as emission sources. Paper presented to the Society of Analytical Chemistry, *Analyst,* 88 (1053) (1963) 904.
295 GRIFFITH, F. D., H. E. PARKER AND J. C. ROGLER, The effect of dietary magnesium and fluoride on the magnesium content of tissues from growing chicks. Abstract in: *Federation Proc.,* 22 (2) (1963) 554.
296 GROENEWALD, I. D., The polarographic determination of lead in antimony sulfide flotation concentrates, *Analyst,* 89 (1964) 140.
297 GUDZINOWICZ, B. J. AND V. J. LUCIANO, Analysis of organometallic fungicides and related compounds by atomic-absorption spectroscopy. Paper presented to the 150th ACS Meeting, Atlantic City, N. J., September 12–17, 1965.
298 GUDZINOWICZ, B. J. AND V. J. LUCIANO, Analysis of organometallic fungicides and related compounds by atomic-absorption spectroscopy. Paper presented to the 5th Annual Conference on Pharmaceutical Analysis, Land O'Lakes, Wis., October 10–14, 1965.
299 GUDZINOWICZ, B. J. AND V. J. LUCIANO, Analysis of organo-metallic fungicides and related compounds by atomic-absorption spectroscopy. Paper presented to the 1965 Anachem Conference, Detroit, Mich., October 19–21, 1965.
300 GULLIKSON, C. W., R. W. LAMP AND D. W. SEEGMILLER, Cesium determination by atomic-absorption spectroscopy. Paper presented to the 4th National Meeting of the Society for Applied Spectroscopy, Denver, Colo., August 30–September 3, 1965.
301 HAGENAH, W. D., K. LAQUA AND V.G. MOSSOTTI, Laser microprobe atomic-absorption analysis. Paper presented to the XII Colloquium Spectroscopicum Internationale, Exeter, England, July 1965.
302 HALLS, D. AND A. TOWNSHEND, Interferences in the atomic-absorption spectrophotometry of magnesium. Paper presented to the Reunion Symposium of the Research School of Analytical Chemistry, Birmingham, England, April 28–29, 1966.
303 HAM, N. S., Communications presented to the 2nd Australian Spectroscopy Conference, *Nature,* 184 (1959) 1195.

304 HAM, N. S. AND A. WALSH, Microwave-powered raman sources, *Spectrochim. Acta*, 12 (1958) 88.
305 HARA, T., T. SAKAGUCHI AND T. YOSHIDA, Absorption spectrophotometry, *Bunseki Kagaku*, (1961) 1R.
306 HARRISON, W. W., Considerations involving the use of atomic-absorption spectroscopy as a quantitative analytical technique. Univ. Microfilms Order No. 65-289, 126 pp., *Dissertation Abstr.*, 25 (8) (1965) 4376.
307 HARRISON, W. W., Factors affecting the selection of a cobalt analysis line for atomic-absorption spectrometry, *Anal. Chem.*, 37 (9) (1965) 1168.
308 HARRISS, R. C. AND G. K. BILLINGS, Major and trace cation determinations in sea water by atomic-absorption spectrometry. To be published in *Texas J. Sci.* According to W. SLAVIN (*692*).
309 HEATON, F. W. AND A. HODGKINSON, External factors affecting diurnal variation in electrolyte excretion with particular reference to calcium and magnesium, *Clin. Chim. Acta*, 8 (1963) 246.
310 HELFER, R. E. AND D. O. RODGERSON, The determination of iron in biological material by atomic-absorption spectrophotometry. Paper presented to the 4th National Meeting of the Society for Applied Spectroscopy, Denver, Colo., August 30–September 3, 1965.
311 HELL, A., Advanced laminar flow burner for atomic-absorption. Paper presented to the 5th Australian Spectroscopy Conference, Perth, West Australia, May 31–June 2, 1965.
312 HELL, A., Important facts about atomic-absorption. Lectures at Beckman Instrument International, S.A. Symposia in Munich, Vienna, Zurich, Paris, London, July 1965.
313 HELL, A., J. RAMÍREZ-MUÑOZ AND N. SHIFRIN, A multipurpose flame accessory for UV visible spectrophotometers. Paper presented to the 4th National Meeting of the Society for Applied Spectroscopy, Denver, Colo., August 30–September 3, 1965.
314 HELL, A., J. RAMÍREZ-MUÑOZ AND N. SHIFRIN, New atomic-absorption accessory for UV visible spectrophotometers. Beckman preprint (1965) 30 p.
315 HELL, A., J. RAMÍREZ-MUÑOZ AND N. SHIFRIN, Nitrous oxide–acetylene burner with improved sample delivery system. Paper presented to the Pittsburgh Conference on Analytical Chemistry and Applied Spectroscopy, Pittsburgh, Pa., February 21–25, 1966.
316 HELL, A., J. RAMÍREZ-MUÑOZ AND N. SHIFRIN, Some recent results with a new multipurpose flame photometry accessory. Paper presented to the Meeting on Inorganic and Analytical Chemistry of the Royal Spanish Society for Physics and Chemistry, Madrid, Spain, February 1966 (in Spanish).
317 HERCUS, G. R., Communication presented to the 4th Australian Spectroscopy Conference, Canberra, Australia, August 20, 1963. According to C. K. COOGAN *et al.* (*153*).
318 HERRMANN, R., Researches on atomizers for emission and absorption flame photometry, *Optik*, 18 (1961) 422 (in German).
319 HERRMANN, R., Absorption flame photometry, *Chemie für Labor und Betrieb*, 14 (2) (1963) 45 (in German).
320 HERRMANN, R., New developments of the flame photometric analytical methods, *Z. Anal. Chem.*, 212 (1) (1965) 1 (in German).
321 HERRMANN, R. AND C. T. J. ALKEMADE, *Flame Photometry*, 2nd ed., Springer, Berlin, 1960 (in German); translated into English by P. T. GILBERT, JR.: *Chemical Analysis by Flame Photometry*, Interscience Publishers, New York, N.Y., 1963.
322 HERRMANN, R. AND W. LANG, Analysis of sodium and potassium in serum by means of absorption flame photometry, *Z. Ges. Exptl. Med.*, 134 (1961) 268 (in German).
323 HERRMANN, R. AND W. LANG, Determination of magnesium in serum and other body fluids by absorption flame photometry, *Z. Ges. Exptl. Med.*, 135 (1962) 569 (in German).
324 HERRMANN, R. AND W. LANG, New advances in emission and absorption flame

photometry, *Arkiv für das Eisenhüttenwesen*, 33 (10) (1962) 643 (in German).
325 HERRMANN, R. AND W. LANG, Quantitative determination of trace elements by flame absorption photometry. Paper presented to the IX Colloquium Spectroscopicum Internationale, Lyons, France, June 1961, *Publ. Group. Avan. Methodes Spectrog.*, 3 (1962) 291.
326 HERRMANN, R. AND W. LANG, Researches on atomizing chambers for emission and absorption flame photometry, *Optik*, 19 (1962) 208 (in German).
327 HERRMANN, R. AND W. LANG, Serum copper analysis by absorption flame photometry, *Z. Klin. Chem.*, 1 (6) (1963) 182 (in German).
328 HERRMANN, R. AND W. LANG, Modulation of the flame-photometric signal by means of intermitent sample feed to the flame, *Z. Anal. Chem.*, 203 (1964) 1 (in German).
329 HERRMANN, R., W. LANG AND K. RUDIGER, Modulation of the flame-photometric signals by means of intermitent sample feed to the flame, *Z. Anal. Chem.*, 206 (1964) 241 (in German).
330 HERRMANN, R., W. LANG AND D. STAMM, Determination of haemoglobin by atomic-absorption flame spectrophotometric determination of iron in whole blood. Blut, *Zeitschrift für Blutforschung*, 11 (1965) 135 (in German).
331 HERRMANN, R. AND W. NEU, The magnesium and zinc contents of chloroplasts, *Experientia*, 21 (1965) 436 (in German).
332 HICKS, D. G., Trisubstituted organophosphorus compounds in analytical chemistry, *Doctoral Thesis*, University of Tennessee, August 1965.
333 Hilger and Watts, Ltd., The use of atomic-absorption spectroscopy for the analysis of copper-based alloys. Research Paper BR 4 (1957) 10 pp.
334 Hilger and Watts, Ltd., Atomic-absorption spectroscopy. A new method of analysis. Bulletin CH407 (1959).
335 Hilger and Watts, Ltd., Lamps and light sources for Hilger instruments. Bulletin CH263/6 (1959) 7 pp.
336 Hilger and Watts, Ltd., The use of atomic-absorption spectroscopy for the determination of some noble metals. Research Report BR 11 (1959) 8 pp.
337 Hilger and Watts, Ltd., Uvispek photoelectric spectrophotometer. Bulletin CH318 14 (1960) 32 pp.
338 Hilger and Watts, Ltd., Atomic-absorption spectroscopy and hollow-cathode sources. BQ 1 Collection of data sheets (1961).
339 Hilger and Watts, Ltd., The Uvispek for versatility. Bulletin CJ 33 (1962) 3 pp.
340 Hilger and Watts, Ltd., A dual-purpose burner, *Hilger J.*, 8 (1963) 34.
341 Hilger and Watts, Ltd., Four channel direct-reading head on medium spectrograph. In *Handbook of Scientific Instruments and Apparatus*, Inst. Physics and Physical Society, 1964 Exhibition, London, January 1964; London, 1964, p. 175.
342 Hilger and Watts, Ltd., Light sources Hilger and Watts Instruments. Bulletin CH 263/7 (1964) 9 p.
343 Hilger and Watts, Ltd., Spectrophotometers. Attachments for Uvispek. Bulletin H 15 (1964) 1 p.
344 HINSON, W. H., An ion exchange treatment of plant ash extracts for removal of interfering anions in the determination of calcium by atomic-absorption, *Spectrochim. Acta*, 18 (1962) 427.
345 HINSON, W. H. AND R. KITCHING, A double-beam atomic-absorption spectrophotometer, *Spectrochim. Acta*, 20 (1964) 245.
346 HOLLANDER, T., Self-absorption, inonization and dissociation of metal vapor in flames. *Thesis*, Utrecht, 1964. Bronder-Offset, Rotterdam, 1964.
347 HONEGGER, N., Analysis of zinc in serum by means of absorption flame photometry, *Das Arztliche Laboratorium*, 2 (1963) 41 (in German).
348 HORN, D. B. AND A. L. LATNER, The estimation of magnesium by atomic-absorption spectrophotometry. Paper presented to the 5th International Congress on Clinical Chemistry, Detroit, Mich., August 19–23, 1963, *Clin. Chim. Acta*, 8 (1963) 974.
349 HUDSON, R. D., Atomic-absorption cross section of sodium vapor between 2400 and 1000 Å, *Phys. Rev.*, 135 (5A) (1964) 1212.

350 HUGHES, R. C., R. MAVRODINEANU AND T. R. KOHLER, Direct reader for flame emission and absorption measurement. Paper presented to the Seventh Conference on Analytical Chemistry in Nuclear Technology, Gatlinburg, Tenn., October 10, 1963

351 HUMPHREY, J. R., Determination of magnesium in uranium by atomic-absorption spectrometry, *Anal. Chem.*, 37 (12) (1965) 1604.

352 HUNT, E. C., Discussion to the paper of A. WALSH (*804*), in *Analytical Chemistry 1962*, Proc. Feigl Anniversary Symp., Birmingham, England, 1962; Elsevier, Amsterdam, 1963, p. 286.

353 HURST, R. J. AND R. R. MCSWINEY, Hilger atomic-absorption apparatus used to determine magnesium in blood plasma, *Hilger J.*, 8 (2) (1963) 25.

354 HUSSEIN, M., R. J. RUTMAN AND P. GEORGE, Determination of copper and iron in urine by atomic-absorption spectrophotometry using consecutive extractions from the same sample. Paper presented to the 5th Annual Conference on Pharmaceutical Analysis, Land O'Lakes, Wis., October 10–14, 1965.

355 HUSSEIN, M., R. J. RUTMAN AND P. GEORGE, Determination of copper and iron in urine by atomic-absorption spectrophotometry using consecutive extractions from the same sample. Paper presented to the 1965 Anachem Conference, Detroit, Mich., October 19–21, 1965.

356 IKENBERRY, L. C. AND N. G. SELLERS, Rapid determination of zinc in iron, steel and flue dusts by atomic-absorption. Paper presented to the Pittsburgh Conference on Analytical Chemistry and Applied Spectroscopy, Pittsburgh, Pa., February 21–25, 1966.

357 ISAAK, G. R., An atomic beam spectrophotometer, *Nature*, 189 (4762) (1961) 373.

358 IVANOV, N. P. AND N. A. KOZYREVA, Determination of copper in chemical reagents by atomic-absorption (exchange of experience), *Ind. Lab. (USSR) (English Trans.)*, 30 (6) (1964) 892; *Zavodsk. Lab.*, 30 (6) (1964) 706 (in Russian).

359 IVANOV, N. P. AND N. A. KOZYREVA, Atomic-absorption determination of magnesium in strontium nitrate with a continuous radiation source (exchange of experience), *Ind. Lab. (USSR) (English Trans.)*, 31 (5) (1965) 697; *Zavodsk. Lab.*, 31 (5) (1965) 556 (in Russian).

360 JACOBS, M. B. AND L. J. GOLDWATER, Ultramicrodetermination of mercury in apples, *Food Technol.*, 15 (1961) 357.

361 JACOBS, M. B., L. J. GOLDWATER AND H. GILBERT, Ultramicrodetermination of mercury in blood, *Am. Ind. Hyg. Assoc. J.*, 22 (1961) 276.

362 Jarrell-Ash Company, Performance characteristics and typical applications of Jarrell-Ash spectroscopic instruments, *Jarrell-Ash Newsletter*, 12 (1961) 4.

363 Jarrell-Ash Company, Atomic-absorption flame spectrometer. Catalogue 82-362 (1964) 8 p.

364 Jarrell-Ash Company, Half-meter Ebert scanning spectrometer. Catalogue 82-000, January 1964.

365 Jarrell-Ash Company, Control model atomic-absorption/flame spectrometer. Advance Information Sheet (1965) 1 p.

366 Jarrell-Ash Company, Multi-channel atomic-absorption/flame spectrometer. Advance Information Sheet (1965) 2 p.

367 JOHANSSON, A., Atomic-absorption spectrophotometry, *Svensk Kem. Tidskr.*, 74 (1962) 415 (in Swedish).

368 JOHNS, J. W. C., The absorption spectrum of BO_2, *Can. J. Phys.*, 39 (1961) 1738.

369 JONES, A. H., The application of atomic-absorption spectrophotometry to the analysis of glass and ceramic frit. Paper presented to the Pittsburgh Conference on Analytical Chemistry and Applied Spectroscopy, Pittsburgh, Pa., March 1965.

370 JONES, A. H., Analysis of glass and ceramic frit by atomic-absorption spectrophotometry, *Anal. Chem.*, 37 (13) (1965) 1761.

371 JONES, D. I. H. AND T. A. THOMAS, The determination of magnesium in plant material and serum by atomic-absorption spectrophotometry, *Hilger J.*, 9 (3) (1965) 39.

372 JONES, W. G. AND A. WALSH, Hollow-cathode discharges. The construction and

characteristics of sealed off tubes for use as spectroscopic light sources, *Spectrochim. Acta*, 16 (1960) 249.

373 KAHN, H. L., Detecting one part in a million ... super sleuthing. Reprint from *Research/Development Magazine*, June 1963, 4 pp.

374 KAHN, H. L., Instrumental procedures in atomic-absorption. Paper presented to the Society for Applied Spectroscopy, 2nd National Meeting, San Diego, Calif., October 18, 1963.

375 KAHN, H. L., The model 303 atomic-absorption spectrophotometer, *Atomic Absorption Newsletter*, (14) (1963) 1.

376 KAHN, H. L., Atomic-absorption newsletter describe new analytical procedures, *Instrument News*, 15 (3) (1964) 5, 11.

377 KAHN, H. L., Uses of atomic-absorption. Reprint from *Laboratory Management*, November–December 1964, 3 pp.

378 KAHN, H. L., Performance of the recorder readout accessory for the model 303 atomic-absorption spectrophotometer, *Atomic Absorption Newsletter*, (24) (1964) 11.

379 KAHN, H. L., Atomic-absorption speeds precision trace-metal analysis, *Food Engineering*, 37 (5) (1965) 105.

380 KAHN, H. L., Cloak and dagger applications of atomic-absorption, *Instrument News*, 15 (4) (1965) 1.

381 KAHN, H. L., Quantitative analysis by atomic-absorption, *Mater. Res. Std.*, 5 (7) (1965) 337.

382 KAHN, H. L. AND D. C. MANNING, A current-regulated source-lamp power supply for the model 303 atomic-absorption spectrophotometer, *Atomic Absorption Newsletter*, 4 (4) (1965) 264.

383 KAHN, H. L., K. J. MIKLUS AND W. SLAVIN, Design and performance of an atomic-absorption spectrophotometer. Paper presented to the Pittsburgh Conference on Analytical Chemistry and Applied Spectroscopy, Pittsburgh, Pa., March 4–8, 1963.

384 KAHN, H. L. AND W. SLAVIN, Atomic-absorption analysis, *International Science and Technology*, 11 (1962) 60, 86.

385 KAHN, H. L. AND W. SLAVIN, An atomic-absorption spectrophotometer, *Appl. Opt.*, 2 (1963) 931.

386 KARLOVITZ, B., Flow phenomena and flame technology, *Chem. Eng. Progr.*, 61 (8) (1965) 56.

387 KASHTAN, M. S., An improvement in the design of a discharge tube with a hollow. cathode, *Instr. Exp. Tech. USSR (English Transl.)*, (October 1963) 190; *Pribory i Tekhn. Eksperim.*, (1963) 262.

388 KAY, J. G., N. A. KUEBLER AND L. S. NELSON, Vacuum ultraviolet absorption spectra of flash-heated lead reacting with various gases, *Nature*, 194, (4829) (1962) 671.

389 KAYE, W. I., Far ultraviolet spectroscopy. II. Analytical applications, *Appl-Spectry.*, 15 (1961) 130.

390 KEATS, G. H., Concentration-reading digital voltmeter for atomic-absorption spectrophotometry, *Atomic Absorption Newsletter*, 4 (7) (1965) 319.

391 KEATS, G. H., A direct concentration reading digital voltmeter for atomic-absorption spectroscopy. Paper presented to the 16th Pittsburgh Conference on Analytical Chemistry and Applied Spectroscopy, Pittsburgh, Pa., March 1965.

392 KENDALL, K. K., (JR.), Interferences in flame photometry. Beckman Bulletin BB-12 (1953).

393 KHALIFA, H., G. SVEHLA AND L. ERDEY, Precision of the determination of copper and gold by atomic-absorption spectrometry, *Talanta*, 12 (1965) 703; see also KHALIFA, H., L. ERDEY AND G. SVEHLA, *Acta Chim. Acad. Sci. Hung.*, 41 (1964) 187.

394 KING, R. B., The measurement of absolute oscillator strengths for lines of neutral atoms, *J. Quant. Spectry. Radiative Transfer*, 3 (1962) 299.

395 KINGSLEY, G. R., Clinical chemistry, *Anal. Chem.*, 37 (5) (1965) 30R.

396 KINSON, K. AND C. B. BELCHER, The determination of nickel in iron and steel by atomic-absorption spectrophotometry, *Anal. Chim. Acta*, 30 (1) (1964) 64.

397 KINSON, K. AND C. B. BELCHER, The determination of minor amounts of copper in iron and steel by atomic-absorption spectrophotometry, *Anal. Chim. Acta*, 31 (2) (1964) 180.
398 KINSON, K., R. J. HODGES AND C. B. BELCHER, The determination of chromium in low-alloy irons and steels by atomic-absorption spectrophotometry, *Anal. Chim. Acta*, 29 (1963) 134.
399 KNISELEY, R. N., Spectroscopic properties and analytical applications of fuel-rich, oxy–acetylene flames. Paper presented to the Eastern Analytical Symposium, New York, N. Y., November 11–13, 1964.
400 KNISELEY, R. N., Atomic-absorption spectroscopy. Paper presented to the 5th Annual Conference on Pharmaceutical Analysis, Land O'Lakes, Wis., October 10–14, 1965.
401 KNISELEY, R. N., Theory of atomic-absorption. Paper presented to the Joint Meeting of the American Society of Clinical Pathologists and College of American Pathologists, Chicago, Ill., October 15–23, 1965.
402 KNISELEY, R. N., The use of a continuum for atomic-absorption spectroscopy. Paper presented to the 1965 Eastern Analytical Symposium, New York, N. Y., November 17–19, 1965.
403 KNISELEY, R. N., Spectroscopic usefulness of induction coupled plasmas. Spectroscopic studies of premixed oxy–acetylene. Paper presented to the 9th Annual Symposium on Modern Methods of Analytical Chemistry, Baton Rouge, La., January 24–27, 1966.
404 KNISELEY, R. N., A. P. D'SILVA AND V. A. FASSEL, A sensitive premixed oxy–acetylene atomizer-burner for flame emission and absorption spectrometry, *Anal. Chem.*, 35 (7) (1963) 910; see also *Angew. Chem.*, 75 (10) (1963).
405 KNISELEY, R. N. AND V. A. FASSEL, The free-atom problem in flame atomic emission and absorption spectroscopy. Paper presented to the Symposium "Unresolved problems in spectrochemical analysis" (Organized and sponsored by the A.S.T.M. Committee E-2 on Emission Spectroscopy) 4th National Meeting of the Society for Applied Spectroscopy, Denver, Colo., September 3, 1965.
406 KNISELEY, R. N. AND V. A. FASSEL, Flame emission spectroscopy—a critical review. Paper presented to the 150th ACS Meeting, Atlantic City, N. J., September 12–17, 1965.
407 KNUTSON, K. E., Flame photometric determination of magnesium in plant material. A study of the emission of magnesium in a highly reducing oxygen–acetylene flame, *Analyst*, 82 (1957) 241.
408 KOIRTYOHANN, S. R. AND C. FELDMAN, Atomic-absorption spectroscopy using long absorption path lengths and a demountable hollow-cathode lamp, *Develop. Appl. Spectry.*, (1964) 3.
409 KOIRTYOHANN, S. R. AND E. E. PICKETT, Background corrections in long path atomic-absorption spectrometry, *Anal. Chem.*, 37 (4) (1965) 601.
410 KOIRTYOHANN, S. R. AND E. E. PICKETT, Spectral interferences in atomic-absorption spectroscopy. Paper presented to the 4th National Meeting of the Society for Applied Spectroscopy, Denver, Colo., August 30–September 3, 1965.
411 KOMETANI, T. Y., The application of atomic-absorption spectroscopy to study the effects of temperature on the volatilization of alkali salts during dry ashing of teflon. Paper presented to the Pittsburgh Conference on Analytical Chemistry and Applied Spectroscopy, Pittsburgh, Pa., February 21–25, 1966.
412 KRAMPITZ, G. AND R. DOEPFMER, Flame photometry in biochemistry and biological analysis, *Rev. Univ. Ind. Santander*, 5 (1963) 361 (in Spanish).
413 KRASIL'SHCHIK, V. Z., Device for working with a hollow-cathode, *Ind. Lab. (USSR) (English Trans.)*, 31 (2) (1965) 305; *Zavodsk. Lab.*, 31 (2) (1965) 251 (in Russian).
414 KUZNETSOV, YU. N. AND L. P. CHABOVSKII, Rapid atomic-absorption determination of Hg in powdered samples, *Uch. Zap. Tsentr. Nauchn. Issled Inst. Olovyan Prom.*, 2 (1964) 75 (in Russian).
415 LAMBIA, D. A., Discussion to the paper of A. WALSH (*804*), in *Analytical Chemistry 1962*, Proc. Feigl Anniversary Symp., Birmingham England, 1962; Elsevier, Am-

sterdam, 1963, p. 287.
416 LANG, W., Limits of quantitative detection of trace elements by means of absorption flame photometry. *Doctoral Thesis*, Giessen, Germany, 1963 (in German).
417 LANG, W., Differentiation of the flame spectrophotometric signal, *Mikrochim. Acta*, (5) (1964) 716 (in German).
418 LANG, W., Flame photometric absorption measurements with a periodically deflected flame, *Mikrochim. Acta*, (5) (1964) 796 (in German).
419 LANG, W. AND R. HERRMANN, A burner for absorption flame photometric analysis, *Optik*, 19 (1962) 422 (in German).
420 LANG, W. AND R. HERRMANN, Absorption flame-photometric absorption spectral analysis with microliter samples, *Mikrochim. Acta*, (5-6) (1963) 872 (in German).
421 LANG, W. AND R. HERRMANN, Flows in pneumatic anular sprayer for flame photometer, *Optik*, 20 (8) (1963) 391 (in German).
422 LANG, W. AND R. HERRMANN, Scale expansion in flame-photometric absorption spectral analysis for intermediate ranges of extinction, *Mikrochim. Acta*, (5-6) (1963) 1053 (in German).
423 LANG, W AND R. HERRMANN, Signal-to-noise ratio in flame-photometric absorption measurements, *Optik*, 20 (7) (1963) 347 (in German).
424 LANG, W. AND R. HERRMANN, On the evaluation of flame-spectrophotometric atomic-absorption measurements by the quotient method, *Z. Anal. Chem.*, 199 (1964) 161 (in German).
425 LANG, W., K. RUDIGER AND R. HERRMANN, A sprayer-burner combination with three suction capillaries for flame spectrophotometry, *Z. Angew. Phys.*, 17 (1964) 277 (in German).
426 LEEN, M. W. AND J. G. ATWOOD, Design of an atomic-absorption spectrophotometer. Paper presented to the Pittsburgh Conference on Analytical Chemistry and Applied Spectroscopy, Pittsburgh, Pa., February–March 1961.
427 LEFEBVRE, J. C., Dissolution techniques in atomic-absorption analysis, *Afinidad*, 22 (237) (1965) 181 (in Spanish).
428 LEITHE, W., Absorption flame photometry in analytical chemistry, *Angew. Chem.*, 73 (14) (1961) 488 (in German).
429 LEITHE, W. AND A. HOFER, Determination of magnesium by atomic-absorption flame photometry. I, *Mikrochim. Acta*, 2 (1961) 268 (in German).
430 LEITHE, W. AND A. HOFER, Determination of magnesium by atomic-absorption flame photometry. II. Determination of magnesium in aluminum alloys, *Mikrochim. Acta*, 2 (1961) 277 (in German).
431 LINDSTROM, O., Rapid microdetermination of mercury by spectrophotometric flame combustion, *Anal. Chem.*, 31 (1959) 461.
432 LOCKYER, R., Some factors affecting performance in atomic-absorption spectroscopy. Paper presented to the Joint Meeting of the Western Section and Physical Methods Group, Society for Analytical Chemistry, *Analyst*, 85 (1012) (1960) 461. See also *Hilger J.*, 5 (1959) 55.
433 LOCKYER, R., Atomic-absorption spectroscopy, in *Analytical Chemistry 1962*, Proc. Feigl Anniversary Symp., Birmingham, England, 1962; Elsevier, Amsterdam, p. 297.
434 LOCKYER, R., Atomic-absorption spectroscopy. *Proceedings of the Conference on Analytical Methods, Malvern, England, October 24–25, 1961*, 1962, p. 9.
435 LOCKYER, R., Atomic-absorption spectroscopy, *Advan. Anal. Chem. Instr.*, 3 (1964) 1.
436 LOCKYER, R. AND G. E. HAMES, The quantitative determination of some noble metals by atomic-absorption spectroscopy, *Analyst*, 84 (1959) 385.
437 LOCKYER, R. AND G. E. HAMES, Atomic-absorption spectroscopy. Some analytical applications and some limitations. Paper presented to the Pittsburgh Conference on Analytical Chemistry and Applied Spectroscopy, Pittsburgh, Pa., March 1960.
438 LOCKYER, R. AND G. E. HAMES, Atomic-absorption spectroscopy, *Lab. Pract.*, 11 (1962) 597.
439 LOCKYER, R., J. E. SCOTT AND S. SLADE, Enhancement of atomic-absorption in the flame by organic solvents, *Nature*, 189 (1961) 830.

440 LONG, D. A., Atomic-absorption spectroscopy, *Chem. Ind. (London)*, (February 16, 1963) 282.
441 L'vov, B. V., The analytical use of atomic-absorption spectra, *Spectrochim. Acta*, 17 (7) (1961) 761.
442 L'vov, B. V., Possibility of absolute analysis using atomic-absorption spectra, *Tr. Gos. Inst. Prikl. Khim.*, 49 (1962) 256 (in Russian).
443 L'vov, B. V., Theory of atomic-absorption analysis, *Zavodsk. Lab.*, 28 (8) (1962) 931 (in Russian).
444 L'vov, B. V., Use of atomic-absorption spectroscopy for solving problems of analysis automation and raising the sensitivity of the analysis. Paper presented to the XX International Congress of Pure and Applied Chemistry, Moscow, U.S.S.R., July 9, 1965.
445 L'vov, B. V., V. I. MOSICHEV AND S. A. SENYUTA, Quantitative spectral determination of the isotopic composition of oxygen, *Ind. Lab. (USSR) (English Trans.)*, 11 (1963) 1404; *Zavodsk. Lab.*, 28 (1962) 1322 (in Russian).
446 MAGEE, R. J., Discussion to the paper of A. WALSH (*804*), in *Analytical Chemistry 1962*, Proc. Feigl Anniversary Symp., Birmingham, England, 1962; Elsevier, Amsterdam, 1963, p. 287.
447 MAKINO, I. AND K. YASUDA, Atomic-absorption spectrophotometry, *Bunseki Kagaku*, 11 (11) (1962) 1211.
448 MAKINO, I., K. YASUDA, S. SATO, M. KURIHARA AND K. AKAMATSU, A single beam atomic-absorption attachment. Paper presented to the Pittsburgh Conference on Analytical Chemistry and Applied Spectroscopy, Pittsburgh, Pa., March 4–8, 1963.
449 MALMSTADT, H. V., Atomic-absorption spectrochemical analysis, *Encyclopedia of Spectroscopy*, G. L. CLARK (Ed.), Reinhold, New York, 1960, pp. 12–18.
450 MALMSTADT, H. V., R. M. BARNES AND P. A. RODRÍGUEZ, A multipurpose high precision recording photometer, *J. Chem. Educ.*, 41 (5) (1964) 263.
451 MALMSTADT, H. V. AND W. E. CHAMBERS, Precision null point atomic-absorption spectrochemical analysis, *Anal. Chem.*, 32 (1960) 225.
452 MANNING, D. C., Magnesium in blood. Sales Lab. Study No. 14, October 1962, Perkin-Elmer Corp., Norwalk, Conn.
453 MANNING, D. C., Detection limits in analytical atomic-absorption spectroscopy. Paper presented to the Society for Applied Spectroscopy, Rocky Mountain Spectroscopy Conference, Denver, Colo., August 12, 1963.
454 MANNING, D. C., Trace metals in blood plasma, *Atomic Absorption Newsletter*, (11) (1963) 3.
455 MANNING, D. C., Atomic-absorption analysis using the premix oxy–acetylene flame. Paper presented to the 3rd National Meeting (SAS) Cleveland, Ohio, September 28–October 2, 1964.
456 MANNING, D. C., The determination of aluminum by atomic-absorption spectroscopy, *Atomic Absorption Newsletter*, (24) (1964) 6.
457 MANNING, D. C., A burner for nitrous oxide–acetylene flames, *Atomic Absorption Newsletter*, 4 (4) (1965) 267.
458 MANNING, D. C. AND H. L. KAHN, Emission and continuous-source absorption experiments on the model 303 atomic-absorption spectrophotometer, *Atomic Absorption Newsletter*, 4 (3) (1965) 224.
459 MANNING, D. C. AND W. SLAVIN, Lithium isotope analysis by atomic-absorption spectrophotometry, *Atomic Absorption Newsletter*, (8) (1962) 1.
460 MANNING, D. C. AND W. SLAVIN, Lithium isotope analysis by atomic-absorption spectrophotometry. Proceedings of the 6th Conference on Analytical Chemistry in Nuclear Reactor Technology, Gatlinburg, Tenn., October 1962, p. 390–9.
461 MANNING, D. C., S. SPRAGUE AND W. SLAVIN, Atomic-absorption spectrophotometry in strongly reducing oxy–acetylene flames. Paper presented to the Pittsburgh Conference on Analytical Chemistry and Applied Spectroscopy, Pittsburgh, Pa., March 4–8, 1963.
462 MANNING, D. C., D. J. TRENT, S. SPRAGUE AND W. SLAVIN, Hollow-cathode lamps and low-temperature flames for the determination of sodium and potassium by atomic-absorption spectrophotometry, *Atomic Absorption Newsletter*, 4 (4) (1965) 255.

463 MANNING, D. C., D. J. TRENT AND J. VOLLMER, Dual-element magnesium–calcium hollow-cathode lamp, *Atomic Absorption Newsletter*, 4 (3) (1965) 234.

464 MANNING, R. J., An atomic-absorption accessory for ultraviolet spectrophotometers. Paper presented to the Mid-America Symposium on Spectroscopy (SAS), Chicago, Ill., June 14–17, 1965.

465 MANNING, R. J., New atomic-absorption instrumentation. Lecture presented to the Beckman Instruments, Inc. Symposium on Atomic-Absorption Flame Photometry, Pico Rivera, Calif., May 11–12, 1965.

466 MANSELL, R. E., Industrial applications of atomic-absorption spectroscopy. Paper presented to the 12th Annual Anachem Conference, Detroit, Mich., October 21–23, 1964.

467 MANSELL, R. E., Atomic-absorption spectroscopy. A promising new analytical tool, atomic-absorption provides fast, sensitive, and accurate analysis of trace elements, *Industrial Research*, (February 1965) 68.

468 MANSELL, R. E., Notes on the extraction of manganese with chelating agents and MIBK, *Atomic Absorption Newsletter*, 4 (5) (1965) 276.

469 MANSELL, R. E. AND H. W. EMMEL, Trace metal extractions from brine with APDC and oxine, *Atomic Absorption Newsletter*, 4 (10) (1965) 365.

470 MANSELL, R. E., H. W. EMMEL AND E. L. MCLAUGHLIN, The determination of alloying elements in magnesium and aluminum alloys by atomic-absorption spectroscopy. Paper presented to the Pittsburgh Conference on Analytical Chemistry and Applied Spectroscopy, Pittsburgh, Pa., February 21–25, 1966.

471 MANSELL, R. E. AND E. J. HUNEMORDER, A photometric method for trace mercury determination using a Beckman DU spectrophotometer, *Anal. Chem.*, 35 (1963) 1981.

472 MANSFIELD, J. M., J. D. WINEFORDNER AND C. VEILLON, High sensitivity determination of zinc, cadmium, mercury, thallium, gallium, and indium by atomic fluorescence flame spectrometry, *Anal. Chem.*, 37 (8) (1965) 1049.

473 MARGOSHES, M., The selection of wavelengths for atomic-absorption spectroscopy. Paper presented to the 4th National Meeting of the Society for Applied Spectroscopy, Denver, Colo., August 30–September 3, 1965.

474 MARGOSHES, H. AND B. F. SCRIBNER, The plasma jet as a spectroscopic source, *Spectrochim. Acta*, 15 (1959) 138.

475 MASON, W. B., Bioanalytical techniques. A report of the 18th Annual Analytical Chemistry Summer Symposium, *Anal. Chem.*, 37 (13) (1965) 1755.

476 MASSMANN, H., Hollow-cathodes for simultaneous excitation. Paper presented to the X Colloquium Spectroscopicum Internationale, College Park, Md., June 1962. Abstract in *Appl. Spectry.*, 16 (1962) 56.

477 MASSMANN, H., Hollow-cathodes for constant intensity ratios of spectra of different elements, *Z. Instrumentenk.*, 71 (1963) 225 (in German).

478 MASSMANN, H., Trace analysis with a multichannel atomic-absorption spectrophotometer and multiple hollow-cathodes. Paper presented to the XII Colloquium Spectroscopicum Internationale, Exeter, England, July 1965.

479 MAVRODINEANU, R. AND H. BOITEUX, *Flame Spectroscopy*, John Wiley and Sons, New York, 1965.

480 MAVRODINEANU, R. AND R. C. HUGHES, Simultaneous determination of sodium, potassium, calcium, and magnesium in biological samples by combined flame emission and atomic-absorption spectrophotometry. Paper presented to the 16th Annual Mid-America Symposium on Spectroscopy, Chicago, Ill., June 14–17, 1965.

481 MAXWELL, D. G., Concluding address in the Symposium on "The analysis of high purity gold", Johannesburg, S. Africa, June 6, 1962, *J. S. African Inst. Mining Met.*, 62 (12, Part II) (1962) 844.

482 MCBRIDE, C. H., Determination of minor nutrients in fertilizers by atomic-absorption spectrophotometry, *Atomic Absorption Newsletter*, 3 (11) (1964) 144.

483 MCBRIDE, C. H., Determination of minor nutrients in fertilizers by atomic-absorption spectrophotometry, *J. Assoc. Offic. Agr. Chemists*, 48 (2) (1965) 406.

484 MCCLENDON, J. H., Simple colorimeter using the 254 mμ line of mercury for continuous monitoring of chromatographic effluents, *Anal. Biochem.*, 3 (1962) 94.

485 McGrath, W. D., P. F. Pickering, R. J. Magee and C. L. Wilson, Analysis of gases and vapours by spectroscopy techniques. II. Review of the absorption spectra of gases and vapours, *Talanta*, 9 (1962) 227. See I A note on emission spectroscopy, *Talanta*, 8 (1961) 892.

486 McGrath, W. D., P. F. Pickering, R. J. Magee and C. L. Wilson, Analysis of gases and vapours by spectroscopy techniques. III. Application of electronic absorption spectra, *Talanta*, 9 (1962) 239.

487 McPherson, G. L., Atomic-absorption spectrophotometry as an analytical tool in a metallurgical laboratory. Paper presented to the 17th BISRA Chemists' Conference, Scarborough, England, June 1964.

488 McPherson, G. L., Atomic-absorption spectrophotometry as an analytical tool in a metallurgical laboratory, *Atomic Absorption Newsletter*, 4 (2) (1965) 186.

489 McPherson, G. L., Some applications of atomic-absorption spectroscopy in the determination of metals in alloys, paints, and plastics. Paper presented to the 4th Australian Spectroscopy Conference, Canberra, Australia, August 20, 1962.

490 McPherson, G. L., J. W. Price and P. H. Scaife, Application of atomic-absorption spectroscopy to the determination of cobalt in steel, alloy steel, and nickel, *Nature*, 199 (4891) (1963) 371.

491 Means, E. A. and D. Ratcliff, Determination of wear metals in lubricating oils by atomic-absorption spectroscopy, *Atomic Absorption Newsletter*, 4 (1) (1965) 174.

492 Menzies, A. C., Spectroscopy of flames in absorption and emission. *Proceedings of the 15th International Congress of Pure and Applied Chemistry (Anal. Chem.), Lisbon, Portugal*, Vol. II (1956) 313.

493 Menzies, A. C., Atomic-absorption spectroscopy. Paper presented to the Society of Analytical Chemistry, *Analyst*, 82 (981) (1957) 778.

494 Menzies, A. C., Trends in automatic spectrochemical analysis. VI Colloquium Spectroscopicum Internationale, *Spectrochim. Acta*, 11 (1957) 106.

495 Menzies, A. C., Atomic emission and absorption in flames, *Z. Instrumentenk.*, 68 (10) (1960) 242 (in German).

496 Menzies, A. C., A study of atomic-absorption spectroscopy, *Anal. Chem.*, 32 (8) (1960) 898.

497 Miklus, K. J. and W. J. Menosky, A high sensitive burner for atomic-absorption spectroscopy. Paper presented to the 5th Conference on Pharmaceutical Analysis, Land O'Lakes, Wis., October 10–14, 1965.

498 Miklus, K. J. and W. J. Menosky, A high sensitivity burner for atomic-absorption spectroscopy. Paper presented to the 1965 Anachem Conference, Detroit, Mich., October 19–21, 1965.

499 Milazzo, G., Atomic-absorption, *Chim. Ind. (Milan)*, 44 (5) (1962) 493 (in Italian).

500 Miller, B., Project surveyor to seek solar origins, *Aviation Week*, (July 1961) 62.

501 Millikan, R. C., Measurement of particle and gas temperatures in a slightly luminous premixed flame, *J. Opt. Soc. Am.*, 51 (1961) 535.

502 Mislan, J. P., A flameless method for producing atomic vapor for atomic-absorption spectrophotometry. I. Determination of cadmium. Atomic Energy of Canada Ltd. Rep. AECL-1941 (1964) 10 p. Paper presented to the 7th Conference on Analytical Chemistry in Nuclear Technology, Gatlinburg, Tenn., October 1963.

503 Mitchell, A. C. G. and M. W. Zemansky, *Resonance Radiation and Excited Atoms*, Cambridge University Press, 1934 (reprinted in 1961).

504 Mitchell, R. L., Trace analysis by spectrochemical methods, in *Analytical Chemistry 1962*, Proc. Feigl Anniversary Symp., Birmingham, England, 1962; Elsevier, Amsterdam, 1963, p. 314.

505 Mitchell, R. L., The spectrochemical analysis of soils, plants, and related materials. Technical Comm. No. 44A, Commonwealth Bureau of Soils, Harpenden, Reprinted with Addendum, Commonwealth Agricultural Bureau, Farnham Royal, Bucks., England, 1964.

506 Mitchell, R. L., Developments in soil and plant analysis. Paper presented to the 5th Australian Spectroscopy Conference, Perth, W. Australia, May 31–June 2, 1965.

507 MOONEY, J. B., Detergent addition in flame photometry, *Appl. Spectry.*, 19 (1) (1965) 36.
508 MORGAN, M. E., The determination of copper in milk by atomic-absorption spectroscopy, *Atomic Absorption Newsletter*, (21) (1964) 1.
509 MOSSOTTI, V. G., The atomic-absorption flame spectra of lanthanide elements. Univ. Microfilms Order No. 65-2044, 140 pp., *Dissertation Abstr.*, 25 (8) (1965) 4429.
510 MOSSOTTI, V. G. AND V. A. FASSEL, The atomic-absorption spectra of the lanthanide elements, *Spectrochim. Acta*, 20 (1964) 1117.
511 MOSTYN, R. A. AND A. F. CUNNINGHAM, Determination of molybdenum in ferrous alloys by atomic-absorption spectrometry, *Anal. Chem.*, 38 (1) (1966) 121.
512 MÜLLER, R. H., Some thoughts on atomic-absorption spectroscopy and electrolitic conductivity, *Anal. Chem.*, 33 (11) (1961) 101A.
513 MÜLLER, R. H., Developments in atomic-absorption spectrometry, *Anal. Chem.*, 36 (2) (1964) 147A.
514 MÜLLER, R. H., Electronics industry shifts to commercial goals, *Anal. Chem.*, 36 (9) (1964) 85A.
515 MÜLLER, R. H., Instrumentation, *Anal. Chem.*, 36 (5) (1964) 140R.
516 MUNY, R. P., Simple constant feed pump. *Atomic Absorption Newsletter*, 3 (10) (1964) 129.
517 MURIE, R. A. AND R. C. BOURKE, Improved burner adjustments for atomic-absorption spectrophotometers, *Appl. Spectry.*, 18 (4) (1964) 116.
518 MUSHA, S., M. MUNEMORI AND Y. NAKANISHI, Determination of zinc, lead, and calcium in poly(vinyl chloride) by atomic-absorption spectrophotometry, *Bunseki Kagaku*, 13 (4) (1964) 330.
519 NELSON, L. S., Intense rapid heating with flash discharge lamps, *Science*, 136 (1962) 296.
520 NELSON, L. S., Spectra of transient high temperature species produced by flash heating. Paper presented to the Conference on Spectroscopy, Instrumentation and Chemistry, San Francisco, Calif., October 22, 1964.
521 NELSON, L. S. AND N. A. KUEBLER, Absorption spectra of gaseous species formed at flash-heated solid surfaces, *J. Chem. Phys.*, 37 (1) (1962) 47.
522 NELSON, L. S. AND N. A. KUEBLER, Kinetic absorption spectra recorded edgewise across flash-heated strips, *Appl. Opt.*, 1 (6) (1962) 775.
523 NELSON, L. S. AND N. A. KUEBLER, Absorption spectra of atoms formed in flash-heated tungsten surfaces. *Proc. Colloq. Spectros. Intern. 10th Univ. Maryland, June, 1962*, (1963) 83.
524 NELSON, L. S. AND N. A. KUEBLER, Vaporization of elements for atomic-absorption spectroscopy with capacitor discharge lamps. Paper presented to the 11th Annual Anachem Conference, Detroit, Mich., October 21, 1963.
525 NELSON, L. S. AND N. A. KUEBLER, Vaporization of elements for atomic-absorption spectroscopy with capacitor discharge lamps, *Spectrochim. Acta*, 19 (4) (1963) 781.
526 NEVILLE, G. J. AND J. E. CARROLL, JR., Determination of lead by atomic-absorption spectrophotometry. Paper presented to the 12th Ottawa Symposium on Applied Spectroscopy, Ottawa, Canada, October 18–20, 1965.
527 NEWBURN, E., Application of atomic-absorption spectroscopy to the determination of calcium in saliva, *Nature*, 192 (4808) (1961) 1182.
528 NIKOLAEV, G. I., Atomic-absorption method for the determination of zinc in metals and alloys, *Zh. Anal. Khim.*, 19 (1964) 63 (in Russian).
529 NIKOLAEV, G. I. AND V. B. ALESKOWSKII, Atomic-absorption micromethod for the determination of aluminum in pure metals and alloys, *Zh. Anal. Khim.*, 18 (7) (1963) 816 (in Russian).
530 NONNENMACHER, G. AND F. H. SCHLESER, Quantitative analysis of metals, specially metal traces, by atomic-absorption spectroscopy, *Z. Anal. Chem.*, 209 (1) (1965) 284 (in German).
531 NORMAND, M., Application of atomic-absorption analysis in atomic energy work. *Afinidad*, 22 (237) (1965) 190 (in Spanish).

532 NORRIS, J. A., Atomic-absorption: problems, solutions, and new instrumental approaches. Paper presented to the 4th National Meeting of the Society for Applied Spectroscopy, Denver, Colo., August 30–September 3, 1965.
533 NORRIS, J. A., Multichannel atomic-absorption analyses. Paper presented to the XII Colloquium Spectroscopicum Internationale, Exeter, England, July 1965.
534 NORRIS, J. A., Role of atomic-absorption in analysis. Paper presented to the Pittsburgh Conference on Analytical Chemistry and Applied Spectroscopy, Pittsburgh, Pa., February 21–25, 1966.
535 OLSON, A. M., Gold assay by atomic-absorption spectrophotometry: a preliminary report, *Atomic Absorption Newsletter*, 4 (5) (1965) 278.
536 Optica, Inc., Atomic-absorption apparatus. Bulletin No. 6-2000 (1961) 4 p.
537 Optica, S.p.A., Densatomic. Spectrophotometer for atomic-absorption and emission flame photometry analysis. Brochure (1965) 3 p.
538 OSBORN, K. R. AND H. E. GUNNING, Determination of Hg-202 and other mercury isotopes in sample of mercury vapor by mercury resonance radiation absorbiometry, *J. Opt. Soc. Am.*, 45 (1955) 552.
539 OSTERRIED, O., Flame photometric determination of the alkalies and aluminum in silicates, *Dissertation*, Technische Hochschule, Munich, Germany, 1962.
540 PACISA, Madrid, Emission and absorption (atomic-absorption) flame photometry accessory for Beckman spectrophotometers. Detectability of the elements. Pamphlet (1965) 2 pp. (in Spanish).
541 PARELLADA-BELLOD, R., Atomic-absorption flame photometry, *Inform. Quim. Anal. (Madrid)*, 17 (5) (1963) 137 (in Spanish).
542 PARKER, H. E., Magnesium, calcium, and zinc in animal nutrition, *Atomic Absorption Newsletter*, (13) (1963) 1.
543 PARKER, H. E., The use of an atomic-absorption spectrometer in mineral metabolism studies. Abstract in *Federation Proc.*, 22 (2) (1963) 260.
544 PASSMORE, W. AND P. B. ADAMS, Determination of iron and zinc in glass by atomic-absorption spectrophotometry, *Atomic Absorption Newsletter*, 4 (4) (1965) 237.
545 PATERSON, J. E., Hollow-cathode tubes and emission tubes for absorption spectroscopy. Paper presented to the 9th Annual Seminar on Spectroscopy, Southeastern Section, SAS, Gainesville, Fla., January 4–6, 1961.
546 PATERSON, J. E., A hollow-cathode tube for spectrochemical analysis. Paper presented to the X Colloquium Spectroscopicum Internationale, College Park, Md., June 1962. Abstract: *Appl. Spectry.*, 16 (1962) 56.
547 PATERSON, J. E., The hollow-cathode tube as a source for optical emission spectroscopy. Paper presented to the Pittsburgh Conference on Analytical Chemistry and Applied Spectroscopy, Pittsburgh, Pa., March 2–6, 1964.
548 PATERSON, J. E., Hollow-cathode technique. Paper presented to the 3rd National Meeting (SAS), Cleveland, Ohio, September 28–October 2, 1964.
549 Perkin-Elmer Corp., Analytical operating data for the model 214 spectrophotometer, *Atomic Absorption Newsletter*, (7) (1962) 6.
550 Perkin-Elmer Corp., Perkin-Elmer model 303 atomic-absorption spectrophotometer. Bulletin No. KHV26310, 6 p.
551 Perkin-Elmer Corp., Analytical methods for atomic-absorption spectrophotometry. Instruction method book for Perkin-Elmer Instrument No. 303,Perkin-Elmer Corp. Norwalk, Conn., 1964.
552 Perkin-Elmer Corp., Perkin-Elmer digital concentration read-out accessory for the model 303 atomic-absorption spectrophotometer. Bulletin (1965) 5 pp.
553 Perkin-Elmer Corp., Perkin-Elmer model 290 atomic-absorption spectrophotometer. Brochure No. L290 (1965) 11 pp.
554 PERKINS, J., Determination of sodium in halo-phosphate phosphors by atomic-absorption spectroscopy, *Analyst*, 88 (1045) (1963) 324.
555 PINTA, M., Research and determination of trace elements. Dunod, Paris, France, (1962) 352.
556 PLASS, G. N., The theory of the absorption of flame radiation by molecular bands *Appl. Opt.*, 4 (2) (1965) 161.

557 PLATTE, J. A. AND V. M. MARCY, Atomic-absorption spectrophotometry—A new tool for the water chemist. Paper presented to the 27th Annual Meeting of American Power Conference, Chicago, Ill., April 27–29, 1965.
558 PLATTE, J. A. AND V. M. MARCY, Atomic-absorption spectrophotometry as a tool for the water chemist, *Atomic Absorption Newsletter*, 4 (6) (1965) 289.
559 PLATTE, J. A. AND V. M. MARCY, A new tool for the water chemist. *Industrial Water Engineering*, (May 1965) 27.
560 POLUÉKTOV, N. S., Atomic-absorption flame-photometry, *Zavodsk. Lab.*, 27 (7) (1961) 830 (in Russian).
561 POLUÉKTOV, N. S., The flame photometric method of analysis, *Ind. Lab. (USSR) (English Trans.)*, 28 (9) (1962) 1138; *Zavodsk. Lab.*, 28 (9) (1962) 1069 (in Russian).
562 POLUÉKTOV, N. S. AND S. E. GRINZAID, Atomic-absorption flame photometry, *Izv. Akad. Nauk SSSR, Ser. Fiz.*, 26 (7) (1962) 948 (in Russian).
563 POLUÉKTOV, N. S. AND S. E. GRINZAID, An instrument for atomic-absorption flame spectrophotometry, *Zavodsk. Lab.*, 29 (8) (1963) 998 (in Russian). Translated into English with the title: A device for atomic-absorption spectrophotometric flame analysis, *Ind. Lab. (USSR) (English Trans.)*, 29 (8) (1963) 1071.
564 POLUÉKTOV, N. S. AND R. A. VITKUN, Atomic-absorption flame photometric determination of cadmium, *Zh. Anal. Khim.*, 17 (1962) 935 (in Russian).
565 POLUÉKTOV, N. S. AND R. A. VITKUN, Atomic-absorption determination of mercury by means of a flame method, *Zh. Anal. Khim.*, 18 (1) (1963) 37 (in Russian).
566 POLUÉKTOV, N. S. AND Y. V. ZELYUKOVA, Absorption flame photometry (survey). *Ind. Lab. (USSR) (English Trans.)*, 30 (1) (1964) 35; *Zavodsk. Lab.*, 30 (1) (1964) 33 (in Russian).
567 POWELL, G., Tissue analysis (Mn, Zn, Cu, K) on muscle and liver by atomic-absorption. Paper presented to the Eastern Analytical Symposium, New York, N.Y., November 11–13, 1964.
568 PRASAD, A. S., D. OBERLEAS AND J. A. HALSTED, Determination of zinc in biological fluids by atomic-absorption spectrophotometry in normal and cirrhotic subjects, *J. Lab. Clin. Med.*, 66 (3) (1965) 508.
569 PREOBRAZHENSKII, N. G., An extension of the limits of applicability of the self absorption method, *Opt. Spectry. (USSR)*, 14 (1963) 183; *Opt. i Spektroskopiya*, 14 (1963) 342 (in Russian).
570 PREUSS, E. AND O. OSTERRIED, A simple method for determination of the effect of liquid flow on flame photometry, *Z. Anal. Chem.*, 198 (1963) 395 (in German).
571 PRICE, W. J., A new instrument for atomic-absorption analysis, *Spectrovision*, 13 (1965) 2.
572 PRIEST, D. E., Design features of a multichannel atomic-absorption photometer. Paper presented to the 10th Detroit Anachem Conference, Detroit, Mich., October 1962.
573 PRUDNIKOV, E. D., Influence of some alcohols and acids on the atomic-absorption and the flame photometric determination of sodium, potassium, rubidium, and cesium, *Vestn. Leningr. Univ.* (20 (10)) *Ser. Fiz. i Khim.*, 2 (1965) 125 (in Russian).
574 PRUGGER, H., Determination of atom concentrations by absorption of resonance lines, *Optik*, 21 (7) (1964) 320 (in German).
575 PUNGOR, E. AND I. KONKOLY-THEGE, On the atomic-absorption research with sodium, *Acta Chim. Acad. Sci. Hung.*, 28 (1–3) (1961) 133 (in German). See also: PUNGOR, E., *Magy. Kem. Lapja*, 15 (1960) 133 (in Hungarian).
576 PÜSCHEL, R., L. SIMON AND R. HERRMANN, Losses of sodium atoms in flame-spectrophotometric analyses with turbulent oxygen–hydrogen flames, *Optik*, 21 (1964) 441 (in German).
577 RAINS, T. C. AND O. MENIS, Determination of the alkaline earth metals in phosphate rock, limestone, feldspar, clay and burnt refractories by flame emission and atomic-absorption spectrophotometry. Paper presented to the Pittsburgh Conference on Analytical Chemistry and Applied Spectroscopy, Pittsburgh, Pa. February 21–25, 1966.
578 RAINS, T. C., H. E. ZITTEL AND M. FERGUSON, Elimination of anionic interferences in the flame spectrophotometric determination of calcium, *Talanta*, 10 (1963) 367.

579 RAMÍREZ-MUÑOZ, J., Discussion to the paper of A. C. MENZIES (*492*). *Proceedings of the 15th International Congress of Pure and Applied Chemistry (Anal. Chem.)*, Vol. II (1956) 313.
580 RAMÍREZ-MUÑOZ, J., Atomic-absorption methods in flame photometry. Lectures in the 1st Interamerican Course on Flame Photometry, organized by the Department of Scientific Affairs, Pan American Union, Bucaramanga, Colombia, August 1962 (in Spanish).
581 RAMÍREZ-MUÑOZ, J., Interference ratios in atomic-absorption flame photometry. Paper presented to 7th Meeting of Philosophical-Scientifical Approximation. Institución Fernando el Católico (High Council of Scientifical Research), Zaragoza, Spain, November 1963 (in Spanish).
582 RAMÍREZ-MUÑOZ, J., The present status of flame photometry, *Rev. Univ. Ind. Santander*, 5 (1) (1963) 387 (in Spanish).
583 RAMÍREZ-MUÑOZ, J., Flame photometry in metallurgical analysis. Extraction methods in flame photometric analysis, *Revista del Instituto del Hierro y del Acero*, 89 (XVII) (1964) 44 (in Spanish).
584 RAMÍREZ-MUÑOZ, J., Analytical applications of atomic-absorption flame photometry. Lecture presented to the Beckman Instruments, Inc. Symposium on Atomic-Absorption Flame Photometry, Pico Rivera, Calif., May 11–12, 1965.
585 RAMÍREZ-MUÑOZ, J., The addition method in emission and atomic-absorption flame photometry, *Inform. Quim. Anal.*, 19 (5) (1965) 154, 183 (in Spanish)[3].
586 RAMÍREZ-MUÑOZ, J., Atomic-absorption flame photometry. Lecture for the Analytical Group of the South California Section (ACS), Los Angeles, Calif. March 1965.
587 RAMÍREZ-MUÑOZ, J., Atomic-absorption spectrophotometry. Lecture for the San Gorgonio Section (ACS), Corona, Calif., March 1965.
588 RAMÍREZ-MUÑOZ, J., Analytical limitations in atomic-absorption flame photometry. Lecture presented to the Joint Local Meeting of the American Chemical Society and Society for Applied Spectroscopy, Syracuse, N. Y., April 13, 1965.
589 RAMÍREZ-MUÑOZ, J., Chemical ways to overcome difficulties in flame photometric analysis. Lecture presented to the Joint Local Meeting of the American Chemical Society and Society for Applied Spectroscopy, Buffalo, N. Y., April 12, 1965.
590 RAMÍREZ-MUÑOZ, J., The dilution method in flame photometry with special attention to its application in biological analysis, *Bol. Soc. Quim. Peru*, 31 (1) (1965) 23 (in Spanish).
591 RAMÍREZ-MUÑOZ, J., Emission and atomic-absorption flame spectrophotometric methods. Lecture presented to the Summer Technical Roundtable Discussion, ACS Orange County Section, Fullerton, Calif., July 15, 1965.
592 RAMÍREZ-MUÑOZ, J., Information on flame photometry. I, *Inform. Quím. Anal.*, 19 (1) (1965) 36 (in Spanish).
593 RAMÍREZ-MUÑOZ, J., Information on flame photometry. II, *Inform. Quím. Anal.*, 19 (3) (1965) 104 (in Spanish).
594 RAMÍREZ-MUÑOZ, J., Information on flame photometry. III, *Inform. Quím. Anal.*, 19 (5) (1965) 162 (in Spanish).
595 RAMÍREZ-MUÑOZ, J., Information on flame photometry. IV, *Inform. Quím. Anal.*, 19 (6) (1965) 198 (in Spanish).
596 RAMÍREZ-MUÑOZ, J., Information on flame photometry. V, *Inform. Quím. Anal.*, 20 (1) (1966) 28 (in Spanish).
597 RAMÍREZ-MUÑOZ, J., Present aspects of atomic-absorption flame photometry. Lecture presented to the Noon Seminar, Beckman Instruments, Inc., Fullerton, Calif., January 1965.
598 RAMÍREZ-MUÑOZ, J., Sensitivity, precision and accuracy in atomic-absorption flame photometry. Lecture presented to the San Diego Section of the Society for Applied Spectroscopy, San Diego, Calif., October 19, 1965.
599 RAMÍREZ-MUÑOZ, J., Nomogram for volume-concentration calculations in the

[3] Paper presented to the IX Latin-American Congress of Chemistry, Puerto Rico, August 1965.

preparation of solutions for flame photometry, *Inform. Quim. Anal.*, 20 (1) (1966) 20 (in Spanish).

600 Ramírez-Muñoz, J., Qualitative and quantitative sensitivity in flame photometry, *Talanta*, 13 (1966) 87[4].

601 Ramírez-Muñoz, J., J. L. Malakoff and C. P. Aime, The use of computer techniques in emission and atomic-absorption flame photometry, *Anal. Chim. Acta*, 36 (1966) 328.[4a]

602 Ramírez-Muñoz, J., N. Shifrin and A. Hell, Quantitative sensitivity in atomic-absorption spectroscopy, *Microchem. J.*, 11(2) (1966) 204[5].

603 Rann, C. S., Aspects of atomic-absorption analysis including the assay of selenium, *M. S. Thesis*, Australian National University, March 1964.

604 Rann, C. S. and A. N. Hambly, The distribution of atoms in flames and its significance in atomic-absorption. Paper presented to the 4th Australian Spectroscopy Conference, Canberra, Australia, August 20, 1963. See also C. K. Coogan *et al.* (*153*).

605 Rann, C. S. and A. N. Hambly, Distribution of atoms in an atomic-absorption flame, *Anal. Chem.*, 37 (7) (1965) 879.

606 Rann, C. S. and A. N. Hambly, The determination of selenium by atomic-absorption spectrophotometry, *Anal. Chim. Acta*, 32 (1965) 346.

607 Rawling, B. S. and M. D. Amos, The application of atomic-absorption spectroscopy in the non-ferrous mining and smelting industry. Paper presented to the 8th Commonwealth Mining and Metallurgical Congress (preprint No. 19), Australia, March 1965.

608 Rawling, B. S., M. D. Amos and M. C. Greaves, Determination of silver in lead sulphide concentrate by atomic-absorption spectroscopy, *Proc. Aust. Inst. Mining Met.*, 199 (1961) 1.

609 Rawling, B. S., M. D. Amos and M. C. Greaves, Determination of silver in lead sulfide concentrate by atomic-absorption spectroscopy, *Trans. Inst. Mining Met.*, 71 (659) (1961–62) 15; (662) (1961–62) 227.

610 Rawling, B. S., M. C. Greaves and M. D. Amos, The determination of silver in lead concentrates by atomic-absorption spectroscopy, *Nature*, 188 (4775) (1960) 137.

611 Rechnitz, G. A., Simplified atomic-absorption spectrophotometer, *J. Chem. Educ.*, 39 (9) (1962) 475.

612 Rich, C. I., Elemental analysis by flame photometry. In C. A. Black, D. D. Evans, J. L. White, L. E. Ensminger, F. E. Clark and R. C. Dinauer, (Eds.), *Methods of Soil Analysis*, Part 2, (No. 9 in the series Agronomy). American Society of Agronomy, Inc. Publ. Madison, Wis., 1965, p. 849.

613 Rigault, G., Application of atomic-absorption spectrophotometry for geochemical research purposes, *Periodico Mineral. (Rome)*, 34 (1) (1965) 117 (in Italian).

614 Robinson, J. W., Progress in atomic-absorption spectroscopy. Paper presented to the Society for Applied Spectroscopy, 11th Annual Symposium on Spectroscopy, Chicago, Ill., June 1960.

615 Robinson, J. W., Atomic-absorption spectroscopy, *Anal. Chem.*, 32 (1960) 17A.

616 Robinson, J. W., Determination of sodium by atomic-absorption spectroscopy, *Anal. Chim. Acta*, 23 (5) (1960) 458.

617 Robinson, J. W., Effect of organic and aqueous solvents on flame photometric emission and atomic-absorption spectroscopy, *Anal. Chim. Acta*, 23 (5) (1960) 479.

618 Robinson, J. W., High temperature flame photometry and atomic-absorption spectrometry. Paper presented to the 13th International Symposium on Modern Methods in Analytical Chemistry, Baton Rouge, La., January 1960.

---

[4] Paper presented to the Pacific Southwest Regional Meeting (ACS), Costa Mesa, Calif., December 1964.

[4a] Paper presented to the Pittsburgh Conference on Analytical Chemistry and Applied Spectroscopy, Pittsburgh, Pa., February 21–25, 1966.

[5] Paper presented to the 149th National ACS Meeting, Detroit, Mich., April 4–9, 1965.

619 ROBINSON, J. W., The application of atomic-absorption spectroscopy. Paper presented to the 18th International Congress on Pure and Applied Chemistry, Montreal, Canada, August 1961.
620 ROBINSON, J. W., Determination of lead in gasoline by atomic-absorption spectroscopy, *Anal. Chim. Acta*, 24 (5) (1961) 451.
621 ROBINSON, J. W., Flame photometry and atomic-absorption spectroscopy, *Progr. Nucl. Energy, Ser. IX*, 2 (1961) 244.
622 ROBINSON, J. W., Mechanism of elemental spectral excitation in flame photometry, *Anal. Chim. Acta*, 24 (1961) 254.
623 ROBINSON, J. W., Recent advances in atomic-absorption spectroscopy, *Anal. Chem.*, 33 (8) (1961) 1067.
624 ROBINSON, J. W., Progress in atomic-absorption spectroscopy, *Develop. Appl. Spectry.*, 1 (1962) 195[6].
625 ROBINSON, J. W., Atomic-absorption spectroscopy, *Ind. Chemist*, 38 (1962) 226, 362.
626 ROBINSON, J. W., Observations in atomic-absorption spectroscopy, *Anal. Chim. Acta*, 27 (5) (1962) 465.
627 ROBINSON, J. W., Atomic-absorption spectroscopy. Paper presented to the Gordon Research Conference, New Hampton, N.H., August 26, 1963.
628 ROBINSON, J. W., Atomic-absorption spectroscopy, its place in analytical chemistry. *The Element* (Technical News Notes from Aztec Instruments, Inc.), No. 1 (November 1964) 4 p.
629 ROBINSON, J. W., The future of atomic-absorption spectroscopy. Paper presented to the 15th Mid-America Symposium on Spectroscopy, Chicago, Ill., June 1964.
630 ROBINSON, J. W., Use of bisolvents in atomic-absorption spectroscopy. Paper presented to the XX International Congress of Pure and Applied Chemistry, Moscow, U.S.S.R., July 9, 1965.
631 ROBINSON, J. W., The future of atomic-absorption spectroscopy, *Develop. Appl. Spectry.*, 4 (1965) 455.
632 ROBINSON, J. W. AND R. J. HARRIS, Mechanical feed burner with total consumption for flame photometry and atomic-absorption spectroscopy, *Anal. Chim. Acta*, 26 (5) (1962) 439.
633 ROBINSON, J. W. AND L. J. KEVAN, Further observations in atomic-absorption spectroscopy, *Anal. Chim. Acta*, 28 (2) (1963) 170.
634 ROBINSON, J. W., T. V. RAMAKRISHNA AND P. W. WEST, The determination of vanadium by means of atomic-absorption spectroscopy. Paper presented to the 4th National Meeting of the Society for Applied Spectroscopy, Denver, Colo., August 30–September 3, 1965.
635 ROSENTHAL, J. E. AND C. F. EYER, Extremely intense light sources with narrow-band spectral emission, *J. Electrochem. Soc.*, 112 (1) (1965) 68.
636 ROSSI, G., Recent developments of spectral emission techniques in the field of nuclear research, *Rev. Univ. Ind. Santander*, 5 (2) (1963) 493 (in Spanish).
637 ROSSOUW, A. J., Discussion to the paper of V. C. O. SCHÜLER *et al.* (*658*), *J.S. African Inst. Mining Met.*, 62 (12, Part II) (1962) 816.
638 ROTH, D. J., Antimony trisulfide–potassium chlorate ratio determination by atomic-absorption spectroscopy. Paper presented to the 16th Annual Mid-America Symposium on Spectroscopy, Chicago, Ill., June 14–17, 1965.
639 ROUSSELET, F., The application of atomic-absorption to clinical biology, *Afinidad*, 22 (237) (1965) 185 (in Spanish).
640 ROUSSELET, F. AND M. L. GIRARD, Application of atomic-absorption flame spectrophotometry to the microdetermination of copper and zinc in biological media, *Compt. Rend.*, 260 (13) (1965) 3780 (in French).
641 RUBEŠKA, I. AND B. MOLDAN, Interference in the determination of magnesium by atomic-absorption spectrophotometry, *Rudy (Prague)*, 12 (6) (1964) 191 (in Czech).

[6] Paper presented to the 12th Annual Symposium on Spectroscopy, Chicago, Ill., May 1961.

642 RUBEŠKA, I., B. MOLDAN AND Z. VALNÝ, Determination of sodium in "pure" limestones by atomic-absorption spectrophotometry, *Anal. Chim. Acta*, 29 (3) (1963) 206.
643 RUBEŠKA, I. AND V. SVOBODA, Some causes of bending of analytical curves in atomic-absorption spectroscopy, *Anal. Chim. Acta*, 32 (1965) 253.
644 RUBEŠKA, I. AND I. VELIČKA, Atomic-absorption spectrophotometry, *Chem. Listy*, 59 (7) (1965) 769 (in Czech).
645 RUMMENS, F. H. A., Absorption spectrophotometry in the ultraviolet and visible regions. In J. KRUGERS AND A. I. M. KEULEMANS (Eds.), *Practical Instrumental Analysis*, Elsevier Publishing Co., Amsterdam, 1965, p. 19.
646 RUSIN, A. D. AND V. M. TATEVSKII, Spectroscopic determination of the concentration of the BO_2 radical in an explosion, *Vestn. Moskov Univ., Ser. II Khim.*, 3 (1962) 21 (in Russian).
647 RUSSELL, B. J., J. P. SHELTON AND A. WALSH, An atomic-absorption spectrophotometer and its application to the analysis of solutions, *Spectrochim. Acta*, 8 (1957) 317.
648 RUSSELL, B. J. AND A. WALSH, Resonance radiation from a hollow-cathode, *Spectrochim. Acta*, 10 (1959) 883.
649 SALTZMAN, R. S., E. S. TAYLOR, R. S. CROWDER AND G. W. REILLY (JR.), Multipoint analyzer for atomic monitoring for p.p.b. organic mercury, *Proc. Ann. Instru. Autom. Conf. Exhibit (ISA)*, Part 2, 40-1-62 (1962) 1.
650 SAPPENFIELD, K. M. AND O. MENIS, Flame photometry. In O. MENIS (Ed.), Quantitative Separations: Titrimetry, Gravimetry, Flame Photometry, Spectrophotometry, Gas Evolution and Isotopic Preparations. July 1964 to June 1965. *Nat. Bur. Std. Tech. Note*, 275 (1965) 12.
651 SAUNDERSON, J. L., A new atomic-absorption photometer. Paper presented to the Pittsburgh Conference on Analytical Chemistry and Applied Spectroscopy, Pittsburgh, Pa., March 1962.
652 SAWYER, R., Atomic-absorption spectrophotometric applications. Paper presented to the Pittsburgh Conference on Analytical Chemistry and Applied Spectroscopy, Pittsburgh, Pa., March 1960.
653 SAWYER, R., Instrumentation and application of atomic-absorption spectroscopy. Paper presented to the 9th Annual Seminar on Spectroscopy of the Society of Applied Spectroscopy, Gainesville, Fla., January 4–6, 1961.
654 SAWYER, R., Absorption spectrophotometry, *Instr. Control Systems*, 34 (11) (1961) 2049.
655 SCHLESER, H., Atomic-absorption spectrophotometry, *Z. Instrumentenk.*, 73 (2) (1965) 25 (in German).
656 SCHRENK, W. G., D. A. LEHMAN AND L. NEUFELD, Atomic-absorption behavior of rhenium. Paper presented to the Fourth National Meeting of the Society for Applied Spectroscopy, Denver, Colo., August 30–September 3, 1965.
657 SCHÜLER, V. C. O. AND A. V. JANSEN, The development of improved atomic-absorption apparatus, *J. S. African Inst. Mining Met.*, 62 (12, Part II) (1962) 790.
658 SCHÜLER, V. C. O., A. V. JANSEN AND G. S. JAMES, The development of atomic-absorption methods for the determination of silver, copper, iron, lead, and zinc in high purity gold and the role of organic additives, *J. S. African Inst. Mining Met.*, 62 (12, Part II) (1962) 807.
659 SCOTT, R. O., The application of direct reading spectrochemical methods to soil analysis, *Trans. Intern. Congr. Soil Sci. 7th, Madison, Wis., 1959*, Vol. II, 2 (1960) 10.
660 SCRIBNER, B. F., Emission spectroscopy, *Anal. Chem.*, 32 (5) (1960) 229R.
661 SCRIBNER, B. F. AND M. MARGOSHES, Emission spectrometry, *Anal. Chem.*, 36 (5) (1964) 329R.
662 SEBENS, C., D. C. MANNING AND W. SLAVIN, Hollow-cathode lamps for atomic-absorption spectrophotometry. Paper presented to the Pittsburgh Conference on Analytical Chemistry and Applied Spectroscopy, Pittsburgh, Pa., March 2–6, 1964.
663 SEBENS, C., J. VOLLMER AND W. SLAVIN, Multi-element hollow-cathode lamps, *Atomic Absorption Newsletter*, 3 (11) (1964) 165.

664 SHAFTO, R. G., The determination of copper, iron, lead, and zinc in nickel plating solutions by atomic-absorption, *Atomic Absorption Newsletter*, 3 (9) (1964) 115.
665 Sharpline Spectro-source[7], Sharpline electrodeless discharge tubes. Bulletin (1965) 2 p.
666 SHELTON, J. P. AND A. WALSH, See comments in *Handbook of 3rd Exhibition of Institute of Physics, Melbourne, Australia*, 1954, 42 pp.
667 SHELTON, J. P. AND A. WALSH, The application of atomic-absorption spectra to chemical analysis, *Proceedings of the 15th International Congress of Pure and Applied Chemistry*, Vol. II (September 1956) 403.
668 SHIFRIN, N., Atomic-absorption accessory for UV visible spectrophotometers. Lecture at the Beckman Instruments, Inc. Meeting, Newport, Calif., December 1964.
669 SHIMAZU, M. AND A. HASHIMOTO, Relation between the shape of analytical curves and spectral line profiles in atomic-absorption analyses, *Sci. Light (Tokyo)*, 11 (3) (1962) 131.
670 SHIN-PIAW CHOONG AND WANG LOONG-SENG, Absorption spectra of silver vapour, *Nature*, 204 (1964) 276.
671 SHTERNBERG, A. N., Use of a hollow-cathode source in routine spectral analysis, *Ind. Lab. (USSR) (English Trans.)*, 29 (9) (1963) 1176; *Zavodsk. Lab.*, 29 (9) (1963) 1084 (in Russian).
672 SIKORSKI, M. E. AND P. L. COPELAND, Application of atomic-absorption spectroscopy to solids. Paper presented to the 8th Annual Symposium on Spectroscopy, Chicago, Ill., April 29–May 1, 1957; *Spectrochim. Acta*, 9 (1957) 361.
673 SIMMONS, E. C., Gold assay by atomic-absorption spectrophotometry, *Atomic Absorption Newsletter*, 4 (5) (1965) 281.
674 SKOGERBOE, R. K., Study of the optimum conditions for the analysis of some rare-earths by atomic-absorption methods, *Ph. D. Thesis*, Montana State College, Bozeman, Mon., 1963.
675 SKOGERBOE, R. K. AND R. A. WOODRIFF, Atomic-absorption spectra of europium, thulium, and ytterbium using a flame as line source, *Anal. Chem.*, 35 (12) (1963) 1977.
676 SLAVIN, W., Agricultural applications of atomic-absorption spectrophotometry, *Atomic Absorption Newsletter*, (4) (1962) 1.
677 SLAVIN, W., The application of atomic-absorption spectrophotometry to metallurgy, *Atomic Absorption Newsletter*, (5) (1962) 1.
678 SLAVIN, W., Applications of atomic-absorption spectrophotometry to isotope analysis. Paper presented to the Sixth Conference on Analytical Chemistry in Nuclear Reactor Technology, Gatlinburg, Tenn., October 1962.
679 SLAVIN, W., Atomic-absorption spectrophotometry without the use of flames, *Atomic Absorption Newsletter*, (7) (1962) 1.
680 SLAVIN, W., Biological applications of atomic-absorption spectrophotometry, *Atomic Absorption Newsletter*, (2) (1962) 1.
681 SLAVIN, W., A burner-atomizer for atomic-absorption spectrophotometry, *Atomic Absorption Newsletter*, (10) (1963) 1.
682 SLAVIN, W., Determination of trace metals in biological materials by atomic-absorption spectrophotometry. Paper presented to the 5th International Congress on Clinical Chemistry, Detroit, Mich., August 19–23, 1963. Abstract: *Clin. Chem.*, 9 (4) (1963) 22.
683 SLAVIN, W., Recent developments in atomic-absorption spectroscopy. Paper presented to the SAS, Pittsburgh, Pa., April 17, 1963.
684 SLAVIN, W., A review of methods for the determination of lead, sodium, copper, iron, and nickel in petroleum products, *Atomic Absorption Newsletter*, (12) (1963) 4.
685 SLAVIN, W., Atomic-absorption instrumentation and technique—a review, *Atomic Absorption Newsletter*, (24) (1964) 15.

---

[7] Sharpline Spectro-source. 1203 Woodcrest Drive, Downers Grove, Ill., U.S.A.

686 Slavin, W., Quantitative metal analysis by atomic-absorption spectrophotometry, *Chim. Indust. (Milan)*, 46 (1964) 60 (in Italian).
687 Slavin, W., Some data on ammonium pyrrolidinedithiocarbamate, *Atomic Absorption Newsletter*, (10) (1964) 141.
688 Slavin, W., Application of atomic-absorption spectroscopy to clinical medicine and toxicology. Lecture before the American Association of Clinical Chemists, Southern California Section, Children's Hospital Auditorium, Los Angeles, Calif., February 2, 1965.
689 Slavin, W., Application of atomic-absorption spectroscopy to analytical biochemistry and toxicology, *Occupational Health Rev.*, 17 (1965) 9.
690 Slavin, W., The application of atomic-absorption spectroscopy to geochemical prospecting and mining, *Atomic Absorption Newsletter*, 4 (4) (1965) 243.
691 Slavin, W., Applications of atomic-absorption spectroscopy in the food industry, *Atomic Absorption Newsletter*, 4 (8) (1965) 330.
692 Slavin, W., An atomic-absorption bibliography for 1964 and index to references, *Atomic Absorption Newsletter*, 4 (2) (1965) 194.
693 Slavin, W., Atomic-absorption spectroscopy. Paper presented to the Fifth Australian Spectroscopy Conference, Perth, W. Australia, May 31–June 2, 1965.
694 Slavin, W., Atomic-absorption spectroscopy. Paper presented to the 1st Joint International Symposium on Analytical Instrumentation and Chemical and Petroleum Instrumentation (ISA), Montreal, Canada, May 1965.
695 Slavin, W., A critical review of atomic-absorption spectroscopy. Paper presented to the 150th ACS Meeting, Atlantic City, New Jersey, September 12–17, 1965.
696 Slavin, W., The determination of various metals in synthetic fibers using atomic-absorption spectrophotometry, *Atomic Absorption Newsletter*, 4 (2) (1965) 192.
697 Slavin, W., Extension of atomic-absorption detection limits. Paper presented to the 4th National Meeting of the Society for Applied Spectroscopy, Denver, Colo., August 30–September 3, 1965.
698 Slavin, W., Instrumentation for atomic-absorption spectroscopy. Paper presented to the Joint Meeting of the American Society of Clinical Pathologists and College of American Pathologists, Chicago, Ill., October 15–23, 1965.
699 Slavin, W., New trends in atomic-absorption instrumentation. Discussion presented to the Symposium "Unresolved problems in spectrochemical analysis" (Organized and sponsored by the A.S.T.M. Committee E-2 on Emission Spectroscopy), 4th National Meeting of the Society for Applied Spectroscopy, Denver, Colo., September 3, 1965.
700 Slavin, W., Recent improvements in analytical atomic-absorption spectrophotometry. Paper presented to the Pittsburgh Conference on Analytical Chemistry and Applied Spectroscopy, Pittsburgh, Pa., March 1965.
701 Slavin, W., The application of atomic-absorption to agricultural and biological chemistry. Paper presented to the Pittsburgh Conference on Analytical Chemistry and Applied Spectroscopy, Pittsburgh, Pa., February 21–25, 1966.
702 Slavin, W., The present status of flame absorption spectrometry in the chemical laboratory. Paper presented to the Phoenix Symposium on Flame Spectrometric Methods of Analysis, Phoenix, Ariz., January 16–21, 1966.
703 Slavin, W. and D. C. Manning, Atomic-absorption spectrophotometry in strongly reducing oxy–acetylene flames, *Anal. Chem.*, 35 (2) (1963) 253.
704 Slavin, W. and D. C. Manning, Performance of lead hollow-cathode lamps for atomic-absorption spectroscopy, *Appl. Spectry.*, 19 (3) (1965) 65.
705 Slavin, W. and C. Sebens, Modern improvements in hollow-cathode lamps for atomic-absorption spectroscopy. Paper presented to the 1965 Eastern Analytical Symposium, New York City, N. Y., November 17–19, 1965.
706 Slavin, W., C. Sebens and S. Sprague, Arsenic hollow-cathodes and the determination of arsenic, *Atomic Absorption Newsletter*, 4 (9) (1965) 341.
707 Slavin, W. and S. Sprague, The determination of trace metals in blood and urine by atomic-absorption spectrophotometry, *Atomic Absorption Newsletter*, (17) (1964) 1.
708 Slavin, W., S. Sprague and D. C. Manning, The determination of calcium by

atomic-absorption spectrophotometry, *Atomic Absorption Newsletter*, (15) (1963) 1.
709 SLAVIN, W., S. SPRAGUE AND D. C. MANNING, Detection limits in analytical atomic-absorption spectroscopy, *Atomic Absorption Newsletter*, (18) (1964) 1.
710 SLAVIN, W., S. SPRAGUE, F. RIEDERS AND V. CORDOVA, The determination of certain toxicological trace metals by atomic-absorption spectrophotometry, *Atomic Absorption Newsletter*, (17) (1964) 7.
711 SLAVIN, W. AND D. J. TRENT, An atomic-absorption spectrophotometer having concentration readout, *Atomic Absorption Newsletter*, 4 (10) (1965) 351.
712 SLAVIN, W., D. J. TRENT AND S. SPRAGUE, The determination of rubidium by atomic-absorption spectrophotometry, *Atomic Absorption Newsletter*, 4 (1) (1965) 180.
713 SMITH, D. M., Conference on limitations of detection in spectrochemical analysis, Exeter, July 1964; *Brit. J. Appl. Phys.*, 15 (1964) 1267.
714 SPRAGUE, S., Some atomic-absorption determinations of calcium and magnesium in blood, *Atomic Absorption Newsletter*, (13) (1963) 8.
715 SPRAGUE, S., Cement analysis, *Atomic Absorption Newsletter*, (14) (1963) 9.
716 SPRAGUE, S., D. C. MANNING AND W. SLAVIN, The determination of selenium and tellurium in copper by atomic-absorption spectrophotometry, *Atomic Absorption Newsletter*, (20) (1964) 1[8].
717 SPRAGUE, S., D. C. MANNING AND W. SLAVIN, Linear working curves in atomic-absorption spectrophotometry. Paper presented to the 16th Annual Mid-America Symposium on Spectroscopy, Chicago, Ill., June 14–17, 1965.
718 SPRAGUE, S. AND W. SLAVIN, Determination of the metal content of lubricating oils by atomic-absorption spectrophotometry, *Atomic Absorption Newsletter*, (12) (1963) 1.
719 SPRAGUE, S. AND W. SLAVIN, The application of atomic-absorption spectrophotometry to the analysis of certain metals in alloys systems. Paper presented to the 15th Mid-America Symposium on Spectroscopy, Chicago, Ill., June 4, 1964.
720 SPRAGUE, S. AND W. SLAVIN, The determination of copper, nickel, cobalt, manganese and magnesium in irons and steels by atomic-absorption spectrophotometry, *Atomic Absorption Newsletter*, (23) (1964) 8.
721 SPRAGUE, S. AND W. SLAVIN, Determination of copper, nickel, cobalt, manganese and magnesium in irons and steels by atomic-absorption spectrophotometry, *Develop. Appl. Spectry.*, 4 (1964) 433 (Publ. 1965).
722 SPRAGUE, S. AND W. SLAVIN, The determination of nickel in urine by atomic-absorption spectrophotometry—preliminary study, *Atomic Absorption Newsletter*, 3 (11) (1964) 160.
723 SPRAGUE, S. AND W. SLAVIN, Determination of very small amounts of copper and lead in potassium chloride by organic extraction and atomic-absorption spectrophotometry, *Atomic Absorption Newsletter*, (20) (1964) 11.
724 SPRAGUE, S. AND W. SLAVIN, Determination of iron, copper, and zinc in blood serum by an atomic-absorption method requiring only dilution, *Atomic Absorption Newsletter*, 4 (3) (1965) 228.
725 SPRAGUE, S. AND W. SLAVIN, Performance of the three-slot Boling burner, *Atomic Absorption Newsletter*, 4 (6) (1965) 393.
726 SPRAGUE, S. AND W. SLAVIN, A rapid method for the determination of trace metals in used aircraft lubricating oils, *Atomic Absorption Newsletter*, 4 (10) (1965) 367.
727 STAAB, R. A., Atomic fluorescence flame photometry as a means of chemical analysis. *Doctoral Thesis*, University of Florida, Gainesville, Fla. University Microfilms, Ann Arbor, Mich., Order No. 64-11, 545, 75 pp.
728 Standards Association of Australia, Committee on Sampling and Analysis of Ferrous Metals, Determination of magnesium in iron by atomic-absorption spectrophotometry, *Proc. Roy. Austr. Chem. Inst.*, 30 (3) (1963) 111.
729 STANSFIELD, J. R. AND R. LOCKYER, Trace determinations in steel by atomic-absorption spectroscopy. Paper presented to the Pittsburgh Conference on Ana-

[8] Paper presented to the Fifteenth Pittsburgh Conference on Analytical Chemistry and Applied Spectroscopy, Pittsburgh, Pa., March 2–6, 1964.

lytical Chemistry and Applied Spectroscopy, Pittsburgh, Pa., February 21–25, 1966.

730 STEWART, W. K., F. HUTCHINSON AND L. W. FLEMING, The estimation of magnesium in serum and urine by atomic-absorption spectrophotometry, *J. Lab. Clin. Med.*, 61 (1963) 858.

731 STRASHEIM, A., A time-resolved spark as a source for atomic-absorption analysis, *Nature*, 196 (4860) (1962) 1194.

732 STRASHEIM, A. AND L. R. P. BUTLER, A versatile hollow-cathode lamp for atomic-absorption spectroscopy, *Appl. Spectry.*, 16 (3) (1962) 109.

733 STRASHEIM, A. AND L. R. P. BUTLER, Simultaneous multi-element analysis by atomic-absorption spectroscopy. Paper presented to the Pittsburgh Conference on Analytical Chemistry and Applied Spectroscopy, Pittsburgh, Pa., March 2–6, 1964.

734 STRASHEIM, A., L. R. P. BUTLER AND E. C. MASKEW, The determination of certain impurities in gold by atomic-absorption spectroscopy, *J. S. African Inst. Mining Met.*, 62 (12, Part II) (1962) 796.

735 STRASHEIM, A., E. NORVAL AND L. R. P. BUTLER, The atomic-absorption determination of traces of lead in fish flour, *J. S. African Chem. Inst.*, 17 (2) (1964) 55.

736 STRASHEIM, A., F. W. E. STRELOW AND L. R. P. BUTLER, Determination of copper by means of atomic-absorption spectroscopy, *J. S. African Chem. Inst.*, 13 (2) (1960) 73.

737 STRASHEIM, A. AND F. VERSTER, The determination of copper and zinc in human tissues by means of atomic-absorption spectroscopy, *Tydskrift vir Natuurwetenskappe*, (September 1961) 197 (in African).

738 STRASHEIM, A. AND G. J. WESSELS, Atomic-absorption determination of some noble metals, *Appl. Spectry.*, 17 (3) (1963) 65. See also M.Sc. in Physics Thesis of G. J. WESSELS, Univ. Stellenbosch (1962).

739 STRELOW, F. W. E., E. C. FEAST, P. M. MATHEWS, C. J. C. BOTHMA AND C. R. VAN ZYL, Determination of gold in cyanide waste solutions by solvent extraction and atomic-absorption spectrometry, *Anal. Chem.*, 38 (1) (1966) 115.

740 STROUTS, C. R. N., H. N. WILSON AND R. T. PARRY-JONES, *Chemical Analysis: The working tools*. 2nd edition, Vol. 2, Oxford Univ. Press, New York, N.Y., 1962.

741 STUMPF, K. E. AND T. GONSIOR, Applicability of atomic-absorption flame spectrometry in the metallurgical laboratory. IX Colloquium Spectroscopicum Internationale, Lyons, France, June 5–10, 1961, *Publ. Group. Avan. Methodes Spectrog.*, 3 (1962) 279 (in German).

742 STUPAR, J., Determination of rubidium in agriculturally important materials by atomic-absorption flame photometry. Ljubljana, Rep. R-425 (1964) 11 pp. (in German). See also *Z. Anal. Chem.*, 203 (1964) 401.

743 STUPAR, J., B. PODOBNIK AND J. KOROSIN, The determination of cadmium in uranium compounds by atomic-absorption spectrophotometry, *Croat. Chem. Acta*, 27 (1965) 141.

744 SULLIVAN, J. V., New techniques in atomic-absorption spectroscopy. 1. High temperature flames and light sources. 2. Isolation and detection of atomic resonance lines. Paper presented to the 9th Annual Symposium on Modern Methods of Analytical Chemistry, Baton Rouge, La., January 24–27, 1966.

745 SULLIVAN, J. V., Recent advances in atomic-absorption spectroscopy. Paper presented to the Pittsburgh Conference on Analytical Chemistry and Applied Spectroscopy, Pittsburgh, Pa., February 21–25, 1966.

746 SULLIVAN, J. V. AND A. WALSH, Paper presented to the 4th Australian Spectroscopy Conference, Canberra, Australia, August 20, 1963. According to C. K. COOGAN *et al.* (*153*).

747 SULLIVAN, J. V. AND A. WALSH, High intensity hollow-cathode lamps, *Spectrochim. Acta*, 21 (4) (1965) 721.

748 SULLIVAN, J. V. AND A. WALSH, Resonance radiation from atomic vapours, *Spectrochim. Acta*, 21 (4) (1965) 727.

749 SUNDERMAN, F. W., Measurements of nickel in biological materials by atomic-absorption spectrometry, *Am. J. Clin. Pathol.*, 44 (2) (1965) 182.

750 SUNDERMAN, F. W. AND J. E. CARROLL, Measurements of serum calcium and magnesium by atomic-absorption spectrometry, *Am. J. Clin. Pathol.*, 43 (4) (1965) 302.
751 SUZUKI, M. AND T. TAKEUCHI, Atomic-absorption spectrophotometry. Determination of magnesium in cast iron by atomic-absorption spectrophotometry, *Kogyo Kagaku Zasshi*, 66 (5) (1963) 690 (in Japanese).
752 SUZUKI, M., M. YANACISAWA AND T. TAKEUCHI, Determination of magnesium by atomic-absorption spectrophotometry after extraction, *Talanta*, 12 (11) (1965) 989.
753 SVEHLA, G., Atomic-absorption spectrophotometry, a new branch of metal analysis, *Kohasz. Lapok*, 95 (1962) 448 (in Hungarian).
754 SVEHLA, G., A. PALL AND L. ERDEY, Improved method for error calculation of quantitative spectrophotometric measurements, *Talanta*, 10 (1963) 719.
755 TABELING, R. W. AND R. K. BREHM, The Jarrell-Ash Ebert scanning spectrometer and its application in flame photometry. Jarrell-Ash Co., Publication No. 82-000(F) (1962) 5 pp.
756 TABELING, R. W. AND J. DEVANEY, Factors influencing sensitivity in atomic-absorption spectroscopy. Paper presented to the 12th Annual Symposium on Spectroscopy (SAS), Chicago, Ill., May 15–18, 1961. Preprint by Jarrell-Ash Co.
757 TABELING, R. W. AND J. DEVANEY, Factors influencing sensitivity in atomic-absorption spectroscopy, *Develop. Appl. Spectry.*, 1 (1962) 175.
758 TAKAHASHI, M., An atomic-absorption spectrometer, *Bunko Kenkyu*, 12 (5) (1964) 197 (in Japanese).
759 TAKAHASHI, M. AND Y. TAKASHIMA, The determination of potassium in sodium salts by atomic-absorption method, *Bunko Kenkyu*, 13 (1) (1964) 14 (in Japanese).
760 TAKAHASHI, M. AND Y. URUNO, Determination of magnesium in uranium by atomic-absorption, *Bunko Kenkyu*, 10 (1962) 110 (in Japanese).
761 TAKEUCHI, T. AND M. SUZUKI, The determination of sodium, potassium, magnesium, manganese, and calcium in cement by atomic-absorption spectrophotometry, *Talanta*, 11 (10) (1964) 1391.
762 TAKEUCHI, T. AND M. SUZUKI, Problems in atomic-absorption spectrophotometry, *Kagaku No Ryoiki*, 18 (1) (1964) 38 (in Japanese).
763 TAKEUCHI, T., M. SUZUKI AND H. MICHIKI, Atomic-absorption spectrophotometry. III. Determination of nickel in iron and steel by atomic-absorption spectrophotometry, *Kogyo Kagaku Zasshi*, 66 (8) (1963) 1194 (in Japanese).
764 TAKEUCHI, T., M. SUZUKI AND K. YASUDA, Atomic-absorption spectrophotometry. I. The effect of other ele mentson the determination of calcium and potassium by atomic-absorption spectrophotometry, *Kogyo Kagaku Zasshi*, 65 (7) (1962) 1025 (in Japanese).
765 TARDON, S., Determination of elements by absorption flame photometry, *Chem. Listy*, 58 (4) (1964) 417.
766 Techtron Pty. Ltd., Chemical analysis by atomic-absorption. Brochure (1963) 3 pp.
767 TELOH, H. A., *Clinical flame photometry*, Thomas, Springfield, Ill., 1959.
768 The Ealing Corp.[9], Spectroscopes, spectrometers, spectral sources. Brochure (1963) 12 pp.
769 THILLIEZ, G., Atomic-absorption spectroscopy. Apparatus, results, and applications, *Chim. Anal.*, 46 (1) (1964) 3.
770 TINDALL, F. M., Silver and gold assay by atomic-absorption spectrophotometry, *Atomic Absorption Newsletter*, 4 (9) (1965) 339.
771 TINTEA, H., C. UNGUREANU AND E. WEISSMANN, Isotopic analysis by optical spectroscopic methods. Atomic spectra, *Acad. Rep. Populare Romine, Studii Cerecetari Fiz.*, 13 (1) (1962) 147 (in Rumanian).
772 TRENT, D. J., The determination of lead in gasoline by atomic-absorption spectroscopy, *Atomic Absorption Newsletter*, 4 (9) (1965) 348.
773 TRENT, D. J. AND D. C. MANNING, Analytical applications of the oxy–acetylene flame in atomic-absorption spectrophotometry. Paper presented to the 16th

---

[9] TheEaling C orporation. 2225 Massachusetts Ave., Cambridge, Mass. 02140, U.S.A.

Pittsburgh Conference on Analytical Chemistry and Applied Spectroscopy, Pittsburgh, Pa., March 1965.
774 TRENT, D. J., D. C. MANNING AND W. SLAVIN, Self-absorption in sodium discharge lamps, *Atomic Absorption Newsletter*, 4 (8) (1965) 335.
775 TRENT, D. AND W. SLAVIN, The direct determination of trace quantities of nickel in catalitic cracking feedstocks by atomic-absorption spectrophotometry, *Atomic Absorption Newsletter*, 3 (10) (1964) 131.
776 TRENT, D. AND W. SLAVIN, Determination of the major metals in granitic and diabasic rocks by atomic-absorption spectrophotometry, *Atomic Absorption Newsletter*, (19) (1964) 1.
777 TRENT, D. J. AND W. SLAVIN, Determination of various metals in silicate samples by atomic-absorption spectrophotometry, *Atomic Absorption Newsletter*, 3 (9) (1964) 118.
778 TRENT, D. AND W. SLAVIN, Factors in the determination of strontium by atomic-absorption spectrophotometry with particular reference to ashed biological samples, *Atomic Absorption Newsletter*, (22) (1964) 1.
779 TRENT, D. J. AND W. SLAVIN, Clinical application of an atomic-absorption spectrophotometer linear in concentration, *Atomic Absorption Newsletter*, 4 (6) (1965) 300.
780 TRUSCHKE, E. J., A study of methods for sample preparation in absorption spectroscopy. Paper presented to the 16th Annual Mid-America Symposium on Spectroscopy, Chicago, Ill., June 14–17, 1965.
781 ULRICH, W. F., Atomic-absorption spectrophotometry. Lecture at the Beckman Instruments, Inc. Meeting, Newport, Calif., December 1964.
782 ULRICH, W. F., Atomic-absorption spectroscopy—past, present and future. Paper presented to the Association of Analytical Chemists of Michigan, Detroit, Mich., September 20, 1965.
783 ULRICH, W. F., Atomic-absorption spectroscopy, instrumentation, theory, and technique. Paper presented to the U.S. Geological Survey Water Resources Conference, Denver, Colo., October 11, 1965.
784 ULRICH, W. F. AND N. SHIFRIN, Atomic-absorption spectrophotometry. I and II. *The Analyzer*, 6 (2) (1965) 10.
785 Unicam Instruments Ltd., Advance Information (1964) 1 p.
786 VALLEE, B. L. AND K. FUWA, Recent studies in atomic-absorption spectroscopy. Paper presented to the Symposium on Recent Developments in Research Methods and Instrumentation, National Institute of Health, Bethesda, Md., October 1963.
787 VALLEE, B. L. AND R. E. THIERS, Flame Photometry, *Treatise Anal. Chem.*, 6 (1965) 3463.
788 VEILLON, C., Fine points in instrumentation (letter to the editor), *Chem. Eng. News*, (March 8, 1965) 4.
789 VEILLON, C. AND J. D. WINEFORDNER, Flame fluorescence spectrometry. Paper presented to the Phoenix Symposium on Flame Spectrometric Methods of Analysis, 151st American Chemical Society Meeting, Phoenix, Ariz., January 16–21, 1966.
790 VIGNOLI, L., R. BADRE, M. C. MOREL AND J. ARDORINO, A comparative study of modern techniques for the micro determination of mercury, *Chim. Anal.*, 45 (1963) 53 (in French).
791 VOINOVITCH, I. A., M. HAMEAU, J. LEGRAND AND L. KATZ, Investigation of the mechanism of the effect of certain organic reagents in flame spectrophotometry. Paper presented to the XX International Congress of Pure and Applied Chemistry, Moscow, U.S.S.R., July 9, 1965.
792 VOLLMER, J., C. SEBENS AND W. SLAVIN, Improved zinc hollow-cathode lamps, *Atomic Absorption Newsletter*, 4 (6) (1965) 306.
793 WACKER, W. E. C., C. IIDA AND K. FUWA, Accuracy of determinations of serum magnesium by flame emission and atomic-absorption spectrometry, *Nature*, 202 (4933) (1964) 659.
794 WALLACE, F. J., The determination of zinc in metallurgical materials by atomic-absorption spectroscopy, *Hilger J.*, 7 (1962) 39.
795 WALLACE, F. J., The determination of copper in metallurgical materials by atomic-absorption spectroscopy, *Hilger J.*, 7 (4) (1963) 65.

796 WALLACE, F. J., Determination of magnesium in aluminum alloys by atomic absorption spectroscopy, *Analyst*, 88 (1045) (1963) 259.
797 WALSH, A., The application of atomic-absorption spectra to chemical analysis, *Spectrochim. Acta*, 7 (1955) 108.
798 WALSH, A., Communication presented to the 2nd Australian Spectroscopy Conference, Melbourne, Australia, June 1959. According to N. S. HAM (*303*).
799 WALSH, A., The application of atomic-absorption spectroscopy to chemical analysis. Paper presented to the Pittsburgh Conference on Analytical Chemistry and Applied Spectroscopy, Pittsburgh, Pa., March 1960.
800 WALSH, A., Application of atomic-absorption spectra to chemical analysis, *Advan. Spectry.*, 2 (1961) 1.
801 WALSH, A., Atomic-absorption spectroscopy, *Proc. Colloq. Spectros. Intern. 10th Univ. Maryland, June, 1962*, (June 1963) 127.
802 WALSH, A., Atomic-absorption spectroscopy, *Spectry., Rept. Conf. Organ. Hydrocarbon Res. Group Inst. Petrol., London, England*, (1962) 13.
803 WALSH, A., Atomic-absorption spectroscopy in Australia. Paper presented to the Louisiana State University Symposium, Baton Rouge, La., February 1962.
804 WALSH, A., Atomic-absorption spectroscopy in Australia, in *Analytical Chemistry 1962*, Proc. Feigl Anniversary Symp., Birmingham, England, 1962; Elsevier, Amsterdam, 1963, p. 281.
805 WALSH, A., Some recent advances in atomic-absorption spectroscopy. Paper presented to the XX International Congress of Pure and Applied Chemistry, Moscow, U.S.S.R., July 9, 1965.
806 WALSH, A., Some recent advances in atomic-absorption spectroscopy. Paper presented to the XII Colloquium Spectroscopicum Internationale, Exeter, England, July 1965.
807 WARING, P. P., R. S. HARDING, J. A. MOORMAN AND Z. Z. ZIPORIN, A comparison of automated calcium determinations by atomic-absorption spectroscopy and colorimetric analysis. Paper presented to the 4th National Meeting of the Society for Applied Spectroscopy, Denver, Colo., August 30–September 3, 1965.
808 WARREN, R. L., A versatile micro-sample flame spectrophotometer. *VIII Colloquium Spectroscopicum Internationale, Lucerne, Switzerland*, Sauerlander, Aarau, Switzerland, 1959, p. 213.
809 WARREN, R. L., Some aspects of atomic-absorption, *Spectroscopy Conference, Institute of Petroleum Symposium*, R. Clay, Bungay, Suffolk, Great Britain, 1962, p. 27.
810 WEBERLING, R. P., J. F. COSGROVE AND D. J. BRACCO, Analysis of small samples of mixed alkaline-earth carbonates. Paper presented to the American Chemical Society, New York (September 1963). According to *Atomic Absorption Newsletter*, (16) (1963) 8.
811 WENNINGER, J. A. AND J. H. JONES, Determination of submicrogram amounts of mercury in inorganic pigments by the photometric mercury vapor procedure, *J. Assoc. Offic. Agr. Chemists*, 46 (1963) 1018.
812 WERNER, G. K., D. D. SMITH, S. J. OVENSHINE, O. B. RUDOLF AND J. R. MCNALLY, Further investigations in the spectro-isotopic assay technique for lithium, *J. Opt. Soc. Am.*, 45 (1955) 203.
813 WESSELS, G. J., Discussion to the paper of V. C. O. SCHÜLER *et al.* (*658*). *J. S. African Inst. Mining and Met.*, 62 (12, Part II) (1962) 817.
814 WEST, P. W., Inorganic microchemistry, *Anal. Chem.*, 34 (5) (1962) 104R.
815 Westinghouse Electric Corporation, Electronic Tube Division, Hollow-cathode spectral tubes for atomic-absorption spectroscopy. Brochure ET-1437-0264-10M, 1964, 4 pp.
816 Westinghouse Electric Corporation, Electronic Tube Division, Westinghouse hollow-cathode tubes don't cover all the elements. Advertisement in *Appl. Spectry.*, 18 (5) (1964) 22A.
817 Westinghouse Electric Corporation, Electronic Tube Division, Hollow-cathode discharge devices for atomic-absorption spectroscopy. Catalog, 1965, 4 pp.
818 Westinghouse Electric Corporation, Electronic Tube Division, Hollow-cathode

tubes. Alphabetic Listing. Single and multiple element types. Catalog (1965) 13 pp.
819 WHITE, J. U., Long optical paths of large aperture, *J. Opt. Soc. Am.*, 32 (1942) 285.
820 WHITTINGTON, C. M. AND J. B. WILLIS, The analysis of trace elements in electroplating solutions by atomic-absorption spectroscopy. Reprint from *Plating*, (August, 1964) 767.
821 WILL, F. (III), Nonferrous metallurgy. I. Light metals, *Anal. Chem.*, 37 (5) (1965) 92R.
822 WILLIAMS, C. H., The use of lanthanum chloride to prevent interferences in the flame photometric determination of exchangeable calcium in soils, *Anal. Chim. Acta*, 22 (1960) 163.
823 WILLIAMS, C. H., D. J. DAVID AND O. IISMAA, The determination of chromic oxide in faeces samples by atomic-absorption spectrometry, *J. Agr. Sci.*, 59 (Part 3) (1962) 381.
824 WILLIS, J. B., Determination of magnesium in blood serum by atomic-absorption spectroscopy, *Nature*, 184 (Suppl. No. 4) (1959) 186.
825 WILLIS, J. B., The determination of calcium and magnesium in blood by atomic-absorption spectroscopy. Paper presented to the 2nd Australian Spectroscopy Conference, Melbourne, Australia, June 1–3, 1959. Abstract in *Spectrochim. Acta*, 15 (9) (1959) 785. See also N. S. HAM (*303*).
826 WILLIS, J. B., The determination of calcium in blood serum by atomic-absorption spectroscopy, *Nature*, 186 (4720) (1960) 249.
827 WILLIS, J. B., Determination of metals in blood serum by atomic-absorption spectroscopy. I. Calcium, *Spectrochim. Acta*, 16 (3) (1960) 259.
828 WILLIS, J. B., Determination of metals in blood serum by atomic-absorption spectroscopy. II. Magnesium, *Spectrochim. Acta*, 16 (3) (1960) 273.
829 WILLIS, J. B., The determination of metals in blood serum by atomic-absorption spectroscopy. III. Sodium and potassium, *Spectrochim. Acta*, 16 (5) (1960) 551.
830 WILLIS, J. B., Paper presented to the 3rd Australian Spectroscopy Conference, Sydney, Australia, August 1961, *Nature*, 192 (4806) (1961) 929. See R. A. DURIE (*203*).
831 WILLIS, J. B., Determination of calcium and magnesium in urine by atomic-absorption spectroscopy, *Anal. Chem.*, 33 (4) (1961) 556.
832 WILLIS, J. B., Determination of lead in urine by atomic-absorption spectroscopy, *Nature*, 191 (4786) (1961) 381.
833 WILLIS, J. B., Atomic-absorption spectroscopy, *Proc. Roy. Australian Chem. Inst.*, (July 1962) 245.
834 WILLIS, J. B., Determination of lead and other heavy metals in urine by atomic-absorption spectroscopy, *Anal. Chem.*, 34 (6) (1962) 614.
835 WILLIS, J. B., Analysis of biological materials by atomic-absorption spectroscopy, *Methods of Biochem. Anal.*, 11 (1962) 1.
836 WILLIS, J. B., The determination of copper in butter and butteroil by atomic-absorption spectroscopy, *Australian J. Dairy Technol.*, 19 (2) (June 1964) 70.
837 WILLIS, J. B., The analysis of biological materials by atomic-absorption spectroscopy, *Clin. Chem.*, 11 (2, Part I) (1965) 251.
838 WILLIS, J. B., Nitrous oxide–acetylene flame in atomic-absorption spectroscopy, *Nature*, 207 (4998) (1965) 715.
839 WILSON, L., Determination of silver in aluminum alloys by atomic-absorption spectroscopy. Commonwealth of Australia, Dept. of Supply, Aeronaut. Res. Lab. Report ARL/MET 46 (1962) 20 pp.
840 WILSON, L., The determination of silver in aluminium alloys by atomic-absorption spectroscopy, *Anal. Chim. Acta*, 30 (1964) 377.
841 WINEFORDNER, J. D., Effect of spectrometer slit width on intensity of atomic emission lines in emission flame photometry, and the effect of sourceline width on absorbance of atomic-absorption lines in absorption flame photometry, *Appl. Spectry.*, 17 (5) (1963) 109.
842 WINEFORDNER, J. D., Atomic fluorescence flame spectrometry. Paper presented

to the Eastern Analytical Symposium, New York, N.Y., November 11–13, 1964.
843 WINEFORDNER, J. D., Atomic fluorescence flame spectrometry—a critical review, Paper presented to the 150th American Chemical Society Meeting, Atlantic City. N. J., September 12–17, 1965.
844 WINEFORDNER, J. D., Atomic fluorescence flame spectrometry. Paper presented to the 9th Annual Symposium on Modern Methods of Analytical Chemistry, Baton Rouge, La., January 24–27, 1966.
845 WINEFORDNER, J. D. AND H. W. LATZ, Quantitative study of factors influencing sample flow rate in flame photometry, *Anal. Chem.*, 33 (12) (1961) 1727.
846 WINEFORDNER, J. D., C. T. MANSFIELD AND T. J. VICKERS, Atomization efficiency of total consumption atomizer-burners in flame photometry, *Anal. Chem.*, 35 (11) (1963) 1607.
847 WINEFORDNER, J. D., C. T. MANSFIELD AND T. J. VICKERS, Temperatures of some typical flames used in flame photometry, *Anal. Chem.*, 35 (11) (1963) 1611.
848 WINEFORDNER, J. D. AND R. A. STAAB, Determination of zinc, cadmium, and mercury by atomic fluorescence flame spectrometry, *Anal. Chem.*, 35 (11) (1963) 1611.
849 WINEFORDNER, J. D. AND R. A. STAAB, Study of experimental parameters in atomic fluorescence flame spectrometry, *Anal. Chem.*, 36 (7) (1964) 1367.
850 WINEFORDNER, J. D. AND C. VEILLON, Instrumental reduction of background signal of fuel-rich oxy–acetylene flames used in atomic-absorption spectrometry, *Anal. Chem.*, 36 (4) (1964) 943.
851 WINEFORDNER, J. D. AND C. VEILLON, Influence of electrometer noise on limit of detectability in atomic-absorption and atomic emission flame photometry, *Anal. Chem.*, 37 (3) (1965) 416.
852 WINEFORDNER, J. D. AND T. J. VICKERS, Atomic fluorescence spectrometry as a means of chemical analysis, *Anal. Chem.*, 36 (1) (1964) 161.
853 WINEFORDNER, J. D. AND T. J. VICKERS, Calculation of the limit of detectability in atomic-absorption flame spectrometry, *Anal. Chem.*, 36 (10) (1964) 1947.
854 WOODSON, T. T., A new mercury vapor detector, *Rev. Sci. Inst.*, 10 (1939) 308.
855 WOODSON, T. T., Industrial mercury-vapor detector, *Ind. Met. 10, Ind. Hyg. Sect.*, 2 (1941) 22.
856 WÜNSCH, A. AND K. TEICHER, The determination of magnesium in plant material by absorption flame spectroscopy, *Z. Pflanzenernahr. Dueng. Bodenk.*, 97 (1962) 101 (in German).
857 YASUDA, K. AND S. MATSUDAIRA, Relation between the Ca-resonance line profile of the hollow-cathode lamp of flame and absorption intensity in atomic-absorption. Paper presented to the Pittsburgh Conference on Analytical Chemistry and Applied Spectroscopy, Pittsburgh, Pa., March 2–6, 1964.
858 YOFÉ, J., R. AVNI AND M. STILLER, Elimination of phosphate interference in flame-photometric determination of strontium and barium. Israel Atomic Energy Comm., Rep. IA-770 (1962) 15 pp.
859 YOFÉ, J., R. AVNI AND M. STILLER, Elimination of phosphate interference in flame photometric determination of strontium and barium, *Anal. Chim. Acta*, 28 (1963) 331.
860 ZAIDEL, A. N., On the determination of the isotopic composition by spectral absorption technique, *Opt. i Spektroskopiya*, 4 (1958) 701 (in Russian).
861 ZAIDEL, A. N., Spectral analysis of isotopic composition, *Usp. Fiz. Nauk.*, 68 (1959) 123 (in Russian).
862 ZAIDEL, A. N., Use of spectral methods for determination of isotopic composition in analytical chemistry. Paper presented to the XX International Congress of Pure and Applied Chemistry, Moscow, U.S.S.R., July 9, 1965.
863 ZAIDEL, A. N., Fundamentals of spectral analysis. To be published in *The Physics and Technology of Spectral Analysis*, Nauka. According to G. B. PREOBRAZHENSKAYA, New Books on spectral analysis, *Ind. Lab. (USSR) (English Transl.)*, 31 (6) (1965) 962; *Zavodsk. Lab.*, 31 (6) (1965) 775 (in Russian).
864 ZAIDEL, A. N. AND E. P. KORENNOI, Spectral determination of the isotopic composition and concentration of lithium in solutions, *Opt. Spectry. (USSR) (English*

Transl.), 10 (1961) 299; *Opt. i Spectroskopiya*, 10 (1961) 570 (in Russian).
865 ZAIDEL, A. N. AND E. P. KORENNOI, Determination of the isotopic composition of lithium by atomic-absorption methods, *Ind. Lab. (USSR) (English Transl.)*, 29 (1964) 1617; *Zavodsk. Lab.*, 29 (1963) 1449 (in Russian).
866 ZAK, B., Recent applications of spectroscopy in clinical chemistry. Paper presented to the 1965 Anachem Conference, Detroit, Mich., October 19–21, 1965.
867 ZEEMAN, P. B. AND L. R. P. BUTLER, Determination of lead, copper, and zinc in wines by atomic-absorption spectroscopy, *Appl. Spectry.*, 16 (4) (1962) 120.
868 ZEEMAN, P. B. AND L. R. P. BUTLER, The determination of lead in wines by atomic-absorption spectroscopy, *Tegnikon*, 3 (10) (1960) 96 (in African).
869 ZELIUKOVA, YU. V. AND N. S. POLUÉKTOV, Atomic-absorption analysis by means of exhaust gases of the flame, *Zh. Analit. Khim.*, 18 (4) (1963) 435 (in Russian).
870 ZETTNER, A., Principles and applications of atomic-absorption spectroscopy, *Advan. Clin. Chem.*, 7 (1964) 1.
871 ZETTNER, A., Clinical calcium, magnesium, and iron determination. Paper presented to the Joint Meeting of the American Society of Clinical Pathologists and College of American Pathologists, Chicago, Ill., October 15–23, 1965.
872 ZETTNER, A. AND E. BERMAN, Manual for workshop on clinical methods of atomic-absorption spectroscopy. Commission on Continuing Education. Council on Clinical Chemistry. American Society of Clinical Pathologists, Chicago, Ill., (1965) 37 pp.
873 ZETTNER, A. AND L. MANSBACH, Application of atomic-absorption spectrophotometry in the determination of iron in urine, *Am. J. Clin. Pathol*, 44 (5) (1965) 517.
874 ZETTNER, A. AND D. SELIGSON, The determination of serum calcium using atomic-absorption spectrophotometry. Paper presented to the 5th International Congress on Clinical Chemistry, Detroit, Mich., August 19–23, 1963. Abstract: *Clin. Chem.*, 9 (4) (1963) 21.
875 ZETTNER, A. AND D. SELIGSON, Application of atomic-absorption spectrophotometry in the determination of calcium in serum, *Clin. Chem.*, 10 (9) (1964) 869.
876 ZETTNER, A., L. SYLVIA AND L. CAPACHO-DELGADO, Application of atomic-absorption spectroscopy to the determination of serum iron and iron binding capacity. Paper presented to the Joint Meeting of the American Society of Clinical Pathologists and College of American Pathologists, Chicago, Ill., October 15–23, 1965.
877 ZHIGLINSKII, A. G., A. N. ZAIDEL AND A. A. PETROV, Spectroscopic analysis of isotopic composition. Paper presented to the 14th Conference on Applied Spectroscopy, Gorki, U.S.S.R., July 1962. According to *Appl. Spectry.*, 18 (4) (1964) 32A.
878 ZHIGLINSKII, A. G., A. N. ZAIDEL AND A. A. PETROV, Special analysis of isotope compositions, *Ind. Lab. (USSR) (English Transl.)*, 29 (5) (1963) 575; *Zavodsk. Lab.*, 29 (5) (1963) 550 (in Russian).
879 ZUEHLKE, C. W. AND A. E. BALLARD, Photometric method for the estimation of minute amounts of mercury. Use of G.E. germicidal ultraviolet intensity meter, *Anal. Chem.*, 22 (1950) 953.

APPENDIX

ADDENDUM TO BIBLIOGRAPHY

This addendum contains references which became available during the period of final revision and typing of the manuscript.

880 AMOS, M. D., Developments in instrumentation for atomic-absorption spectroscopy. Paper presented to the Pittsburgh Conference on Analytical Chemistry and Applied Spectroscopy, Pittsburgh, Pa., February 21–25, 1966.
881 Anonymous, Evans model EEL-140 atomic-absorption spectrophotometer. Fisher Scientific Co. Product Bulletin 14-380 (1965) 8 pp.
882 Anonymous, Fisher certified atomic-absorption standards for accurate metal determinations. Fisher Scientific Co. Product Data. Brochure (1965) 2 pp.

883 Anonymous, Instrument makers court atomic-absorption, *Chem. Eng. News*, 43 (4) (January 25, 1965) 48.
884 Anonymous, New instruments, products and procedures. The Beckman Atomic Absorption Accessory, *Afinidad*, 22 (1965) 373 (in Spanish).
885 Anonymous, A report on the newest atomic-absorption spectrophotometer, *The Laboratory*, 33 (4) (1965) 106.
886 Anonymous, Atomic-absorption instruments proliferate, *Chem. Eng. News*, 44 (10) (1966) 56.
887 Anonymous, Determination of refractory elements by atomic-absorption is now routine, *Instrument News*, 16 (3) (1966) 12.
888 Anonymous, Hollow-cathode discharge tubes for atomic-absorption spectrometry. Fisher Scientific Co. Bulletin No. 14-380-5 (1966) 4 pp.
889 Anonymous, New Hitachi Perkin-Elmer Model 139 Atomic Absorption Spectrophotometer, *Scientific Products Review*, (January–February, 1966) 3.
890 Anonymous, Spectrometry heads Louisiana State University Symposium, *Anal. Chem.*, 38 (3) (1966) 58 A.
891 Barras, R. C. and H. W. Smith, The determination of vanadium by atomic-absorption spectrophotometry. Paper presented to the Pittsburgh Conference on Analytical Chemistry and Applied Spectroscopy, Pittsburgh, Pa., February 21–25, 1966.
892 Beckman Instruments, Inc., The Beckman Atomic Absorption Accessory for ultraviolet spectrophotometers. Bulletin No. 7064-A (1965) 7 pp.
893 Belt, C. B. (Jr.), Far-red photomultiplier for the Perkin-Elmer model 214 spectrophotometer, *Atomic Absorption Newsletter*, 5 (1) (1966) 11.
894 Berman, E., Application of atomic-absorption spectrophotometry to trace metal analysis of biological materials. Paper presented to the Anachem Meeting, Detroit, Mich., October 19–21, 1965.
895 Berman, E., Clinical copper, lead, mercury and thallium determination. Paper presented to the Joint Meeting of the American Society of Clinical Pathologists and College of American Pathologists, Chicago, Ill., October 15–23, 1965.
896 Bermejo-Martínez, F., Instrumental methods of analysis. IV. New techniques in atomic-absorption spectrophotometry, *Quím. Ind. (Bilbao)*, 11 (5) (1964) 123 (in Spanish).
897 Billings, G. L., Light scattering in trace-element analysis by atomic-absorption, *Atomic Absorption Newsletter*, 4 (10) (1965) 357.
898 Brech, F., Improved technology in atomic-absorption including multi-channel approaches. Preprint (1965) 7 pp.
899 Burger, J. C., Hollow-cathode tubes and their applications. Paper presented to the Pittsburgh Conference on Analytical Chemistry and Applied Spectroscopy, Pittsburgh, Pa., February 21–25, 1966.
900 Capacho-Delgado, L. and D. C. Manning, Determination of metals in cements by atomic-absorption spectroscopy. Paper presented to the Pittsburgh Conference on Analytical Chemistry and Applied Spectroscopy, Pittsburgh, Pa., February 21–25, 1966.
901 Capacho-Delgado, L. and D. C. Manning, Determination of vanadium in steels and gas oils, *Atomic Absorption Newsletter*, 5 (1) (1966) 1.
902 Capacho-Delgado, L. and S. Sprague, Calcium interference in atomic-absorption analysis for barium, *Atomic Absorption Newsletter*, 4 (10) (1965) 363.
903 Carl Zeiss, Flame spectrophotometer for emission and absorption analysis with the flame attachment FA 2 and PMQ II. Brochure 50-657/FA2-e (1965) 6 pp.
904 Cellier, K. M. and H. C. T. Stace, Determination of optimum operating conditions in atomic-absorption spectroscopy, *Appl. Spectry.*, 20 (1) (1966) 26.
905 Chang, T. L., T. A. Gover and W. W. Harrison, Determination of magnesium and zinc in human brain by atomic-absorption spectroscopy, *Anal. Chim. Acta*, 34 (1966) 17.
906 Dagnall, R. M., T. S. West and P. Young, Determination of lead in steels, brass and bronze by atomic-absorption spectrometry, *Anal. Chem.*, 38 (2) (1966) 558.

907 DeKalb, E. L., R. N. Kniseley and V. A. Fassel, Purification of materials. Optical emission as an analytical tool. U.S. Atomic Energy Comm. IS-1237 (1965) 40 pp.
908 Dumanski, J., Adaptation and modification in determining copper, zinc and manganese in plant materials by atomic-absorption spectroscopy, *Roczniki Nauk Rolniczych Ser A.*, 90 (3) (1965) 431 (in Polish).
909 Fassel, V. A., V. G. Mossotti, W. E. L. Grossman and R. N. Kniseley, Evaluation of spectral continua as primary sources in atomic-absorption spectroscopy, *Spectrochim. Acta*, 22 (2) (1966) 347.[10]
910 Ginzburg, V. L., D. M. Livshits and G. I. Satarina, Atomic-absorption spectrophotometric determination of silver, gold, palladium, platinum and rhodium, *Zh. Analit. Khim.*, 19 (9) (1964) 1089 (in Russian).
911 Goleb, J. A., The determination of uranium isotopes by atomic-absorption spectrophotometry, *Anal. Chim. Acta*, 34 (1966) 135.
912 Hameau, M., Comparison between flame spectrophotometry and atomic-absorption in the analysis of minerals. Lecture presented at the Symposium on Atomic Absorption of the Chemical Institute of Sarriá, Barcelona, Spain, March 22–26, 1965.
913 Hameau, M., Quantitative determination of calcium, iron, and magnesium in silicocalcareous minerals by atomic-absorption spectroscopy, *Afinidad*, 22 (237) (1965) 176 (in Spanish).
914 Herrmann, R., Fundamentals and applications of atomic-absorption flame spectroscopy, *Z. Klin. Chem.*, 3 (6) (1965) 178.
915 Herrmann, R., Atomic-absorption flame photometry, *Fortschr. Chem. Forsch.*, 5 (3) (1966) 515 (in German).
916 Hitachi, Ltd., Accessories for Hitachi UV-VIS Spectrophotometer model 139. Brochure EX-E120A (1966) 27 pp.
917 Joyner, T. and J. S. Finley, The determination of manganese and iron in sea water by atomic-absorption spectrometry, *Atomic Absorption Newsletter*, 5 (1) (1966) 4.
918 Kahn, H. L., Instrumentation for atomic-absorption. I. and II, *J. Chem. Educ.*, 43 (1) (1966) A 7; (2) (1966) A 103.
919 Kahnke, M. J., Atomic-absorption spectrophotometry applied to the determination of zinc in formalinized human tissue, *Atomic Absorption Newsletter*, 5 (1) (1966) 7.
920 Lefebvre, J. C., Atomic-absorption in organic chemistry. Lecture presented at the Symposium on Atomic Absorption of the Chemical Institute of Sarriá, Barcelona, Spain, March 22–26, 1965.
921 Lefebvre, J. C., Atomic-absorption in petrochemistry. Lecture presented at the Symposium on Atomic Absorption of the Chemical Institute of Sarriá, Barcelona, Spain, March 22–26, 1965.
922 Margoshes, M. and M. M. Darr, Atomic-absorption spectrometry. In Spectrochemical Analysis: Optical spectrometry, X-ray fluorescence spectrometry, and electron probe microanalysis techniques. July 1964 to June 1965, *Natl. Bur. Std., Tech. Note*, 272 (1965) 18.
923 Masumura, T., M. Sugawara and S. Ariyoshi, Atomic-absorption spectroscopy method for mineral analysis of mixed feeds and ingredients. I. Determination of calcium and magnesium, *Nippon Nogeikagaku Kaishi*, 39 (10) (1965) 402.
924 McBride, C. H., Determination of minor nutrients in fertilizers by atomic-absorption spectrometry: second collaboration study, *J. Assoc. Offic. Agr. Chemists*, 48 (6) (1965) 1100. See ref. (*483*).
925 Negri, R. G., Trace analysis and detectable limits of the elements. Lecture presented at the Symposium on Atomic Absorption of the Chemical Institute of Sarriá, Barcelona, Spain, March 22–26, 1965.
926 Negri, R. G., Theoretical fundamentals of atomic-absorption. Lecture presented

[10] Paper presented to the XII Colloquium Spectroscopicum Internationale, Exeter, England, July, 1965.

at the Symposium on Atomic Absorption of the Chemical Institute of Sarriá, Barcelona, Spain, March 22–26, 1965.
927 OBIOLS-SALVAT, J., Atomic-absorption spectroscopy, *Afinidad*, 22 (237) (1965) 173.
928 PATERSON, J. E., Moderator (J. C. BURGER, V. A. FASSEL, R. E. MANSELL, J. A. NORRIS AND W. SLAVIN), Atomic Absorption. Panel Discussion at the Pittsburgh Conference on Analytical Chemistry and Applied Spectroscopy, Pittsburgh, Pa., February 21–25, 1966.
929 PREVOT, A. AND C. BARBATI, Determination of sodium and potassium in fats by atomic-absorption, *Rev. Franc. Corps Gras*, 11 (1965) 657 (in French).
930 PRUGGER, H., Development of absorption flame photometry for technical methods in the chemical laboratorium, *Zeiss-Informationen*, (56) (1965) 54.
931 RAMÍREZ-MUÑOZ, J., Practical use of concentration limits in atomic-absorption flame photometry, *Rev. Univ. Ind. Santander*, 7 (4) (1965) 233 (in Spanish).
932 RAMÍREZ-MUÑOZ, J., On the adoption of the word "analito" in the scientific literature published in Spanish on analytical chemistry, *Inform. Quím. Anal.*, 20 (1) (1966) 25 (in Spanish).
933 RAMÍREZ-MUÑOZ, J., Determinations of zinc in plant materials by atomic-absorption flame photometry, *Anales Inst. Edafol. Biol. Veg.* (in press, in Spanish).
934 RAMÍREZ-MUÑOZ, J., High-sodium systems in atomic-absorption flame photometry. Paper presented to the XIII Colloquium Spectroscopium Internationale, Ottawa, Canada, June 19–23, 1967.
935 RAMÍREZ-MUÑOZ, J., Relationship between accuracy and sensitivity in atomic-absorption flame photometry, *Microchem. J.*, 12 (2) (1967) 196.
936 RAMÍREZ-MUÑOZ, J., The significance of absolute limits in atomic-absorption flame photometry, *Bol. Soc. Quim Peru*, 32 (2) (1966) 57 (in Spanish).[11]
937 RAMÍREZ-MUÑOZ, J., Scale expansion in atomic-absorption flame photometry (not yet submitted for publication).
938 RAMÍREZ-MUÑOZ, J., Two standard method in emission and atomic-absorption flame photometry (not yet submitted for publication).
939 ROTH, D. J., Ratio determination of antimony trisulfide and potassium chlorate by atomic-absorption spectrophotometry, *U.S. At. Energy Comm. MLM-1289-J*, (1965) 9 pp.
940 ROUSSLET, F., Biological and pharmaceutical applications of atomic-absorption. Lecture presented at the Symposium on Atomic Absorption of the Chemical Institute of Sarriá, Barcelona, Spain, March 22–26, 1965.
941 SKEWES, H. R., Determination of gold in mill cyanide solutions by atomic-absorption spectroscopy, *Australasian Inst. Min. Met. Proc.*, (211) (1964) 217.
942 SLAVIN, W., Comments on "Light scattering in trace-element analysis", *Atomic Absorption Newsletter*, 4 (10) (1965) 361. See G. L. BILLINGS (*897*).
943 SLAVIN, W., Burner notes, *Atomic Absorption Newsletter*, 5 (1) (1966) 11.
944 SLAVIN, W., Use of Osram lamp power supply, *Atomic Absorption Newsletter*, 5 (1) (1966) 12.
945 SPRAGUE, S. AND W. SLAVIN, A simple method for determination of lead in blood, *Atomic Absorption Newsletter*, 5 (1) (1966) 9.
946 STIEHLER, R. D. AND J. MANDEL, Evaluation of analytical methods by the sensitivity criterion, *Anal. Chem.*, 29 (4) (1957) 17 A. See also J. MANDELL AND R. D. STIEHLER, *J. Res. Natl. Bur. Std.*, 1954, 155.53, R.P. 2527, and *Natl. Bur. Std. Tech. News Bull.*, 40 (1956) 139.
947 TILCH, J., U. RANHUT AND F. WALTER, Analysis of ruby by atomic-absorption, *Rev. Roumaine Chim.*, 10 (8) (1965) 691 (in German).
948 VOLLMER, J., Bismuth hollow-cathode lamp, *Atomic Absorption Newsletter*, 5 (1) (1966) 12.
949 WENDT, R. H. AND V. A. FASSEL, Atomic-absorption with induction-coupled plasmas, *Anal. Chem.*, 38 (2) (1966) 337.

[11] Paper presented to the VII Peruvian Congress of Chemistry, Lima, Peru, October 18–23, 1965.

950 Westinghouse Electric Corporation, Electronic Tube Division, Hollow-cathode discharge devices for atomic-absorption spectroscopy. Bulletin HCDD (1966) 16 pp.

A new periodic publication, *Flame Notes. Beckman*, has appeared and covers topics on emission and atomic-absorption flame photometry. Volumes I and II have been published during 1966 and 1967. Several articles of the present author have been included in this publication; a few of them have been mentioned in the foot notes corresponding to Tables 13–4 and 13–5.
Two new notes of the series "Information on flame photometry" *(592-596)*. Notes VI and VII, have been published in *Inform. Quim. Anal.*, 20 (5) (1966) 146, and 21 (2) (1967) 75 resp.

Junior Author Index

ADAMS, J. A. S., *ref. 101*
ADAMS, P. B., *ref. 544*
ADLER, S., *ref. 223*
AIME, C. P., *ref. 601*
AKAMATSU, K., *ref. 448*
ALESKOWSKII, V. B., *ref. 529*
ALKEMADE, C. T. J., *ref. 321*
AMOS, M. D., *ref. 607, 608, 609, 610*
ARAS, A., *ref. 190*
ARDORINO, J., *ref. 790*
ARIYOSHI, S., *ref. 923*
ATUYA, I., *ref. 292*
ATWOOD, J. G., *ref. 426*
AVNI, R., *ref. 858, 859*

BADRE, R., *ref. 790*
BALLARD, A. E., *ref. 879*
BARBATI, C., *ref. 929*
BARNES, R. M., *ref. 450*
BEALE, P. A. A., *ref. 193*
BELCHER, C. B., *ref. 396, 397, 398*
BERMAN, E., *ref. 872*
BERRY, C. T., *ref. 294*
BILLINGS, G. K., *ref. 308*
BLOOM, A. L., *ref. 86*
BOITEUX, A. L., *ref. 479*
BOTHMA, C. J. C., *ref. 739*
BOURKE, R. C., *ref. 517*
BOYLE, J. F., *ref. 69*
BRACCO, D. J., *ref. 810*
BRACE, R. O., *ref. 150*
BRAY, H. M., *ref. 80*
BRECH, F., *ref. 195*
BREHM, R. K., *ref. 755*
BRINK, D., *ref. 130*
BRODY, J. K., *ref. 287*
BROOKS, K. A., *ref. 81*
BUTLER, L. R. P., *ref. 732, 733, 734, 735, 736, 867, 868*

CAPACHO-DELGADO, L., *ref. 876*
CARNES, W. J., *ref. 189*
CARROLL (JR.), J. E., *ref. 526*
CARROLL, J. E., *ref. 750*
CHABOVSKII, L. P., *ref. 414*
CHAKRABARTI, C. L., *ref. 199*
CHAMBERS, W. E., *ref. 451*
CLAUS, R. W., *ref. 110*
COOKE, W. D., *ref. 262, 263, 264, 265, 266*
COPELAND, P. L., *ref. 672*
COSGROVE, J. F., *ref. 810*
CORDOVA, V., *ref. 710*
COWLEY, T. C., *ref. 232*
CROWDER, R. S., *ref. 649*
CUNNINGHAM, A. F., *ref. 511*
CURRY, R. H., *ref. 201, 229, 230*

DAGNALL, R. M., *ref. 83*
DARR, M. M., *ref. 922*
DAVID, D. J., *ref. 823*
DECKER, L. E., *ref. 190*
DEVANEY, J., *ref. 756, 757*
DHUMWARD, R. K., *ref. 238*
DIEFENDERFER, A. J., *ref. 249*
DOEPFMER, R., *ref. 412*
DOMINGUEZ, M., *ref. 137*
DOWLING, F. B., *ref. 146*
D'SILVA, A. P., *ref. 404*

ELLIS, D. J., *ref. 183, 184*
EMMEL, H. W., *ref. 469, 470*
ENVALI, B., *ref. 64*
ERDEY, L., *ref. 393, 754*
EYER, C. F., *ref. 635*

FASSEL, V. A., *ref. 191, 200, 201, 404, 405, 406, 510, 907, 949*
FEAST, E. C., *ref. 133, 739*
FELDMAN, C., *ref. 408*
FERGUSON, M., *ref. 578*
FINLEY, J. S., *ref. 917*
FIORINO, J., *ref. 233*
FLEMING, L. W., *ref. 730*
FOSTER, J. E., *ref. 157*
FUWA, K., *ref. 786, 793*

GANNON, W. C., *ref. 157*
GARTON, F. W. J., *ref. 66*
GEORGE, P., *ref. 354, 355*
GEYER, R., *ref. 196, 197*
GIBSON, J. H., *ref. 154*
GIDLEY, J. A. F., *ref. 212, 213, 214, 215*
GILBERT, H., *ref. 361*
GILLIES, W., *ref. 119, 120, 121*
GIRARD, M. L., *ref. 640*
GOLDWATER, L. J., *ref. 360, 361*
GOLIGHTLY, D., *ref. 232*
GONSIOR, T., *ref. 741*
GOULDEN, R. J., *ref. 157*
GOVER, T. A., *ref. 905*
GRAYSTONE, J. E., *ref. 149*
GREAVES, M. C., *ref. 608, 609, 610*

GRINZAID, S. E., *ref. 562, 563*
GROSSMAN, W. E., *ref. 154, 236, 263, 264, 265, 266, 909*
GUNNING, H. E., *ref. 538*

HAMBLY, A. N., *ref. 604, 605, 606*
HAMEAU, M., *ref. 791*
HAMES, G. E., *ref. 436, 437, 438*
HARDING, R. S., *ref. 807*
HARRIS, R. J., *ref. 632*
HARRISON, W. W., *ref. 905*
HASHIMOTO, A., *ref. 669*
HASTED, J. A., *ref. 568*
HEATON, F. W., *ref. 185*
HEERDT, J. C., *ref. 126*
HELL, A., *ref. 602*
HELWIG, J. D., *ref. 70*
HERRMANN, R., *ref. 419, 420, 421, 422, 423, 424, 425, 576*
HODGES, R. J., *ref. 398*
HODKINSON, A., *ref. 309*
HOFER, A., *ref. 429, 430*
HOLT, A. B., *ref. 149*
HUGHES, R. C., *ref. 480*
HUNEMORDER, E. J., *ref. 471*
HUTCHINSON, F., *ref. 730*

IIDA, C., *ref. 793*
IISSMAA, O., *ref. 823*
IKEDA, S., *ref. 292*

JAMES, G. S., *ref. 658*
JANSEN, A. V., *ref. 214, 657, 658*
JIMÉNEZ-SECO, J. L., *ref. 290*
JONES, I. L., *ref. 294*
JONES, J. H., *ref. 811*
JONES, J. T., *ref. 270, 271*

KAHN, H. L., *ref. 458*
KATZ, L., *ref. 791*
KEVAN, L. J., *ref. 633*
KINSON, K., *ref. 82*
KITCHING, R., *ref. 345*
KNISELEY, R. N., *ref. 191, 200, 201, 229, 230, 231, 232, 233, 236, 907, 909*
KOHLER, T. R., *ref. 350*
KOLTAI, L., *ref. 217*
KONKOLI-THEGE, I., *ref. 575*
KORENNOI, E. P., *ref. 864, 865*
KOROSIN, J., *ref. 743*
KOZYREVA, N. A., *ref. 358*
KUEBLER, N. A., *ref. 388, 521, 522, 523, 524, 525*
KURIHARA, M., *ref. 448*

LAMP, R. W., *ref. 300*
LANG, W., *ref. 322, 323, 324, 325, 326, 327, 328, 329, 330*
LAQUA, K., *ref. 301*
LATNER, A. L., *ref. 348*
LATZ, H. W., *ref. 845*
LEGRAND, J., *ref. 791*
LEHMAN, D. A., *ref. 656*
LIVSHITS, D. M., *ref. 910*
LOCK, D. N., *ref. 242*
LOCYER, R., *ref. 729*
LORD (JR), S. S., *ref. 87*
LUCIANO, V. J., *ref. 297, 298, 299*
LYLES, G. R., *ref. 146*
LYNCH, J., *ref. 86*

MCKAY, R., *ref. 250*
MCLAUGHLIN, E. L., *ref. 470*
MCNALLY, J. R., *ref. 812*
MCSWINEY, R. R., *ref. 353*
MAGEE, R. J., *ref. 218, 485, 486*
MALAKOFF, J. L., *ref. 601*
MALISSA, H., *ref. 291*
MANDEL, J., *ref. 946*
MANNING, D. C., *ref. 138, 139, 140, 382, 662, 703, 704, 708, 709, 716, 717, 773, 774, 900, 901*
MANSBACH, L., *ref. 873*
MANSFIELD, C. T., *ref. 846, 847*
MARCY, V. M., *ref. 557, 558, 559*
MARGOSHES, M., *ref. 661*
MASKEW, E. C., *ref. 734*
MATHEWS, P. M., *ref. 133, 739*
MATSUDAIRA, S., *ref. 857*
MAVRODINEANU, R., *ref. 350*
MENIS, O., *ref. 577, 650*
MENOSKI, W. J., *ref. 497, 498*
MICHIKI, H., *ref. 763*
MIKKELEIT, W., *ref. 202*
MIKLUS, K. J., *ref. 383*
MILATZ, M. W., *ref. 5, 6*
MOLDAN, B., *ref. 641, 642*
MOORMAN, J. A., *ref. 807*
MOREL, M. C., *ref. 790*
MORRISON, J. D., *ref. 153*
MOSICHEV, V. I., *ref. 445*
MOSSOTTI, V. G., *ref. 231, 232, 234, 235, 236, 301, 909*
MUELLER, G., *ref. 196, 197*
MUNEMORI, M., *ref. 518*
MURAOKA, T. T., *ref. 116*
MYERS, R. B., *ref. 201, 230*

NAKANISHI, Y., *ref. 518*
NELSON, L. S., *ref. 388*
NEU, W., *ref. 331*
NEUFELD, L., *ref. 656*
NEVILLE, G. J., *ref. 143*
NICHOLS, P. N. R., *ref. 22*
NITZSCHE, U., *ref. 198*

NORRIS, J. A., *ref. 114*
NORVAL, E., *ref. 735*

OBERLEANS, D., *ref. 658*
OSTERRIED, O., *ref. 570*
OVENSHINE, S. J., *ref. 812*

PALL, A., *ref. 754*
PALMER, R., *ref. 193*
PARKER, H. E., *ref. 295*
PASSMORE, W. O., *ref. 1*
PASZTOR, L. C., *ref. 77*
PETROV, A. A., *ref. 877, 878*
PFORR, G., *ref. 202*
PICKERLING, P. F., *ref. 485, 486*
PICKETT, E. E., *ref. 409, 410*
PODOBNIK, B., *ref. 743*
POLUÉKTOV, N. S., *ref. 869*
PRICE, J. W., *ref. 490*
PULIDO, P., *ref. 250*
PURDY, W. C., *ref. 239*

RAFAELE, I., *ref. 117*
RAHNUT, U., *ref. 947*
RAMAKRISHNA, T. V., *ref. 634*
RAMÍREZ-MUÑOZ, *ref. 110, 111, 125, 150, 313, 314, 315, 316*
RATCLIFF, D., *ref. 491*
REILLY (JR.), G. W., *ref. 649*
RIEDERS, F., *ref. 710*
RIEMENS, J., *ref. 208*
RODGERSON, D. O., *ref. 310*
RODRÍGUEZ, P. A., *ref. 450*
ROGLER, J. C., *ref. 295*
RUDIGER, K., *ref. 329, 425*
RUDOLF, O. B., *ref. 812*
RUTMAN, R. J., *ref. 354, 355*

SAKAGUCHI, T., *ref. 305*
SATARINA, G. I., *ref. 282, 910*
SATO, S., *ref. 448*
SAWYER, R. R., *ref. 223*
SCAIFE, P. H., *ref. 490*
SCHLESER, F. H., *ref. 530*
SCOTT, J. E., *ref. 439*
SCRIBNER, B. F., *ref. 474*
SEBENS, C., *ref. 705, 706, 792*
SEEGMILLER, D. W., *ref. 300*
SELIGSON, D., *ref. 874, 875*
SELLERS, N. G., *ref. 356*
SENYUTA, S. A., *ref. 445*
SHELTON, J. P., *ref. 647*
SHIFRIN, N., *ref. 313, 314, 315, 316, 602, 784*
SHREIDER, E. YA., *ref. 103*
SIMON, L., *ref. 576*
SLADE, S., *ref. 439*
SLAVIN, W., *ref. 259, 383, 384, 385, 459, 460, 461, 462, 662, 663, 716, 717, 718, 719, 720, 721, 722, 723, 724, 725, 726, 774, 775, 776, 777, 778, 779, 792, 945*
SMITH, D. D., *ref. 812*
SMITH, H. W., *ref. 69, 891*
SPRAGUE, S., *ref. 259, 461, 462, 706, 707, 708, 709, 710, 712, 902*
STAAB, R. A., *ref. 848, 849*
STACE, H. C. T., *ref. 144, 904*
STAMM, D., *ref. 330*
STEVENS, R. E., *ref. 246*
STILLER, M., *ref. 858, 859*
STRASHEIM, A., *ref. 131, 132, 133*
STRELOW, F. W. E., *ref. 133, 736*
SUGAWARA, M., *ref. 923*
SULLIVAN, J. V., *ref. 107, 255*
SUZUKI, M., *ref. 761, 762, 763, 764*
SVEHLA, G., *ref. 216, 217, 393*
SVOBODA, V., *ref. 643*
SYKES, B. J., *ref. 206*
SYLVIA, L., *ref. 876*

TAKASHIMA, Y., *ref. 759*
TAKEUCHI, T., *ref. 751, 752*
TATEVSKII, V. M., *ref. 646*
TAYLOR, E. S., *ref. 649*
TEICHER, K., *ref. 856*
THIERS, R. E., *ref. 787*
THOMAS, P. E., *ref. 18, 19*
THOMAS, T. A., *ref. 371*
TOWNSHEND, A., *ref. 302*
TRENT, D. J., *ref. 462, 463, 711, 712*

ULRICH, W. F., *ref. 281*
UNGAR, S. G., *ref. 223*
UNGUREANU, C., *ref. 771*
URUNO, Y., *ref. 760*
USSARY, J. P., *ref. 260*

VALLEE, B. L., *ref. 250, 251, 252, 253*
VALNY, Z., *ref. 642*
VAN ZYL, C. R., *ref. 739*
VEILLON, C., *ref. 472, 850, 851*
VELIČKA, I., *ref. 644*
VENN, R., *ref. 179*
VERSTER, F., *ref. 737*
WEST, P. W., *ref. 634*
VICKERS, T. J., *ref. 846, 847, 852, 853*
VITKUN, R. A., *ref. 564, 565*
VOIGT, R., *ref.* 205
VOLLMER, J., *ref. 463, 663*

WALSH, A., *ref. 107, 108, 109, 153, 255, 256, 257, 304, 372, 647, 648, 666, 667, 746, 747, 748*
WALTER, F., *ref. 947*
WANG L.-S., *ref. 670*
WEISSMANN, E., *ref. 771*

WENDT, R. H., *ref. 233*
WESSELS, G. J., *ref. 738*
WEST, T. S., *ref. 83, 158, 906*
WILLIS, J. B., *ref. 20, 126, 179, 249, 258, 820*
WILMSHURST, J. K., *ref. 153*
WILSON, C. L., *ref. 485, 486*
WILSON, H. N., *ref. 740*
WINEFORDNER, J. D., *ref. 472, 789*
WOODRIFF, R. A., *ref. 675*

YAMASAKI, G. K., *ref. 120, 121*
YANACISAWA, M., *ref. 752*
YASUDA, K., *ref. 447, 448, 764*
YOKOYAMA, Y., *ref. 288, 289*
YOSHIDA, T., *ref. 305*
YOUNG, P., *ref. 906*

ZAIDEL, A. N., *ref. 877, 878*
ZELYUKOVA, Y. V., *ref. 566*
ZEMANSKI, M. W., *ref. 503*
ZIPORIN, Z. Z., *ref. 807*
ZITTEL, H. E., *ref. 578*

Subject Index

A

abcissae at the arbitrary absorbance origin, 223
absorbance, 40, 220
–/ absorption (%) correlation, 320, 321
– conversion into absorption (%) or transmission (%) (Table), 392
–/ fuel pressure curves, 92
–/ support gas pressure curves, 90
–/– temperature curves, 91
absorbing cell, 38, 39
– medium, 38
absorption, background, 171
–, comparison with emission, 15
–, detection of, 13
–, integrated, 39
–, percentage of, 40, 220
– by molecular bands, theory, *ref. 556*
– coefficient, 39
– (%) conversion into absorbance (Table), 392
– lines (see lines, absorption, and lines, analytical)
– path, long (see adapters, long path)
– phenomena produced by the flame, 104
– process, 29, 32
– –, quantitative aspects, 38
– source (see lamps, hollow-cathode)
– system, 45, 87
– system, mechanical parts, 131
absorptivity, 40
accuracy, 175, 256, 258, 268, 296, 300; *ref. 598*
–, relationship with sensitivity, *ref. 935*
– in magnesium determination in blood serum, *ref. 793*
acetic acid interferences on calcium, 268
– – on magnesium, 268
acetone, 303
–, effect on flame temperature, 96
8-acetoxyquinoline as chelating agent, 309
acetylacetone as chelating agent, 309
acetylene flames, incandescent, 99, 100
–, rich, 99
acids, halogenated, interferences by, 267
–, perturbations by, 267
– interferences, 358
– – on cesium, potassium, rubidium, and sodium, *ref. 573*
– – on zinc, 354
adapters, 16
–, elongated horizontal tube, 135, 137
–, long beam path, 134
–, long path, 96, 175, 215, 251; *ref. 253, 408, 409*
–, long tube, influence of diameter, 138
–, –, influence of length, 138
–, T-form, 134–136
addition, standard (see addition method), 330
– method, 258, 304, 306, 328, 336, 381, 382, 385; *ref. 97, 175, 585*
– –, graphical extrapolation, 332
– –, increment (see addition method), 330
– –, multi-addition technique, 333
– –, standard (see addition method), 330
– – in urine analysis, 367
additions, 290, 301
–, method of (see addition method), 330
–, group, 305
–, heterogeneous, 306
–, homogeneous, 305
–, massive, 306, 310
–, moderate, 305, 306
–, single, 305
– of non-aqueous solvents, 302
additives, 302, 304
admixture method (see addition method), 330
adsorption, selective, 298
aerosol, 124, 125, 130
–, efficiency of the, in the flame, 126, 127
–, enriched, 131
–, liquid–gas, 33, 125
–, solid–gas, 33, 125
Agazzi, instrument described by, 175
agricultural analysis (see also agricultural materials analysis), *ref. 8*
agricultural materials, magnesium determination in, 353
– –, rubidium determination in, *ref. 742*
– –, zinc determination in, 353; *ref. 12*
– – analysis, 353; *ref. 8, 505, 676, 701*
air, compressed, 99, 129
–, enriched, as support gas, 89
–, lead determination in, 182
– absorption, 211
– as spraying gas, 124
– as support gas, pre-heating of, 130

– pollution, *ref. 221*
– –, determination of iron, lead, magnesium and manganese, 388
– pressure variation, 89
air–acetylene flames, 97–99, 118, 182; *ref. 15*
– –, absorption curves, 106
– –, enriched, 103
– –, fuel-rich, 100
– –, oxygen-enriched, 103
air–butane flames, 182
air–coal gas flames, 94, 97, 98, 109
aircraft engines, monitoring, 374; *ref. 106*
air–hydrogen flames, 97, 98, 277
– –, absorption curves, 106
– –, air variation curves, 89
– –, fuel-rich, 101, 122, 130; *ref. 150*
– –, fuel variation curves, 93
– –, turbulent, 122
air–natural gas flames, 118
air–oxygen mixture, 116
air–propane flames, 94, 98, 118
– –, absorption curves, 106
air–propane–butane flames, 179
alcoholic beverages, 267
– –, zinc determination in, 303
alcohols interferences on cesium, potassium, rubidium, sodium, *ref. 573*
alkali metals, volatilization of, in dry ashing of teflon, *ref. 411*
– – determination in ceramic frit, 386
– – – in silicates, *ref. 539*
– – interferences on magnesium, *ref. 243*
alkaline earths, interferences by aluminum on, 271
– – carbonates, mixed, analysis of, *ref. 810*
– –, alkaline-earths determination, 385
– – determination in alkaline-earth carbonates, 385
– – – in burnt refractories, *ref. 577*
– – – in ceramic frit, 386
– – – in clays, feldspars, limestones, and phosphate rocks *ref. 577*
– – – in glass, *ref. 1*
Allan, instrument described by, 176
alloy steels, cobalt determination in, *ref. 490*
alloys, aluminum determination in, 389; *ref. 529*
–, lithium determination in, 389
–, magnesium determination in, 389
–, metals determination in, *ref. 719*
–, non-ferrous, aluminum determination in, 377
–, potassium determination in, 389
–, zinc determination in, 378, 389; *ref. 528*
– analysis, *ref. 256, 489*
aluminous materials, zinc determination in, *ref. 222*
aluminum, barium determination in the presence of, 271
–, calcium determination in the presence of, 271
–, fluctuational concentration limit, 246
–, iron determination in, traces of iron, *ref. 59*
–, light pipes, 101
–, magnesium determination in, 379
–, operating conditions, 401
–, percentual concentration limit, 244
–, percentual concentration limit with nitrous oxide–acetylene flame, 104
–, percentual concentration limit with plasmas, 148
–, silicon determination in (sputtering chamber), 151
– alloys, aluminum determination in, 379
– –, determination of cadmium, calcium, cobalt, lead, sodium and zinc, 380
– –, iron determination in, traces of iron, *ref. 59*
– –, magnesium determination in, 377, 379, 380; *ref. 430, 796*
– –, silver determination in, 380; *ref. 839, 840*
– – analysis, 376; *ref. 470*
– as releaser, 308, 378
– determination, *ref. 19, 146, 199, 249, 456*
– –, ntrous oxide burner, *ref. 51*
– – in alloys, 389; *ref. 529*
– – in aluminum alloys, 379
– – in cements, 383
– – in non-ferrous alloys, 377
– – in pure metals, *ref. 529*
– – in silicates, *ref. 539*
– – with addition of organic solvents, 302
– – with fuel-rich flames, 100, 101
– – with oxygen enriched air–acetylene flames, 103
– interferences, 270, 358
– – on alkaline earths, 271
– – on calcium, 352
– – on magnesium, 104, 126, 271, 352, 378
– – on rhodium, 101
– – on silver, 381
– – on strontium, 352
– materials, zinc determination in, 380
ammonium pyrrolidine dithiocarbamate, 299, 300, 351, 356, 360, 384, 386; *ref. 687*
– trace, metals in brines, extraction, *ref. 469*

Amos and Thomas, burner described by, 116
amplification, 161
amplifiers, 161
"analito" in Spanish scientific literature, *ref. 932*
analysis, multielement, sequential, *ref. 67*
–, sequential, multielement, 67
analyte, 7
– emission, 162, 164, 166
analytical information, 174
– methods evaluation, *ref. 946*
– process, known, 281
– –, unknown, 283
– qualitative factors, 339
– systems, 174
Andrew and Nichols, instrument described by, 176
animal materials, zinc determination in, *ref. 261*
– metabolism, applications in, 388
– nutrition, determination of calcium, magnesium and zinc in, *ref. 542*
– organisms, zinc determination in, 388
anion exchange resins, 360
antarctic ice cores, determination of lithium, magnesium and potassium, 389
antimony, fluctuational concentration limit, 246
–, operating conditions, 401
–, percentual concentration limit, 244
– determination in mineral products, 373
– – in parafin casts, 388
– emission in the reaction zone, *ref. 189*
antimony trisulfide/potassium chlorate ratio, 389; *ref. 638, 939*
apples, mercury determination in (ultramicrodetermination), *ref. 360*
applications, general (see also reviews), 349; *ref. 27, 35, 84*
–, miscellaneous, 386
argon, purging with, 211
– as a filling gas, 56, 59
– lines, 56
arsenic, fluctuational concentration limit, 246
–, operating conditions, 401
–, percentual concentration limit, 215, 244
– determination, *ref. 706*
– –, ashing, 297
– – in fuel-rich air–hydrogen flames, 103
– – in glass, 386
– – in gold, 386
– – in methanearsonic acid, 386
– – in plant materials, 386
– – in soils, 386
– emission in the reaction zone, *ref. 189*
– hollow cathodes, *ref. 706*
asher, low temperature dry (LTA-600), 297
ashing, 297
aspiration, alternating, 171
– rate, 127
atom, free, short life, 109
– concentration, free, increase, 90
– – determination, *ref. 574*
– distribution in the flame, 110
Atomic Absorption & Electronic Corporation instruments, description, 180, 182, 183
– Model 100 atomic absorption spectrophotometer, *ref. 58*
atomic-absorption analysis by the flame, 4
– flame photometer, general scheme, 46
– flame photometry (see also flame photometry, atomic-absorption)
– –, automatic, *ref. 133*
– –, choose of, 22
– –, definition, 6
– –, nomenclature, 8, 9
– spectroscopy, 4, 6, 10
– –, advantages, 18
– –, bibliographies on, 26
– –, conferences on, 26
– –, current trends, 28
– –, disadvantages, 20
– –, future perspectives, 27
– –, lectures on, 26, 27
– –, literature on, 24
– –, meetings, 26
– –, origin of the method, 5, 7
– –, precision in, 21
– –, repeatability of, 19
– –, reviews on (see also reviews on atomic-absorption spectroscopy) 25
– –, sensitivity in, 19; *ref. 18*
– –, special chapters on, 24
– –, stability in, *ref. 18*
– –, theory, 29; *ref. 401, 443*
– –, theses, 26; *ref. 306, 332, 346, 509, 539, 603, 674, 727*
– –, versatility of, 19
– – in the far ultraviolet region, 22; *ref. 17*
– – in the vacuum ultraviolet region, 151
– – with gases above the flame, 276
– – without the use of flames, 6, 146; *ref. 679*
Atomic and Spectral lamps (hollow-cathode), 56
atomic energy, applications in, 388; *ref. 531*
– vapor, efficiency of generating, 250
– vapors, 6, 33

atomic-fluorescence flame photometry, 28, 51; *ref. 289, 472, 727, 842, 843, 844, 848, 852*
– – spectrophotometry (see atomic-fluorescence flame photometry)
atomising chambers (see chamber, spraying)
atomization, 6
–, free-atom problem, *ref. 405*
–, lack of, 103
–, partial, 103
– efficiency, 120; *ref.* 846
– fluctuations, 167
atomize (to), 7
atomizer-burners (see sprayer-burners)
atomizers (see sprayers, if used as spraying devices)
atoms, distribution in flames, *ref. 604, 605*
–, excited, *ref. 503*
–, excited state, 29, 33, 37, 38
–, free, distribution, 138
–, –, half life, 112
–, –, long life, 135
–, ground state, 29, 33, 35, 37, 38
–, retention time, 116
Australia, spectroscopy in, *ref. 803, 804*
Australian Spectroscopy Conference, second, *ref. 303*
– – –, third, *ref. 203*
automatic analysis, *ref. 494*
– instruments, *ref. 184*
automatization, *ref. 259*
autoreleasing action, 308
autostandards, 302
Aztec burner (Techtron burner), 123

B

background absorption, 171
– corrections, *ref. 409*
– signal reduction, *ref. 850*
backing-off procedure, 273
Baker and Garton, burner described by, 117
– – –, instrument described by, 176
band emission, 18
bands, 107, 215
barium, fluctuational concentration limit, 246
–, interferences by calcium on, *ref. 902*
–, interferences by phosphates on, elimination of, *ref. 858*
–, operating conditions, 401
–, percentual concentration limit, 244
– determination in the presence of aluminum, 271
– – with fuel-rich air–hydrogen flames, 103
– – with fuel-rich flames, 101
– emission intensity, 276
Bayer liquor, copper determination in, 383
– –, zinc determination in, 383
beam, analysis, 170
–, multiple passage, 16
–, optical path, 251
–, reference, 170
– combiners, 140
bearing alloys analysis, 386
Beckman Instruments, Inc. atomic-absorption spectrophotometers, *ref. 71, 72*
– burner, 113, 120, 123, 124, 175, 179, 215
– instruments, 179; *ref. 313, 314, 316, 464, 465, 471, 540, 668, 884, 892*
– –, description, 180, 182, 184
– laminar flow burner (see also burner, laminar flow), 119
– Model 979 atomic-absorption spectrophotometer, 83, 209, 210, 255, 318, 319
– No. 97900 atomic-absorption spectrophotometer (see Beckman Instruments, Inc. Model 979)
– Model DB spectrophotometer, 318, 319
– Model DU spectrophotometer, 57, 81, 82, 84, 85, 178, 179, 315
– Model DU-2 spectrophotometer, 69, 75, 80, 89, 93, 157
– monochromator, 176
– triple pass devices, 142, 144, 145
– tnrbulent flow burner (see burner, turbulent flow)
beer, determination of calcium, copper, iron, potassium and sodium in, 382, *ref. 248*
Beer's law, 39, 97, 168
Beer–Lambert law (see also Beer's law,) *ref. 252*
Belcher and Bray, instrument described by, 176
beryllium, fluctuational concentration limit, 246
–, operating conditions, 401
–, percentual concentration limit, 244
–, – – –, with nitrous oxide–acetylene flame, 104
– determination by sputtering techniques, 151
– – with fuel-rich flames, 101
beverages analysis, 382
bibliographies, *ref. 27, 35, 692*
bioanalytical techniques, *ref. 475*

biochemistry, applications in (see biological materials analysis)
biological fluids (see biological materials analysis)
– –, zinc determination in, 364; *ref. 568*
biological materials, calcium determination in, 4, 270, 364; *ref. 42, 480, 871*
– –, copper determination in, *ref. 91, 640, 895*
– –, iron determination in, *ref. 310, 871*
– –, lead determination in, *ref. 895*
– –, magnesium determination in, 4, 364, 382; *ref. 42, 185, 480, 871*
– –, mercury determination in, *ref. 895*
– –, nickel determination in, *ref. 749*
– –, potassium determination in, 269; *ref. 480*
– –, sodium determination in, *ref. 480*
– –, strontium determination in, *ref. 173*
– –, thallium determination in, *ref. 895*
– –, trace elements (metals) determination in, *ref. 94, 682, 894*
– –, zinc determination in, *ref. 42, 250, 640*
– – analysis, 361; *ref. 34, 148, 149, 182, 183, 412, 680, 701, 779, 835, 837, 866, 872, 940*
– – –, determinable elements (cadmium, calcium, chromium, cobalt, copper, iron, lead, magnesium, manganese, mercury, molybdenum, potassium, sodium, thallium, zinc), 363
– – –, microsamples, 363
– – –, reviews, 361, 362
– samples (see also biological materials)
– –, ashed, strontium determination in, *ref. 778*
biotites (see information given in feldspars)
–, iron determination in, 372
bismuth, fluctuational concentration limit, 246
–, operating conditions, 401
–, percentual concentration limit, 244
–, working curve, air–acetylene flame, 95
–, – –, air–coal gas flame, 95
– determination in steels, 376
– – in urine, 367
– emission in the reaction zone, *ref. 189*
– extraction, 300
– hollow-cathode lamp, *ref. 948*
blank absorption in the flame, 106
blanks, 12, 88, 297
blood, calcium determination in, *ref. 714, 825*
–, lead determination in, *ref. 92, 945*
–, lead extraction, 299
–, magnesium determination in, *ref. 452, 714, 825*
–, mercury determination in, *ref. 361*
–, trace elements determination in, *ref. 707*
–, whole, iron determination in, *ref. 330*
– analysis, 362
– –, interferences, 364
– –, preparation of samples, 362
– –, standards, 365
– plasma, magnesium determination in, 365, 369; *ref. 353*
– –, trace elements (metals) determination in, *ref. 454*
– –, zinc determination in, 364
– – analysis, 362
– serum, accuracy in magnesium determination in, *ref. 793*
– –, calcium, determination in, 99, 270, 364; *ref. 28, 750, 826, 827, 874, 875*
– –, copper determination in, *ref. 93, 327, 724*
– –, iron determination in, *ref. 724, 876*
– –, magnesium determination in, 364; *ref. 28, 323, 371, 730, 750, 824, 828*
– –, determination of potassium and sodium in, *ref. 322, 829*
– –, zinc determination in, *ref. 347, 724*
– – analysis, 362
– – –, protein addition to standards, 363
blue cone, 109
– –, height above the, 109
– edge, 109
– zone, 109
BO_2, absorption spectrum, *ref. 368*
– radical determination, 389; *ref. 646*
body fluids, magnesium determination in, *ref. 323*
Bolin, burner described by, 117; *ref. 725*
bone, strontium determination in, 366
– ash, determination of calcium, magnesium, potassium and sodium in, *ref. 36*
bones, determination of calcium, magnesium, potassium, sodium and strontium, 369
– analysis, 369
books (see under flame photometry)
boron, fluctuational concentration limit, 246
–, operating conditions, 401
–, percentual concentration limit, 244
– determination with fuel-rich flames, 100
Bouguer–Lambert–Bernard law (see Beer's law), 39
Box and Walsh, instrument described by, 176
brain, human, magnesium and zinc determination in, *ref. 905*
brass, lead determination in, *ref. 906*
brines, copper determination in, 351

–, lead determination in, 351
–, purified, magnesium determination in, 384
–, trace metals extraction (ammonium pyrrolidine dithiobarbamate and oxine), *ref. 469*
– analysis, 384
bromides determination, 205
bronze, lead determination in, *ref. 906*
buffering, 306
–, homogeneous, 306
–, radiation, 310
Bunsen and Kirchhoff identification of emission spectra, 7
burner, Boling, 177; *ref. 725*
–, height of the, 108
–, optimum height of the, 108
–, – with organic solvents, 109
– adjustment, *ref. 517*
– alignment, 132
– – plate, 132
– efficiency, 127
– functions, 113
– head, multi-hole, 119
– –, multi-slot, 118
– – baffle, 115, 116
– holding bar, 109
– path, 262
– raising mechanism, 109
– rotation, 131–135, 253
– vertical displacement, 131
burners, 45, 87, 113; *ref. 151, 419, 479 498, 943*
–, auxiliary mechanisms, 131
–, characteristics, 262
–, commercial, 123
–, cooled, 117–120
–, different kinds, 114
–, double slot, 116, 117
–, dual purpose, *ref. 340*
–, forced-feed, 122
–, glass, 120
–, internal turbulence, 114
–, laminar flow, 115; *ref. 63, 75, 311*
–, – –, modified, 104
–, longitudinal slot, 113
–, long slot, 251
–, mechanical-feed, *ref. 632*
–, mechanical mount, Perkin-Elmer Corp. Model 214, *ref. 85*
–, multiple, 251
–, multi-slot, 116
–, nitrous oxide–acetylene, *ref. 315, 457*
–, – –, determination of aluminum, titanium and vanadium, *ref. 51*
–, non-premix gases, 115, 121
–, non-spraying, 113–116
–, oscillating, 122
–, oxygen–acetylene, *ref. 135, 404*
–, –, premixed, *ref. 404*
–, perforated plate, 113
–, plastic, 117; *ref. 129*
–, platinum, 137, 139
–, premix gases, 115
–, rotating, 117, 119
–, sheathed, 16
–, swinging, 171
–, three slots (triple slot), 116, 117; *ref. 725*
–, total consumption, 94
–, turbulent flow, 96, 121, 124; *ref. 76*
–, – –, air variation curves, 89
– mounted in a row, 122
burning velocity, 115, 121
Butler, burner described by, 117
– and Strasheim, instrument described by, 176
butter, copper determination in, *ref. 836*
butteroil, copper determination in, *ref. 836*

C

cadmium, atomic vapor, flameless method, *ref. 502*
–, fluctuational concentration limit, 246
–, – – – by furnace technique, 150
–, operating conditions, 401
–, percentual concentration limit, 244
– analysis, 387
– determination, 182; *ref. 564*
– – by atomic-fluorescence flame photometry, *ref. 472, 848*
– – in aluminum alloys, 380
– – in cadmium plating solutions, 387
– – in copper alloys, 380
– – in feldspars and biotites, 371
– – in galvanized and protective coatings, 376
– – in industrial waste water, *ref. 99*
– – in polyvinylchloride, 376
– – in rat kidney, 367
– – in stainless steel, 380
– – in uranium compounds, 385; *ref. 743*
– – in urine, 367
– – in waste water, 351
– – in water, 376
– extraction, 300
– hollow-cathode lamp, 60
– nitrate, copper determination in, 384
– plating solutions, determination of cadmium, lead and zinc, 387
– sensitivity with continuum sources, 48
– vapor lamp, 179
calcium, effects of the variation of air pressure, 89

–, effects of the variation of hydrogen pressure, 93
–, elimination of anionic interferences in determinations of, *ref. 578*
–, flame processes, 35
–, fluctuational concentration limit, 246
–, interferences by acetic acid on, 268
–, – by aluminum on, 352
–, – by chlorides on, 272
–, – by magnesium on, 352
–, – by phosphates on, 271, 352, 364, 365
–, – by potassium on, 269, 357
–, – by silicates on, 271
–, – by silicon on, 352, 365
–, – by sodium on, 269, 272, 352, 357, 364
–, – by sulfates on, 271
–, – on, 271; *ref. 578, 764*
–, operating conditions, 401
–, percentual concentration limit, 244
–, – – – with plasmas, 148
–, protein-bound, 304
– and sulfuric acid as releaser, 308
– as releaser, 308, 368, 378, 383
– determination, *ref. 184, 708*
– –, automated, *ref. 807*
– – by sputtering technique, 151
– – in aluminum alloys, 380
– – in animal nutrition, *ref. 542*
– – in beer, 382; *ref. 248*
– – in biological materials, 4, 270, 346; *ref. 42, 480, 871*
– – in blood, *ref. 714, 825*
– – in blood serum, 99, 270, 364; *ref. 750, 826, 827, 874, 875*
– – in bone ash, *ref. 36*
– – in bones, 369
– – in cast iron, 380, 381; *ref. 292*
– – in cements, 383; *ref. 761*
– – in cerebrospinal fluid, 370; *ref. 190*
– – in copper alloys, 380
– – in electrolyte excretion studies, *ref. 309*
– – in feeding stuffs, 382
– – in feldspars and biotites, 371
– – in granitic and diabasic rocks, 371
– – in human blood serum, *ref. 28*
– – in igneous minerals and rocks, 372
– – in limestones, 373
– – in microcultures, 388
– – in mixed feeds, *ref. 923*
– – in parotid saliva of sheep, *ref. 141*
– – in plant ash, *ref. 344*
– – in plant materials, 355
– – in plants, 4, 269; *ref. 163*
– – in polyvinylchloride, 385; *ref. 518*
– – in saliva, 365; *ref. 527*
– – in sediments, 373
– – in silicate samples, 386
– – in silicocalcareous minerals, *ref. 913*
– – in slags, 380, 381; *ref. 292*
– – in soils, exchangeable, 4; *ref. 166*
– – in the presence of aluminum, 271
– – in tissues, 369
– – in urine, 364; *ref. 631*
– – in water, *ref. 130*
– – in zincblende and catalysts, 182
– – with air–coal gas flames, 109
– – with fuel-rich air–hydrogen flames, 103
– – with fuel-rich flames, 101
– – with reversed oxygen–acetylene flame, 89
– emission intensity, 276
– enhancement by potassium (serum, plants), 304
– – by sodium (serum, plants), 304
– hollow-cathode lamp, *ref. 857*
– interferences on barium, *ref. 902*
– – on gold, 371
– – on rhodium, 101
– – on sodium, 352, 383
– nitrate, copper determination in, 384
– phosphate, sodium determination in, 384
– resonance line profile, *ref. 857*
– separation, 304
– working curves, 316, 317
calcium–magnesium–aluminum hollow-cathode lamp (Ne and Ar), emission curves, 57
– – –, warm-up curve, 68
calculation of the variations of concentrations, 338
calculations, 290, 338
–, postphotometric, 339
–, routine, 340
–, special cases, 341
– of the expressions of concentration, 339
calibration, 313
–, analytical, 313
Carl Zeiss instruments, *ref. 903*
– –, description, 180, 186, 196
– monochromator, 176, 179
cast iron, calcium determination in, 380, 381; *ref. 292*
– –, chromium, copper and nickel determination in, *ref. 98*
– –, magnesium determination in, 376–378, 380, 381; *ref. 98, 751*
– –, manganese determination in, *ref. 98, 292*
catalysts, vanadium determination in, 5
– analysis, 182
cationic inhibition, 271
caustic solutions, determination of cobalt and manganese, 383

cells, barrier-layer, 160
–, long absorbing, 139
cements, aluminium determination in, 383
–, calcium, magnesium, manganese, potassium, and sodium determination in, 383;
–, iron determination in, 383
–, metals determination in, *ref. 900*
– analysis, 383; *ref. 715*
ceramic frit analysis, *ref. 369, 376*
– – –, determination of alkali metals, alkaline earths, cobalt, copper, magnesium, nickel and zinc, 386
ceramics analysis, 386
cerebrospinal fluid, calcium determination in, 370; *ref. 190*
– –, magnesium determination in, 370; *ref. 190*
cerium, fluctuational concentration limit, 246
–, operating conditions, 401
–, percentual concentration limit, 244
cesium, fluctuational concentration limit, 246
–, interferences by acids and alcohols on, *ref. 573*
–, operating conditions, 401
–, percentual concentration limit, 244
– determination, 268; *ref. 46, 300*
– – in fission products, 389
– – in graphites, 389
– – with addition of organic solvents, 303
– emission intensity, 276
– standard solutions, 291
Chambers, instrument described by, 177
chambers, atomising (see chambers, spray)
–, condensing, 117, 118, 126
–, –, cooled, 130
–, –, efficiency of the, 126
–, drip, 126
–, solvent condensing, 118
–, spray (spraying), 115, 126, 262; *ref. 326*
–, –, cold, 130
–, –, efficiency of the, 126
–, –, heated, 117–119, 130, 250, 312
–, –, infrared heated, 118
–, sputtering, 87
chart, step-by-step, 311
chelating agents, 126, 309
– –, manganese extraction, *ref. 468*
Chelex-100, 351
chemical products analysis, 384
– reagents, copper determination in, *ref. 358*
– systems, applications in, 389
chemiluminescence, 18
– phenomena, 16
chimneys, 139
–, side windows, 139
–, silica windows, 139
chlorides determination, 205
– –, indirect, 389
– interferences on calcium, 272
chloroform, 376
chloroplasts, magnesium and zinc determination in, 355; *ref. 331*
choppers, 45, 69, 70, 165, 178, 179, 252
–, reflecting, 141
chromic oxide determination in feces, *ref. 823*
chromium, atomic-absorption spectroscopy of, *ref. 239*
–, flame profile, air–hydrogen turbulent flame, 111
–, fluctuational concentration limit, 246
–, magnesium determination in, 182
–, operating conditions, 401
–, percentual concentration limit, 244
– determination in brines, *ref. 192*
– – in cast iron, *ref. 98*
– – in feces, 368; *ref. 823*
– – in iron, 377, 382
– – in iron (low-alloy), *ref. 398*
– – in lubricating oil, 375
– – in nickel alloys, 377, 382; *ref. 204*
– – in plating solutions, 383
– – in rat kidney, 367
– – in sodium chloride solutions, 384
– – in stainless steels, 376
– – in steels, 377, 382; *ref. 98*
– – in steels (low-alloy), *ref. 398*
– – in sub-p.p.m. levels, *ref. 192*
– – in zincblende and catalysts, 182
– – with addition of organic solvents, 302
– – with fuel-rich air–hydrogen flames, 103
– – with fuel-rich flames, 100
– extraction, 298, 299, 284
clays, alkaline-earth determination in, *ref. 577*
clean-up (hollow-cathode lamps), 56, 72, 74
clinical applications (see biological materials)
clinical biology (see also biological materials), *ref. 639*
clinical chemistry (see also biological materials), *ref. 91, 395*
– –, instruments for, *ref. 38*
– medicine (see also biological materials), *ref. 688, 689*
Clinton, burner described by, 117, 176
clotlets, 125
clots, 125

coal ash, strontium determination in, 386; *ref. 81*
coatings, galvanized and protective, determination of cadmium and lead, 376
cobalt, fluctuational concentration limit, 246
–, line selection, *ref. 307*
–, operating conditions, 402
–, percentual concentration limit, 244
–, slit, 156
– chloride, copper determination in, 384
– determination, *ref. 10*
– – in alloy steel, *ref. 490*
– – in aluminum alloys, 380
– – in caustic solutions, 383
– – in ceramic frit, 386
– – in copper alloys, 380
– – in feldspars and biotites, 371
– – in iron, 377; *ref. 721*
– – in marine sediments, 388
– – in metallurgical products, 376
– – in natural water, 351; *ref. 123*
– – in nickel, *ref. 490*
– – in recent sediments, *ref. 122*
– – in steel, 376, 377; *ref. 490, 721*
– – in zincblende and catalysts, 182
– extraction, 300
– – from NaOH solutions, 299
– lines, 208
– nitrate, copper determination in, 384
– sensitivity with continuum sources, 48
coefficient of variation (relative standard deviation), 232, 234, 235, 259, 260
combustion, 121
– gases, trace species in, *ref. 245*
– wave, 121
– zone, 121
compensation, 305
competiting ions, 307
composition gradient, 114
computer techniques, 340, 341; *ref. 601*
computers, integrating analog, 168; *ref. 105*
–, logarithmic analog, 169
concentrates, antimony sulfide flotation, lead determination in, *ref. 296*
–, lead determination in, 372
–, zinc determination in, 372
concentration, added, 256
–, preliminary, 254, 296, 298, 301
–, variations of, 301
– conversion factors (Table), 400
– dynamic ranges, 131; *ref. 111*
– factor, 301, 339
– limits (see limits, concentration)
– range, 175, 292, 327, 407
– –, dynamic (see concentration dynamic ranges)
– –, –, linear, 254
– –, –, abbreviated expression, 328; *ref. 111*
– reading digital voltmeters, *ref. 390, 391*
– readouts, *ref. 711*
– –, digital, *ref. 52*
condensers, 168
contaminants, 344, 345
contaminations, 343
continuous source (see sources, continuum)
continuum as background source, 47
– sources (see sources, continuum)
control links, 174
conversion factors, 339
cookbooks, *ref. 45*
copper, fluctuational concentration limit, 246
–, interferences by sodium, 272
–, – on, 381
–, operating conditions, 402
–, percentual concentration limit, 244
–, phosphorous determination in (sputtering chamber), 151
–, selenium and tellurium determination in, 377; *ref. 716*
–, silver determination in (sputtering chamber), 151
– alloys, copper determination in, 378
– –, determination of cadmium, calcium, cobalt, lead, magnesium, silver, sodium, and zinc, 380
– – analysis, *ref. 210*
– as releaser, 308
– determination, *ref. 11, 393*
– – by extraction (in urine), *ref. 354, 355*
– – in Bayer liquor, 383
– – in beer, 382
– – in biological materials, *ref. 91, 640, 895*
– – in blood serum, *ref. 93, 327, 724*
– – in brines, 351
– – in butter, *ref. 836*
– – in butteroil, *ref. 836*
– – in cadmium nitrate, 384
– – in calcium nitrate, 384
– – in cast iron, *ref. 98*
– – in ceramic frit, 386
– – in chemical reagents, *ref. 358*
– – in cobalt chloride, 384
– – in cobalt nitrate, 384
– – in copper alloys, 378
– – in copperized superphosphates, 354
– – in dried liver and muscle, 369
– – in drill core samples, 372
– – in electroplating solutions, 383
– – in foods, 382
– – in gold bullion, 378

– – in high purity gold, *ref. 658*
– – in human tissues, *ref. 737*
– – in industrial waste waters, *ref. 99*
– – in iron, 377; *ref. 379, 721*
– – in lead-base alloys, *ref. 224*
– – in liver, *ref. 567*
– – in lubricating oils, 375
– – in magnesium chloride, 384
– – in manganese chloride, 384
– – in metallurgical materials, *ref. 794*
– – in milk, 366; *ref. 508*
– – in muscle, *ref. 567*
– – in nickel chloride, 384
– – in nickel plating solutions, 383; *ref. 664*
– – in ore samples, 372; *ref. 224*
– – in petroleum products, *ref. 684*
– – in plant materials, *ref. 908*
– – in potassium chloride, 384; *ref. 723*
– – in rat kidney, 367
– – in rocks, silicate, *ref. 88*
– – in steel, 377, 381; *ref. 98, 397, 721*
– – in tissues, 369; *ref. 93*
– – in type metal, 378
– – in urine, 367; *ref. 93*
– – –, by extraction, *ref. 354, 355*
– – in waste water, 351
– – in water, 352; *ref. 130*
– – in wine, *ref. 867*
– – in zincblende and catalysts, 182
– – with addition of organic solvents, 303
– extract, 360
– extraction, 299, 300, 356, 384, 386
– –, potassium chloride analysis, 299
– –, rocks analysis, 299
– – from NaOH solutions, 299
– – with cupferron, 300
– hollow-cathode lamp, warm-up curve, 68
– lines, 208
– –, absorption of, 209
– oscillator strength (3247 Å), 150
– sensitivity with continuum sources, 48
– standard solutions, 291
copper-base alloys (see also copper alloys)
– –, iron determination in, 378
– –, lead determination in, 378; *ref. 214, 333*
– –, nickel determination in, 378
counterinterferents, 302
criminology, applications in, 388
cupferron, 352, 384
curves, absorbance/concentration, 314, 316, 318
–, absorbance/pressure, 92
–, absorbance/support gas pressure, 90
–, absorbance/support gas temperature, 91
–, absorption/concentration, 320, 323
–, analytical, bending, *ref. 643*
–, –, shape of, *ref. 669*
–, calibration, 313
–, –, curvature, 230, 322, 324
–, –, types, 313
–, effect/variable, 311
–, interference, 270
–, noise/fuel pressure, 92
–, sensitivity/fuel pressure, 92
–, working, 314, 315
–, –, change with support gas pressure, 91
–, –, curvature, 164
–,–, linear, *ref. 717*
–, –, log–log, 222
–, –, ordinary, 222
–, –, shape of, 48, 322
–, –, special cases, 328
–, –, types, 314
cyanide solutions, gold determination in, 383; *ref. 941*
– wastes, gold determination in, *ref. 739*

D

damping, 168, 169, 248, 251, 252
data collection, *ref. 104*
– processing links, 174
Davey, instrument described by, 177
David, instrument described by, 177
Dawson and Ellis, instrument described by, 177
De-Acidite FF, 298
deionizers, 302
density variations, 268
detectability, 219, 220; *ref. 73*
detectabilities of elements, 219
detection, 160
–, limitations in, *ref. 713*
–, photographic, 160
– limits (see limits, detection)
– sensitivity (see sensitivity, detection)
detectors, 1P22, 160
detergent addition, 310; *ref. 507*
determination, direct, 205
–, indirect, 205
developments (see reviews)
dextrose as protector, 309
diaphragms, 109
–, masking, 140
differential method, 341
diethyldithiocarbamate, 300, 379
diets, magnesium determination in, *ref. 295*
digital concentration readouts (see concentration readouts, digital)
– readout, 160

– voltmeter, 169
dilution, preliminary, 296
–, previous, 300
– factors, 339
– method, 304, 306, 336, 338; *ref. 590*
– process, 289
– ratios, 217, 231
– series, 288
– values, 217
dimethylglyoxime, 383
2,4-dimethylquinoline as chelating agent 309
dioxan, 303
diphenylthiocarbazone, 300, 384
direct reading method, *ref. 659*
discharge tubes (see lamps, hollow-cathode)
discussions, *ref. 145, 155, 415*
dissociation, *ref. 346*
–, thermal, 33
– equilibrium, 99
– process, 100, 101
dissolution, 296
– technique, *ref. 427*
disturbances, 260
dithiol, 384
dithizone, 299, 300
Doerffel *et al.*, instrument described by, 178
Doppler broadening, 42, 84
– effect, 41, 42, 70
double-beam, 98
– instruments (see also double-beam systems), 160, 170, 171, 178, 179; *ref. 345*
– method, spectral selection, *ref. 5, 6*
– operation, 170
– systems (see also double-beam instruments), 69, 71, 122, 140, 141, 170
drift, 251
drill core samples, copper determination in, 372
drop size, 125
dry asher, low temperature, *ref. 96*
dynamic ranges, concentration, 131; *ref. 111*
dysprosium, fluctuational concentration limit, 246
–, operating conditions, 402
–, percentual concentration limit, 244
– determination with fuel-rich flames, 100

E

Ealing Corp. (The) instruments, *ref. 768*
EDTA, 309, 350, 356, 359, 363–365
efficiency studies, 129, 130
electrodeless discharge tubes, 85
electrodes, auxiliary, 149
–, sample, 148
–, sample holder, 149
electrolitic excretion studies (see calcium and magnesium determination)
electroplating solutions, determination of copper and zinc, 383
– –, trace elements determination in, *ref. 820*
elements, determinable by direct atomic-absorption methods, 205, 206
–, determinable by emission flame photometry, 207
–, emitting (see also elements, strongly emitting, and elements, high emitting), 156, 167
–, heavy, 255
–, high emitting, 107
– –, (Na and Li), 99
–, non-metallic, 211
–, strongly emitting, 273, 276, 277; *ref. 110*
emission, background, 325
–, continuous, 99
–, discrete, by molecular bands, 215
–, residual, 326
–, source, 326
– effects, decreasing of, 272
– process, comparison with adsorption process, 31
– system, 45, 47
– work, fuel-rich flames, 101
emitter drifts, 170
emitters, continuum (see also sources, continuum), 47
–, –, evaluation as primary sources, 48
–, –, hydrogen arc, 48
–, –, low brightness of, 47
–, –, low radiance of, 47
–, –, stability, 48
–, –, resolution, 48
–, discrete, 47, 49
–, line, 47
–, spectra of the, 210
–, uninterrupted, 107
emitting elements, strongly, *ref. 110*
enhancers, 302
equalization, 305
erbium, fluctuational concentration limit, 246
–, operating conditions, 402
–, percentual concentration limit, 244
– determination with fuel-rich flames, 100
errors, 256, 260
–, calculation, 340; *ref. 754*
–, relative (in concentration), 257

ethanol, 300, 302, 303
– addition, 100
ether, 303
ethyl acetate, 299, 300
ethylene glycol, 303
– as protector, 309
ethylenetetracetic acid (see EDTA)
europium, flame as a source, 101
–, fluctuational concentration limit, 246
–, operating conditions, 402
–, percentual concentration limit, 244
– determination with fuel-rich flames, 100
– spectrum, *ref. 675*
Evans Electroselenium Ltd. burner, 113
– instruments, description, 180, 186, 196
– Model 140 atomic absorption spectrophotometer, *ref. 219, 881*
– spectrophotometers, *ref. 219, 220*
– sprayer, 125, 176, 179, 371
excitation (in flames), factor affecting, *ref. 262*
–, mechanism of, *ref. 622*
– in flames, *ref. 3*
– processes (in flames), *ref. 263, 266*
excretions, calcium determination in, *ref. 309*
–, magnesium determination in, 370; *ref. 309*
exhaust gases of the flame, analysis by means of, *ref. 869*
experimental process, 281
extinction, 340
extractions, bulk, 298
–, chelating, 299
–, group, 298
–, selective, 298
–, solvent, 379, 384; *ref. 739*
– in metallurgical materials analysis, *ref. 583*
extracts, organic, lead determination in, *ref. 158*

F

Fabricand *et al.*, instrument described by, 178
factors, 339
–, concentration conversion (Table), 400
–, fluctuational correction, 233
–, limiting (see limiting factors)
–, volume, 231
far ultraviolet region, atomic-absorption spectroscopy in the, *ref. 17*
fats, potassium determination in, 370; *ref. 929*
–, sodium determination in, 370; *ref. 929*
feces, chromium (chromic oxide) determination in, 368; *ref. 823*
–, magnesium determination in, 368
– analysis, 368
feed rate, 127, 231, 250, 342
– – curves as a function of support gas pressure, 128, 129
– – variation, 128, 129
– time, 231
feeding, forced, 113
–, tube (tubing), 131
– rate (see feed rate)
– stuffs, determination of calcium, magnesium and zinc, 382
– system, *ref. 249*
feeds, mixed, calcium determination in, *ref. 923*
–, –, magnesium determination in, *ref. 923*
feedstocks, catalytic cracking, nickel determination in, 376; *ref. 775*
feldspars, alkaline earths determination in, *ref. 577*
– and biotites, determination of cadmium, calcium, cobalt, iron, magnesium, nickel, potassium, rubidium, sodium, and strontium, 371
ferrous alloys, molybdenum determination in, *ref. 511*
fertilizers, magnesium determination in, 182
–, zinc determination in, *ref. 261*
– analysis, 353; *ref. 260, 482, 483, 924*
– –, determinable elements (cobalt, copper, iron, magnesium, manganese, molybdenum, nickel, potassium, strontium, and zinc), 354 (see also iron and manganese in p. 355)
– –, interferences, 354
– –, preparation of samples, 353
– –, standards, 354
fibers, synthetic, manganese determination in, 385
filters, 153, 177, 179
–, color, 153
–, interferences, 153
–, red cut-off, 153
–, selection by, 153, 154
–, – (sodium and potassium), 153
–, –, wavelength band, 153
fish flour, lead determination in, 382; *ref. 735*
Fisher standard solutions, *ref. 882*
fission products, cesium determination in, 389
flame, 87
–, absorption phenomena produced by the, 104
–, active role of the, 88

–, air–acetylene (see air–acetylene flames)
–, air–hydrogen, fuel-rich (see air–hydrogen flames, fuel-rich)
–, excitation in the, *ref. 3*
–, exhaust gases of the, analysis by means of, *ref. 869*
–, nitrous oxide–acetylene (see nitrous oxide–acetylene flames)
–, oxygen acetylene, reaction zone, *ref. 142*
–, reversed, 16, 89
–, spectroscopy of, *ref. 492*
–, type of, 407
–, uses of, 88
– absorption, 211
– – at short wavelengths, 106
– as a carrier, 7, 38
– as a line source (see flame as a source)
– as a source, 49, 50; *ref. 65, 675*
– – – in isotope analysis, 50
– background, 120, 156, 157, 250
– – emission, 162, 163
– characteristics, 88
– cross-section, 96, 97
– dimensions, 96
– emission, 99, 122, 252, 262
– flickering, 230, 273
– fluctuations, 167
– gases, 88
– height, 97
– – in turbulent flames, 97
– noise component, 107
– – contribution, 167
– opacity, 106
– pathlength, 96, 97
– patterns, 110–112
– –, optical device to obtain, 112
– photometer, versatile micro-sample, *ref. 808*
– photometry, absorption, 4, 6
– –, atomic-absorption (see also atomic-absorption flame photometry)
– –, –, automatic, *ref. 133*
– –, –, books, 24; *ref. 213*
– –, –, definition, 6
– –, –, nomenclature, 8, 9
– –, –, semiautomatic, *ref. 133*
– –, atomic-fluorescence (see atomic-fluorescence flame photometry)
– –, emission, 4; *ref. 125, 787*
– –, –, books, *ref. 125, 186, 321, 479, 767*
– –, –, reviews, *ref. 612, 650*
– –, recent developments in, *ref. 4*
– pre-operative characteristics, 88
– profiles, 111, 272
– –, air–hydrogen turbulent flames, 111
– –, atomic-absorption, 275
– –, emission, 275
– –, long-tube, 137, 138
– regulation, 88
– spectrophotometry, absorption, 6, 9
– speed, 104, 105
– technology, flow phenomena, *ref. 386*
– temperature, 88, 94, 101, 108; *ref. 847*
– –, excessive, 270
– – measurement, 94, 96
– transmission (hydrogen, acetylene, propane), 211
– turbulence, 121, 122
– width, 97
flames, colored, 99
–, cool, 94, 122
–, different kinds of, 97
–, dry, 94
–, excessively bright, 98
–, fish-tail, 113, 253
–, fuel-rich, 16, 99
–, –, as a source (europium, thulium, yttrium), 101
–, high-emitting, 107
–, high temperature, *ref. 618, 744*
–, hot, 272
–, laminar, 88
–, –, flow pattern, 115
–, –, shapes, 114
–, low temperature, 99
–, luminous, 101, 106
–, other techniques than, 146
–, periodically deflected, *ref. 418*
–, plasma, 125; *ref. 202*
–, premix, *ref. 501*
–, premixed, high temperature, *ref. 20*
–, reducing, 99, 272
–, turbulent, 88, 94, 277
–, zone of higher atom concentration, 110, 111
– as emitters, 87
flash backs (see also strike backs), 120
– heating, 152
flash-heated strips, wires or sheets, 152
flash-heating techniques, 152; *ref. 388, 519, 520, 521, 522, 523, 524, 525*
flasks, volumetric, 288
floculant agent, Separan NP-10 as, 297
flow rate variation, 130
– rates, 102
– ratio, 88
flowmeters, 93, 94
flows, 94
fluctuation, peak-to-peak (see noise, peak-to-peak), 242, 243, 248
fluctuations, 228
flue dusts, zinc determination in, *ref. 356*
food industry, *ref. 691*
foods, copper determination in, 382
– analysis, 382

foundry products analysis, 386
four-channel direct reading head, *ref. 341*
Fraunhofer observations, 7
frequency, resonant, 29
fuel-rich flames (see under flames and under the name of the flames according to the gases used: for instance, oxygen–acetylene flames)
fungicides, determination of iron, manganese and zinc, 385
– analysis, 385
– –, organometallic components, *ref. 297, 298, 299*
furnace techniques, 149, 150
furnaces, 87
Fuwa tube (see also adapter, long tube) 139

G

gadolinium, fluctuational concentration limit, 246
–, operating conditions, 402
– percentual concentration limit, 244
– determination with fuel-rich flames, 100, 101
galena, selenium determination in, 372
gallium, fluctuational concentration limit, 246
–, operating conditions, 402
–, percentual concentration limit, 244
– determination by atomic-fluorescence flame photometry, *ref. 472*
gas, fuel, 89
–, leakage, 91
–, suppert, 89
–, –, pressure, 90
–, –, temperature, 90
–, supporting, 89
–, town (see town gas)
– oils, vanadium determination in, *ref. 901*
– tanks, 99
gases, premixed, 94
–, streaming velocity, 114, 116
–, flow, 88
– regulation, 88, 94
gas-line, lead determination in, 182
gasoline, lead determination in, 375; *ref. 158, 620, 772*
Gatehouse and Willis, instrument described by, 178
Geissler tubes 86
general principles 11
geochemical prospecting, *ref. 690*
– – applications in, 371
– research, applications in, *ref. 613*
geological materials, *ref. 100, 101, 124*
– problems, applications in, 388
egrmanium, fluctuational concentration limit, 246
–, operating conditions, 402
–, percentual concentration limit, 244
– determination with fuel-rich flames, 100
glass, alkaline earth determination in, *ref. 1*
–, arsenic determination in, 386
–, iron determination in, 386; *ref. 544*
–, optical, analysis of, *ref. 137*
–, zinc determination in, 383; *ref. 544*
– analysis, 383; *ref. 369, 370*
glassware, 288
glycerol, 303
–, use in interferences on calcium, 309
– as a protector, 309
gold, arsenic determination in, 386
–, fluctuational concentration limit, 246
–, high purity, determination of copper, iron, lead, silver, zinc in, *ref. 658*
–, – –, fineness of, *ref. 242*
–, impurities determination in, *ref. 734*
–, interferences by calcium on, 371
–, operating conditions, 402
–, percentual concentration limit, 244
– analysis, 377, 379
– –, impurities in, *ref. 242*
– as internal standard, 173
– as monitor, 173
– assay, 371, 379; *ref. 535, 673, 770*
– bullion, determination of copper and silver, 378
– determination, 182, 371, 381; *ref. 293, 393, 910*
– – in carbonate rocks, 372
– – in cyanide wastes, *ref. 739*
– – in mill cyanide solutions, 383; *ref. 941*
– – in mine solutions, *ref. 133*
– – in waste solutions, gold mining, 383
– extraction, 371
– mining, waste solutions, gold determination, 383
– standard solutions, 291
graphical aids, 292
graphite cell, 150
– crucible, 149
graphites, cesium determination in, 386
ground state, multiple, 37

H

haemoglobin determination, 370; *ref. 330*

hafnium, fluctuational concentration limit, 246
–, operating conditions, 402
–, percentual concentration limit, 244
halogen acids, interferences on zinc, *ref. 241*
Hamamatsu photomultipliers, 160
Handigas, 94, 120
hay, strontium determination in, 356, 366
head, four-channels, direct reading, 177
height, optimum, 274
helium as a filling gas, 56, 58, 59
Hell, burner described by, 117
Herrmann and Lang, instrument described by, 178
hexone, 299, 300
high-sodium systems (see sodium (high-) systems)
Hilger and Watts Ltd. atomic-absorption unit, 179
– burner, 123
– instruments, 176; *ref. 343, 353*
– –, description, 180, 188, 196
– monochromator, 177
– spectrograph, 176, 177
– Uvispek spectrophotometer, 178; *ref. 337, 339*
Hinson and Kitching, burner described by, 119
– – –, instrument described by, 178
Hitachi Limited instruments, *ref. 889, 916*
– –, description, 180, 188, 196
hit-and-run accidents, 388
hollow-cathode lamps (see lamps, hollow-cathode)
– source (see lamps, hollow-cathode)
– tubes (see tubes, hollow-cathode)
holmium, fluctuational concentration limit, 246
–, operating conditions, 403
–, percentual concentration limit, 244
– determination with fuel-rich flames, 100
Holtsmark effect, 41
Honeywell–Brown recorder, 176
Hudson furnace method, 150
hydrochloric acid interferences on zinc, 381
hydrogen arc, 48
hydrogen flames, rich, 101, 102
hydrogen peroxide, tin determination in, 384; *ref. 2*
hydrogen tube DVS-25, 48

I

identification, 217
–, qualitative, 218
impurities determination in gold, *ref. 734*
increments, method of (see addition method), 330
indirect analysis, 21
indium, determination of magnesium and nickel, 380
–, fluctuational concentration limit, 246
–, operating conditions, 403
–, percentual concentration limit, 244
– determination by atomic-fluorescence flame photometry, *ref. 472*
industrial products analysis, 383
– solutions analysis, 383
information, analytical, 174
–, readable, 174
–, stored, 174
– on the quantitative composition of the sample, 174
– sources, 174
instrument adjustment, 281
instrumental systems, 12, 45, 174
instrumentation (see also instruments), *ref. 778*
instruments, 174; *ref. 31, 33, 41, 50, 55, 109, 117, 160, 180, 251, 258, 426, 448, 450, 563, 571, 651, 657, 758, 885, 886*
–, automatic, *ref. 184*
–, commercial, 180, 182
–, direct reading, *ref. 350*
–, home made, 175
–, multichannel, 161, 179, 307; *ref. 114, 184, 478, 533, 572, 898*
–, simplified, *ref. 611*
– for clinical chemistry, *ref. 38*
– – – laboratories, *ref. 38*
integration with condensers, 178
intensities, relative emission, 276
intensity, constant, 12
interconal zone, *ref. 232*
interference effects (see also interferences), 19
– phenomena, graphic representation, 277
– ratios, 340; *ref. 581*
– –, ponderal, 340
interferences, 256, 258, 260, 261, 265, 266; *ref. 66, 410, 588, 589*
– (hyper-), 272
–, absorption by flame or solvent, 261
–, anionic, 269, 270
–, –, elimination in determinations of calcium, *ref. 578*
–, background, 261
–, cationic, 270

–, chemical, 103, 126, 261, 265, 266, 268
–, –, suppression, 272
–, classification of, 261
–, condensed-phase, 268, 270
–, dissociation chemical, 269
–, element specific, 261
–, elimination of *ref. 174*
–, emission, 273
–, excitation, 265, 268
–, –, chemical, 270
–, flame emission, 102, 261
–, flame photometry, *ref. 392*
–, inhibition chemical, 270
–, instrument type, 261
–, instrumental, 266
–, inter-element, 265, 298
–, ionization, 104, 268
–, –, chemical, 269
–, non-specific, 261
–, physical, 128, 261
–, radiation, 261, 265
–, sample inter-element, 65
–, source inter-element, 64
–, spectral (spectroscopic), 64, 261, 266
–, – absorption, 261
–, vapor-phase, 268–270
– by flame emission, 47
interfering anions, removal, exchange, *ref. 344*
– effects (see also interferences), 265
internal standard, gold as, 173
– –, palladium as, 383
– – operation, 172
– standards, 172, 177, 302, 306
iodides determination, 205
iodine determination, 211
ion-exchange column, *ref. 177*
ion-exchange resins, 356, 357
ionization, *ref. 346*
– equilibrium, 267
iridium, fluctuational concentration limit, 246
–, operating conditions, 403
–, percentual concentration limit, 244
iron, cast (see cast iron)
–, chromium determination in, 377, 382
– (low alloy), chromium determination in, *ref. 398*
–, cobalt determination in, 377; *ref. 721*
–, copper determination in, 377; *ref. 379, 721*
–, effects of the variation of the air pressure, 89
–, effects of variations of hydrogen pressure, 93
–, fluctuational concentration limit, 246
–, interferences by sodium on, 272
–, magnesium determination in, 376, 377; *ref. 79, 80, 721, 728*
–, manganese determination in, 377; *ref. 82, 721*
–, nickel determination in, 377, 379, 381, 382; *ref. 396, 721, 763*
–, operating conditions, 403
–, percentual concentration limit, 244
–, slit, 156
–, zinc determination in, *ref. 356*
– binding capacity determination, *ref. 876*
– carbonyl determination in town gas, 389; *ref. 193*
– coprecipitation, 351
– determination, 266; *ref. 9*
– – by extraction (urine), *ref. 354, 355*
– – in air polution, 388
– – in aluminum, traces of iron, *ref. 59*
– – in aluminum alloys, traces of iron, *ref. 59*
– – in beer, 382; *ref. 248*
– – in biological materials, *ref. 310, 871*
– – in biotites, 372
– – in blood serum, *ref. 724, 876*
– – in cements, 383
– – in copper-base alloys, 378
– – in feldspars and biotites, 371
– – in fungicides, 385
– – in glass, 386; *ref. 544*
– – in granitic and diabasic rocks, 371
– – in high purity gold, *ref. 658*
– – in igneous minerals and rocks, 372
– – in industrial waste water, *ref. 99*
– – in lubricating oils, 375
– – in marine sediments, 388
– – in nickel plating solutions, 383; *ref. 664*
– – in niobium, 380; *ref. 157*
– – in plants, *ref. 171*
– – in plating solutions, 383
– – in petroleum products, *ref. 684*
– – in protein solutions, *ref. 37*
– – in sea water, *ref. 917*
– – in sediments, 373; *ref. 122*
– – in silicate samples, 386
– – in silicocalcareous minerals, *ref. 913*
– – in stainless steels, 380
– – in steels, 381
– – in tantalum, 380; *ref. 157*
– – in tungsten carbide, 377, 382; *ref. 78*
– – in urine, 367, 368; *ref. 873*
– – – – by extraction, *ref. 354, 355*
– – in vegetable matter, 176
– – in waste water, 351
– – in water, *ref. 130*
– – in whole blood, *ref. 330*
– – with addition of organic solvents, 302
– – with fuel-rich air–hydrogen flames, 103

– extraction, 384
– – with cupferron, 300
– interferences on magnesium, 271; *ref. 243*
– – on rhodium, 101
– – on zinc, *ref. 243*
– sensitivity variations with slit, 157
– – with continuum sources, 48
– (high-) systems, 272
isoquinoline as chelating agent, 309
isopropanol, 302
– addition, 271
isotope analysis (see also isotopic analysis), 211; *ref. 678*
– –, overlaping in, 211
– composition, determination of, *ref. 861, 862, 864, 865, 877, 878*
– shift, 58
isotopes, lithium, determination (see lithium isotopes determination)
–, uranium, determination (see uranium, isotopes determination)
isotopic analysis (see also isotope analysis), 5, 266, 387; *ref. 771*

J

Jarrell-Ash Company instruments, 124; *ref. 362, 363, 364, 365, 366, 755*
– –, description, 180, 190, 196
– monochromator, 175
Jadec-type plug-in-base (hollow-cathode lamps), 71, 76
Jobin-Yvon instruments, description, 180, 192, 196

K

kidney, rat (see rat kidney)
King furnace, 149
Kniseley *et al.*, burner described by, 115, 120; *ref. 62*
knowns, 296
–, blank, 297
Koirtyohann and Pickett, instrument described by, 178

L

lactose as protector, 309
laminar flow burners (see burners, laminar flow)
lamp background, 153, 154, 156
– connectors, 76
– current, 250, 252, 407
lamps, *ref. 335, 342*
–, brass cathode, 156
–, capacitor discharge, 152
–, discharge, sodium, self-absorption, *ref. 774*
–, electrodeless, 84
–, –, selenium, 85
–, high-pressure xenon arc, 48
–, hollow-cathode, 51; *ref. 43, 60, 74, 102, 119, 120, 121, 128, 205, 286, 287, 338, 372, 387, 413, 462, 476, 477, 545, 546, 547, 548, 648, 662, 671, 704, 705, 888, 899*
–, –, adjustable, 67, 68
–, –, alloy cathodes, 64
–, –, air leakage, 72, 73
–, –, Al–Mg cathodes, 64
–, –, anode, 52
–, –, background emission, 70, 79, 81
–, –, boosting discharge, 78
–, –, bases, 67
–, –, cathode, 52, 53
–, –, classification, 59
–, –, clean-up, 72, 74
–, –, coated cathodes, 63
–, –, concentric cathodes, 65, 66
–, –, cooled, 59, 63, 64
–, –, Corning glass windows, 56
–, –, cup shaped cathode, 60
–, –, current, 70
–, –, curve absorbance vs. current (Zn), 75
–, –, Cu–Zn cathodes, 64
–, –, demountable, 59, 61, 62; *ref. 408*
–, –, detachable, graphite cathode, 179
–, –, drift, 72
–, –, dual (Mg–Ca), *ref. 463*
–, –, effect of current, 61
–, –, electrical supply, 69
–, –, elongated cathode, 53, 54
–, –, emission curves, 80
–, –, – –, europium, 81
–, –, – –, gallium, 82
–, –, – –, potassium, 83
–, –, – –, silver, 84
–, –, – –, tin, 85
–, –, filling gas, 56
–, –, firing, 74
–, –, flicker, 72
–, –, getter, 75, 77
–, –, glass windows, 56
–, –, graded seals, 55
–, –, high-brightness, 77
–, –, high-intensity, 76–79, 157, 158; *ref. 747*
–, –, – –, nickel, 78, 80
–, –, high-radiance, 78
–, –, ignition, 70
–, –, intensity/current curves, 71

–, –, lateral emission, 79
–, –, lead cathode, 60
–, –, leaded brass cathode, 60, 63
–, –, life, 71, 72, 74
–, –, low melting cathode, 61
–, –, manufacturers, 59
–, –, Mn–Cu cathodes, 64
–, –, multiple, 282; *ref. 478*
–, –, multi-cathode, 59, 64–66, 75, 82
–, –, –, life, 75
–, –, multi-element, 59, 64, 65, 75, 177, 282; *ref. 663*
–, –, –, Ca–Mg–Al, 178
–, –, multi-ring cathodes, 65, 67, 75, 177
–, –, noise, 71
–, –, open-ended cathode, 61
–, –, operation, electrical aspects, 69
–, –, –, mechanical aspects, 67
–, –, pins, 71
–, –, Pyrex windows, 56
–, –, power supplies, 70, 72–74
–, –, – –, current stabilized, 71
–, –, – –, regulated, 71
–, –, presence of hydrogen, 80
–, –, protective sleeve, 54, 56
–, –, quartz windows, 56
–, –, regeneration, 74
–, –, ring shaped anode, 55
–, –, sealed, 59
–, –, shapes, 53
–, –, spherical cavity cathodes, 72
–, –, signal frequency, 165
–, –, single cathode, 59, 60, 63
–, –, sintered cathodes, 63
–, –, stability, 71
–, –, tabulated data, 395
–, –, tandem mounting, 61, 63, 177
–, –, tubular cathodes, 72
–, –, uncooled, 59
–, –, use of pulsating short time signals, 70
–, –, versatile, *ref. 732*
–, –, voltage, 70
–, –, warming-up, 69
–, –, warm-up curve, 68, 69
–, –, – time, 68, 71
–, –, wax seals, 55
–, –, window, 52, 53
–, –, –, transmittance curves, 55
–, –, zinc, argon, 59
–, –, –, helium, 59
–, –, Zn–Ca cathodes, 64
–, hydrogen, 48
–, –, as reference emitter, 48
–, laboratory vapor-discharge, 50
–, mercury, excited with microwaves, 51
–, Osram, 51; *ref. 60*
–, –, power supply, *ref. 944*
–, –, quartz envelopes, 51
–, Philips, 51
–, self-absorption in sodium arc discharge, 51
–, switching, 282
–, tungsten, 48
–, vapor discharge, alkali metals, *ref. 86*
–, worn-out, 262
Lang, burner (oscillating) described by, 122
Lang and Herrmann, burner described by, 119
Lang *et al.*, burner described by, 122
lanthanides determination with fuel-rich flames, 101
– elements, atomic-absorption spectra of *ref. 509, 510*
lanthanum, fluctuational concentration limit, 246
–, operating conditions, 403
–, percentual concentration limit, 244
– addition, 270
– as releaser, 307, 308, 352, 356–359, 363–366, 368, 369, 371, 373, 386
– chloride, preventing interferences on calcium in soil analysis, *ref. 822*
– determination with fuel-rich flames, 100
laser, 147
– microprobe atomic-absorption analysis, *ref. 301*
N-lauryl-β-aminopropionic acid, 310
lead, flame profile, air–hydrogen turbulent flame, 111
–, fluctuational concentration limit, 246
–, operating conditions, 403
–, percentual concentration limit, 244
– bullion analysis, 387
– concentrates, silver determination in, 371; *ref. 608, 609, 610*
– determination, *ref. 526*
– – in aluminum alloys, 380
– – in antimony sulfide flotation concentrates, *ref. 296*
– – in aqueous solutions, *ref. 158*
– – in air, 182
– – in air pollution, 388
– – in biological materials, *ref. 895*
– – in blood, *ref. 92, 945*
– – in brass, *ref. 906*
– – in brines, 351
– – in bronzes, *ref. 906*
– – in cadmium plating solutions, 387
– – in concentrates, 372
– – in copper alloys, 380
– – in copper-base alloys, 378; *ref. 214, 333*
– – in fish flour, 382; *ref. 735*
– – in gas-line, 182
– – in gasoline, 375; *ref. 158, 622, 772*

– – in high purity gold, *ref. 658*
– – in industrial waste water, *ref. 99*
– – in galvanized and protective coatings, 376
– – in lubricating oils, 375
– – in mineral products, 373
– – in nickel plating solutions, 383; *ref. 664*
– – in organic extracts, *ref. 158*
– – in petroleum products, 5; *ref. 684*
– – in polyvinyl chloride, 376, 385; *ref. 518*
– – in potassium chloride, 384; *ref. 723*
– – in stainless steel, 380
– – in steel, 376–378; *ref. 214, 906*
– – in urine, 367; *ref. 92, 832, 834*
– – in waste water, 351
– – in water, 352, 376
– – in wine, 382; *ref. 867, 868*
– – with addition of organic solvents, 302
– – with fuel-rich air–hydrogen flames, 103
– extraction, 299, 300, 376
– –, blood, 299
– –, potassium chloride, 299
– –, urine, 299
– hollow-cathode lamp, 56, 60
– sensitivity with continuum sources, 48
lead sulfide concentrate (see lead concentrates)
– – – analysis, 386
lead-base alloys, determination of copper and zinc in, *ref. 224*
– bearing metals, 378
leaves, tree, manganese determination in, 356
–, –, zinc determination in, 356
lenses, 109, 140
–, auxiliary, 157
–, converging (convergent), 140–142
–, quartz, 140
–, spherical, 140
–, sphero cylindrical, 140
ligands, 389
light ducts, 173, 177
– pipes, (V, Sn, Al), 101
– scattering in trace element determination, *ref. 897, 942*
– signals, comparison of two, 171
– sources (see sources, light)
– – for line spectra (see sources, light)
limestones, alkaline earths determination in, *ref. 577*
–, calcium determination in, 373
–, pure, sodium determination in, *ref. 642*
–, sodium determination in, 373
– analysis, 385
liming materials analysis, 385
limit of detectability (see limits, detectability)
– of resolution, 221
limitations, *ref. 588*
– in atomic absorption, 256
limiting factors, operational, in the absorption system, 265
– –, –, in the emission system, 263
– – –, in the recording system, 265
– –, –, in the selection system, 264
– – associated with operation, 263
– – depending on the instrumental system, 262
– – – on the sample, 265
– – in the absorption systems, 262
– – in the emission system, 262
– – in the photometric system, 263
– – in the selection system, 263
limits, 231
–, absolute, 219, 230 231, 241
–, –, correlation, 231
–, –, definition, 236
–, –, significance of, *ref. 936*
–, – fluctuational, 232
–, – – qualitative, 236
–, – – quantitative, 236
–, – minimum qualitative, 218
–, – – quantitative, 218
–, – percentual qualitative, 236
–, – – quantitative, 236
–, concentration, 223
–, –, correlation, 231, 239, 240
–, –, determination, 241
–, –, practical use, 241; *ref. 931*
–, detectability, *ref. 851*
–, –, calculation, *ref. 853*
–, detection, 224, 231; *ref. 15, 416, 453, 697, 709, 925*
–, determination, 231
–, fluctuational concentration, 219, 226–229, 232, 237, 246
–, – –, table, 246
–, – qualitative concentration, 99, 231, 236
–, – – –, determination, 242
–, – quantitative concentration, 99, 231, 236
–, percentual concentration, 224–226, 229, 244
–, – –, table, 244
–, – qualitative concentration, 224, 225, 231, 236, 241
–, – – –, determination in log–log scales, 242
–, – – –, determination in ordinary scales, 241
–, – quantitative concentration, 231, 236

–, qualitative, 221, 231
–, – fluctuational concentration, 233–235
–, – percentual concentration, 233, 235
–, quantitative, 231, 232
–, – fluctuational concentration, 233, 235
–, – percentual concentration, 233
–, relative, 219, 231
–, –, definition, 236
–, –, detection, 221
–, – fluctuational concentration, 228
–, – percentual concentration, 224
–, – – detection, 224
–, – – qualitative concentration, 224
–, units to express, 218
linearity, 175
– expansion, 254
– loss, 48
line profiles, measurement, 215
– spectra, light sources for, *ref. 208*
– width, source, 47
– –, –, effect on absorbance, *ref. 841*
lines, absorption, *ref. 15*
–, analytical, 407
–, argon, 56
–, atomic resonance, detection, *ref. 744*
–, – –, isolation, *ref. 107, 744*
–, choice of, 208
–, halfwidth of, 41
–, intensity of, 208
–, internal standard, ratios, 173
–, less sensitive, 211
–, monitor, ratios, 173
–, neon, 56
–, non-resonant monitor, 172
–, resonance, 29, 37, 53, 208; *ref. 574*
–, –, definition, 11
–, –, isolation, 155
–, –, profiles of, 215
–, –, pure, 79
–, selection by spectrography, 48
–, spectral, profiles, *ref. 669*
–, width, significance of, 41
– in the far ultraviolet, 211
– used in atomic-absorption, 215
– – – – (1800–4200 Å), 212
– – – – (4200–6600 Å), 213
– – – – (6600–8600 Å), 214
liquid flow, effect of, *ref. 570*
lithium, fluctuational concentration limit, 246
–, operating conditions, 403
–, percentual concentration limit, 244
–, strong emission, 326
– determination in alloys, 389
– – in antarctic ice cores, 389
– flame profiles, 275, 277
– isotope analysis (see lithium isotope determination)
– – assay, *ref. 818*
– – determination, 387; *ref. 288, 289, 459, 460, 864, 865*
– emission intensity, 276
Littrow spectrograph, 176
– system, 182
liver, determination of copper, manganese, potassium and zinc in, *ref. 567*
–, dried, determination of copper, manganese and zinc, 369
Lorentz broadening, 53
– effect, 41
– shift, 53
low temperature dry asher (LTA-600) (see asher, low temperature dry)
lubricating oils, determination of chromium, copper, iron, lead, magnesium, nickel, and silver, 375
– –, wear metal analysis, *ref. 126*
– – analysis, 374; *ref. 126*
– – –, standards, 290
Lundegårdh burner, 113, 176
– sprayer, 125
lutetium, fluctuational concentration limit, 246
–, operating conditions, 403
–, percentual concentration limit, 244
– determination with fuel-rich flames, 100
L'vov furnace, 149

M

magnesium, absorption/concentration curves, 322
–, dissociation of oxides, 100
–, effects of the variation of air pressure, 89
–, – – of hydrogen pressure, 93
–, extraction methods, *ref. 752*
–, fluctuational concentration limit, 246
–, hollow-cathode lamp warm-up curve, 69
–, interferences by acetic acid on, 268
–, by alkalis on, *ref. 243*
–, – by aluminum on, 104, 126, 271, 352, 378
–, – by iron on, 271; *ref. 243*
–, – by phosphates on, 271, 352
–, – by silicon on, 352, 381
–, – by silicates on, 271
–, – by sodium on, 272, 365
–, – by sulfates on, 271
–, – on, *ref. 302, 641*
–, operating conditions, 404
–, percentual concentration limit, 244

–, – – – with plasmas, 148
–, rubidium determination in, 379
– alloys, magnesium determination in, 380
– – analysis, *ref. 470*
– and sulfuric acid as releaser, 308
– chloride, copper determination in, 384
– determination, *ref. 7, 184, 348, 429*
– – by sputtering techniques, 151
– – in agricultural materials, 353
– – in air pollution, 388
– – in alloys, 389
– – in aluminum, 379
– – in aluminum alloys, 377, 379, 380; *ref. 430, 796*
– – in animal nutrition, *ref. 542*
– – in antarctic ice cores, 389
– – in biological materials, 4, 364, 382; *ref. 42, 185, 480, 871*
– – in blood, *ref. 452 714, 825*
– – in blood plasma, 365, 369; *ref. 353*
– – in blood serum, 364; *ref. 323, 371, 730, 750, 824, 828*
– – – –, accuracy in, *ref. 793*
– – in body fluids, *ref. 323*
– – in bone ash, *ref. 36*
– – in bones, 369
– – in cast iron, 376–378, 380, 381; *ref. 98, 292, 751*
– – in cements, 383; *ref. 761*
– – in ceramic frit, 386
– – in cerebrospinal fluid, 370; *ref. 190*
– – in chloroplasts, 355
– – in chromium, 182
– – in copper alloys, 380
– – in diets, *ref. 295*
– – in electrolytic excretion studies, 370; *ref. 309*
– – in electronic nickel, *ref. 21, 22*
– – in feces, 368
– – in feeding stuffs, 382
– – in feldspars and biotites, 371
– – in fertilizers, 182
– – in granitic and diabasic rocks, 371
– – in human blood serum, *ref. 28*
– – in human brain, *ref. 905*
– – in indium, 380
– – in iron, 376, 377; *ref. 79, 80, 721, 728*
– – in lubricating oils 375
– – in magnesium alloys, 380
– – in metabolism studies, 370
– – in metallurgical products, 376
– – in mixed feeds, *ref. 923*
– – in molybdenum, 182
– – in nickel, 378
– – in nickel alloys, 377, 378, 382; *ref. 21, 22, 204*
– – in parotid saliva of sheep, *ref. 141*
– – in phosphates, 182
– – in plant materials, 4, 355; *ref. 371, 407, 856*
– – in purified brines, 384
– – in rat heart and muscle, 369
– – in silicate samples, 386
– – in silicocalcareous minerals, *ref. 913*
– – in slags, 380, 381; *ref. 292*
– – in sodium bicarbonate, 384
– – in sodium carbonate, 384
– – in soil extracts, 156
– – in soils, exchangeable, 4; *ref. 166*
– – in stainless steel, 380
– – in steel, 377; *ref. 98, 721*
– – in strontium nitrate, 384; *ref. 359*
– – – – – with continuum source, 48
– – in the presence of sodium, 156
– – in tissues, 369
– – – – of chicken, *ref. 295*
– – in uranium, 378, 389; *ref. 351, 760*
– – in urine, 364; *ref. 730, 831*
– – in water, *ref. 130*
– – in zinc chloride, 182
– – with addition of organic solvents, 302
– – with fuel-rich air–hydrogen flames, 103
– – with fuel-rich flames, 101
– extraction, 300, 384
– hollow-cathode lamp, coated, 182
– interferences on calcium, 352
– – on rhodium, 101
– – on sodium, 352
– sensitivity with continuum sources, 48
– spectrum, 159
– – isolated by resonance monochromator, 159
– working curves, 255, 315
major component determination in sea water, *ref. 308*
Malmstadt *et al.*, instrument described by, 178
manganese, effects of the variation of air pressure, 89
–, – – of hydrogen pressure, 93
–, fluctuational concentration limit, 246
–, interferences by molybdenum on, 381
–, – by silicon on, 381
–, – by sodium on, 272
–, – by tungsten on, 381
–, – on, 381
–, operating conditions, 404
–, percentual concentration limit, 244
– chloride, copper determination in, 384
– determination, 266, 381; *ref. 9*
– – in air pollution, 388
– – in cast iron, *ref. 98*

– – in caustic solutions, 383
– – in cements, 383; *ref. 761*
– – in dried liver and muscle, 369
– – in fungicides, 385
– – in granitic and diabasic rocks, 371
– – in iron, 377; *ref. 82, 721*
– – in liver, *ref. 567*
– – in muscle, *ref. 567*
– – in nickel alloys, 377, 382; *ref. 204*
– – in plants, *ref. 171, 908*
– – in rat kidney, 367
– – in sea water, *ref. 917*
– – in stainless steel, 380
– – in steel, 377; *ref. 82, 98, 721*
– – in synthetic fibers, 385
– – in tree leaves, 356; *ref. 116*
– – in vegetable matter, 176
– – in zincblende and catalysts, 182
– – with fuel-rich air–hydrogen flames, 103
– extraction, 300, 384
– – with cupferron, 300
– – with chelating agents and methyl isobutyl ketone, *ref. 468*
– sensitivity with continuum sources, 48
– working curves, 315–317
manganese–copper hollow-cathode lamp warm-up curve, 68
Manning, burner described by, 119
mannitol as protector, 309
mano-reducers, 94
marine sediments, determination of cobalt, iron and nickel, 388
masking devices, 140
– diphragms, 140
– slits, 140
measurement, 161
–, by difference, 12
–, densitometric, 211
–, digital voltmeter for, 169
–, direct, 12
–, electrical differentiation procedure for, 169
–, integration of signal for, 169
–, short interval wavelength scanning for, 169
–, experimental, 311
–, order of, 312
Meker burner, 113, 117, 176, 178, 179
Menzies, instrument described by, 178
mercury, fluctuational concentration limit, 246
–, operating conditions, 404
–, percentual concentration limit, 215,244
– determination, 8, 179, 349; *ref. 238, 431, 471, 484, 565, 649, 780, 879* (see also references included in the foot note of p. 349)
– – by atomic-fluorescence flame photometry, *ref. 472, 848*
– – in apples (ultramicrodetermination), *ref. 360*
– – in biological materials, *ref. 895*
– – in blood, *ref. 361*
– – in pigments, *ref. 811*
– – in powdered samples, 8; *ref. 414*
– – in urine, 367, 368
– isotopes, *ref. 538*
– lamps, excited with microwaves, 51
– lines, 215
– vapor detector, *ref. 854, 855*
– – spectrum, 215
metabolism, mineral, *ref. 543*
– studies, magnesium determination in, 370
metal, type, copper determination in, 378
– analysis, plant control, *ref. 70*
– complexes determination in organic solvents, *ref. 291*
– determination in alloys, *ref. 39*
– – in lubricating oils, wear metals, *ref. 126*
– – in oils, *ref. 49*
– – in plating solutions, *ref. 40*
– traces (see trace elements)
metallic samples (see metallurgical materials analysis)
metallurgical applications (see metallurgical materials analysis)
– materials, copper determination in, *ref. 794*
– –, zinc determination in, *ref. 270, 271, 528, 794*
– – analysis (see also metallurgical products analysis), 376; *ref. 67, 209, 215, 218, 268, 487, 488, 583, 677, 741*
– – –, determinable elements (aluminum, bismuth, cadmium, calcium, chromium, copper, gold, iron, lead, magnesium, manganese, molybdenum, nickel, palladium, platinum, rhodium, rubidium, selenium, silver, sodium, tellurium, vanadium, zinc), 379, 380
– – –, extractions, in, *ref. 583*
– – –, interferences, 380
– – –, standards, 381
– products, cobalt determination in, 376
– –, magnesium determination in, 376
– –, silver determination in, 376
– –, zinc determination in, 376
– – analysis (see also metallurgical materials analysis), 376
– – –, preparation of samples, 377
– – –, reviews, 376
metallurgy, applications in (see also metallurgical materials analysis), *ref. 677*

–, ferrous, *ref. 77*
–, nonferrous, light metals, *ref. 821*
metals, heavy, *ref. 216*
–, –, determination in urine, *ref. 834*
–, noble, determination, *ref. 336, 436, 738*
–, non-ferrous, *ref. 207*
–, pure, aluminum determination in, *ref. 529*
–, refractory, 243
–, trace elements determination in, *ref. 379*
– analysis, *ref. 256, 257*
– determination in alloys, *ref. 719*
– – in cements, *ref. 900*
– (major) – in diabasic rocks, *ref. 776*
– (major) – in granitic rocks, *ref. 776*
– – in lubricating oils, *ref. 718*
– (wear) – in lubricating oils, *ref. 491*
– – in silicate samples, *ref. 777*
– – in synthetic fibers, *ref. 696*
methanearsonic acid, arsenic determination in, 386
methanol, 130, 303
methanol–chloroform, 388
4-methyl-1,2-dimercaptobenzene, 384
methyl isobutyl ketone, 297, 298, 300, 303, 376, 379, 383, 384, 386
– – –, manganese extraction, *ref. 468*
methyl n-amyl ketone, 299
microbiology, applications in, 388
microchemistry, inorganic, *ref. 814*
microcultures, calcium determination in, 388
microliter samples, *ref. 420*
microwave field on flame emission, 50
microwave-powered Raman sources, *ref. 304*
milk, copper determination in, 366; *ref. 508*
–, powdered, strontium determination in, 366, 382
– analysis, 366
mill cyanide solutions, gold determination in, 383; *ref. 941*
– intermediate products analysis, 386
mine solutions, gold determination in, *ref. 133*
mineral products, antimony determination in, 373
– –, lead determination in, 373
– – analysis, 370
– – (solid) –, 370
– – –, determinable elements (antimony, cadmium, calcium, cobalt, copper, gold, iron, lead, magnesium, manganese, nickel, potassium, rubidium, selenium, silver, sodium, strontium, and zinc), 372
– – –, extraction, 373
– – –, interferences, 373
– – –, preparation of samples, 371
– – –, standards, 373
minerals, igneous, determination of calcium, iron, potassium, rubidium, sodium and strontium), 372
–, silicocalcareous, determination of calcium, iron and magnesium in, *ref. 913*
–, silver determination in, *ref. 290*
–, sodium determination in, *ref. 197*
– analysis, *ref. 912*
mining, 371; *ref. 690*
–, non-ferrous, *ref. 607*
mirrors, 146, 263
– (semi-), 141
–, half silvered, 178
–, polka-dot, 141
Mislan furnace method, 150
mist, 131
–, sample solution, 115
mixture method (see addition method), 330
modulation, 101, 107, 153, 156, 164–167, 263, 273, 326
–, flame, *ref. 328, 329*
–, selective, *ref. 107*
– in sputtering techniques, 167
– frequency, 107
molecular absorption, 7, 49, 215, 261
– – spectroscopy, 7
– bands, absorption by, theory, *ref. 556*
– entities, 211
molybdenum, fluctuational concentration limit, 246
–, magnesium determination in, 182
–, operating conditions, 404
–, percentual concentration limit, 244
– determination, *ref. 165, 168*
– – in brines, *ref. 192*
– – in ferrous alloys, *ref. 511*
– – in sodium chloride solutions, 384
– – in steels, 377, 378
– – in sub-p.p.m. levels, *ref. 192*
– – in uranium, 389
– – with fuel-rich flames, 100, 101
– – with reducing flames, 100
– extraction, 384
– interferences on manganese, 381
– – on nickel, 381
monitor elements 173
monochromators, 155
mount, adjustable, *ref. 206*
multi-burner couplings, 124
multichannel instruments (see instruments, multichannel)
– photometers (see instruments, multichannels)
multi-component analysis, 18

multi-element analysis, 291; *ref. 131, 132*
– –, simultaneous, *ref. 733*
– determinations, 159
– instruments, 172
– measurements, 172
multi-layer path devices, 142
multi-pass devices, 96, 97, 124, 251
– –, angular zig-zag, 142, 144, 145
– –, circular, 142, 146
– –, optical, 142
muscle, determination of copper, manganese, potassium and zinc in, *ref. 567*
–, dried, determination of copper, manganese and zinc, 369

N

National Bureau of Standards standards, 375, 378, 385
neodymium, fluctuational concentration limit, 246
–, operating conditions, 404
–, percentual concentration limit, 244
– determination with fuel-rich flames, 100
neon as a filling gas, 56
– lines, 56
new developments (see reviews)
nickel, cobalt determination in, *ref. 490*
–, effects of the variation of the air pressure, 89
–, – – of the hydrogen pressure, 93
–, electronic, magnesium determination in, *ref. 21, 22*
–, fluctuational concentration limit, 246
–, interferences by molybdenum on, 381
–, – by phosphates on, 381
–, – by sulfates on, 381
–, magnesium determination in, 378
–, operating conditions, 404
–, percentual concentration limit, 244
–, slit, 156
– alloys, chromium determination in, 377, 382; *ref. 204*
– –, magnesium determination in, 377, 378, 382; *ref. 21, 22, 204*
– –, manganese determination in, 377, 382; *ref. 204*
– carbonyl determination in town gas, 389; *ref. 192*
– determination, *ref. 10*
– – in biological materials, *ref. 749*
– – in cast iron, *ref. 98*
– – in catalytic cracking feedstocks, 376; *ref. 775*
– – in ceramic frit, 386
– – in copper-base alloys, 378
– – in feldspars and biotites, 371
– – in indium, 380
– – in industrial waste water, *ref. 99*
– – in iron, 377, 379, 381, 382; *ref. 396, 721, 763*
– – in lubricating oils, 375
– – in natural water, 351; *ref. 123*
– – in petroleum products *ref. 684*
– – in sediments (marine and recent sediments), 388; *ref. 122*
– – in stainless steel, 380, 381
– – in steel, 377, 379; *ref. 98, 396, 721, 763*
– – in urine, 367; *ref. 722*
– – in waste water, 351
– – in zincblende and catalysts, 182
– – with fuel-rich air–hydrogen flames, 103
– extraction, 300, 384
– –, urine, 299
– – from NaOH solutions, 299
– – with cupferron, 300
– lines, 208
– sensitivity with continuum sources, 48
nickel chloride, copper determination in, 384
niobium, atomic-absorption spectrum, *ref. 234, 235*
–, fluctuational concentration limit, 246
–, iron determination in, 380; *ref. 157*
–, operating conditions, 404
–, percentual concentration limit, 244
– determination with fuel-rich flames, 100, 101
nitric acid interferences on silver, 381
nitrogen, purging with, 211
– as support gas, 89, 94
– as spraying gas, 124
nitrogen monoxide–acetylene flame, 104
nitrous oxide as spraying gas, 124
– – as support gas, 89
– – –acetylene burner (see burner, nitrous oxide–acetylene)
– – –acetylene flames, 16, 98, 103, 104, 117, 118, 120, 245, 408; *ref. 838*
– – – –, slot dimensions for, 103
noble metals, (see metals, noble)
noise, 167
–, blank, 250
–, electrometer, 230
–, –, effect of *ref. 851*
–, methods of minimizing, 251
–, peak-to-peak, 227, 234, 242, 243, 248
–, recorder, 248
–, shot, 167, 230, 259
– at 0% absorption, 230
– level, 167, 251, 259
–/ pressure curves, 92

nomenclature, 6, 8
nomogram, volume–concentration calculation, 292, 293; *ref. 599*
–, – –, auxiliary scales, 294
nuclear research, applications in, *ref. 636*
– spin, 58
null-point circuits, 170
– method, precision, 177, 260; *ref. 147, 451*
nutrition, animal (see animal nutrition)

O

OH emission profiles, 96
oil analysis by emission spectrometric methods, *ref. 106*
oils, crude, vanadium determination in, 5
–, lubricating, metals determination in, *ref. 718*
–, –, metals (wear) determination in, *ref. 491*
–, metal determination in, *ref. 49*
–, used aircraft lubricating, trace metals (elements) determination in, *ref. 726*
–, vanadium determination in, 104
oleic acid as additive, 352
opacity by salt particles, 107
operating conditions, optimum, 281, 284; *ref. 144, 904*
– – for determinations by atomic-absorption flame photometry, 401
operations, auxiliary, 296
Optica S. p. A. CF4 monochromator, 177, 178
– instruments, *ref. 536, 537*
– –, description, 180, 192, 196
– sprayer, 178
optical density, 340
– path, 116, 140
– paths, long, large aperture, *ref. 819*
optimization, 284
–, complete factorial procedure, 285
–, response surface investigation, 285
ore samples, copper and zinc determination in, 372; *ref. 224*
ores, silver determination in, 373
organic additives, *ref. 658*
– chemistry, atomic absorption in, *ref. 920*
– extracts, 303
– reagents, *ref. 791*
– solvent extractions (see also organic solvents), *ref. 723*
– solvents, 109, 302, 303, 361; *ref. 13, 291 439, 617*
– –, bisolvents, *ref. 630*
oscillator strength, 39, 42, 255; *ref. 394*
– –, measurement, 389
osmium, operating conditions, 404
–, percentual concentration limit, 244
– conditions, 408
– determination, 245, 408
Osram lamps (see lamps, Osram)
output, uninterrupted, 107
oxide-type compounds formed in the flame, 110
oxine, 300, 376, 379, 384
–, trace metals in brines, extraction, *ref. 469*
– as chelating agent, 309
oxy–acetylene flames (see oxygen–acetylene flames)
oxygen, use instead of air, 98
– as spraying gas, 124
– as support gas, 89
oxygen–acetylene burners (see burners, oxygen–acetylene)
– flames, 94, 97, 98, 130; *ref. 773*
– –, fuel-rich, 99–101, 120; *ref. 226, 399*
– –, incandescent, 100
– –, premix, *ref. 455*
– –, premixed fuel-rich, *ref. 200, 228, 230, 232*
– –, strongly reducing, *ref. 461, 703*
oxygen–cyanogen flames, 97, 98
oxygen–hydrogen flames, 94, 97, 98, 130

P

p%, 238, 239
paints analysis, 385; *ref. 489*
palladium, fluctuational concentration limit, 246
–, operating conditions, 404
–, percentual concentration limit, 244
– as internal standard, 383
– determination, 381; *ref. 218, 910*
– – with addition of organic solvents, 303
– extraction, 300
parafin casts, antimony determination in, 388
path length, 38, 39
p*C*, 219, 238, 239, 278
p*D*, 219
p*D'*, 219
peak absorption method, 324, 325
– of the absorption line, 6
peaks, obtained with premix burners, *ref. 89*
performance, analytico-chemical, 174
–, factors affecting, *ref. 432*
–, physical, 174
periscope coupling, 144–146
Perkin-Elmer Corp. (The) instruments, *ref. 383, 385, 458, 918*

– – description, 180, 194, 196
– Model 13, 178, 179
– Model 214 atomic-absorption spectrophotometer, *ref. 29, 549, 893*
– – –, cesium and rubidium determination, *ref. 46*
– Model 290 atomic-absorption spectrophotometer, *ref. 53, 553*
– Model 303 atomic-absorption spectrophotometer, *ref. 375, 550, 551, 552*
– – –, recorder readout, *ref. 378*
– – –, source lamp, power supply, *ref. 382*
Perkins, instrument described by, 179
petrochemistry, atomic absorption in, *ref. 921*
petroleum analysis, 374
– industry, applications in, *ref. 68*
– products (see also oil analysis)
– –, determination of copper, iron, lead, nickel and sodium in, *ref. 684*
– – analysis, 374
– – –, determinable elements (barium, chromium, copper, iron, lead, nickel, silver, sodium, and vanadium), 375
pharmaceutical materials analysis, *ref. 940*
phenol as chelating agent, 309
Philips lamps, 51
phosphates, magnesium determination in, 182
– as releaser, 308
– interferences (see also phosphorus interferences), 358
– – on barium, elimination of, *ref. 858*
– – on calcium, 98, 104, 271, 352, 364, 365
– – on magnesium, 271, 352
– – on nickel, 381
– – on strontium, 271, 352
– – – –, elimination of, *ref. 858, 859*
– separation, ion exchange column, 364
– – in biological materials analysis, 298
– – in vegetable matter analysis, 298
phosphors, fluorescent, sodium determination in, 386
–, halo-phosphate, sodium determination in, *ref. 554*
phosphorus determination, 211
– – in copper (sputtering chamber), 151
– interferences (see also phosphates interferences), 270
photodetection, 160
–, continuous recording, 149
photodetectors, 160
photographic methods, 325
photometers, multichannel (see instruments, multichannel)
photometric system, 46, 160
– –, tuned, 164, 165
photomultipliers, 160, 177
–, 1P28, 160
–, far red, *ref. 893*
pigments, mercury determination in, *ref. 811*
pin holes, 140
pipettes, 288
plant analysis (see also plant materials analysis; see also vegetable materials, vegatable matter, and plants), 355; *ref. 172*
– ash, calcium determination in, *ref. 344*
– (industrial) control, metal analysis, *ref. 70*
– materials, arsenic determination in 386
– –, calcium determination in, 4, 269, 255; *ref. 163*
– –, magnesium determination in, 355; *ref. 371, 407, 856*
– –, potassium determination in, 355
– –, sodium determination in, 355
– –, zinc determination in, 355, 356, 358; *ref. 161, 908, 933*
– – analysis (see also plant analysis), 355; *ref. 162, 170, 505, 506*
– – –, determinable elements (calcium, cobalt, copper, iron, magnesium, manganese, nickel, potassium, rubidium, selenium, sodium, strontium, and zinc), 357
– – –, interferences, 357
– – –, preparation of samples, 355
– – –, standards, 358
plants, copper determination in, *ref. 908*
–, iron determination in, *ref. 171*
–, manganese determination in, *ref. 171, 908*
plasma flames, 125; *ref. 202*
– jet as spectroscopic source, *ref. 474*
plasmas, 147
–, high pressure, as emission source, *ref. 294*
–, induction coupled, 147; *ref. 403, 949*
–, percentual concentration limits (Al, Ca, Mg, V), 148
–, radiofrequency-induced, 147
plastics analysis, 385; *ref. 489*
plating solutions, chromium determination in, 383
– – (electro-), determination of copper and zinc, 383
– –, iron determination in, 383
– –, metal determination in, *ref. 40*
– –, nickel, determination of copper, iron, lead and zinc in, 383; *ref. 664*
platinum, fluctuational concentration limit, 246

–, operating conditions, 404
–, percentual concentration limit, 244
– determination, 182, 381; *ref. 910*
platinum–rhodium alloys, rhodium determination in, 182
Poiseuille equation, 128
Poluéktov and Grinzaid, instrument described by, 179
polyethylene bottles, 289
polyvinylchloride, cadmium determination in, 376
–, calcium and zinc determination in, 385; *ref. 518*
–, lead determination in, 376, 385; *ref. 518*
potassium, fluctuational concentration limit, 246
–, interferences by acids and alcohols on, *ref. 573*
–, – by sodium on, 272, 365
–, – on, *ref. 764*
–, ionization interferences on, 270
–, operating conditions, 404
–, percentual concentration limit, 244
–, rubidium determination in, 379
–, working curves, air–(lean)acetylene flame, 95
–, – –, air–(rich)acetylene flame, 95
–, – –, air–coal gas flame, 95
– determination (see also alkali metals determination), 268, 269; *ref. 184, 462*
– – in alloys, 389
– – in antarctic ice cores, 389
– – in beer, 382; *ref. 248*
– – in biological materials, 269; *ref. 480*
– – in blood serum, *ref. 322, 829*
– – in bone ash, *ref. 36*
– – in bones, 369
– – in cements, 383; *ref. 761*
– – in fats, 370; *ref. 929*
– – in feldspars and biotites, 371, 372
– – in granitic and diabasic rocks, 371
– – in igneous minerals and rocks, 372
– – in liver and muscle *ref. 567*
– – in plant materials, 355
– – in soda ash, 385
– – in sodium iodide, 385
– – in sodium salts, 385; *ref. 759*
– – in soils, exchangeable, *ref. 166*
– – in water, *ref. 130*
– – with addition of organic solvents, 303
– emission intensity, 276
– interferences on calcium, 269, 357
– Osram lamp, 83
potassium chloride, copper and lead determination in, 384; *ref. 723*
– –, copper extraction, 299
– –, lead extraction, 299
powdered samples, mercury determination in, *ref. 414*
power supplies, 45
p.p.b., 219
p.p.m., 219
p.p.t., 219
praeseodymium, fluctuational concentration limit, 246
–, operating conditions, 404
–, percentual concentration limit, 244
– determination with fuel-rich flames, 100
precautions, 341
–, instrumental, 341
– of personal nature, 343
– with respect to the sample, 343
precision, 232, 234, 256, 258, 259, 268, 296, 300; *ref. 598*
–, parameters influencing, 259
– null-point method (see null-point method, precision)
preparatory process, 349
pressure shift in the flame, 58
Priest, instrument described by, 179
printers, 160, 161, 169
prisms, beam splitting, 178
pro analisi products, 258
propane, 94
propanol, 303
protectors, 302, 309
protein solutions, iron determination in, *ref. 37*
publications, *ref. 376*
pump, constant feed, *ref. 516*
pumping effect, 263
pumps auxiliary feed, 140
–, impellent piston, 130
purification of materials, *ref. 191, 907*

Q

qualitative analysis, 13, 17, 22
– – with continuum sources, 49
– characteristics, 13
– tests, specific, 22
quantitative analysis, 17
– characteristics, 13
quotient method, *ref. 424*

R

radiation, resonance, 53; *ref. 503, 648, 748*
Raman sources, microwave-powered, *ref. 304*

range, dynamic (see also concentration range, dynamic), 216
–, useful (see also concentration range, dynamic), 216
rare-earth elements, flame spectra, *ref. 229*
– –, spectrum, atomic-absorption, *ref. 234, 235*
– – determination, *ref. 674*
– – – with continuum sources, 48
– – spectra, *ref. 201*
rat kidney, determination of cadmium, chromium, copper, manganese and zinc, 367
– heart and muscle, magnesium determination in, 369
Rawling *et al.*, instrument described by, 179
reaction zone, emission in the (As, Bi, and Sb), *ref. 189*
– – in oxygen–acetylene flame, *ref. 142*
reading time, 250
– –, methods of decreasing, 251
readings, 161, 162
–, apparent, 162
–, distorted, 162
–, experimental, 7
read-out, digital concentration, *ref. 52*
– device, 161
recent sediments, determination of cobalt, iron and nickel in, *ref. 122*
recent developments (see reviews)
Rechnitz, instrument described by, 179
recombination rates, 110
recorder, damped, 168
recorders, 160, 242
–, ratio, 170, 179
–, strip-chart, 168
recording, 168
–, photographic, 211
red blood cells, zinc determination in, 364
refractories, burnt, alkaline earths determination in, *ref. 577*
– analysis, 385
– elements, 20; *ref. 887*
regulators, long term drift, 92
–, short term fluctuations, 92
releasers (see also releasing agents; see also Sr, Ca, and La as releasers), 302, 307, 381
releasing agents (see also releasers), 98, 307, 382
repeatability, 175, 259, 260
Research and Control Instruments instruments, description, 180, 197, 202
resolution, 263
–, high, 155
resonance detectors, 159
– monochromators, 159
– radiation, *ref. 503*
– –, use of, 258
response: stimulus ratio, 175, 241
reviews on atomic-absorption spectroscopy (including general papers, general applications and general reviewing lectures), *ref. 16, 23, 24, 25, 26, 30, 32, 48, 56, 57, 95, 112, 113, 118, 127, 134, 136, 152, 153, 156, 164, 169, 176, 178, 181, 187, 188, 194, 195, 227, 228, 231, 233, 247, 273, 274, 275, 276, 277, 278, 279, 281, 305, 306, 312, 319, 320, 324, 334, 367, 373, 374, 377, 380, 381, 384, 400, 406, 428, 433, 434, 435, 437, 438, 440, 441, 442, 444, 447, 449, 466, 467, 493, 495, 496, 499, 512, 513, 514, 515, 532, 534, 541, 560, 561, 562, 566, 580, 582, 584, 586, 587, 591, 592, 593 594, 595, 596, 597, 614, 615, 619, 621, 623, 624, 625, 626, 627, 628, 629, 631, 633, 644, 647, 652, 653, 654, 655, 667, 683, 685, 686, 693, 694, 695, 698, 699, 700, 702, 744, 745, 753, 762, 781, 782, 783, 784, 786, 796, 797, 800, 801, 802, 803, 804, 805, 806, 809, 833, 870, 880, 883. 890, 896, 898, 914, 915, 922, 926, 927, 930*
rhenium, atomic-absorption spectrum, *ref. 235*
–, fluctuational concentration limit, 246
–, operating conditions, 405
–, percentual concentration limit, 244
– determination, *ref. 656*
– – with fuel-rich flames, 100
rhodium, fluctuational concentration limit, 101, 246
–, interferences on, 101
–, operating conditions, 405
–, percentual concentration limit, 244
– determination, 381; *ref. 910*
– – in platinum–rhodium alloys, 182
– – with fuel-rich flames, 101
Ringbom curves, 321, 324
– relationship, 320
Robinson, burner described by, 122
–, instrument described by, 179
rocks, carbonate, gold determination in, 372
–, copper determination in silicate, *ref. 88*
–, – extraction, 299
–, diabasic, major metals determination in, *ref. 776*
–, G-1 and W-1, determination of rubidium and strontium, 373
–, granitic, major metals determination in, *ref. 776*
–, grantic and diabasic, determination on calcium, iron, magnesium, manganese,

potassium, and sodium, 371
–, igneous, determination of calcium, iron, potassium and rubidium, 372
–, phosphate, alkaline earths determination in, *ref. 577*
–, silicate, analysis of, 271
–, –, zinc determination in, *ref. 88*
– analysis, *ref. 90, 246*
rubidium, fluctuational concentration limit, 246
–, interferences by acids and alcohols on, *ref. 573*
–, – on, 358
–, operating conditions, 405
–, percentual concentration limit, 244
– determination, 268; *ref. 46, 712*
– – in agricultural materials, *ref. 742*
– – in feldspars and biotites, 371
– – in G-1 and W-1 rocks, 373
– – in igneous minerals and rocks, 372
– – in magnesium, 379
– – in potassium, 379
– – in soils, 359
– – in water, 352
– – with addition of organic solvents, 303
– emission intensity, 276
– flame profiles, 275, 277
– standard solutions, 291
ruby analysis, 389; *ref. 947*
ruthenium, fluctuational concentration limit, 246
–, operating conditions, 405
–, percentual concentration limit, 244
– determination with fuel-rich flames, 100

S

saliva, calcium determination in, 365; *ref. 527*
– analysis, 365
– of sheep, parotid, calcium and magnesium determination in, *ref. 141*
salinity, 306
samarium, fluctuational concentration limit, 246
–, operating conditions, 405
–, percentual concentration limit, 245
– determination with fuel-rich flames, 100
sample consumption, 127
– flow rate, *ref. 845*
– intake, 127
– – rate, 127
– preparation, *ref. 780*
– size, 220
– solution intake, 90, 102
samples, certified, 256
–, drain losses of, 130
–, preparation of, 296
–, secondary preparation, 301
–, solid, treatment, 297
sandwiching method, 291, 313
saturators (homo- and hetero-), 302
scale, full, 318
–, restricted, 318
– expansion, 168, 169, 251, 252; *ref. 422, 937*
scandium, atomic-absorption spectrum, *ref.* 235
–, fluctuational concentration limit, 246
–, operating conditions, 405
–, percentual concentration limit, 245
– determination with fuel-rich flames, 100
– spectrum, *ref. 201*
scanning, automatic, 84
–, spectral, 171
scattering, 107, 261, 267
– of luminous radiation, 126
Schüller and Jansen, burner described by, 120
– – –, instrument described by, 179
sea water analysis (see water, sea)
sectors, rotating split, 141
sediments, determination of calcium, iron and strontium, 373
selection, monochromator, 162, 163
–, spectral, 153
– by monochromator, 155
– system, 46, 153
selenium, concentration limit, 135
–, fluctuational concentration limit, 247
–, operating conditions, 405
–, percentual concentration limit, 215, 245
–, slit, 156
– determination, *ref. 603, 606*
– – ashing, 297
– – in copper, 377; *ref. 716*
– – in galena, 372
– – in wheat, 356
– – with air–propane flame, 135
– lamp, 156
self-absorption, 60; *ref. 346, 569*
self-reversal, 51
self-standardization method (see addition method), 330
semiquantitative analysis, 17, 22
– – with continuum sources, 49
sensitivity (-ies), 175, 216, 231, 268; *ref. 143, 598*
–, absolute, 149, 230
–, –, factors governing, 220
–, – concepts, 216

–, – fluctuational, 232
–, – qualitative, 220
–, analytical, 221
–, correlation, 231, 239, 240
–, definitions, 216
–, detection, 231
–, –, theory, *ref. 280*
–, determination, 231, 241
–, experimental reduction, 253, 254
–, factors influencing, 250; *ref. 756, 757, 765, 766, 769*
–, – which decrease, 252
–, fluctuational, 228, 237
–, – qualitative, 229
–, instrumental, 229, 230
–, percentual, 137
–, –, graphical representation, 249
–, –, increase, 238
–, –, relation with fluctuational sensitivity, 228
–, – qualitative, 224, 229
–, qualitative, 216, 217, 221, 231
–, quantitative, 216, 231, 232; *ref. 600, 602*
–, relationship with accuracy, *ref. 935*
–, relative, 223
–, –, definitions, 220
–, – concepts, 216
–, – fluctuational, 228
–, – percentual, 224
–, – – qualitative, 224
–, superior values in atomic-absorption, 248
–, variations of, with slit, 157
–, symbols, 218
– as a function of an arbitrary absorption, 221
– – of experimental fluctuations, 221, 226
– coefficient, 225
– decrease, 253
–/fuel pressure curves, 92
– in atomic-absorption spectroscopy, *ref. 18*
– in emission methods, 17
– obtainable by atomic-absorption, 243
– reduction, 253
– values, 224
– –, advantage of their use, 237
– – variation, 217
– variations, 217
Separan NP-10 as floculant agent, 297, 372
separations, 296, 297
–, chemical, 297
–, physical, 297
– by adsorption, 298
– by extraction, 298
SF-4 spectrophotometer, 179
Sharpline spectro-source, *ref. 665*
– –, electrodeless discharge tubes, 85
shellfish, strontium determination in, 366, 370
Shelton and Walsh, instrument described by, 179
shot noise, 99
signal differentiation, *ref. 417*
signal-to-background ratio, 252
signal-to-noise ratio, 99, 167, 168; *ref. 423*
silica bricks analysis, 385
– separation, 378
silicate samples (see minerals analysis)
– –, determination of calcium, copper, iron, magnesium and strontium, 386
– –, metals determination in, *ref. 777*
silicates, alkali-metals and aluminum determination in, *ref. 539*
– analysis, 385
– interferences on calcium (see also silicon interferences), 271
– – on magnesium, 271
– – on strontium, 271
silicon, fluctuational concentration limit, 247
–, operating conditions, 405
–, percentual concentration limit, 245
– determination by sputtering techniques, 151
– – in aluminum (sputtering chamber), 151
– – in steel (sputtering chamber), 151
– – with fuel-rich flames, 100
– interferences (see also silicates interferences), 358
– – on calcium, 352, 365
– – on magnesium, 352, 381
– – on manganese, 381
– – on strontium, 352
– oscillator strength (2516 Å), 150
– percentual sensitivity (concentration limit) with nitrous oxide–acetylene flame, 104
silver, flame profile, air–hydrogen turbulent flame, 111
–, fluctuational concentration limit, 247
–, interferences by aluminum on, 381
–, – by nitric acid on, 381
–, operating conditions, 405
–, percentual concentration limit, 245
– assay, 379; *ref. 770*
– determination, 182, 381; *ref. 83, 293, 910*
– – in aluminum alloys, 380; *ref. 839, 840*
– – in copper (sputtering chamber), 151
– – in copper alloys, 380

– – in fuel-rich air–hydrogen flames, 102
– – in gold bullion, 378
– – in high purity gold, *ref. 658*
– – in lead concentrates, *371*; *ref. 608, 609, 610*
– – in lead sulfide concentrates (see silver determination in lead concentrates)
– – in lubricating oils, 375
– – in metallurgical products, 376
– – in minerals, *ref. 290*
– – in ores, 373
– extraction, 299
– lines, 208
– –, absorption of, 210
– sensitivity with continuum sources, 48
– vapor, absorption spectra of, 150; *ref. 670*
simulation, 305
single beam, 98
single-standard method, 313, 328, 329
sinter samples analysis, 387
Si-Ro-Spec instrument, 182; *ref. 108*
Skinner burner, 123
Skogerboe, instrument described by, 179
slags, calcium and magnesium determination in, 380, 381; *ref. 292*
– analysis, 387
Slavin, burner described by, 120
slit, focusing on the, 157
–, sensitivity variations with the, 157
– assymetry, 158
– width, 407
– –, effect on emission, *ref. 841*
slits, masking, 140
–, narrow, noise with, 158
slope, 224, 229, 230, 250, 326
–, calculation of, 225
–, methods to increase, 250
– values, 225, 229
slot, 96
– dimensions, 116, 120
smelting industry, *ref. 607*
soda ash, potassium determination in, 385
sodium, atomic-absorption cross section, *ref. 349*
–, discharge lamps, self-absorption, *ref. 774*
–, flame processes, 34
–, fluctuational concentration limit, 247
–, interferences by acids and alcohols on, *ref. 573*
–, – by calcium on, 352, 383
–, – by magnesium on, 352
–, – on, 267
–, ionization interferences, 270
–, magnesium determination in the presence of, 156
–, operating conditions, 405
–, percentual concentration limit, 245
–, selection by filters, 153
– arc discharge lamps, self-absorption in, 51
– atom losses (turbulent oxygen–hydrogen flames), *ref. 576*
– determination (see also alkali metals determination), 266, 267, 301; *ref. 115, 184, 197, 462, 575, 616*
– – by sputtering techniques, 151
– – in aluminum alloys, 380
– – in beer, 382; *ref. 248*
– – in biological materials, *ref. 480*
– – in blood serum, *ref. 322, 829*
– – in bone ash, *ref. 36*
– – in bones, 369
– – in calcium phosphate, 384
– – in cements, 383; *ref. 761*
– – in copper alloys, 380
– – in fats, 370; *ref. 929*
– – in feldspars and biotites, 371
– – in fluorescent phosphors, 386
– – in granitic and diabasic rocks, 371
– – in limestones, 373
– – in halo-phosphate phosphors, *ref. 554*
– – in igneous minerals, 372
– – in minerals, *ref. 196*
– – in petroleum products, *ref. 684*
– – in plant materials, 355
– – in pure limestones, *ref. 642*
– – in soils, exchangeable, *ref. 166*
– – in tungstic acid, 384
– – in water, 352; *ref. 130*
– – with addition of organic solvents, 303
– emission intensity, 276
– interferences, *ref. 934*
– – in water analysis, 352
– – on calcium, 269, 272, 352, 357, 364
– – on copper, 272
– – on iron, 272
– – on magnesium, 272, 365
– – on manganese, 272
– – on potassium, 272, 365
– – on zinc, 272
– lines, 301
– salts, potassium determination in, 385; *ref. 759*
– (high-) systems, 272; *ref. 934*
– vapor, atomic-absorption cross section, 150
– – lamp, 178, 179
sodium bicarbonate, magnesium determination in, 384
sodium carbonate, magnesium determination in, 384
sodium chloride solutions, determination of chromium and molybdenum, 384

sodium iodide, potassium determination in, 385
soils, arsenic determination in, 386
–, determination of exchangeable calcium, magnesium, potassium, sodium, 4; *ref. 166*
–, rubidium determination in, 359
–, strontium determination in, exchangeable, *ref. 173*
–, zinc determination in, *ref. 261*
– analysis, 358; *ref. 162, 505, 506, 659*
– –, determinable elements (calcium, copper, iron, magnesium, manganese, potassium, rubidium, selenium, sodium, strontium, and zinc), 360
– –, extractant solutions, 358
– –, extraction with organic solvents, 361
– –, interferences, 360
– –, preparation of samples, 359
– –, standards, 360
– extracts, magnesium determination in, 156
solid, evaporation of, 33
–, vaporization of, 33
– analysis, *ref. 672*
solution flow rate, 127
solutions, aqueous, lead determination in, *ref. 158*
–, coloidal, 267
–, high saline, 267
–, mechanisms for suplying the, 140
–, modification of the composition of, 304
–, sample, preparation of, 281
–, standard, 286, 287
–, –, dilution series (Table), 399
–, stock, 281, 287
–, storage, 289
– prepared for analysis, 296
– – for determination, 296
solvents, absorption by, 20, 107
–, organic (see under the name of the solvent)
–, non-aqueous, 267
source instability, 170
– noise, 252
– power supply (see under power supply)
sources, background emission, 162, 163
–, continuum (see also emitters, continuum), 58; *ref. 154, 228, 236, 264, 265, 359, 402, 458, 909*
–, –, advantages, 49
–, discharge tubes, *ref. 288, 289*
–, emission, spectra of, 211
–, intense, *ref. 635*
–, light, *ref. 282, 335, 342*
–, –, for line spectra, *ref. 208*
–, microwave powered, 86; *ref. 304*
–, pulse spark, time-resolved, 86
–, quartz-iodine, 48
–, radiation, 45
–, time-resolved spark, *ref. 731*
spark, 148
–, time-resolved, as a source, *ref. 731*
spark-in-spray, 148
spectra, absorption, 6
–, –, of gases and vapors, *ref. 485, 486*
–, atomic-absorption, *ref. 254*
–, discrete, 58
–, vacuum ultraviolet absorption, *ref. 388*
spectral selection, double-beam method, *ref. 5, 6*
spectroanalysis by flame methods, 6
spectrographic inspection, 211
spectrometer, scanning, high speed, *ref. 184*
spectrometers (see instruments, and under manufacturer company names)
spectrometry, emission, *ref. 661*
spectrophotometers, *ref. 357*
spectroscopy, emission, *ref. 660*
–, far ultraviolet, *ref. 389*
splitting devices, 140
spoilers, 120, 126
spray, 88, 89, 125
– (to), 7
sprayer efficiency, 126, 127, 130, 250, 265, 268
– noise, 130, 167
– section, 126
sprayer-burners, 113; *ref. 425, 681*
–, total consumption, *ref. 846*
–, torch-like, 122
– with premix gases, 120
sprayers, 7, 87, 124; *ref. 318*
–, adjustable, 124; *ref. 179*
–, anular, flows in, *ref. 421*
–, characteristics, 262
–, optimum conditions, 126
–, ultrasonic, 124, 125; *ref. 202*
spraying chambers (see chambers, spraying)
– efficiency (see also sprayer efficiency), 87
– process, 87, 266
spread of values, 228
sputtering, 52
– chambers, 151, 152
– technique, cathodic, 150–152
stability in atomic-absorption spectroscopy, *ref. 18*
– of instrumental systems, 228
standard addition technique (see addition method)
– deviation, 259
– –, blank 234
– –, relative (see coefficient of variation)

– –, signal, 234
– preparation, 281
standards, 281
–, calibration, 286, 291
–, dilution series (Table), 399
–, group series, 291
–, internal, 172, 177, 302, 306
–, series of, 291
–, single-analyte series, 291
–, substances for the preparation of, 286
–, two close, 291
–, working, 286, 291
Stark effect, 41
steels, bismuth determination in, 376
–, chromium determination in, 377, 382
– (low-alloy), chromium determination in, *ref. 398*
–, cobalt determination in, 376, 377; *ref. 490, 721*
–, copper determination in, 377, 381; *ref. 397, 721*
–, iron determination in, 381
–, lead determination in, 376, 377, 378; *ref. 214, 906*
–, magnesium determination in, 377; *ref. 82, 721*
–, manganese determination in, 377; *ref. 721*
–, molybdenum determination in, 377, 378
–, nickel determination in, 377, 379, 381; *ref. 396, 721, 763*
–, silicon determination in (sputtering chamber), 151
–, stainless, chromium determination in, 376
–, –, determination of cadmium, iron, lead, magnesium, manganese, and nickel, 380
–, trace element determination in, *ref. 729*
–, trace metals determination in, 380
–, vanadium determination in, 104; *ref. 901*
–, zinc determination in, *ref. 356*
streaming velocity, 121, 130
strike backs (flash backs), 113, 116, 120, 342
strip chart recording, 161
strongly emitting elements (see elements, strongly emitting)
strontium, fluctuational concentration limit, 247
–, interferences by aluminum on, 352
–, – by phosphates on, 271, 352
–, – –, elimination of, *ref. 858, 859*
–, – by silicates on, 271
–, – by silicon on, 352
–, – by sulfates on, 271
–, – on, 366
–, operating conditions, 405
–, percentual concentration limit, 245
– as releaser, 98, 307, 308, 351, 352, 357, 359, 364, 365, 378, 381
– determination, *ref. 165*
– – in ashed biological samples, *ref. 778*
– – in biological materials, *ref. 173*
– – in bones, 366, 369
– – in coal ash, 386; *ref. 81*
– – in feldspars and biotites, 371
– – in G-1 and W-1 rocks, 373
– – in hay, 356, 366
– – in igneous minerals, 372
– – in powdered milk, 366, 382
– – in sediments, 373
– – in shellfish, 366, 370
– – in silicate samples, 386
– – in soils, exchangeable, *ref. 173*
– – with fuel-rich air–hydrogen flames, 103
– emission intensity, 276
strontium nitrate, magnesium determination in, 384; *ref. 359*
studies, general, 349
–, special, 388
sulfates interferences on calcium, 271
– – on magnesium, 272
– – on nickel, 381
– – on strontium, 271
Sullivan and Walsh, instrument described by, 182
superphosphates, copperized, copper determination in, 354
suspensions, analysis of, 16, 21
synthetic fiber, metals determination in, *ref. 696*
systems a.c., 273
–, d.c., 273
syringes, motor driven, 130, 140

T

tantalum, fluctuational concentration limit, 247
–, iron determination in, 380; *ref. 157*
–, operating conditions, 405
–, percentual concentration limit, 245
tape puncher, 160
Techtron Pty. Ltd. instruments, description, 180, 198, 202
– Model AA-3 atomic-absorption spectrophotometer, *ref. 61*
teflon, alkali-metals volatilization in dry ashing of, *ref. 411*
tellurium, fluctuational concentration limit, 247
–, operating conditions, 406

–, percentual concentration limit, 245
– determination in copper, 377; *ref. 716*
temperature gradient, 114
terbium, fluctuational concentration limit, 247
–, operating conditions, 406
–, percentual concentration limit, 245
– determination with fuel-rich flames, 100
term diagrams, 33
terminology, 8
tert-butanol, 303
Tesla coil, 74
tetraethyllead, 375, 376
tetramethyllead, 376
thallium, fluctuational concentration limit, 247
–, operating conditions, 406
–, percentual concentration limit, 245
– determination by atomic-fluorescence flame photometry, *ref. 472*
– – in biological materials, *ref. 895*
Thilliez, instrument described by, 182
thorium, fluctuational concentration limit, 247
–, operating conditions, 406
–, percentual concentration limit, 245
thulium, flame as source, 101
–, fluctuational concentration limit, 247
–, operating conditions, 406
–, percentual concentration limit, 245
– determination with fuel-rich flames, 100
– spectrum, *ref. 675*
time constant, 168
tin, flame profile, air–hydrogen turbulent flame, 111
–, fluctuational concentration limit, 247
–, light pipes, 101
–, operating conditions, 406
–, percentual concentration limit, 245
–, working curve, air–acetylene flame, 95
–, – –, air–coal gas flame, 95
– determination, *ref. 138, 139*
– – in hydrogen peroxide, 384; *ref. 2*
– – with fuel-rich flames 100
– – – –, air–hydrogen, 103
tissues, calcium determination in, 369
–, copper determination in, 369; *ref. 93*
–, human, determination of copper and zinc in, *ref. 737*
–, –, formalinized, zinc determination in *ref. 919*
–, magnesium determination in, 369
–, zinc determination in, 369
– analysis, 369; *ref. 237*
– –, standards, 369
– of chicken, magnesium determination in, *ref. 295*
titanium, atomic-absorption spectrum, *ref. 234, 235*
–, fluctuational concentration limit, 247
–, operating conditions, 406
–, percentual concentration limit, 245
–, – – – with nitrous oxide–acetylene flame, 104
– determination, nitrous oxide burner, *ref. 51*
– – with fuel-rich flames, 100
toluene, 300
total absorption method, 324, 325
total-consumption burner (see burners, total consumption)
town gas, iron carbonyl and nickel carbonyl determination in, 389; *ref. 192*
toxicology, applications in, 368; *ref. 688, 689*
trace analysis, *ref. 211*
trace elements, light scattering in, *ref. 897, 942*
– determination (see also trace metals determination), *ref. 504, 530, 555, 925*
– –, light scattering in, *ref. 897, 942*
– –, toxicological, *ref. 710*
– (metals) – in biological materials, *ref. 94, 682, 894*
– – in blood, *ref. 707*
– – in blood plasma, *ref. 454*
– – in electroplating solutions, *ref. 820*
– – in metals, *ref. 379*
– – in sea water, *ref. 223, 308*
– (metals) – in steels, 380; *ref. 729*
– – in urine, *ref. 707*
– – in used aircraft lubricating oil, *ref. 726*
– (metals) extraction with ammonium pyrrolidine dithiocarbamate and oxine, in brines, *ref. 469*
– (metals) in therapeutical methods, *ref. 240*
trace metals determination (see also trace elements determination), *ref. 69, 94, 240, 269*
trace species in combustion gases, *ref. 245*
transducers, 174
transitions between two energy levels, 30
transmission, percentage of, 40
– (%) conversion into absorbance (Table), 392
transparency, lack of, 211
tree leaves, manganese and zinc determination in, *ref. 116*
tube, long path (see adapters long path, and adapters, long tube)
tubes, hollow-cathode (see lamps, hollow cathode)
tungsten, fluctuational concentration limit, 247

–, operating conditions, 406
–, percentual concentration limit, 245
–, – – – with nitrous oxide–acetylene flame, 104
– determination with fuel-rich flames, 100, 101
– interferences on manganese, 381
tungsten carbide, iron determination in, 377, 382; *ref. 78*
tungstic acid, sodium determination in, 384
turbulence, optical path, 252
two-detector systems, 161
two-standard method, 291, 313, 328, 329, 330; *ref. 938*

U

ultrasonic atomizer (sprayer) (see sprayer, ultrasonic)
ultraviolet, far, 22; *ref. 17*
–, vacuum, 151, 211
– region beyond 2000 Å, 211
Unicam Instruments Ltd instruments, *ref. 785*
– –, description, 180, 200, 202
uranium, fluctuational concentration limit, 247
–, magnesium determination in, 378, 389; *ref. 351, 760*
–, molybdenum determination in, 389
–, operating conditions, 406
–, percentual concentration limit, 245
– compounds, cadmium determination in, 385; *ref. 743*
– determination by sputtering techniques, 151
– isotopes determination (analysis), 387; *ref. 283, 284, 285, 911*
urine, bismuth determination in, 367
–, cadmium determination in, 367
–, calcium determination in, 364; *ref. 831*
–, copper determination in, 367; *ref. 93*
–, copper determination in, by extraction, *ref. 354, 355*
–, heavy metals determination in, *ref. 834*
–, iron determination in, 367, 368; *ref. 873*
–, – –, by extraction, *ref. 354, 355*
–, lead determination in, 367; *ref. 92, 832, 834*
–, – extraction, 299
–, magnesium determination in, 364; *ref. 730, 831*
–, mercury determination in, 367, 368
–, nickel determination in, 367; *ref. 722*
–, – extraction, 299
–, trace elements determination in, *ref. 707*
–, zinc determination in, 364; *ref. 44*
– analysis, 366
– –, addition method, 367
– –, determinable elements (bismuth, cadmium, calcium, chromium, copper, gold, iron, lead, magnesium, mercury, nickel, potassium, silver, sodium, thallium, and zinc), 367
– –, extractions, 367
– –, interferences, 368
– –, standards, 368

V

valve, quick cut-off, 342
vanadium, atomic-absorption spectrum, *ref. 234, 235*
–, fluctuational concentration limit, 247
–, light pipes, 101
–, operating conditions, 407
–, percentual concentration limit, 245
–, – – – with nitrous oxide–acetylene flame, 104
–, – – – with plasmas, 148
– determination, *ref. 140, 634, 891*
– –, nitrous oxide burner, *ref. 51*
– – in catalysts, 5
– – in crude oils, 5
– – in drinking water, 352
– – in gas oils, *ref. 901*
– – in oils, 104
– – in steels, 104; *ref. 901*
– – with fuel-rich flames, 100, 101
– extraction with cupferron, 352
vaporization, fractional, 149
variable, qualitative, 11, 13, 87
–, quantitative, 11, 12
variables, predeterminable, 311
vegetable materials, zinc determination in, *ref. 261*
– matter, manganese determination in, 176
– –, iron determination in, 176
vent tubes, 139
vents, 139, 344
Venturi effect, 122
Vidale furnace technique, 150
volume–concentration calculation, nomogram for (see under nomogram)
volume factor, 231
– required, 230, 240, 250
– –, correlation, 231
– –, minimum, 220
voltage stabilizers, 71

W

warm-up curves, 68, 69
– time, 68, 281, 282
Warren, burner described by, 113, 122, 176
–, instrument described by, 182
washings, intermediate, 312
water, borehole natural, 351
–, cadmium determination in, 376
–, calcium determination in, *ref. 130*
–, concentration of, 351
–, copper determination in, 352; *ref. 130*
–, demineralized, 287
– deposits from, 350
–, dilution of, 351
–, distilled, 287
–, double demineralized, 287
–, drinking, vanadium determination in, 352
–, filtration, 351
–, industrial effluents, 351
–, – waste, determination of cadmium, copper, iron, lead, nickel and zinc in, *ref. 99*
–, iron determination in, *ref. 130*
–, lead determination in, 352, 376
–, lysimeter, 350
–, magnesium determination in, *ref. 130*
–, natural, analysis, *ref. 123, 244*
–, –, cobalt and nickel determination in, 351; *ref. 123*
–, potassium determination in, *ref. 130*
–, preliminary concentration, 351
–, river, 351
–, rubidium determination in, 352
–, sea, 351
–, –, iron and manganese determination in, *ref. 917*
–, –, major components determination in, *ref. 308*
–, –, trace metals determination in, *ref. 223, 308*
–, sewage, 351
–, sodium determination in, 352; *ref. 130*
–, twice-distilled, 287
–, waste, cadmium determination in, 351
–, –, copper determination in, 351
–, –, iron determination in, 351
–, –, lead determination in, 351
–, –, nickel determination in, 351
–, –, zinc determination in, 351
– analysis, 350; *ref. 557, 558, 559*
– –, industrial waste, *ref. 99*
– –, determinable elements (calcium, copper, iron, magnesium, manganese, nickel, potassium, sodium, and zinc), 350
– –, – – (rubidium, sodium, and vanadium), 352
– –, interferences, 352
– –, preparation of samples, 351
– –, reviews, 350
– –, standards, 353
– for biological samples, 287
wavelength selection, 253; *ref. 473*
weighing bottles, 289
– procedure, 289
Westinghouse Electric Corporation, hollow-cathode lamps, 52, 56; *ref. 815, 816, 817, 818, 950*
–, – tubes (see Westinghouse Electric Corporation, hollow-cathode lamps)
wheat, selenium determination in, 356
Willis, burner described by, 120
wine, copper determination in, *ref. 867*
–, lead determination in, 382; *ref. 867, 868*
–, zinc determination in, 303; *ref. 867*

Y

ytterbium, flames as source, 101
–, fluctuational concentration limit, 247
–, operating conditions, 407
–, percentual concentration limit, 245
– determination with fuel-rich flames, 100
yttrium, atomic absorption spectrum, *ref. 235, 675*
–, fluctuational concentration limit, 247
–, operating conditions, 407
–, percentual concentration limit, 245
– determination with fuel-rich flames, 100, 101

Z

zeroing, 88, 104, 106, 313, 314
zinc, absolute limit in grafite cell, 150
–, fluctuational concentration limit, 247
–, interferences by acids on, 354
–, – by halogen acids on, *ref. 241*
–, – by hydrochloric acid on, 381
–, – by sodium on, 272
–, operating conditions, 407
–, percentual concentration limit, 245
–, slit, 156
– absorption, 129
– analysis, 387
– contamination, 139
– determination, *ref. 198*
– – , accuracy of, *ref. 217*
– – by atomic–fluorescence flame photometry, *ref. 472, 848*

– – in agricultural materials, 353
– – in alcoholic beverages, 303
– – in alloys, 378, 389; *ref. 528*
– – in aluminous materials, *ref. 222*
– – in aluminum alloys, 380
– – in aluminum materials, 380
– – in animal materials, *ref. 261*
– – in animal nutrition, *ref. 542*
– – in animal organisms, 388
– – in Bayer liquor, 383
– – in biological fluids, 364; *ref. 568*
– – in biological materials; *ref. 42, 250, 640*
– – in blood plasma, 364
– – in blood serum, *ref. 347, 724*
– – in cadmium plating solutions, 387
– – in chloroplasts, 355; *ref. 331*
– – in concentrates, 372
– – in copper alloys, 380
– – in dried liver and muscle, 369
– – in electroplating solutions, 383
– – in feeding stuffs, 382
– – in fertilizers, *ref. 261*
– – in flue dusts, *ref. 356*
– – in fungicides, 385
– – in glass, 386; *ref. 544*
– – in high purity gold, *ref. 658*
– – in human brain, *ref. 905*
– – in human tissues, *ref. 737*
– – –, formalinized, *ref. 919*
– – in industrial waste water, *ref. 99*
– – in iron, *ref. 356*
– – in lead-base alloys, *ref. 224*
– – in liver, *ref. 567*
– – in metallurgical materials, *ref. 270, 271, 528, 794*
– – in metallurgical products, 376
– – in muscle, *ref. 567*
– – in nickel plating solutions, 383; *ref. 664*
– – in ore samples, 372; *ref. 224*
– – in plant materials (see also zinc determination in vegetable materials), 355, 356, 358; *ref. 161, 908, 933*
– – in polyvinylchloride, 385; *ref. 518*
– – in rat kidney, 367
– – in red blood cells, 364
– – in rocks, silicate, *ref. 88*
– – in soils, *ref. 261*
– – in steels, *ref. 356*
– – in tissues, 369
– – in tree leaves, 356; *ref. 116*
– – in urine, 364; *ref. 44*
– – in vegetable matter (see also zinc determination in plant materials), *ref. 261*
– – in waste water, 351
– – in wine, 303; *ref. 867*
– – in zincblende and catalysts, 182
– – in zirconium alloys 378
– – with addition of organic solvents, 302
– – with long tube adapters, 137
– extraction, 299, 300
– hollow-cathode lamp, 60; *ref. 792*
– sensitivity with continuum sources, 48
zinc chloride, magnesium determination in, 182
zinc sulfide concentrates analysis, 386
zincblende analysis, 182
zirconium, fluctuational concentration limit, 247
–, operating conditions, 407
–, percentual concentration limit, 245
– alloys, zinc determination in, 378
– determination with fuel-rich flames, 101
zone, absorption, 274
–, emission, 274
–, optimum, 108, 251
–, –, for atomic absorption, 108
–, –, for emission, 108
–, selected, 108
–, selection, 274, 407